DYDE

Stanley C

AUSTF

CONCISE

STAMP CATALOGUE

Second edition, 1991

Stanley Gibbons Publications Ltd
London and Ringwood

*By Appointment to Her Majesty The Queen
Stanley Gibbons Ltd., London
Philatelists*

Published by **Stanley Gibbons Publications Ltd.**
Editorial, Sales Offices and Distribution Centre:
5 Parkside, Christchurch Road, Ringwood,
Hants BH24 3SH

**First Edition – February 1989
Second Edition – February 1991**

© Stanley Gibbons Publications Ltd., 1991

ISBN: 0–85259–289–2

Item No. 2892 (91)

Typeset by Black Bear Press Limited, Cambridge, England
Printed in Great Britain by Butler and Tanner Ltd., Frome, Somerset

THE AUSTRALIA CONCISE CATALOGUE

Second Edition

The publication of the first edition of this catalogue in 1989 was so warmly welcomed by collectors requiring a handy one-country listing that it became clear that further, regular, editions would be required.

This second edition incorporates a number of revisions, including further details for the listed New South Wales Sydney View varieties, notes on the complicated modern Australia stamp papers and "koala" new printings, and a revised Stamp Booklet section with many of the cover designs illustrated for ease of reference. Watermarks from the colonial period which were used for the stamps of more than one State have been added to the Philatelic Information pages.

The following stamps, other than New Issues recorded in the *Gibbons Stamp Monthly* Catalogue Supplements, have been added since the last edition:

Tasmania. 148b, 251ba, 252a, F36c

Australia. 1a, 155a, 224ab, 525a, 591Ea, 930a, 1169a, 1170a, 1179b/ba, 1230b/ba, B64a, B69a, O6*a*, O21*a*, O41*a*/*c*, O49*a*, O64a, O75*b*, O81*a*, O118*a*/*b*

B.C.O.F. J1b, J4c, J5c

Papua New Guinea–New Guinea. 70*b*

Papua. 48a, 91*a*

The listings in the *Concise* are based on those of the Stanley Gibbons *Part 1* (*British Commonwealth*) catalogue, but there is much additional material within its pages.

Australia inverted watermarks.

First Day Cover prices for commemoratives from 1937 and of definitives from 1970.

Post Office Souvenir Packs, Year and Heritage Books.

P.O. Postcards.

Stamp Booklets from 1913.

We continue to provide both unmounted and mounted mint prices for the popular King George VI issues and a design index from 1942 also appears.

In addition to issues for Australia and the Australian States the *Concise* also includes British Commonwealth Occupation Force (Japan), Australian Antarctic Territory, Christmas Island, Cocos (Keeling) Islands, Nauru (to 1966), Norfolk Island and Papua New Guinea (to 1975).

Each stamp is listed with the internationally-recognised SG catalogue number and many of the prices have been reviewed specially for this publication.

It is hoped to extend the coverage still further in subsequent editions and suggestions as to possible improvements are very welcome.

David J. Aggersberg

Stanley Gibbons International Ltd.

HEAD OFFICE, 399 STRAND, LONDON WC2R 0LX

Auction Room and Specialist Departments. Open Monday–Friday, 9.30 a.m. to 5 p.m.

Shop: Open Monday 9.30 a.m. to 5.30 p.m., Tuesday–Friday 8.30 a.m. to 5.30 p.m.
   Telephone 071-836 8444 and Telex 28883 for all departments.

RINGWOOD OFFICE

Stanley Gibbons Publications and Promotions, Parkside, Christchurch Road, Ringwood, Hants
   BH24 3SH.
   Telephone 0425 472363.

OVERSEAS BRANCHES

Stanley Gibbons (Australia) Pty. Ltd., P.O. Box 863J, Melbourne 3001, Australia.
   Telephone (01 0613) 670-3332 and Telex AA 37223.

Stanley Gibbons (Singapore) Pte Ltd., Raffles City, P.O. Box 1689, Singapore 9117, Republic of
   Singapore.
   Telephone (010 65) 3361998.

Contents

Specialist Philatelic Societies

British Society of Australian Philately. Secretary—Mr. T. R. Finlayson, 86 Clarence Road, Fleet, Hants GU13 9RS.

Pacific Islands Study Circle of Great Britain. Honorary Secretary—Mr. J. D. Ray, 24 Woodvale Avenue, London SE25 4AE.

Papuan Philatelic Society. Secretary—Mr. G. Amedro, 12 Main Street, Gorebridge, Midlothian EH23 4BX.

STANLEY GIBBONS PUBLICATIONS LIMITED

OVERSEAS REPRESENTATION

Stanley Gibbons Publications Ltd. are represented overseas by the following sole distributors (*) and main agents (**)

Australia*
Lighthouse Philatelic (Aust.) Pty Ltd
Box 62
Chippendale 2008
New South Wales
Australia

Belgium and Luxembourg**
Philac
Rue du Midi 48
Bruxelles
Belgium 1000

Canada*
Lighthouse Publications (Canada)
Ltd
255 Duke Street
Montreal
Quebec
Canada H3C 2M2

Denmark**
Nordfrim
DK 5450
Otterup
Denmark

France*
Davo France SARL
11 Rue de Chateaudun
75009 Paris
France

Germany and Austria*
Ka-Be Briefmarkenalben-Verlag
Volkhardt GMBH
Daimlerstrasse 15
Goppingen
Germany

Hong Kong**
Po-on Stamp Service
GPO Box 2498
Hong Kong

Israel**
Capital Stamps
PO Box 3769
Jerusalem 91036
Israel

Italy*
Secrian Srl
Via Pantelleria 2
Milano
1-20156
Italy

Japan**
Japan Philatelic Co Ltd
PO Box 2
Suginami-Minami
Tokyo
Japan

Netherlands*
Davo Publications
PO Box 411
7400 AK Deventer
Netherlands

New Zealand*
Philatelic Distributors Ltd
PO Box 863
New Plymouth
New Zealand

Norway**
Wennergren-Cappelen AS
Nedre Vollgate 4
PO Box 738
Sentrum N-0105
Oslo 1
Norway

South Africa**
Stanley Gibbons (Pty) Ltd
PO Box 930
Parklands
RSA 2121

Republic Coin and Stamp
Accessories (Pty) Ltd
PO Box 260325
Excom 2023
Johannesburg
RSA

Sweden*
Chr Winther Soerensen AB
Box 43
S-310 Knaered
Sweden

Switzerland**
Dove of Basle
Birsigstrasse 111
4011 Basle
Switzerland

USA*
Lighthouse Publications Inc
274 Washington Avenue
Hackensack
New Jersey 07601
USA

West Indies/Caribbean**
Hugh Dunphy
PO Box 413
Kingston 10
Jamaica
West Indies

Prices

The prices quoted in this catalogue are the estimated selling prices of Stanley Gibbons Ltd at the time of publication. They are, *unless it is specifically stated otherwise*, for examples in fine condition for the issue concerned. Superb examples are worth more; those of a lower quality considerably less.

All prices are subject to change without prior notice and Stanley Gibbons Ltd may from time to time offer stamps below catalogue price in consequence of special purchases or particular promotions.

No guarantee is given to supply all stamps priced, since it is not possible to keep every catalogued item in stock.

Quotation of prices. The prices in the left-hand column are for unused stamps and those in the right-hand column are for used.

A dagger (†) denotes that the item listed does not exist in that condition and a blank, or dash, that it exists, or may exist, but no market price is known.

Prices are expressed in pounds and pence sterling. One pound comprises 100 pence (£1 = 100p).

The method of notation is as follows: pence in numerals (e.g. 5 denotes five pence); pounds and pence up to £100, in numerals (e.g. 4·25 denotes four pounds and twenty-five pence); prices above £100 expressed in whole pounds with the "£" sign shown.

Unused and Used stamps. The prices for unused stamps of Queen Victoria to King George V are for lightly hinged examples. King George VI mint stamps (1937–52) are priced in both unmounted (left-hand column) and mounted (centre column) condition. Mint stamps of the present reign are priced in unmounted condition only (though when not available, mounted mint stamps are often supplied at a lower price). The used prices are normally for stamps postally used, but may be for stamps cancelled-to-order where this practice exists.

Prices quoted for bisects on cover or on large piece are for those dated during the period officially authorised.

Minimum price. The minimum price quoted is ten pence. This represents a handling charge rather than a basis for valuing common stamps, for which the 10p price should not be reckoned automatically, since it covers a variation in real scarcity.

Set prices. Set prices are generally for one of each value, excluding shades and varieties, but including major colour changes. Where there are alternative shades, etc., the cheapest is usually included. The number of stamps in the set is always stated for clarity.

The mint prices for sets containing *se-tenant* pieces are based on the prices quoted for such combinations, and not on those for the individual stamps. The used set price is for single stamps.

Used on Cover prices. To assist collectors, cover prices are quoted for issues up to 1945 at the beginning of each country.

The system gives a general guide in the form of a factor by which the corresponding used price of the loose stamp should be multiplied when found in fine average condition on cover.

Care is needed in applying the factors and they relate to a cover which bears a single of the denomination listed; strips and blocks would need individual valuation outside the scope. If more than one denomination is present the most highly priced attracts the multiplier and the remainder are priced at the simple figure for used singles in arriving at a total.

The cover should be of non-philatelic origin, bearing the correct postal rate for the period and distance involved and cancelled with the markings normal to the offices concerned. Purely philatelic items have a cover value only slightly greater than the catalogue value for the corresponding used stamps. This applies generally to those high-value stamps used philatelically rather than in the normal course of commerce.

Oversized covers, difficult to accommodate on an album page, should be reckoned as worth little more than the corresponding value of the used stamps. The condition of a cover affects its value. Except for "wreck covers", serious damage or soiling reduce the value where the postal markings and stamps are ordinary ones. Conversely, visual appeal adds to the value and this can include freshness of appearance, important addresses, old-fashioned but legible handwriting, historic town-names, etc. The prices quoted are a base on which further value would be added to take account of the cover's postal historical importance in demonstrating such things as unusual, scarce or emergency cancels, interesting routes, significant postal markings, combination usage, the development of postal rates, and so on.

First Day Cover prices. Prices are quoted for commemorative first day covers from 1937 onwards. These prices are for special covers (from 1945) franked with complete sets and cancelled by ordinary operational postmarks or the various standard "First Day of Issue" markings from 1962.

The Australian Post Office introduced its own first day covers from 16 March 1970. From that date until 29 September 1971 the catalogue quotes prices for both commercial and P.O. first day covers.

Thereafter prices are for Post Office examples only.

Prices for constant varieties. Prices are for unmounted mint single stamps, unless otherwise stated. Prices are not quoted for used stamps, since varieties tend not to be collected in this condition.

When ordered in pairs or positional blocks the extra stamps are charged at the prices of normals.

Guarantee

All stamps are guaranteed genuine originals in the following terms:

If not as described, and returned by the purchaser, we undertake to refund the price paid to us in the original transaction. If any stamp is certified as genuine by the Expert Committee of the Royal Philatelic Society, London, or by B.P.A. Expertising Ltd, the purchaser shall not be entitled to make any claim against us for any error, omission or mistake in such certificate.

Consumers' statutory rights are not affected by the above guarantee.

The recognised Expert Committees in this country are those of the Royal Philatelic Society, 41 Devonshire Place, London W1N 1PE, and B.P.A. Expertising Ltd, P.O. Box 163, Carshalton Beeches, Surrey SM5 4QR. They do not undertake valuations under any circumstances and fees are payable for their services.

Printers

B.D.T.	B.D.T. International Security Printing Ltd, Dublin, Ireland.
B.W.	Bradbury Wilkinson & Co, Ltd.
Courvoisier	Imprimerie Courvoisier S.A., La-Chaux-de-Fonds, Switzerland
D.L.R.	De La Rue & Co, Ltd, London, and (from 1961) Bogota, Colombia.
Enschedé	Joh. Enschedé en Zonen, Haarlem, Netherlands.
Format	Format International Security Printers, Ltd, London.
Harrison	Harrison & Sons, Ltd, High Wycombe.
J.W.	John Waddington Security Print, Ltd, Leeds
Questa	Questa Colour Security Printers, Ltd, London.
Walsall	Walsall Security Printers, Ltd.
Waterlow	Waterlow & Sons, Ltd, London.

General Abbreviations

Alph	Alphabet
Anniv	Anniversary
Brt	Bright (colour)
C, c	Chalky paper
C.	Overprinted in carmine
Des	Designer; designed
Dp	Deep (colour)
Eng	Engraver; engraved
Horiz	Horizontal; horizontally
H/S	Handstamped
Imp, Imperf	Imperforate
Inscr	Inscribed
L	Left
Litho	Lithographed
Lt	Light (colour)
mm	Millimetres
MS	Miniature sheet
O, o	Ordinary paper
Opt(d)	Overprint(ed)
P, Pf or Perf	Perforated
Photo	Photogravure
Pl	Plate
Pr	Pair
Ptd	Printed
Ptg	Printing
PVA	Polyvinyl alcohol (gum)
R	Right
R.	Row
Recess	Recess-printed
T	Type
Typo	Typographed
Un	Unused
Us	Used
Vert	Vertical; vertically
W or wmk	Watermark
Wmk s	Watermark sideways

(†) = Does not exist.

(—) (or blank price column) = Exists, or may exist, but no market price is known.

/ between colours means "on" and the colour following is that of the paper on which the stamp is printed.

Contacting the Catalogue Editor

The Editor is always interested in hearing from people who have new information which will improve or correct the Catalogue. As a general rule he must see and examine the actual stamps before they can be considered for listing; photographs or photocopies are insufficient evidence.

Submissions should be made in writing to the Catalogue Editor, Stanley Gibbons Publications Ltd. The cost of return postage for items submitted is appreciated, and this should include the registration fee if required.

Where information is solicited purely for the benefit of the enquirer, the Editor cannot undertake to reply if the answer is already contained in these published notes or if return postage is omitted. Written communications are greatly preferred to enquiries by telephone and the Editor regrets that he or his staff cannot see personal callers without a prior appointment being made. Correspondence may be subject to delay during the production period of each new edition.

Please note that the following classes or material are outside the scope of this Catalogue:

(a) Non-postal revenue or fiscal stamps.
(b) Postage stamps used fiscally.
(c) Local carriage labels and private local issues.
(d) Punctured postage stamps (perfins) prepared by state governments or private firms.
(e) Telegraph stamps.
(f) Bogus or phantom stamps.
(g) Railway or airline letter fee stamps, bus or road transport company labels.
(h) Postal stationery cut-outs.
(i) All types of non-postal labels and souvenirs.
(j) Documentary labels for the postal service, e.g. registration, recorded delivery, airmail etiquettes, etc.
(k) Privately applied embellishments to official issues and privately commissioned items generally.
(l) Stamps for training postal staff.

> We regret we do not give opinions as to the genuineness of stamps, nor do we identify stamps or number them by our Catalogue.

Philatelic Information

CATALOGUE NUMBERS

The catalogue number appears in the extreme left column. The boldface Type numbers in the next column are merely cross-reference to illustrations. Catalogue numbers in the Gibbons *Stamp Monthly* Supplement are provisional only and may need to be altered when the lists are consolidated.

Our catalogue numbers are universally recognised in specifying stamps and as a hallmark of status.

Subsidiary classes of stamps are placed at the end of each country as separate lists, with a distinguishing prefix letter, for example D for postage due or O for official, in the catalogue number. Stamp booklets are also at the end of the country and have B numbers.

Inverted and other watermark varieties incorporate "Wi" within the number. Other items which only appear in the *Australia Concise* incorporate "Ea", etc.

CATALOGUE ILLUSTRATIONS

Stamps are illustrated at three-quarters linear size. Stamps not illustrated are the same size and format as the value shown, unless otherwise indicated. Overprints, surcharges and watermarks are normally actual size. Illustrations of varieties are often enlarged to show the detail.

BOOKLET STAMPS

Single stamps from booklets are listed if they are distinguishable in some way (such as design or watermark) from similar sheet stamps.

Se-tenant pane with label

Booklet panes are listed where they contain stamps of different denominations *se-tenant*, where stamp-size labels are included, or where such panes are otherwise identifiable. Booklet panes are placed in the listing under the lowest denomination present.

COIL STAMPS

Stamps only issued in coil form are given full listing. If stamps are issued in both sheets and coils, the coil stamps are listed separately only where there is some feature (e.g. watermark or perforation) by which single stamps can be distinguished.

Examples of the special coil perforation introduced in the Australia 1937–48 definitive are listed as coil pairs or, for those subsequently placed on sale in sheets, as coil blocks of four.

COLOUR IDENTIFICATION

The 100 colours most used for stamp identification are given in the Stanley Gibbons Colour Guide; these, plus a further 100 variations for more specialised use, are included in the Stanley Gibbons Stamp Colour Key. The Catalogue has used the Guide and Key as standards for describing new issues for some years. The names are also introduced as lists are rewritten, though exceptions are made for those early issues where traditional names have become universally established.

In compound colour names the second is the predominant one, thus:

orange-red = a red tending towards orange;

red-orange = an orange containing more red than usual.

When comparing actual stamps with colour samples in the Guide or Key, view in a good north daylight (or its best substitute: fluorescent "colour-matching" light). Sunshine is not recommended. Choose a solid portion of the stamp design; if available, marginal markings such as solid bars of colour or colour check dots are helpful. Shading lines in the design can be misleading as they appear lighter than solid colour. Furthermore, the listings refer to colours as issued: they may deteriorate into something different through the passage of time.

Shades are particularly significant when they can be linked to specific printings, in general, shades need to be quite marked to fall within the scope of this Catalogue.

Modern colour printing by lithography is prone to marked differences of shade, even within a single run, and variations can occur within the same sheet. Such shades are not listed.

The listings use the following abbreviations for stamp colours: bl (blue); blk (black); brn (brown); car, carm (carmine); choc (chocolate); clar (claret); emer (emerald); grn (green); ind (indigo); mag (magenta); mar (maroon); mult (multicoloured); mve (mauve); ol (olive); orge (orange); pk (pink); pur (purple); scar (scarlet); sep (sepia); turq (turquoise); ultram (ultramarine); verm (vermilion); vio (violet); yell (yellow).

Overprints and surcharges are in black unless otherwise stated. The following abbreviations may be used to describe overprint or surcharge colours: (B.) = blue, (Blk.) = black, (Br.) = brown, (C.) = carmine, (G.) = green, (Mag.) = magenta, (Mve.) = mauve, (Ol.) = olive, (O.) = orange, (P.) = purple, (Pk.) = pink, (R.) = red, (Sil.) = silver, (V.) = violet, (Vm.) or (Verm.) = vermilion, (W.) = white, (Y.) = yellow.

ERRORS OF COLOUR

Major colour errors in stamps or overprints which qualify for listing are: wrong colours; albinos (colourless impressions), where these have Expert Committee certificates; colours completely omitted, but only on unused stamps (if found on used stamps the information is usually footnoted) and with good credentials, missing colours being frequently faked.

Colours only partially omitted are not recognised. Colour shifts, however spectacular, are not listed.

DATES OF ISSUE

Where local issue dates differ from dates of release by agencies, "date of issue" is the local date. Fortuitous stray usage before the officially intended date is disregarded in listing.

DESIGNERS

Designers' names are quoted where known, though space precludes naming every individual concerned in the production of a set. In particular, photographers supplying material are usually named only when they also make an active contribution in the design stage; posed photographs of reigning monarchs are, however, an exception to this rule.

FIRST DAY COVERS

This catalogue provides listings for commemorative first day covers from 1937 onwards and for definitives from the introduction of the full Australia Post Service on 16 March 1970.

For further details see under "Prices" on page vii.

GUM

All stamps listed are assumed to have gum of some kind and original gum (o.g.) means that which was present on the stamp as issued to the public. Deleterious climates and the presence of certain chemicals can cause gum to crack and, with early stamps, even make the paper deteriorate. Unscrupulous fakers are adept in removing it and regumming the stamp to meet the unreasoning demand often made for "full o.g." in cases where such a thing is virtually impossible.

MINIATURE SHEETS AND SHEETLETS

A miniature sheet contains a single stamp or set with wide inscribed or decorated margins. The stamps usually also exist in normal sheet format. This Catalogue lists, with **MS** prefix, complete miniature sheets which have been sold by the Post Office as indivisible entities and which are valid for postal purposes.

Norfolk Island miniature sheet containing
a set of stamps

A sheetlet or small sheet differs in that the individual stamps are intended to be purchased separately for postal purposes. For sheetlets, all the component postage stamps are numbered individually and the composition explained in a footnote. (The 1978 Christmas Island Christmas sheetlet, Nos. 99/107, is an example.) Note that the definitions refer to post office sale—not how items may be subsequently offered by stamp dealers.

Production as sheetlets is a modern marketing development chosen by postal administrations to interest collectors in purchasing the item complete; if he has done so he should, as with all *se-tenant* arrangements, keep the sheetlet intact in his collection.

OVERPRINTS AND SURCHARGES

Overprints of different types qualify for separate listing. These include overprints in different colours; overprints from different printing processes such as litho and typo; overprints in totally different typefaces, etc.

Major errors in machine-printed overprints are important and listable. They include: overprint inverted or omitted; overprint double (treble, etc.); overprint diagonal; overprint double, one inverted; pairs with one overprint omitted, e.g.

from a radical shift to an adjoining stamp; error of colour; error of type fount; letters inverted or omitted, etc. If the overprint is handstamped, few of these would qualify and a distinction is drawn. We continue, however, to list pairs of stamps where one has a handstamped overprint and the other has not.

Varieties occurring in overprints will often take the form of broken letters, slight differences in spacing, rising spaces, etc.

PAPER TYPES

All stamps listed are deemed to be on "ordinary" paper of the wove type and white in colour; only departures from this are normally mentioned.

A coloured paper is one that is coloured right through (front and back of the stamp). In the Catalogue the colour of the paper is given in *italics*, thus:

purple/*yellow* = purple design on yellow paper.

Papers have been made specially white in recent years by, for example, a very heavy coating of chalk. We do not classify shades of whiteness of paper as distinct varieties.

The availability of many postage stamps for revenue purposes made necessary some safeguard against the illegitimate re-use of stamps with removable cancellations. This was at first secured by using fugitive inks and later by printing on chalky (chalk-surfaced) paper, both of which made it difficult to remove any form of obliteration without also damaging the stamp design. We have indicated the existence of the papers by the letters "**O**" (ordinary) and "**C**" (chalky) after the description of all stamps where the chalky paper may be found. Where no indication is given the paper is "ordinary".

Our chalky paper is specifically one which shows a black mark when touched with a silver wire. Stamps on chalk-surfaced paper can easily lose this coating through immersion in water.

PERFORATION MEASUREMENT

The gauge of a perforation is the number of holes in a length of 2 cm.

The Gibbons *Instanta* gauge is the standard for measuring perforations. The stamp is viewed against a dark background with the transparent gauge put on top of it. Though the gauge measures to decimal accuracy, perforations read from it are generally quoted in the Catalogue to the nearest half. For example:

Just over perf $12\frac{3}{4}$ to just under $13\frac{1}{4}$ = perf 13
Perf $13\frac{1}{4}$ exactly, rounded up   = perf $13\frac{1}{2}$
Just over perf $13\frac{1}{4}$ to just under $13\frac{3}{4}$ = perf $13\frac{1}{2}$
Perf $13\frac{3}{4}$ exactly, rounded up   = perf 14

However, where classification depends on it, actual quarter-perforations are quoted. Perforations are usually abbreviated (and spoken) as follows, though sometimes they may be spelled out for clarity.

P 14: perforated alike on all sides (read: "perf 14").

P 14 × 15: the first figure refers to top and bottom, the second to left and right sides (read: "perf 14 by 15"). This is a compound perforation.

Such headings as "*P* 13 × 14 (*vert*) and *P* 14 × 13 (*horiz*)" indicate which perforations apply to which stamp format—vertical or horizontal.

In rouletting, an early form of separation, the paper is cut, usually in a series of short lines parallel to the edge of the stamp, but none of it is removed.

PERFORATION ERRORS

Authenticated errors, where a stamp normally perforated is accidentally issued imperforate, are listed provided no traces of perforation (blind holes or indentations) remain. They must be provided as pairs, both stamps wholly imperforate, and are only priced in that form.

Pairs described as "imperforate between" have the line of perforations between the two stamps omitted.

Imperf between (*horiz pair*): a horizontal pair of stamps with perfs all around the edges but none between the stamps.

Imperf between (*vert pair*): a vertical pair of stamps with perfs all around the edges but none between the stamps.

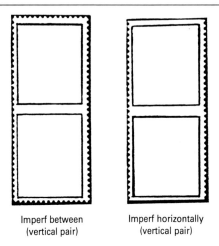

Imperf between   Imperf horizontally
(vertical pair)   (vertical pair)

Where several of the rows have escaped perforation the resulting varieties are listable. Thus:

Imperf vert (horiz pair): a horizontal pair of stamps perforated at top and bottom; all three vertical directions are imperf—the two outer edges and between the stamps.

Imperf horiz (vert pair): a vertical pair perforated at left and right edges; all three horizontal directions are imperf—the top, bottom and between the stamps.

Varieties of double, misplaced or partial perforation caused by error or machine malfunction are not listable, neither are freaks such as perforations placed diagonally from paper folds, nor missing holes caused by broken pins.

Items imperforate between stamp and margin are outside the scope of this catalogue.

PHOSPHOR ISSUES

Australian experiments in electronic sorting which had been going on since 1963, were based on a substance known commercially as "helecon", one of the zinc sulphide group. Helecon becomes luminescent in the orange-red spectrum when subjected to ultra-violet rays and has the property of "residual phosphorescence", i.e. it retains the luminescence for a brief period after the UV light is removed enabling the "tagged' stamp to be detected by the scanners during the instant of lamp black-out. The point of this is that envelope paper, often treated by the manufacturer with a whitening agent, may also react under UV light but would cease to do so when the light source is removed. The success of the operation therefore depends on the UV lamp using a rapid on-off cycle, while the adjoining sensing mechanism is on "continuous alert".

Helecon has been incorporated in stamps in two different ways, either in the ink with which the stamps are printed, or included in the surface coating of the stamp paper.

The only certain method of positively identifying stamps containing helecon in ink or paper is to subject them to ultra-violet light within the 3,000–4,000 Angstrom range, preferably viewing through a suitable filter to retard visible blue light, when the helecon stamps should fluoresce brightly in orange-red colours.

Owing to the difficulty of identification without the use of a UV lamp we do not list the helecon stamps separately.

POSTCARDS

From 1987 the Post Office produced sets of picture cards to accompany some commemorative issues. Each card shows an enlarged colour reproduction of one stamp.

Cards are priced in fine used condition for complete sets as issued, each franked with the appropriate stamp depicted and cancelled with an official postmark for first day of issue.

PRESENTATION AND SOUVENIR PACKS

Special packs comprising slip-in cards with printed commemorative inscriptions and notes on the back and with protective covering, were introduced in 1969 for the Christmas issue. Notes will be found in the listings to describe souvenir books issued on special occasions.

Australia 1970 Royal Visit Presentation Pack

Souvenir Packs, containing commemoratives not issued in individual Presentation Packs, were introduced in 1970. Special Post Office Yearbooks were first available in 1981. They contain all the commemorative issues for one year in a hardbound book, illustrated in colour complete with slip case. These are listed and priced.

PRINTING ERRORS

Errors in printing are of major interest to the Catalogue. Authenticated items meriting consideration would include: background, centre or frame inverted or omitted; centre or subject transposed; error of colour; error or omission of value; double prints and impressions; printed both sides; and so on. Designs *tête-bêche*, whether intentionally or by accident, are listable. Colours only partially omitted are not listed. However, stamps with embossing, phosphor or both omitted and stamps printed on the gummed side are included.

Printing technology has radically improved over the years, during which time photogravure and lithography have become predominant. Varieties nowadays are more in the nature of flaws which are almost always outside the scope of this book.

In no catalogue, however, do we list such items as: dry prints, kiss prints, doctor-blade flaws, colour shifts or registration flaws (unless they lead to the complete omission of a colour from an individual stamp), lithographic ring flaws, and so on. Neither do we recognise fortuitous happenings like paper creases or confetti flaws.

PUNCTURED STAMPS

Perforation holes can be punched into the face of the stamp. Patterns of small holes, often in the shape of initial letters, were applied as devices against pilferage. Private "perfins" are outside the scope of the listings.

This catalogue does, however, list those "OS" punctured stamps which were produced by the federal government or by the administration of Papua.

SE-TENANT COMBINATIONS

Se-tenant means "joined together". Some sets include stamps of different design arranged *se-tenant* as blocks or strips and, in mint condition, these are usually collected unsevered as issued. Such *se-tenant* combinations can often be supplied in used condition at a premium over the used prices of the individual stamps. See also the note on Set Prices.

Australia 1980 "Waltzing Matilda"
se-tenant strip

SHEET SIZES

In describing the sheet arrangement we always give the number of stamps across the sheet first. For example, "50 (5 × 10)" indicates a sheet of fifty stamps in ten horizontal rows of five stamps each.

From 1971 most Crown Agents stocks were in sheets of 25, the stocks sent direct to the territories being often in double, uncut sheets of 50 (i.e. two panes of 25).

To qualify for listing any variety or flaw must be *constant* and so occur throughout the entire printing run, although instances can happen where the flaw gradually corrects itself or—having been noticed—it is corrected by the printer. Before constant varieties and flaws can be listed their sheet position must be known.

The notation for position is based on counting the rows downwards and the stamps across the row. Hence in this Catalogue R. 10/1 = row 10, stamp 1 (the first stamp in the tenth row down); the alternative designation for this position as used in "Through the Magnifying Glass" (Gibbons *Stamp Monthly*) is R. 10, S1 = row 10, stamp 1.

SPECIMEN STAMPS

Originally, stamps overprinted SPECIMEN were circulated to postmasters or kept in official records, but after the establishment of the Universal Postal Union supplies were sent to Berne for distribution to the postal administrations of member countries.

During the period 1884 to 1928 most of the stamps of British Crown Colonies required for this purpose were overprinted SPECIMEN in various shapes and sizes by their printers from typeset formes. Some locally produced provisionals were handstamped locally, as were sets prepared for presentation. From 1928 stamps were punched with holes forming the word SPECIMEN, each firm of printers using a different machine or machines. From 1948 the stamps supplied to U.P.U. distribution were no longer punctured.

Stamps of some other Commonwealth territories were overprinted or handstamped locally, while stamps of Great Britain and those overprinted for use in overseas postal agencies (mostly of the higher denominations) bore SPECIMEN overprints and handstamps applied by the Inland Revenue or the Post Office.

This catalogue records those Specimen overprints or perforations intended for distribution by the U.P.U. to member countries. In addition the Specimen overprints of Australia and its dependent territories, which were sold to collectors by the Post Office, are also included.

All other Specimens are outside the scope of this volume.

WATERMARK TYPES

Stamps are on unwatermarked paper except where the heading to the set states otherwise.

Watermarks are detected for Catalogue description by one of four methods: (1) holding stamps to the light; (2) laying stamps face down on a dark background; (3) by use of the Morley-Bright Detector, which works by revealing the thinning of the paper at the watermark; or (4) by the more complex electric watermark detectors such as the Signoscope.

The diagram below shows how watermark position is described in the Catalogue. Watermarks are usually impressed so that they read normally when looked through from the printed side. However, since philatelists customarily detect watermarks by looking at the back of the stamp, the watermark diagram also makes clear what is actually seen. Note that "G v R" is only an example and illustrations of the different watermarks employed are shown in the listings. These illustrations are actual size and shown in normal positions (from the front of the stamps).

AS DESCRIBED (Read through front of stamp)		AS SEEN DURING WATERMARK DETECTION (Stamp face down and back examined)
GvR	Normal	Яvუ
Яʌუ	Inverted	ꓶʌꓤ
Яvუ	Reversed	GvR
ꓶʌꓤ	Reversed and inverted	Яʌუ
GvR (sideways)	Sideways	ꓶʌꓤ (sideways)
GvR (sideways)	Sideways inverted	Яvუ (sideways)

Australian States Watermark Types, used in more than one State, as seen from the front of the stamp.

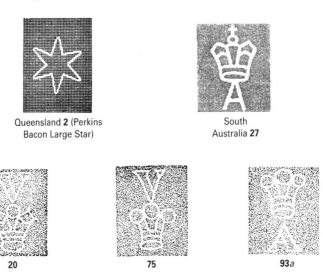

Queensland **2** (Perkins
Bacon Large Star)

South
Australia **27**

20   **75**   **93**_a_

Victoria

Australian Watermark Types as seen through the front of the stamp.

2   **5**   **6**   **6**_a_

7   **15**

Crown Agents Watermark Types as seen through the front of the stamp.

w **4**	w **6**	w **7**
Crown over CC	Crown over CA	Crown over CA

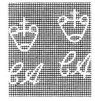

w **12**	w **14**	w **16**
Multiple St. Edward's Crown Block CA	Multiple Crown Block CA Diagonal	Multiple Crown Script CA Diagonal

WATERMARK ERRORS AND VARIETIES

Watermark errors are recognised as of major importance. They comprise stamps showing the wrong watermark devices or stamps printed on paper with the wrong watermark. Stamps printed on paper showing broken or deformed bits on the dandy roll, are not listable.

This Catalogue includes watermark inverted and sideways inverted varieties on the stamps of Australia and the dependent territories.

CATALOGUE NEW ISSUE SUPPPLEMENTS

The first Supplement recording new stamps not in this Catalogue appeared in the February 1991 number of *Gibbons Stamp Monthly*. See page ix for a FREE copy and subscription details.

Australian States

12 Pence   = 1 Shilling
20 Shillings = 1 Pound

NEW SOUTH WALES

PRICES FOR STAMPS ON COVER

Nos. 1/83	from×	2
Nos. 84/108	from×	3
Nos. 109/10		—
No. 110b	from×	3
Nos. 111/13	from×	2
Nos. 114		—
Nos. 115/24	from×	2
Nos. 125/6		—
Nos. 127/53	from×	2
Nos. 154/70	from×	3
Nos. 171/2		—
No. 173	from×	2
Nos. 174/81		—
Nos. 186/202	from×	2
Nos. 203/6	from×	10
Nos. 207/21	from×	5
Nos. 222/39	from×	6
Nos. 240/1	from×	2
Nos. 241a/3	from×	10
Nos. 244/52		—
Nos. 253/73	from×	10
Nos. 274/80		—
Nos. 281/4	from×	15
Nos. 285/7	from×	10
Nos. 287c/d	from×	2
Nos. 288/97	from×	10
Nos. 298/312	from×	12
Nos. 313/28	from×	10
No. 329		—
Nos. 330/45	from×	12
No. 346		—
Nos. 347/60	from×	12
No. O1		—
Nos. O2/12	from×	4
Nos. O13/18		—
Nos. O19/34	from×	20
Nos. O35/8		—
Nos. O39/47	from×	40
Nos. O48/53		—
Nos. O54/8	from×	20
No. O59		—
Nos. D1/7	from×	50
Nos. D8/10		—
Nos. D11/15	from×	50

PRINTERS. The early issues of New South Wales were printed on a press supervised by the Inspector of Stamps. On 1 January 1857 this responsibility passed to the Government Printer who produced all subsequent issues, *unless otherwise stated.*

SPECIMEN OVERPRINTS. Those listed are from U.P.U. distributions between 1892 and 1903. Further "Specimen" overprints exist, but these were used for other purposes. From 1891 examples of some of these Specimens, together with cancelled stamps, were sold to collectors by the N.S.W. Post Office.

1

2

(Eng Robert Clayton, Sydney)

1850 (1 Jan). *T* **1**. *Plate I. No clouds.* (*a*) *Soft yellowish paper.*

1	1d. crimson-lake	£4000	£450
2	1d. carmine	£3750	£400
3	1d. reddish rose	£3500	£375
4	1d. brownish red	£3750	£400

(*b*) *Hard bluish paper*

5	1d. pale red	£3500	£350
6	1d. dull lake	£3500	£350

1850 (Aug). *T* **2**. *Plate I, re-engraved by H. C. Jervis, commonly termed Plate II. With clouds.* (*a*) *Hard toned white to yellowish paper.*

7	1d. vermilion	£2000	£300
8	1d. dull carmine	£2000	£300
	a. No trees on hill (R. 2/2)	£4500	£450
	b. Hill unshaded (R. 2/3)	£4500	£450
	c. Without clouds (R. 3/5)	£4500	£450

(*b*) *Hard greyish or bluish paper*

9	1d. crimson-lake	£2250	£300
10	1d. gooseberry-red	£2750	£425
11	1d. dull carmine	£2000	£250
12	1d. brownish red	£2000	£250
	a. No trees on hill (R. 2/2)	£4500	£450
	b. Hill unshaded (R. 2/3)	£4500	£450
	c. Without clouds (R. 3/5)	£4500	£450

(*c*) *Laid paper*

13	1d. carmine	£3500	£475
14	1d. vermilion	£4000	£450
	a. No trees on hill (R. 2/2)	—	£750
	b. Hill unshaded (R. 2/3)	—	£750
	c. Without clouds (R. 3/5)	—	£750

The varieties quoted with the letters "a", "b", "c" of course exist in each shade; the prices quoted are for the commonest shade, and the same applies to the following portions of this list.

Nos. 1/14 were printed in sheets of 25 (5×5).

3

4

A (Pl I)

Illustrations A, B, C and D are sketches of the lower part of the inner circular frame, showing the characteristic variations of each plate.

(Eng John Carmichael)

1850 (1 Jan). *Plate I. Vertical-lined background. T* **3**.

(*a*) *Early impressions, full details of clouds, etc.*

15	2d. greyish blue	£4000	£300
16	2d. deep blue	—	£350
	a. Double lines on bale (R. 2/7)	—	£550

(*b*) *Intermediate impressions*

16b	2d. greyish blue	£2750	£250
16c	2d. deep blue	£3000	£275

(*c*) *Later impressions, clouds, etc., mostly gone. T* **4**.

17	2d. blue	£1900	£120
18	2d. dull blue	£1500	£110

(*d*) *Stamps in the lower row partially retouched* (end Jan)

19	2d. blue	£2500	£190
20	2d. greyish blue	£2250	£160

5   B (Pl II)   C (Pl III)

(Plate entirely re-engraved by H. C. Jervis)

1850 (Apr). *T 5. Plate II. Horizontal-lined background. Bale on left side, supporting the seated figure, dated. Dot in centre of the star in each corner.* (a) *Early impressions.*

21	2d. indigo	£3250	£250
22	2d. lilac-blue	—	£1000
23	2d. grey-blue	£3250	£200
24	2d. bright blue	£3250	£200
	a. Fan as in Pl II, but with shading outside (R. 1/1)	—	£375
	b. Fan as in Pl III, but without shading, and inner circle intersects the fan (R. 1/2)	—	£375
	c. Pick and shovel omitted (R. 1/10)	—	£375
	d. "CREVIT" omitted (R. 2/1)	—	£500
	e. No whip (R. 1/4, 1/8, 2/8)	—	£300

(b) *Worn impressions*

25	2d. dull blue	£1600	£100
26	2d. Prussian blue	£1700	£150
	a. Fan as in Pl III, but with shading outside (R. 1/1)	—	£300
	b. Fan as in Pl III, but without shading, and inner circle intersects the fan (R. 1/2)	—	£300
	c. Pick and shovel omitted (R. 1/10)	—	£300
	d. "CREVIT" omitted (R. 2/1)	—	£350
	e. No whip (R. 1/4, 1/8, 2/8)	—	£200

(c) *Bottom row retouched with dots and dashes in lower spandrels* (Aug)

27	2d. Prussian blue	£2250	£180
28	2d. dull blue	£2000	£110
	a. No whip (R. 2/8)	—	£250
	b. "CREVIT" omitted (R. 2/1)	—	£300

(Plate re-engraved a second time by H. C. Jervis)

1850 (Sept). *Plate III. Bale not dated and single-lined, except on No. 30c, which are double-lined. No dots on stars.*

29	2d. ultramarine	£1900	£140
30	2d. deep blue	£1800	£140
	a. No whip (R. 2/3, 2/7)	—	£225
	b. Fan with 6 segments (R. 2/8)	—	£375
	c. Double lines on bale (R. 1/7, 1/10, 1/12)	—	£225

(Plate re-engraved a third time by H. C. Jervis)

1851 (Jan). *Plate IV. Double-lined bale, and circle in centre of each star.*

(a) *Hard bluish grey wove paper.*

31	2d. ultramarine	£2250	£140
32	2d. Prussian blue	£1900	£110
33	2d. bright blue	£2000	£120
	a. Hill not shaded (R. 1/12)	—	£200
	b. Fan with 6 segments (R. 2/8)	—	£200
	c. No clouds (R. 2/10)	—	£200
	d. Retouch (R. 2/1)	—	£275
	e. No waves (R. 1/9, 2/5)	—	£190

(b) *Stout yellowish vertically laid paper*

34	2d. ultramarine	£2250	£140
35	2d. Prussian blue	£2500	£120
	a. Hill not shaded (R. 1/12)	—	£225
	b. Fan with 6 segments (R. 2/8)	—	£225
	c. No clouds (R. 2/10)	—	£225
	d. Retouch (R. 2/1)	—	£300
	e. No waves (R. 1/9, 2/8)	—	£200
	f. "PENOE" (R. 2/12)		

The retouch, Nos. 33d and 35d, occurs outside the left margin line on R. 2/1.

6   D (Pl V)   7

(Plate re-engraved a fourth time by H. C. Jervis)

1851 (Apr). *T 6. Plate V. Pearl in fan.* (a) *Hard greyish wove paper.*

36	2d. ultramarine	£2000	£120
37	2d. dull blue	£2000	£120
	a. Pick and shovel omitted (R. 2/5)	—	£250
	b. Fan with 6 segments (R. 2/8)	—	£250

(b) *Stout yellowish vertically laid paper*

38	2d. dull ultramarine	£3500	£250
	a. Pick and shovel omitted (R. 2/5)	—	£400
	b. Fan with 6 segments (R. 2/8)	—	£400

Nos. 15/38 were printed in sheets of 24 (12 × 2), although the existence of inter-panneau *tête bêche* pairs from Plate II, and reportedly Plate III, indicates that the printer applied two impressions of the plate to each sheet of paper. The two pairs were normally separated before issue.

The original plate, I, was re-cut four times to form Plate II to V. An interesting variety occurs on R. 1/9–11 and 2/7 in all five plates. It consists of ten loops of the engine-turning on each side of the design instead of the normal nine loops.

(Eng H. C. Jervis)

1850. *T 7.* (a) *Soft yellowish wove paper.*

39	3d. yellow-green	£2500	£200
40	3d. myrtle-green	£10000	£1000
41	3d. emerald-green	£2750	£200
	a. No whip (R. 4/3–4)	—	£375
	b. "SIGIIIUM" for "SIGILLUM" (R. 5/3)	—	£375

(b) *Bluish to grey wove paper*

42	3d. yellow-green	£1900	£190
43	3d. emerald-green	£1900	£190
	b. No whip (R. 4/3–4)	—	£225
	c. "SIGIIIUM" for "SIGILLUM" (R. 5/3)	—	£300

(c) *Yellowish to bluish laid paper*

43d	3d. bright green	£5000	£400
43e	3d. yellowish green	£4500	£350
	f. No whip (R. 4/3–4)	—	£600
	g. "SIGIIIUM" for "SIGILLUM" (R. 5/3)	—	£600

Nos. 39/43e were printed in sheets of 25 (5 × 5).

8   9

(Des A. W. Manning from sketch by W. T. Levine; eng on steel by John Carmichael, Sydney)

1851 (18 Dec)–**52**. *T 8. Imperf.* (a) *Thick yellowish wove paper.*

44	1d. carmine	£1700	£180
	a. No leaves right of "SOUTH"	—	£350
	b. Two leaves right of "SOUTH"	—	£350
	c. "WALE"	—	£400

(b) *Bluish medium wove paper* (1852)

45	1d. carmine	£1000	£120
46	1d. scarlet	£1000	£120
47	1d. vermilion	£900	£100
48	1d. brick-red	£900	£100
	a. No leaves right of "SOUTH" (Nos. 7 and 8)	—	£200
	b. Two leaves right of "SOUTH" (No. 15)	—	£300
	c. "WALE" (No. 9)	—	£300

(c) *Thick vertically laid bluish paper* (1852?)

49	1d. orange-brown	£2750	£300
50	1d. claret	£2750	£300
	a. No leaves right of "SOUTH"	—	£500
	b. Two leaves right of "SOUTH"	—	£500
	c. "WALE"	—	£500

(Eng on steel by John Carmichael)

1851 (24 July). *T 8. Plate I. Imperf.* (a) *Thick yellowish wove paper.*

51	2d. ultramarine	£650	80·00

(b) *Fine impressions, blue to greyish medium paper*

52	2d. ultramarine	£700	30·00
53	2d. chalky blue	£600	30·00
54	2d. dark blue	£600	30·00
55	2d. greyish blue	£600	30·00

(c) Worn plate, blue to greyish medium paper
56	2d. ultramarine	£425	30·00
57	2d. Prussian blue	£425	30·00

(d) Worn plate, blue wove medium paper
58	2d. ultramarine	£325	30·00
59	2d. Prussian blue	£300	30·00

(Plate II eng H. C. Jervis)

1853 (Oct).   *T* **9**. *Plate II. Stars in corners. Imperf.*

(a) Bluish medium to thick wove paper
60	2d. deep ultramarine	£900	£110
61	2d. indigo	£1000	80·00
	a. "WAEES" (No. 23)	—	£350

(b) Worn plate, hard blue wove paper
62	2d. deep Prussian blue	£900	£100
	a. "WAEES" (No. 23)	—	£325

1855 (Sept).   *Plate III, being Plate I re-engraved by H. C. Jervis. Background of crossed lines. Imperf.*

(a) Medium bluish wove paper
63	2d. Prussian blue	£450	55·00
	a. "WALES" covered with wavy lines (No. 3)	—	£150

(b) Stout white wove paper
64	2d. Prussian blue	£450	55·00
	a. "WALES" covered with wavy lines (No. 3)	—	£190

(Eng John Carmichael)

1852 (3 Dec).   *T* **8**. *Imperf. (a) Medium greyish blue wove paper.*
65	3d. deep green	£1600	£200
66	3d. green	£1300	£140
67	3d. dull yellow-green	£1200	£100
	a. "WAEES" (No. 37)	—	£350

(b) Thick blue wove paper
69	3d. emerald-green	£1300	£200
71	3d. blue-green	£1300	£200
	a. "WAEES" (No. 37)	—	£500

1853 (Apr).   *As T* **8**. *Fine background. Imperf.*

(a) Medium white wove paper
72	6d. vandyke-brown	—	£900
	a. "WALLS" (No. 8)	—	£1500

(b) Medium bluish grey wove paper
73	6d. vandyke-brown	£1700	£250
74	6d. yellow-brown	£1800	£275
75	6d. chocolate-brown	£1700	£250
76	6d. grey-brown	£1600	£250
	a. "WALLS" (No. 8)	—	£500

1853 (June).   *Plate I re-engraved by H. C. Jervis. Coarse background. Imperf.*
77	6d. brown	£1800	£300
78	6d. grey-brown	£1700	£300

(Eng H. C. Jervis)

1853 (May).   *Medium bluish paper. Imperf.*
79	8d. dull yellow	£3250	£500
80	8d. orange-yellow	£3250	£550
81	8d. orange	£3500	£500
	a. No bow at back of head (No. 9)	—	£1200
	b. No leaves right of "SOUTH" (No. 21)	—	£1200
	c. No lines in spandrel (Nos. 12, 22 and 32)	—	£800

10   13   14

1854 (Feb).   *T* **8**. *Wmk* "**1**", *T* **10**. *Imperf. Yellowish wove paper.*
82	1d. red-orange	£170	15·00
83	1d. orange-vermilion	£170	15·00
	a. No leaves right of "SOUTH" (Nos. 7 and 21)	£325	85·00
	b. Two leaves right of "SOUTH" (No. 15)	£425	£120
	c. "WALE" (No. 9)	£425	£120

1854 (Jan).   *Plate III. Wmk* "**2**". *Imperf.*
84	2d. ultramarine	£100	10·00
85	2d. Prussian blue	£100	10·00
86	2d. chalky blue	£100	7·00
	a. "WALES" partly covered	£400	50·00

1854 (Mar).   *Wmk* "**3**". *Imperf.*
87	3d. yellow-green	£180	25·00
	a. "WAEES" (No. 37)	—	£120
	b. Error. Wmk "2"	—	£2250

(Eng John Carmichael)

1856 (1 Jan).   *For Registered Letters. T* **13**. *No wmk. Imperf. Soft medium yellowish paper.*
88	(6d.) vermilion and Prussian blue	£700	£150
	a. Frame printed on back	£2500	£1000
89	(6d.) salmon and indigo	£700	£170
90	(6d.) orange and Prussian blue	£700	£200
91	(6d.) orange and indigo	£700	£180

1859 (Apr)–**60**.   *Hard medium bluish wove paper, with manufacturer's wmk in sans-serif, double-lined capitals across sheet and only showing portions of letters on a few stamps in a sheet. (a) Imperf.*
92	(6d.) orange and Prussian blue	£700	£130
92a	(6d.) vermilion and Prussian blue	£850	£180

(b) P 12 (2.60)
93	(6d.) orange and Prussian blue	£350	40·00
94	(6d.) orange and indigo	£325	40·00

1860 (Feb)–**62**.   *Coarse yellowish wove paper having the manufacturer's wmk in Roman capitals. (a) P* 12.
95	(6d.) rose-red and Prussian blue	£250	35·00
96	(6d.) rose-red and indigo	£325	80·00
97	(6d.) salmon and indigo		

(b) P 13 (1862)
98	(6d.) rose-red and Prussian blue	£225	50·00

1863 (May).   *Yellowish wove paper. Wmk* "**6**". *P* 13.
99	(6d.) rose-red and Prussian blue	90·00	15·00
100	(6d.) rose-red and indigo	£140	17·00
101	(6d.) rose-red and pale blue	65·00	15·00
	a. Double impression of frame	—	£1500

(T **14/21** and **24** printed by the New South Wales Govt Ptg Dept from plates engraved by Perkins, Bacon & Co)

Two plates of the 2d. and 6d. were used. On Plate II of the 2d. the stamps are wider apart and more regularly spaced than on Plate I.

1856 (6 Apr).   *Wmk* "**1**". *Imperf.*
102	**14** 1d. orange-vermilion	£130	22·00
	a. Error. Wmk "**2**"		
103	1d. carmine-vermilion	£130	22·00
104	1d. orange-red	£130	22·00
	a. Printed on both sides	—	£1400

1856 (7 Jan).   *Plate I. Wmk* "**2**". *Imperf.*
105	**14** 2d. light ultramarine	£140	8·00
106	2d. Prussian blue	£130	8·00
107	2d. dull blue	£130	8·00
108	2d. pale blue	£130	8·00
	a. Error. Wmk "1"	—	£4000
	b. Error. Wmk "5"	£450	60·00
	c. Error. Wmk "8"		

1858.   *Plate I, retouched.*
109	**14** 2d. dull blue	£1800	£450

1859 (3 Aug).   *Lithographic transfer of Plate I.*
110	**14** 2d. pale cobalt-blue	—	£750
	a. Retouched	—	£2500

1860 (Jan).   *Plate II. Recess. Stamps printed wider apart.*
110b	**14** 2d. blue	£350	12·00

1856 (10 Oct). *Wmk "3". Imperf.*

111	**14**	3d. yellow-green	£700	80·00
112		3d. bluish green	£750	80·00
113		3d. dull green	£750	80·00
		a. Error. Wmk "2"	—	£3000

In the 3d. the value is in block letters on a white ground.

15   17

19   21

(6d. and 1s. des E. H. Corbould after sketches by T. W. Levinge)

1855 (1 Dec). *Wmk "5". Imperf.*

114	**15**	5d. dull green	£1000	£475

1854 (Feb)–**59**. *Wmk "6". Imperf.*

115	**17**	6d. deep slate	£450	32·00
116		6d. greenish grey	£350	32·00
117		6d. slate-green	£350	£100
		a. Printed both sides		
118		6d. bluish grey	£400	55·00
119		6d. fawn	£450	95·00
		a. Error. Wmk "8" (15.8.59)	£1500	£100
120		6d. grey	£400	55·00
121		6d. olive-grey	£400	32·00
122		6d. greyish brown	£400	32·00
		a. Error. Wmk "8" (15.8.59)	£1500	£100

1855 (1 Dec). *Wmk "8". Imperf.*

125	**19**	8d. golden yellow	£3000	£700
126		8d. dull yellow-orange	£3000	£700

1854 (Feb). *Wmk "12". Imperf.*

127	**21**	1s. rosy vermilion	£650	65·00
		a. Error. Wmk "8" (20.6.57)	£1900	£170
128		1s. pale red	£650	65·00
129		1s. brownish red	£700	75·00

1860 (Feb)–**63**. *Wmk double-lined figure of value. P 12.*

131	**14**	1d. orange-red	£170	16·00
		a. Imperf between (pair)		
		b. Double impression		
132		1d. scarlet	£100	16·00
133		2d. cobalt-blue (Pl I)	£500	£140
		a. Retouched	—	£1300
134		2d. greenish blue (Pl II)	90·00	10·00
136		2d. Prussian blue (Pl II)	90·00	10·00
		a. Error. Wmk "1"	—	£2750
		b. Retouched (shades)	—	£400
137		2d. Prussian blue (Pl I) (3.61)	£110	11·00
138		2d. dull blue (Pl I)	£100	10·00
139		3d. yellow-green (1860)	£1000	55·00
140		3d. blue-green	£550	42·00
141	**15**	5d. dull green (1863)	£100	36·00
142		5d. yellowish green (1863)	£100	36·00
143	**17**	6d. grey-brown	£275	45·00
144		6d. olive-brown	£275	55·00
145		6d. greenish grey	£350	45·00
146		6d. fawn	£325	65·00
147		6d. mauve	£300	35·00
148		6d. violet	£275	16·00
		a. Imperf between (pair)		
149	**19**	8d. lemon-yellow	—	£1400
150		8d. orange	£2000	£600
151		8d. red-orange	£2000	£600

152	**21**	1s. brownish red	£450	48·00
153		1s. rose-carmine	£450	48·00
		a. Imperf between (pair)		

No. 133 was made by perforating a small remaining stock of No. 108.
Nos. 137/8 were printed from the original plate after its return from London, where it had been repaired.

1862–72. *Wmk double-lined figure of value. (a) P 13.*

154	**14**	1d. scarlet (1862)	55·00	8·00
155		1d. dull red	55·00	8·00
156		3d. blue-green (12.62)	45·00	11·00
157		3d. yellow-green	50·00	8·50
		a. Error. Wmk "6" (7.72)	50·00	12·00
158		3d. dull green	50·00	8·00
		a. Error. Wmk "6" (7.72)	55·00	15·00
160	**15**	5d. bluish green (12.63)	35·00	15·00
161		5d. bright yellow-green (8.65)	38·00	24·00
162		5d. sea-green (1866)	38·00	17·00
162a		5d. dark bluish green (11.70)	28·00	17·00
163	**17**	6d. reddish purple (Pl I) (7.62)	60·00	5·00
164		6d. mauve	60·00	5·00
165		6d. purple (Pl II) (1864)	55·00	4·50
		a. Error. Wmk "5" (7.66)	£350	25·00
		b. Error. Wmk "12" (12.66)	£275	20·00
166		6d. violet	55·00	6·00
167		6d. aniline mauve	£900	£120
167a	**19**	8d. red-orange	£140	55·00
167b		8d. yellow-orange	£140	40·00
167c		8d. bright yellow	£140	40·00
168	**21**	1s. rose-carmine	70·00	7·50
169		1s. carmine	70·00	8·00
170		1s. crimson-lake	70·00	8·00

(b) *Perf compound 12 × 13*

171	**14**	1d. scarlet	—	£1700
172		2d. dull blue	£2000	£250

23

1864 (June). *W 23. P 13.*

173	**14**	1d. pale red	30·00	12·00

24   25

(Des E. H. Corbould, R.I.)

1861–88. *W 25. Various perfs.*

174	**24**	5s. dull violet, p 12 (1861)	£1000	£325
		a. Perf 13 (1861)	£160	28·00
175		5s. royal purple, p 13 (1872)	£275	45·00
176		5s. deep rose-lilac, p 13 (1875)	95·00	28·00
177		5s. deep purple, p 13 (1880)	£150	40·00
		a. Perf 10 (1882)	£150	45·00
178		5s. rose-lilac, p 10 (1883)	£110	40·00
179		5s. purple, p 12 (1885)	—	45·00
		a. Perf 10 × 12 (1885)	—	£120
180		5s. reddish purple, p 10 (1886)	£110	40·00
		a. Perf 12 × 10 (1887)	£275	45·00
181		5s. rose-lilac, p 11 (1888)	—	£120

This value was replaced by Nos. 261, etc. in 1888 but reissued in 1897, *see* Nos. 297c/e.

28   **36**   **37**   **38**

(Printed by De La Rue & Co, Ltd, London and perf at Somerset House, London)

1862–65. *Surfaced paper. P* 14. (i) *W* **23**.
186	**26**	1d. dull red (Pl I) (4.64)	80·00	28·00

(ii) *No wmk*
187	**26**	1d. dull red (Pl II) (1.65)	60·00	28·00
188	**28**	2d. pale blue (3.62)	60·00	28·00

(Printed from the De La Rue plates in the Colony)

1862 (12 Apr). *Wmk double-lined "2". P* 13.
189	**28**	2d. blue	45·00	7·00
		a. Perf 12	£120	12·00
		b. Perf 12 × 13	£400	

1864–65. *W* **23**. *P* 13.
190	**26**	1d. dark red-brown (Pl I)	70·00	14·00
191		1d. brownish red (Pl II)	18·00	1·50
192		1d. brick-red (Pl II)	18·00	1·50
		a. Highly surfaced paper (1865)	£180	
194	**28**	2d. pale blue	£110	3·50

Plates I and II were made from the same die; they can only be distinguished by the colour or by the marginal inscription.

1865–66. *Thin wove paper. No wmk. P* 13.
195	**26**	1d. brick-red	90·00	15·00
196		1d. brownish red	90·00	15·00
197	**28**	2d. pale blue	40·00	3·00

1863–69. *W* **29**. *P* 13.
198	**26**	1d. pale red (3.69)	70·00	11·00
199	**28**	2d. pale blue	8·50	50
		a. Perf 12	£110	
200		2d. cobalt-blue	8·50	50
201		2d. Prussian blue	21·00	3·50

1862 (Sept). *Wmk double-lined "5". P* 13.
202	**28**	2d. dull blue	60·00	8·50

32   **34**

33   **35**

1867 (Sept)–**93**. *W* **33** *and* **35**.
203	**32**	4d. red-brown, *p* 13	32·00	3·00
204		4d. pale red-brown, *p* 13	32·00	3·00
205	**34**	10d. lilac, *p* 13 (Optd S. £25)	12·00	3·00
		a. Imperf between (pair)	£400	
206		10d. lilac, *p* 11 (1893)	13·00	3·00
		a. Perf 10	15·00	4·50
		b. Perf 10 and 11, compound	20·00	7·50
		c. Perf 12 × 11	£110	15·00

NINEPENCE

(39)

From 1871 to 1903 the 9d. is formed from the 10d. by a *black* surch. (T **39**), 15 mm long on Nos. 219 to 220h, and 13½ mm long on subsequent issues.

1871–85. *W* **36**.
207	**26**	1d. dull red, *p* 13 (8.71)	5·00	20
		a. Imperf vert (horiz pair)		
208		1d. salmon, *p* 13	5·00	20
		a. Perf 10	£250	15·00
		b. Perf 13 × 10	16·00	20
		c. *Scarlet.* Perf 10	—	£180
209	**28**	2d. Prussian-blue, *p* 13 (11.71).	6·50	20
		a. Perf 11 × 12, comb	£250	40·00
		b. Imperf vert (horiz pair)	—	£500
210		2d. pale blue, *p* 13	6·50	20
		aa. "TWO PENCE" double impression at right	—	30·00
		a. Perf 10	£250	22·00
		b. Perf 13 × 10	7·00	20
		c. Surfaced paper. Perf 13		
211	**14**	3d. yellow-green (3.74), *p* 13	18·00	2·40
		a. Perf 10	65·00	5·50
		b. Perf 11	£150	£100
		c. Perf 12	—	£150
		d. Perf 10 × 12	£150	32·00
		e. Perf 12 × 11	£120	32·00
212		3d. bright green, *p* 10	£120	11·00
		a. Perf 10 × 13	£110	15·00
213	**32**	4d. pale red-brown (8.77), *p* 13	50·00	6·00
214		4d. red-brown, *p* 13	50·00	6·00
		a. Perf 10	£180	50·00
		b. Perf 13 × 10	75·00	3·50
215	**15**	5d. bluish green (8.84), *p* 10	15·00	8·00
		a. Perf 12 (5.85)	£250	£100
		b. Perf 13 × 10		
		c. Perf 10 × 12	19·00	9·00
216	**37**	6d. bright mauve (1.72), *p* 13	30·00	1·00
		a. Imperf between (horiz pair)	—	£500
217		6d. pale lilac, *p* 13	35·00	1·00
		a. Perf 10	£180	12·00
		b. Perf 13 × 10	55·00	1·90
		c. Imperf between (horiz pair). Perf 13 × 10	—	£500
218	**19**	8d. yellow (3.77), *p* 13	90·00	17·00
		a. Perf 10	£250	24·00
		b. Perf 13 × 10	£170	22·00
219	**34**	9d. on 10d. pale red-brown (8.71), *p* 13	20·00	4·50
220		9d. on 10d. red-brown, *p* 13 (Optd S. £25) . .	20·00	6·00
		a. Perf 10	11·00	4·50
		b. Perf 12	11·00	4·50
		c. Perf 11	26·00	7·00
		d. Perf 10 × 12	£250	£160
		e. Perf 10 × 11	42·00	9·00
		f. Perf 12 × 11	14·00	5·50
		g. Perf 11 × 12, comb	14·00	5·50
		h. In black and blue. Perf 11	£110	
221	**38**	1s. black (4.76), *p* 13	80·00	2·50
		a. Perf 10	£325	12·00
		b. Perf 10 × 13	£170	4·50
		c. Perf 11		
		d. Imperf between (horiz pair)	—	£750

Collectors should note that the classification of perforations is that adopted by the Royal Philatelic Society, London. "Perf 12" denotes the perforation formerly called "11½, 12" and "perf 13" that formerly called "12½, 13".

40   41

1882–97. *W* **40.**

222	**26**	1d. salmon, *p* 10	9·50	20
		a. Perf 13		
		b. Perf 10 × 13	28·00	1·50
223		1d. orange *to* scarlet, *p* 13	8·00	20
		a. Perf 10		
		ab. Imperf between (horiz pair)		
		b. Perf 10 × 13	£120	6·00
		c. Perf 10 × 12	£250	65·00
		d. Perf 10 × 11	£450	£120
		e. Perf 12 × 11	—	£120
		f. Perf 11 × 12, comb	5·50	25
		h. Perf 11	—	£130
224	**28**	2d. pale blue, *p* 13	£450	90·00
		a. Perf 10	9·00	25
		b. Perf 13 × 10	65·00	2·00
225		2d. Prussian blue, *p* 10	17·00	25
		a. Perf 13 × 10	65·00	1·90
		b. Perf 12	—	£225
		c. Perf 11	—	£100
		d. Perf 12 × 11	—	£100
		e. Perf 12 × 10	£225	65·00
		f. Perf 10 × 11	£450	£100
		g. Perf 11 × 12, comb	12·00	15
226	**14**	3d. yellow-green (1886), *p* 10	5·00	80
		a. Perf 10 × 12	£160	15·00
		b. Perf 11	5·00	80
		c. Perf 11 × 12 or 12 × 11	5·00	80
		d. Perf 12	9·00	1·00
		e. Imperf between (horiz pair)	£130	
		f. Imperf (pair)	£110	
227		3d. bluish green, *p* 10	5·00	80
		a. Perf 11	5·00	80
		b. Perf 10 × 11	15·00	1·50
		c. Perf 12 × 11	5·00	1·00
		d. Perf 12 × 10	75·00	3·00
228		3d. emerald-green, *p* 10 (1893)	55·00	7·50
		a. Perf 10 × 11	55·00	3·00
		b. Perf 12 × 10	80·00	8·00
229	**32**	4d. red-brown, *p* 10	32·00	2·00
		a. Perf 10 × 12	—	£130
		b. Perf 11 × 12, comb	42·00	1·25
230		4d. dark brown, *p* 10	42·00	2·75
		a. Perf 12	—	35·00
		b. Perf 10 × 12	—	90·00
		c. Perf 11 × 12, comb	14·00	1·00
231	**15**	5d. dull green, *p* 10 (1890), (Optd S. £25)	12·00	90
		a. Perf 11 × 10	30·00	2·00
		b. Perf 12 × 10 (4.85)	80·00	3·50
232		5d. bright green, *p* 10 (4.82)	32·00	4·50
		a. Perf 11 (12.85)	—	4·50
		b. Perf 10 × 11 (12.85)	38·00	4·50
		c. Perf 12 × 10 (4.85)	£150	6·50
233		5d. blue-green, *p* 10 (4.82)	8·50	90
		a. Perf 12 (4.85)	11·00	90
		b. Perf 11 (12.85)	8·50	55
		c. Perf 10 × 11 (12.85)	24·00	1·60
		d. Perf 11 × 12 or 12 × 11	6·50	55
		e. Imperf (pair)	£275	
234	**37**	6d. pale lilac, *p* 10	30·00	1·00
		a. Perf 10 × 13 or 13 × 10	—	£300
		b. Perf 10 × 12 or 12 × 10	38·00	1·50
235		6d. mauve, *p* 10	35·00	1·00
		a. Perf 12	80·00	2·50
		b. Perf 11	80·00	8·00
		c. Perf 10 × 12 or 12 × 10	32·00	1·00
		ca. Imperf between (horiz pair). Perf 12 × 10	—	£650
		d. Perf 11 × 12 or 12 × 11	32·00	1·40
		e. Perf 10 × 11	55·00	1·00
236	**19**	8d. yellow, *p* 10 (1883)	£100	15·00
		a. Perf 12	£150	24·00
		b. Perf 11	£100	17·00
		c. Perf 10 × 12	£130	22·00

236*d*	**34**	9d. on 10d. red-brown, *p* 11 × 12 (1897) (Optd S. £25)	8·00	3·75
		da. Perf 12	11·00	5·00
		db. Perf 11	11·00	5·50
		dc. Surch double, *p* 11	£140	£120
236*e*		10d. violet, *p* 11 × 12 (1897) (Optd S. £25)	12·00	3·25
		ea. Perf 12 × 11½	12·00	3·25
		eb. Perf 12	15·00	4·00
		ec. Perf 11	15·00	4·00
237	**38**	1s. black, *p* 10	65·00	2·00
		a. Perf 11	£200	9·00
		b. Perf 10 × 12		
		c. Perf 10 × 13	—	11·00
		d. Perf 11 × 12, comb	65·00	2·00

1886–87. *W* **41.**

238	**26**	1d. scarlet, *p* 10	11·00	3·75
		a. Perf 11 × 12, comb	3·50	90
239	**28**	2d. deep blue, *p* 10	32·00	5·00
		a. Perf 11 × 12, comb	12·00	95
		b. Imperf		

1891 (July).   *Wmk* "10" *as T* **35.** *P* 10.

240	**14**	3d. green (Optd S. £25)	12·00	80·00
241		3d. dark green	5·00	17·00

42   43

NOTE. The spacing between the Crown and "NSW" is 1 mm in T **42**, as against 2 mm in T **40**.

1903–8. *W* **42.**

241*a*	**14**	3d. yellow-green, *p* 11	6·00	90
		b. Perf 12	5·00	90
		c. Perf 11 × 12	5·00	90
242		3d. dull green, *p* 12	19·00	1·75
		a. Perf 11 × 12	7·00	1·00
243	**15**	5d. dark blue-green, *p* 11 × 12	5·50	90
		a. Perf 11	12·00	90
		b. Perf 12	19·00	3·50
		c. Imperf (pair)	£125	
		d. Wmk sideways		

1885–86. *W* **41.** (i) *Overprinted* "POSTAGE", *in black.*

244	**43**	5s. green and lilac, *p* 13		
		a. Perf 10		
		b. Perf 12 × 10	£300	80·00
245		10s. claret and lilac, *p* 13	£400	£120
		a. Perf 12		
246		£1 claret and lilac, *p* 13	—	£2000
		a. Perf 12	£2000	£900

(ii) *Overprinted in blue*

247	**43**	10s. claret and mauve, *p* 10 (Optd S. £60)	£450	£100
		a. Perf 12	£130	40·00
		b. Perf 12 × 11	£225	
248		£1 claret and rose-lilac, *p* 12 × 10	£2250	£1000

44

1894. *Overprinted "POSTAGE" in blue. W 44.*

249	**43**	10s. claret and mauve, *p* 10	£200	38·00
249*a*		10s. claret and violet, *p* 12	£110	28·00
		b. Perf 11	£100	28·00
		c. Perf 12 × 11	£100	28·00
250		10s. aniline crimson and violet, *p* 12 × 11 . . .	£120	30·00
		a. Perf 12	£140	40·00
250*b*		£1 claret and violet, *p* 12 × 11		

1903–04. *Optd "POSTAGE" in blue. Chalk-surfaced paper. W 44.*

250*c*	**43**	10s. aniline crimson and violet, *p* 12 × 11 . . .		
251		10s. rosine and violet, *p* 12 (1904)	£100	28·00
		a. Perf 11	£120	28·00
		b. Perf 12 × 11	£120	28·00
252		10s. claret and violet, *p* 12 × 11 (1904)	£170	28·00

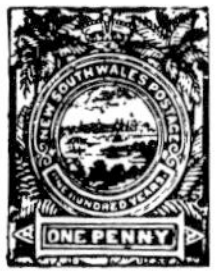

45 View of Sydney   47 Captain Cook

48 Queen Victoria   49 Superb Lyrebird    50 Eastern
and Arms of Colony   Grey Kangaroo

51 Map of Australia    52 Capt. Arthur Phillip, first
                         Governor and Lord Carrington,
                         Governor in 1888

(Des M. Tannenberg (1d., 6d.), Miss Devine (2d., 8d.), H. Barraclough (4d.), Govt Ptg Office (1s.), C. Turner (5s.), Mrs. F. Stoddard (20s.). Eng W. Bell).

1888 (1 May)–**89.** *Centenary of New South Wales. (a) W 40. P 11 × 12.*

253	**45**	1d. lilac (9.7.88)	3·75	10
		a. Perf 12 × 11½	17·00	90
		b. Perf 12	5·00	10
		c. Imperf (pair)		
		d. Mauve	3·75	10
		da. Imperf between (pair)		
		db. Perf 12 × 11½	6·00	25
		dc. Perf 12	5·50	25
254	**46**	2d. Prussian blue (1.9.88)	3·25	10
		a. Imperf (pair)	£100	
		b. Imperf between (pair)	£350	
		c. Perf 12 × 11½	7·00	10
		d. Perf 12	5·00	10
		e. Chalky blue	3·25	10
		ea. Perf 12 × 11½		
		eb. Perf 12	4·25	25
255	**47**	4d. purple-brown (8.10.88)	9·00	3·00
		a. Perf 12 × 11½	28·00	7·50
		b. Perf 12	24·00	3·25
		c. Perf 11	£300	90·00
		d. Red-brown	9·00	3·00
		da. Perf 12 × 11½	13·00	2·75
		db. Perf 12	13·00	2·75
		e. Orange-brown, p 12 × 11½	13·00	2·75
		f. Yellow-brown, p 12 × 11½	10·00	3·00

256	**48**	6d. carmine (26.11.88)	20·00	2·50
		a. Perf 12 × 11½	25·00	3·00
		b. Perf 12	21·00	2·50
257	**49**	8d. lilac-rose (17.1.89)	11·00	1·50
		a. Perf 12 × 11½	35·00	10·00
		b. Perf 12	11·00	1·75
		c. Magenta	75·00	9·00
		ca. Perf 12 × 11½	11·00	1·75
		cb. Perf 12	11·00	2·25
258	**50**	1s. maroon (21.2.89)	12·00	90
		a. Perf 12 × 11½	14·00	90
		b. Perf 12	18·00	90
		c. Violet-brown	12·00	90
		ca. Imperf (pair)	£550	
		cb. Perf 12 × 11½	38·00	1·25
		cc. Perf 12	38·00	90

(b) W 41. P 11 × 12

259	**45**	1d. lilac (1888)	9·00	
		a. Mauve	7·50	10
260	**46**	2d. Prussian blue (1888)	40·00	3·00

(c) W 25. P 10

261	**51**	5s. deep purple (13.3.89)	£225	45·00
		a. Deep violet	£200	42·00
262	**52**	20s. cobalt-blue	£300	£110
		Set of 6 (1*d.* to 1s.) *optd "Specimen"* . .	£150	

Nos. 255c and 261/2 are line perforated, the remainder are comb.

53   54

1890. *W 53 (5s.) or 54 (20s.). P 10.*

263	**51**	5s. lilac	£150	27·00
		a. Perf 11	£225	38·00
		ab. Imperf between (horiz pair)		
		b. Perf 12	£300	38·00
		c. Perf 10 × 11 or 11 × 10	£225	27·00
		d. Mauve	£225	27·00
		da. Perf 11	£225	38·00
264	**52**	20s. cobalt-blue	£225	80·00
		a. Perf 11	£300	75·00
		b. Perf 11 × 10		
		c. Ultramarine, p 11	£225	75·00
		ca. Perf 12	£325	£130
		cb. Perf 11 × 12 or 12 × 11	£225	75·00
		Set of 2 *optd "Specimen"*	£225	

55 Allegorical figure   (56)   (57)
of Australia

SEVEN-PENCE

Halfpenny   **HALFPENNY**

1890 (22 Dec). *W 40.*

281	**55**	2½d. ultramarine, *p* 11 × 12 *comb* (Optd S. £25)	2·00	40
		a. Perf 12 × 11½, comb	45·00	
		b. Perf 12, comb	7·00	40

1891 (5 Jan). *Surch as T 56 and 57. W 40.*

282	**26**	½d. on 1d. grey, *p* 11 × 12 *comb*	1·50	1·75
		a. Surch omitted		
		b. Surch double	£120	

283	**37**	7½d. on 6d. brown, *p* 10	3·50	2·00
		a. Perf 11	3·50	2·00
		b. Perf 12	4·00	3·00
		c. Perf 11 × 12	3·75	2·75
		d. Perf 10 × 12	4·00	2·75
284	**38**	12½d. on 1s. red, *p* 10	7·50	6·50
		a. Perf 11	8·50	6·50
		b. Perf 11 × 12, comb	7·50	6·00
		c. Perf 12 × 11½, comb	5·00	6·00
		d. Perf 12, comb	9·00	6·00
		Set of 3 optd "Specimen"	70·00	

58

Die I

1892 (21 Mar)–**99**. *T* **58**. *Die I. Narrow "H" in "HALF"*. *W* **40**.

285	½d. grey, *p* 10	12·00	45
	a. Perf 11	60·00	5·00
	b. Perf 10 × 12	55·00	7·50
	c. Perf 11 × 12 (Optd S. £20)	70·00	10
	d. Perf 12	90·00	10
286	½d. slate, *p* 11 × 12 (1897).	80	10
	a. Perf 12 × 11½	80	10
	b. Perf 12	80	10
	c. Imperf between (horiz pair). Perf 11 × 12	£400	
287	½d. bluish green, *p* 11 × 12 (1899).	1·50	10
	a. Perf 12 × 11½	70	10
	b. Perf 12	80	10

The perforations 11 × 12, 12 × 11½, 12, are from comb machines.

58a

58b

(Des C. Turner. Typo Govt Printing Office, Sydney)

1897. *Charity. T* **58***a and* **58***b. W* **40**. *P* 12 × 11 (1*d*.) *or* 11 (2½*d*.).

287*c*	**58***a*	1d. (1s.) green and brown (22.6)	40·00	40·00
287*d*	**58***b*	2½d. (2s. 6d.) gold, carmine & blue (28.6) .	£150	£150
		Set of 2	£190	£190
		Set of 2 optd "Specimen"	£200	

These stamps, sold at 1s. and 2s. 6d. respectively, paid postage of 1d. and 2½d. only, the difference being given to a Consumptives' Home.

59

60

61

Dies of the 1d.

Die I   Die II

1d. Die I. The first pearl on the crown on the left side is merged into the arch, the shading under the fleur-de-lis is indistinct, the "S" of "WALES" is open.

Die II. The first pearl is circular, the vertical shading under the fleur-de-lis clear, the "S" of "WALES" not so open.

Dies of the 2½d.

Die I    Die II

2½d. Die I. There are 12 radiating lines in the star on the Queen's breast. Die II. There are 16 radiating lines in the star and the eye is nearly full of colour.

1897–**99**. *W* **40** (*sideways on* 2½*d*.).

288	**59**	1d. carmine (Die I), *p* 11 × 12	1·75	10
		a. Perf 12 × 11½	2·00	10
289		1d. scarlet (Die I), *p* 11 × 12	1·75	10
		a. Perf 12 × 11½	4·50	40
		b. Perf 12	4·50	50
		ba. Imperf horiz (vert pair)		
290		1d. rose-carmine (Die II), *p* 11 × 12	1·75	10
		a. Perf 12 × 11½	1·50	10
		b. Perf 12	1·50	10
		c. Imperf between (pair)	£400	
291		1d. salmon-red (Die II), *p* 12 × 11½	1·75	10
		a. Perf 12	3·25	30
292	**60**	2d. deep dull blue, *p* 11 × 12	1·75	10
		a. Perf 12 × 11½	1·75	10
		b. Perf 12	4·50	10
293		2d. cobalt-blue, *p* 11 × 12	3·00	10
		a. Perf 12 × 11½	2·50	10
		b. Perf 12	3·00	10
294		2d. ultramarine, *p* 11 × 12	2·50	10
		a. Perf 12 × 11½	1·75	10
		b. Perf 12	1·75	10
		c. Imperf between (pair)		
295	**61**	2½d. purple (Die I), *p* 12 × 11	5·00	1·25
		a. Perf 11½ × 12	6·00	80
		b. Perf 11	6·00	1·75
296		2½d. deep violet (Die II), *p* 12 × 11	3·50	80
		a. Perf 11½ × 12	6·00	1·25
		b. Perf 12	3·25	1·25
297		2½d. Prussian blue, *p* 12 × 11	6·00	
		a. Perf 11½ × 12	4·00	80
		b. Perf 12	3·25	80
		Set of 4 (*both colours of* 2d.) *optd* "Specimen"	60·00	

The perforations 11 × 12, 12 × 11½ and 12 are from comb machines, the perforation 11 is from a single-line machine.

1897. *Reissue of T* **24**. *W* **25**. *P* 11.

297*c*	5s. reddish purple (*shades*)	30·00	12·00
	ca. Imperf between (pair)	£2750	
	d. Perf 12	38·00	20·00
	e. Perf 11 × 12 or 12 × 11	30·00	19·00

1898–99. *W* **40**. *P* 11 × 12.

297*f*	**48**	6d. emerald-green (Optd. S. £20)	30·00	5·00
		fa. Perf 12 × 11½	22·00	5·00
		fb. Perf 12	22·00	5·00
297*g*		6d. orange-yellow (1899)	14·00	3·00
		ga. Perf 12 × 11½	13·00	2·50
		gb. Perf 12	23·00	4·50
		gc. Yellow, p 12 × 11½	14·00	1·25

1899 (Oct). *Chalk-surfaced paper. W* **40** *(sideways on 2½d.). P* 12 × 11½ *or* 11½ × 12 *(2½d.), comb.*

298	**58**	½d. blue-green (Die I)	90	10
		a. Imperf (pair)	50·00	30·00
299	**59**	1d. carmine (Die II)	80	10
		a. Imperf horiz (vert pair)	£200	
300		1d. scarlet (Die II)	80	10
301		1d. salmon-red (Die II)	80	10
		a. Imperf (pair)	40·00	38·00
302	**60**	2d. cobalt-blue	1·75	10
		a. Imperf (pair)	40·00	
303	**61**	2½d. Prussian blue (Die II)	2·75	70
		a. Imperf (pair)	45·00	
303*b*	**47**	4d. red-brown	9·00	3·00
		c. Imperf (pair)	£200	
304		4d. orange-brown	9·00	3·00
305	**48**	6d. deep orange	11·00	90
		a. Imperf (pair)	£140	
306		6d. orange-yellow	11·00	90
307		6d. emerald-green	38·00	2·00
		a. Imperf (pair)	£175	
308	**49**	8d. magenta	11·00	2·50
309	**34**	9d. on 10d. dull brown	8·00	4·00
		a. Surch double	90·00	70·00
		b. Without surcharge	80·00	
310		10d. violet	12·00	2·75
311	**50**	1s. maroon	12·00	80
312		1s. purple-brown	12·00	1·25
		a. Imperf (pair)	£150	

62 Superb Lyrebird

63

1902. *Chalk-surfaced paper. W* **42** *(sideways on 2½d.). P* 12 × 11½ *or* 11½ × 12 *(2½d.), comb.*

313	**58**	½d. blue-green, (Die I)	2·75	10
		a. Perf 12 × 11	2·75	
314	**59**	1d. carmine (Die II)	80	10
315	**60**	2d. cobalt-blue	1·50	10
316	**61**	2½d. dark blue (Die II)	2·75	10
317	**47**	4d. orange-brown	18·00	3·25
318	**48**	6d. yellow-orange	16·00	90
319		6d. orange	15·00	90
320		6d. orange-buff	15·00	90
321	**49**	8d. magenta	11·00	1·75
322	**34**	9d. on 10d. brownish orange	8·00	3·50
323		10d. violet	18·00	3·00
324	**50**	1s. maroon	12·00	80
325		1s. purple-brown	13·00	80
326	**62**	2s. 6d. green (Optd S. £35)	42·00	14·00

(Typo Victoria Govt Printer, Melbourne)

1903 (18 July). *W* **75** *of Victoria (double-lined V over Crown).*

327	**63**	9d. brown & ultramarine, *p* 12¼ × 12½, *comb* (Optd S. £27)	7·50	1·75
328		9d. brown & deep blue, *p* 12¼ × 12½, *comb*	7·50	1·75
329		9d. brown and blue, *p* 11	£450	£275

Die II. Broad "H" in "HALF"

66

1905–10. *Chalk-surfaced paper. W* **66** *(sideways on 2½d.). P* 12 × 11½ *or* 11½ × 12 *(2½d.) comb, unless otherwise stated.*

330	**58**	½d. blue-green (Die I)	1·75	10
		a. Perf 11½ × 11		
331		½d. blue-green (Die II)	90	10
		a. Perf 11½ × 11	1·75	
332	**59**	1d. rose-carmine (Die II)	75	10
		a. Perf 11½ × 11	1·75	
333	**60**	2d. deep ultramarine	1·75	10
		b. Perf 11½ × 11	2·00	
333*d*		2d. milky blue (1910)	1·75	10
		da. Perf 11	45·00	
		db. Perf 11½ × 11		
334	**61**	2½d. Prussian blue (Die II)	2·75	80
335	**47**	4d. orange-brown	8·00	3·00
336		4d. red-brown	8·50	3·00
337	**48**	6d. dull yellow	13·00	1·00
		a. Perf 11½ × 11	21·00	
338		6d. orange-yellow	13·00	90
		a. Perf 11 × 11½	27·00	
339		6d. deep orange	11·00	90
		a. Perf 11	£150	
339*b*		6d. orange-buff	11·00	90
		c. Perf 11½ × 11	17·00	2·75
340	**49**	8d. magenta	11·00	2·00
341		8d. lilac-rose	11·00	2·25
342	**34**	10d. violet	14·00	2·75
		a. Perf 11½ × 11	13·00	2·50
		b. Perf 11	13·00	2·50
343	**50**	1s. maroon	11·00	85
344		1s. purple-brown (1908)	12·00	85
345	**62**	2s. 6d. blue-green	38·00	14·00
		a. Perf 11½ × 11	27·00	12·00
		b. Perf 11	30·00	15·00

67

1905 (Dec). *Chalk-surfaced paper. W* **67**. *P* 11.

346	**52**	20s. cobalt-blue	£180	60·00
		a. Perf 12	£180	60·00
		b. Perf 11 × 12 or 12 × 11	£180	60·00

(Typo Victoria Govt Printer, Melbourne)

1906 (Sept). *W* **93***a of Victoria (double-lined "A" and Crown). P* 12 × 12½, *comb.*

347	**63**	9d. brown and ultramarine	6·00	1·10
		a. Perf 11	42·00	35·00
348		9d. yellow-brown and ultramarine	6·00	90

1907 (July). *W* **93***a of Victoria. P* 12 × 11½ *or* 11½ × 12 *(2½d.), comb, unless otherwise stated.*

349	**58**	½d. blue-green (Die I)	2·00	10
351	**59**	1d. dull rose (Die II)	1·75	10
352	**60**	2d. cobalt-blue	1·75	10
353	**61**	2½d. Prussian blue (Die II)	42·00	
354	**47**	4d. orange-brown	8·50	3·50
355	**48**	6d. orange-buff	20·00	4·00

356	48	6d. dull yellow	18·00	4·00
357	49	8d. magenta	11·00	3·50
358	34	10d. violet, *p* 11	18·00	
359	50	1s. purple-brown	16·00	3·00
		a. Perf 11		
360	62	2s. 6d. blue-green	45·00	25·00

OFFICIAL STAMPS

O S　　　O S　　　O S

(O 1)　　　(O 2)　　　(O 3)

The space between the letters is normally 7 mm as illustrated, except on the 5d. and 8d. (11–11½ mm), 5s. (12 mm) and 20s. (14 mm). Later printings of the 3d., W **40**, are 5½ mm, and these are listed. Varieties in the settings are known on the 1d. (8 and 8½ mm), 2d. (8½ mm) and 3d. (9 mm).

Varieties of Type O **1** exist with "O" sideways.

Nos. O1/35 overprinted with Type O **1**

1879. *Wmk double-lined "6". P* 13.

O1	14	3d. dull green	—	£400

1879 (Oct)–**85.** *W* **36.** *P* 13.

O 2	26	1d. salmon	8·50	2·00
		a. Perf 10 (5.81)	£180	30·00
		b. Perf 13×10 (1881)	20·00	3·50
O 3	28	2d. blue	10·00	1·25
		a. Perf 10 (7.81)	£225	32·00
		b. Perf 13×10 (1881)	20·00	2·50
		c. Perf 10×13 (1881)	45·00	7·00
		d. Perf 11×12 (11.84?)	—	£225
O 4	14	3d. dull green (R.) (12.79)	£200	£200
O 5		3d. dull green (3.80)	£250	45·00
		a. Perf 10 (1881)	£140	40·00
		b. Yellow-green. Perf 10 (10.81)	£140	25·00
		c. Ditto. Perf 13×10 (1881)	£140	25·00
		d. Ditto. Perf 12 (4.85)	£200	50·00
		e. Ditto. Perf 12×10 (4.85)	£200	50·00
O 6	32	4d. red-brown	£140	7·50
		a. Perf 10 (1881)	—	£190
		b. Perf 13×10 (1881)	£200	90·00
		c. Perf 10×13 (1881)	£200	11·00
O 7	15	5d. green, *p* 10 (8.84)	18·00	10·00
O 8	37	6d. pale lilac	£200	4·50
		a. Perf 10 (1881)	—	40·00
		b. Perf 13×10 (1881)	£150	40·00
O 9	19	8d. yellow (R.) (12.79)	—	£130
O10		8d. yellow (1880)	—	15·00
		a. Perf 10 (1881)	£250	75·00
O11	34	9d. on 10d. brown, *p* 10 (30.5.80) (Optd S. £60)	£275	£150
O12	38	1s. black (R.)	£200	7·50
		a. Perf 10 (1881)	—	16·00
		b. Perf 13×10 (1881)	—	9·00
		c. Perf 10×13 (1881)	—	45·00

Other stamps are known with red overprint but their status is in doubt.

1880–88. *Wmk "5/-", W* **25.** (*a*) *P* 13.

O13	24	5s. deep purple (15.2.80)	£400	80·00
		a. Royal purple	—	£300
		b. Deep rose-lilac	—	£300

(*b*) *P* 10

O14	24	5s. deep purple (9.82)	£400	£160
		b. Rose-lilac (1883)	£275	£100

(*c*) *P* 10×12

O15	24	5s. purple (10.86)	—	£100

(*d*) *P* 12×10

O16	24	5s. reddish purple (1886)	£300	£100

(*e*) *P* 12

O17	24	5s. purple	—	£150

(*f*) *P* 11

O18	24	5s. rose-lilac (1888)	£160	60·00

1880 (31 May). *Wmk "10", W* **35.** *P* 13.

O18*a*	34	10d. lilac (Optd S. £60)	£130	80·00
		ab. Perf 10 and 11, compound	£200	£180

1882–85. *W* **40.** *P* 10.

O19	26	1d. salmon	7·00	2·00
		a. Perf 13×10	—	£130
O20		1d. orange *to* scarlet	6·00	1·50
		a. Perf 10×13	—	£130
		b. Perf 11×12, comb (1.84)	4·00	1·40
		c. Perf 10×12 (4.85)	—	£110
		d. Perf 12×11 (12.85)		
O21	28	2d. blue	5·00	1·00
		a. Perf 13×10		
		b. Perf 10×13	£190	75·00
		c. Perf 11×12, comb (1.84)	5·00	1·00
		d. Ditto. Opt double		
		e. Perf 12×11 (12.85)		
O22	14	3d. yellow-green (7 *mm*)	5·50	3·50
		a. Perf 12 (4.85)	£120	80·00
		b. Perf 12×10 (4.85)		
O23		3d. bluish green (7 *mm*)	5·50	3·50
		a. Perf 12 (4.85)	£120	80·00
		b. Perf 12×10 (4.85)		
		c. Perf 10×12 (12.85)		
O24		3d. yellow-green (5½ *mm*)	5·50	3·50
		a. Perf 12×10 or 10×12 (4.85)	5·50	
		b. Perf 10×11 or 11×10 (12.85)		
O25		3d. bluish green (5½ *mm*) (Optd S. £35)	5·50	3·50
		a. Perf 12×10 or 10×12 (4.85)	6·00	3·50
		b. Perf 10×11 or 11×10 (12.85)	5·00	3·50
O26	32	4d. red-brown	30·00	4·00
		a. Perf 11×12, comb (1.84)	12·00	3·00
		b. Perf 10×12 (4.85)	—	70·00
O27		4d. dark brown	15·00	3·00
		a. Perf 11×12, comb (1.84)	12·00	3·00
		b. Perf 12 (4.85)	£200	£150
		c. Perf 10×12 (4.85)	£200	90·00
O28	15	5d. dull green (Optd S. £35)	12·00	8·00
		a. Perf 12×10 (4.85)		
O29		5d. blue-green	13·00	9·00
		a. Perf 12 (4.85)		£100
		b. Perf 10×11	13·00	9·00
O30	37	6d. pale lilac	18·00	3·00
		a. Perf 11 (12.85)	19·00	2·75
O31		6d. mauve	18·00	3·00
		a. Perf 12 (4.85)	—	45·00
		b. Perf 11×12 (12.85)	18·00	2·75
		c. Perf 10×12 (4.85)	80·00	38·00
		d. Perf 11×10 (12.85)	18·00	2·75
		e. Perf 12×11 (12.85)	55·00	15·00
O32	19	8d. yellow	20·00	10·00
		a. Perf 12 (4.85)	£130	38·00
		b. Perf 12×10 or 10×12 (4.85)	20·00	9·00
		d. Perf 11 (12.85)	22·00	10·00
		da. Opt double		
		db. Opt treble	†	
O33	38	1s. black (R.)	22·00	3·50
		a. Perf 10×13	—	55·00
		b. Perf 11×12, comb (1.84)	22·00	3·50
		c. Ditto. Opt double		

1886–87. *W* **41.** *P* 10.

O34	26	1d. scarlet	20·00	3·00
O35	28	2d. deep blue		
		a. Perf 11×12		

1887–89. *Nos. 247/8 overprinted in black.* (*a*) *With Type* O **1.**

O36	43	10s. claret and mauve, *p* 12	—	£300

(*b*) *With Type* O **2** (April 1889)

O37	43	10s. claret and mauve, *p* 12 (Optd S. £75)	£1100	£500
		a. Perf 10	£2000	£1300

(*c*) *With Type* O **3** (Jan 1887)

O38	43	£1 claret and rose-lilac, *p* 12×10	£2250	£2250
		a. Opt double		

1888 (17 July)–**90.** *Optd as Type* O **1.** (*a*) *W* **40.** *P* 11×12.

O39	45	1d. lilac	1·75	10
		a. Perf 12	1·75	10
		b. Mauve	1·75	10
		ba. Perf 12	1·75	10
O40	46	2d. Prussian blue (15.10.88)	2·00	10
		a. Perf 12	2·00	10
O41	47	4d. purple-brown (10.10.89)	7·50	2·00
		a. Perf 12	9·00	2·00
		b. Perf 11		
		c. Red-brown	7·50	2·00
		ca. Perf 12	8·50	2·00
O42	48	6d. carmine (16.1.89)	8·00	2·50
		a. Perf 12	9·50	2·50

O43	49	8d. lilac-rose (1890)...............		14·00	6·50
		a. Perf 12		—	9·00
O44	50	1s. maroon (9.1.90)...............		12·00	2·50
		a. Perf 12		13·00	2·50
		b. Purple-brown		12·00	2·50
		ba. Opt double			
		bb. Perf 12		12·00	2·50

(b) W 41. P 11 × 12 (1889)

O45	45	1d. mauve......................			
O46	46	2d. blue			

(c) W 25. P 10

O47	51	5s. deep purple (9.1.90)..........		£500	£400
O48	52	20s. cobalt-blue (10.3.90).........		£1000	£400
		Set of 6 (1d. to 1s.) optd "Specimen" .		£200	

1890 (Feb)–**91**. *Optd as Type* O **1**. *W* **53** (5s.) *or* **54** (20s.). *P* 10.

O49	51	5s. lilac......................		£130	60·00
		a. Mauve		£150	65·00
		b. Dull lilac, p 12		£550	
O50	52	20s. cobalt-blue (3.91).........		£1500	£500
		Set of 2 optd "Specimen"		£200	

1891 (Jan)–**92**. *Nos. 281/5 optd as Type* O **1**. *W* **40**. *P* 11 × 12.

O54	55	2½d. ultramarine		6·00	2·50
O55	26	½d. on 1d. grey.................		45·00	40·00
O56	37	7½d. on 6d. brown, p 10		32·00	27·00
O57	38	12½d. on 1s. red		55·00	50·00
O58	58	½d. grey (5.92).................		6·00	5·00
		a. Perf 10		7·00	9·00
		b. Perf 12		6·00	6·00
		c. Perf 12 × 11½		10·00	
		Set of 5 optd "Specimen"		£160	

Official stamps were withdrawn from the government departments on 31 December 1894.

POSTAGE DUE STAMPS

D 1

(Dies eng by A. Collingridge. Typo Govt Printing Office, Sydney)

1891 (1 Jan)–**92**. *W* **40**. *P* 10.

D 1	D 1	½d. green (21.1.92)		2·50	2·00
D 2		1d. green		3·50	90
		a. Perf 11		3·75	90
		b. Perf 12		13·00	2·50
		c. Perf 12 × 10		—	1·75
		d. Perf 10 × 11		6·50	90
		e. Perf 11 × 12 or 12 × 11		4·00	90
D 3		2d. green		5·50	80
		a. Perf 11		5·50	80
		b. Perf 12		—	8·00
		c. Perf 12 × 10		15·00	3·00
		d. Perf 10 × 11		7·00	1·50
		e. Perf 11 × 12 or 12 × 11		5·50	80
D 4		3d. green		9·00	2·75
		a. Perf 10 × 11		9·00	2·75
D 5		4d. green		7·50	80
		a. Perf 11		8·50	80
		b. Perf 10 × 11		7·50	80
D 6		6d. green		14·00	2·00
D 7		8d. green		60·00	6·00
D 8		5s. green		£120	30·00
		a. Perf 11		£200	75·00
		b. Perf 11 × 12		—	£250
D 9		10s. green (early 1891)		£180	45·00
		a. Perf 12 × 10		£120	80·00
D10		20s. green (early 1891)		£300	80·00
		a. Perf 12		£300	
		b. Perf 12 × 10		£175	£100
		Set of 10 optd "Specimen"		£200	

1900. *Chalk-surfaced paper. W* **40**. *P* 11.

D11	D 1	½d. emerald-green			
D12		1d. emerald-green		3·50	1·75
		a. Perf 12		10·00	3·50
		b. Perf 11 × 12 or 12 × 11		3·50	1·00
D13		2d. emerald-green		6·50	2·75
		a. Perf 12		—	12·00
		b. Perf 11 × 12 or 12 × 11		5·50	2·50
D14		3d. emerald-green, p 11 × 12 or 12 × 11.		12·00	3·00
D15		4d. emerald-green		7·50	2·25

The six former colonies of New South Wales, Queensland, South Australia, Tasmania, Victoria and Western Australia united to form the Commonwealth of Australia on 1 January 1901.

On 1 March 1901 control of the postal service passed to the federal administration. The first national postage due stamps appeared in July 1902, but it was not until January 1913 that postage stamps inscribed "AUSTRALIA" were issued.

QUEENSLAND

The area which later became Queensland was previously part of New South Wales known as the Moreton Bay District. The first post office, at Brisbane, was opened in 1834 and the use of New South Wales stamps from the District became compulsory from 1 May 1854.

Queensland was proclaimed a separate colony on 10 December 1859, but continued to use New South Wales issues until 1 November 1860.

Post Offices opened in the Moreton Bay District before 10 December 1859, and using New South Wales stamps, were

Office	Opened	Numeral Cancellation
Brisbane	1834	95
Burnett's Inn (became		
Goodes Inn)	1850	108
Callandoon	1850	74
Condamine	1856	151
Dalby	1854	133
Drayton	1846	85
Gayndah	1850	86
Gladstone	1854	131
Goodes Inn	1858	108
Ipswich	1846	87
Maryborough	1849	96
Rockhampton	1858	201
Surat	1852	110
Taroom	1856	152
Toowoomba	1858	214
Warwick	1848	81

PRICES
First column = Mounted Mint
Second column = Used

PRICES FOR STAMPS ON COVER

Nos. 1/3	from × 2
Nos. 4/56	from × 3
Nos. 57/8	—
Nos. 59/73	from × 4
Nos. 74/82	from × 2
Nos. 83/109	from × 3
Nos. 110/13	from × 2
Nos. 116/17	from × 3
Nos. 118/27	—
Nos. 128/50	from × 4
Nos. 151/65	—
Nos. 166/78	from × 10
Nos. 179/83	from × 4
Nos. 184/206	from × 15
No. 207	—
Nos. 208/54	from × 15
Nos. 256/64	from × 10
Nos. 264a/b	from × 2
Nos. 265/6	from × 20
Nos. 267/9	from × 5
Nos. 270/80a	—
Nos. 281/5	from × 10
Nos. 286/308	from × 12
No. 309	—
Nos. F1/37	—

1

2 Large Star

3 Small Star

(Dies eng W. Humphrys. Recess P.B.)

1860 (1 Nov). *W* **2**. *Imperf.*

1	**1**	1d. carmine-rose	£2250	£800
2		2d. blue	£5000	£1700
3		6d. green	£3500	£800

1860 (Nov). *W* **2**. *Clean-cut perf* 14–15½.

4	**1**	1d. carmine-rose (1.11)	£1000	£250
5		2d. blue (1.11)	£400	£100
		a. Imperf between (pair)		
6		6d. green (15.11)	£450	60·00

1860–61. *W* **3**. *Clean-cut perf* 14–15½.

7	**1**	2d. blue	£450	£100
		a. Imperf between (horiz pair)	—	£900
8		3d. brown (15.4.61)	£250	50·00
		a. Re-entry	—	£200
		b. Retouch (R. 2/8)	—	£200
9		6d. green	£500	50·00
10		1s. violet (15.11.60)	£475	70·00
11		"REGISTERED" (6d.) olive-yellow (1.61)	£325	70·00
		a. Imperf between (pair)	£2750	

The perforation of the 3d. is that known as "intermediate between clean-cut and rough".

The 3d. re-entry shows doubling of the left-hand arabesque and the retouch has redrawn spandrel dots under "EN" of "PENCE", a single dot in the centre of the circle under "E" and the bottom outer frame liner closer to the spandrel's frame line.

1861 (July (?)). *W* **3**. *Clean-cut perf* 14.

12	**1**	1d. carmine-rose	£100	35·00
13		2d. blue	£275	50·00

1861 (Sept). *W* **3**. *Rough perf* 14–15½.

14	**1**	1d. carmine-rose	75·00	28·00
15		2d. blue	90·00	28·00
		a. Imperf between (pair)		
16		3d. brown	50·00	30·00
		a. Imperf between (pair)	£1400	
		b. Re-entry	£200	£110
		c. Retouch (R. 2/8)	—	£110
17		6d. deep green	£100	27·00
18		6d. yellow-green	£200	27·00
19		1s. violet	£325	80·00
20		"REGISTERED" (6d.) orange-yellow	45·00	35·00

(Printed and perforated in Brisbane)

1862–67. *Thick toned paper. No wmk.* (a) *P* 13 (1862–63).

21	**1**	1d. Indian red (16.12.62)	£250	60·00
22		1d. orange-vermilion (2.63)	60·00	12·00
		a. Imperf (pair)	—	£500
		b. Imperf between (pair)		
23		2d. blue (16.12.62)	40·00	9·00
24		2d. pale blue	80·00	27·00
		a. Imperf (pair)	—	£500
		b. Imperf between (horiz pair)	—	£850
25		3d. brown	55·00	30·00
		a. Re-entry	—	£110
		b. Retouch (R. 2/8)	—	£110
26		6d. apple-green (17.4.63)	90·00	15·00
27		6d. yellow-green	80·00	12·00
		a. Imperf between (horiz pair)	—	£950
28		6d. blue-green	£130	27·00
		a. Imperf (pair)	—	£500
29		1s. grey (14.7.63) (H/S S. £40)	£130	22·00
		a. Imperf between (horiz pair)	—	£850
		b. Imperf between (vert pair)		

The top or bottom row of perforation was sometimes omitted from the sheet, resulting in stamps perforated on three sides only.

(b) *P* 12½ × 13 (1867)

30	**1**	1d. orange-vermilion	60·00	27·00
31		2d. blue	48·00	20·00
32		3d. brown	65·00	25·00
		a. Re-entry	—	95·00
		b. Retouch (R. 2/8)	—	95·00
33		6d. apple-green	85·00	27·00
34		6d. yellow-green	85·00	27·00
35		1s. grey	£170	32·00
		a. Imperf between (horiz pair)		

The previously listed stamps perforated 13 round holes come from the same perforating machine as Nos. 21/9 after the pins had been replaced. The holes vary from rough to clean-cut.

1864–66. *W* **3**. (a) *P* 13.

44	**1**	1d. orange-vermilion (1.65)	55·00	20·00
		a. Imperf between (horiz pair)	£375	
45		2d. pale blue (1.65)	50·00	16·00
46		2d. deep blue	50·00	16·00
		a. Imperf between (vert pair)	£850	
		b. Bisected (1d.) (on cover)	†	£1800
47		6d. yellow-green (1.65)	£120	22·00
48		6d. deep green	£140	22·00

49	1	"REGISTERED" (6d.) orange-yell (21.6.64)	65·00	30·00
		a. Double printed	£750	
		b. Imperf		

(b) P 12½ × 13

50	1	1d. orange-vermilion	95·00	40·00
50a		2d. deep blue		

1866 (24 Jan). *Wmk "QUEENSLAND/POSTAGE—POSTAGE/STAMPS—STAMPS" in three lines in script capitals with double wavy lines above and below the wmk and single wavy lines with projecting sprays between each line of words. There are ornaments ("fleurons") between "POSTAGE" "POSTAGE" and between "STAMPS" "STAMPS". Single stamps only show a portion of one or two letters of this wmk.* (a) P 13.

51	1	1d. orange-vermilion	£130	25·00
52		2d. blue	45·00	17·00

(b) P 12½ × 13

52a	1	1d. orange-vermilion		
52b		2d. blue		

1866 (24 Sept). *Lithographed on thick paper. No wmk. P 13.*

53	1	4d. slate (H/S S. £40)	£150	20·00
		a. Re-entry	—	85·00
		b. Retouch (R. 2/8)	—	85·00
55		4d. lilac	90·00	16·00
		a. Re-entry	—	75·00
		b. Retouch (R. 2/8)	—	75·00
56		4d. reddish lilac	90·00	16·00
		a. Re-entry	—	75·00
		b. Retouch (R. 2/8)	—	75·00
57		5s. bright rose (H/S S. £40)	£275	80·00
58		5s. pale rose	£200	55·00
		a. Imperf between (vert pair)		£600

The 4d. is from a transfer taken from the 3d. die, and the 5s. was taken from the 1s. die, the final "s" being added. The alteration in the values was made by hand on the stone, and there are many varieties, such as tall and short letters in "FOUR PENCE", some of the letters of "FOUR" smudged out, and differences in the position of the two words.

4

1868–74. *Wmk small truncated Star, W 4 on each stamp, and the word "QUEENSLAND" in single-lined Roman capitals four times in each sheet.* (a) P 13.

59	1	1d. orange-vermilion (18.1.71)	45·00	4·50
60		2d. pale blue	45·00	4·50
61		2d. blue (3.4.68)	40·00	2·75
62		2d. bright blue	50·00	2·75
63		2d. greenish blue	85·00	2·50
64		2d. dark blue	45·00	2·50
		a. Imperf		
65		3d. olive-green (27.2.71)	80·00	5·00
		a. Re-entry	—	30·00
		b. Retouch (R. 2/8)	—	30·00
66		3d. greenish grey	95·00	5·50
		a. Re-entry	—	32·00
		b. Retouch (R. 2/8)	—	32·00
67		3d. brown	80·00	5·50
		a. Re-entry	—	32·00
		b. Retouch (R. 2/8)	—	32·00
68		6d. yellow-green (10.11.71)	£130	7·00
69		6d. green	£130	10·00
70		6d. deep green	£170	17·00
71		1s. greenish grey (13.11.72)	£325	32·00
72		1s. brownish grey	£325	32·00
73		1s. mauve (19.2.74)	£200	22·00
		Set of 5 (ex Nos. 67, 71) H/S "Specimen" .	£175	

(b) P 12 (about Feb 1874)

74	1	1d. orange-vermilion	£250	24·00
75		2d. blue	—	35·00
76		3d. greenish grey	—	£120
		a. Re-entry		
		b. Retouch (R. 2/8)		

77	1	3d. brown	£250	£120
		a. Re-entry		
		b. Retouch (R. 2/8)		
78		6d. green	£850	40·00
79		1s. mauve	—	40·00

(c) P 13 × 12

80	1	1d. orange-vermilion	—	£150
81		2d. blue	£850	40·00
82		3d. greenish grey		

Reprints were made in 1895 of all five values on the paper of the regular issue, and perforated 13; the colours are:—1d. orange and orange-brown, 2d. dull blue and bright blue, 3d. deep brown, 6d. yellow-green, 1s. red-violet and dull violet. The "Registered" was also reprinted with these on the same paper, but perforated 12. One sheet of the 2d. reprint is known to have had the perforations missing between the fourth and fifth vertical rows.

5　　　　　　　　　　　　6

(4d., litho. Other values recess)

1868–78. *Wmk Crown and Q, W 5.* (a) P 13 (1868–75).

83	1	1d. orange-vermilion (10.11.68)	50·00	4·50
		a. Imperf	£150	
84		1d. pale rose-red (4.11.74)	48·00	8·50
85		1d. deep rose-red	95·00	9·00
86		2d. pale blue (4.11.74)	48·00	1·75
87		2d. deep blue (20.11.68)	38·00	4·50
		a. Imperf (pair)	£275	
		b. Imperf between (vert pair)		
88		3d. brown (11.6.75)	70·00	12·00
		a. Re-entry	—	55·00
		b. Retouch (R. 2/8)	—	55·00
89		4d. yellow (1.1.75) (H/S S. £60)	£750	40·00
90		6d. deep green (9.4.69)	£120	9·00
91		6d. yellow-green	95·00	6·50
92		6d. pale apple-green (1.1.75)	£130	9·00
		a. Imperf	£160	
93		1s. mauve	£130	29·00

(b) P 12 (1876–78)

94	1	1d. deep orange-vermilion	38·00	5·00
95		1d. pale orange-vermilion	40·00	5·00
		a. Imperf between (vert pair)		
96		1d. rose-red	45·00	10·00
97		1d. flesh	60·00	10·00
98		2d. pale blue	80·00	15·00
99		2d. bright blue	22·00	1·00
100		2d. deep blue	25·00	1·50
101		3d. brown	60·00	9·00
		a. Re-entry	—	45·00
		b. Retouch (R. 2/8)	—	45·00
102		4d. yellow	£600	25·00
103		4d. buff	£600	20·00
104		6d. deep green	£140	7·00
105		6d. green	£130	4·25
106		6d. yellow-green	£140	4·50
107		6d. apple-green	£140	7·00
108		1s. mauve	40·00	9·00
109		1s. purple	£140	5·00
		a. Imperf between (pair)		

(c) P 13 × 12 or 12 × 13

110	1	1d. orange-vermilion	—	85·00
110a		1d. rose-red		
111		2d. deep blue	£1100	£130
112		4d. yellow		
113		6d. deep green	—	£150

(d) P 12½ × 13

114	1	1d. orange-vermilion		
115		2d. deep blue		
115a		6d. yellow-green		

(e) P 12½

115b **1** 2d. deep blue . . . .
    Reprints exist of the 1d., 2d., 3d., 6d. and 1s. on thicker paper, Wmk *W* **6**, and in different shades from the originals.

1879. *No wmk. P 12.*
116 **1** 6d. pale emerald-green . . . . £150   25·00
    a. Imperf between (horiz pair) . . . .   —   £550
117   1s. mauve *(fiscal-cancel* £5) . . . .   95·00   48·00
    No. 117 has a very indistinct lilac *burelé* band at back.
    Nos. 116/17 can be found showing portions of a papermaker's watermark, either T. H. Saunders & Co or A. Pirie & Sons.

1881. *Lithographed from transfers from the 1s. die. Wmk Crown and Q, W* **6**. *P 12.*
118 **1** 2s. pale blue (6 Apr) . . . . 60·00   22·00
119   2s. blue *(fiscal-cancel* £3) . . . . 60·00   22·00
    a. Imperf vert (horiz pair) . . . .
120   2s. deep blue *(fiscal-cancel* £3) . . . . 75·00   22·00
121   2s. 6d. dull scarlet (28 Aug) . . . . £110   40·00
122   2s. 6d. bright scarlet *(fiscal-cancel* £3) . . . . . £130   40·00
123   5s. pale yellow-ochre (28 Aug) . . . . £150   60·00
124   5s. yellow-ochre *(fiscal-cancel* £4) . . . . £150   60·00
125   10s. reddish brown (Mar) £350   £110
    a. Imperf £375
126   10s. bistre-brown £350   £110
127   20s. rose *(fiscal-cancel* £6) £700   £130
    Of the 2s. and 20s. stamps there are five types of each, and of the other values ten types of each.
    Beware of fiscally used copies that have been cleaned and provided with forged postmarks.

7

       Die I   Die II

Dies I and II often occur in the same sheet.
Die I. The white horizontal inner line of the triangle in the upper right-hand corner merges into the outer white line of the oval above the "L".
Die II. The same line is short and does not touch the inner oval.

1879–80. *Typo. P 12. (a) Wmk Crown and Q, W* **5**.
128 **7** 1d. reddish brown (Die I) . . . . 65·00   15·00
    a. Die II . . . . £100   15·00
    ab. "QOEENSLAND" £850   £150
129   1d. orange-brown (Die I) . . . . £100   15·00
130   2d. blue (Die I) . . . . 55·00   10·00
    a. "PENGE" (R. 12/6) . . . . 65·00   £110
    b. "QUEENSbAND" (R. 5/6) . . . .   —   £110
    c. "QU" joined . . . .
131   4d. orange-yellow . . . . £300   35·00

(b) No wmk, with lilac burelé band on back
132 **7** 1d. reddish brown (Die I) . . . . £275   35·00
    a. Die II . . . . £300   65·00
    ab. "QOEENSLAND" . . . .   —   £1400
133   2d. blue (Die I) . . . . £350   17·00
    a. "PENGE" (R. 12/6) £3250   £600
    b. "QUEENSbAND" (R. 5/6) . . . .

(c) Wmk Crown and Q, W **6**
134 **7** 1d. reddish brown (Die I) . . . . 32·00   5·00
    a. Imperf between (pair) . . . .   —   £200
    b. Die II . . . . 40·00   5·00
    ba. "QOEENSLAND" . . . . £200   40·00
    bb. Imperf between (pair) . . . .   —   £200
135   1d. dull orange (Die I) . . . . 9·00   3·00
    a. Die II . . . . 9·00   3·00
    ab. "QOEENSLAND" . . . . 55·00   20·00
136   1d. scarlet (Die I) . . . . 12·00   1·75
    a. Die II . . . . 14·00   2·25
    ab. "QOEENSLAND" . . . . 80·00   24·00

137 **7** 2d. blue (Die I) . . . . 25·00   1·00
    a. "PENGE" . . . . £120   40·00
    b. "QUEENSbAND" . . . . £120   40·00
    c. Die II . . . . 27·00   3·00
138   2d. grey-blue (Die I) . . . . 25·00   1·00
    a. "PENGE" . . . . £120   40·00
    b. "QUEENSbAND" . . . . £120   40·00
    c. Die II . . . .
139   2d. bright blue (Die I) . . . . 28·00   1·00
    a. "PENGE" . . . . £130   40·00
    b. "QUEENSbAND" . . . . £130   4·00
    c. Imperf between (pair) £375
    d. Die II . . . .
140   2d. deep blue (Die I) . . . . 30·00   1·00
    a. "PENGE" . . . . £140   40·00
    b. "QUEENSbAND" . . . . £140   40·00
    c. Die II . . . . 24·00   4·50
141   4d. orange-yellow . . . . £100   10·00
    a. Imperf between (pair) . . . .
142   6d. deep green . . . . 55·00   4·50
    a. Imperf between (pair) . . . .
143   6d. yellow-green . . . . 60·00   4·50
144   1s. deep violet . . . . 50·00   4·50
145   1s. pale lilac . . . . 45·00   5·50
    The variety "QO" is No. 48 in the first arrangement, and No. 44 in a later arrangement on the sheets.
    All these values have been seen imperf and unused, but we have no evidence that any of them were used in this condition.
    The above were printed in sheets of 120, from plates made up of 30 groups of four electrotypes. There are four different types in each group, and two such groups of four are known of the 1d. and 2d., thus giving eight varieties of these two values. There was some resetting of the first plate of the 1d., and there are several plates of the 2d.; the value in the first plate of the latter value is in thinner letters, and in the last plate three types in each group of four have the "TW" of "TWO" joined, the letters of "PENCE" are larger and therefore much closer together, and in one type the "O" of "TWO" is oval, that letter being circular in the other types.

   (8)   9   10

1880 (21 Feb). *Surch with T* **8**.
151 **7** ½d. on 1d. (No. 134) (Die I) . . . . £160   90·00
    a. Die II £425   £350
    ab. "QOEENSLAND" £850   £700
    Examples with "Half-penny" reading downwards are forged surcharges.

1882–86. *Recess. P 12. (a) Thin paper. W* **5** *twice sideways.*
152 **9** 2s. bright blue . . . . 60·00   17·00
153   2s. 6d. vermilion . . . . 50·00   20·00
154   5s. rose . . . . 45·00   22·00
155   10s. brown . . . . 95·00   40·00
156   £1 deep green £225   £120
    a. Re-entry (R. 1/2) . . . .   —   £180
    b. Retouch (R. 6/4) . . . .   —   £180
    Set of 4 (ex 2s. 6d.) *H/S "Specimen"* . . . £150

(b) Thin paper. W **6** *twice sideways*
157 **9** 2s. 6d. vermilion . . . . 40·00   30·00
158   5s. rose . . . . 45·00   20·00
159   10s. brown . . . . £180   50·00
160   £1 deep green . . . . £180   60·00
    a. Re-entry (R. 1/2) . . . .   —   £100
    b. Retouch (R. 6/4) . . . .   —   £100

(c) Thick paper. W **10**
161 **9** 2s. bright blue . . . . 70·00   20·00
162   2s. 6d. vermilion . . . . 38·00   20·00
163   5s. rose . . . . 35·00   28·00
164   10s. brown . . . . 95·00   40·00
165   £1 deep green . . . . £170   60·00
    a. Re-entry (R. 1/2) . . . .   —   £100
    b. Retouch (R. 6/4) . . . .   —   £100
    The re-entry on the £1 shows as a double bottom frame line and the retouch occurs alongside the bottom left numeral.
    See also Nos. 270/1.

11 12

In T **12** the shading lines do not extend entirely across, as in T **11**, thus leaving a white line down the front of the throat and point of the bust.

1882–83. *W* **6**. (*a*) *P* 12.

166	**11**	1d. pale vermilion-red	3·00	30
		a. Double impression		
167		1d. deep vermilion-red	3·00	30
168		2d. blue	4·25	30
		a. Imperf between (horiz pair)		
169		4d. pale yellow	12·00	1·40
		a. "PENGE" for "PENCE" (R. 8/1)	£120	40·00
		b. "EN" joined in "PENCE" (R. 4/6)		
170		6d. green	9·00	70
171		1s. violet	16·00	1·90
172		1s. lilac	11·00	1·75
173		1s. deep mauve	11·00	1·40
174		1s. pale mauve	12·00	1·40
		a. Imperf	†	—

(*b*) *P* 9½×12

176	**11**	1d. pale red	45·00	16·00
177		2d. blue	£200	25·00
178		1s. mauve	90·00	19·00

The above were printed from plates made up of groups of four electrotypes as previously. In the 1d. the words of value are followed by a full stop. There are four types of the 4d., 6d. and 1s., eight types of the 1d., and twelve types of the 2d.

1887–89. *W* **6**. (*a*) *P* 12.

179	**12**	1d. vermilion-red	2·75	30
180		2d. blue	5·00	30
		a. Oval white flaw on Queen's head behind diadem (R. 12/5)		
181		2s. deep brown	55·00	23·00
182		2s. pale brown	50·00	20·00

(*b*) *P* 9½×12

183	**12**	2d. blue	£150	22·00

These are from new plates; four types of each value grouped as before. The 1d. is without stop. In all values No. 2 in each group of four has the "L" and "A" of "QUEENSLAND" joined at the foot, and No. 3 of the 2d. has "P" of word "PENCE" with a long downstroke.

The 2d. is known bisected and used as a 1d. value.

13 14

1890–94. *W* **6** (*sideways on* ½*d.*). *P* 12½, 13 (*comb machine*).

184	**13**	½d. pale green	2·75	50
185		½d. deep green	2·75	50
186		½d. deep blue-green	3·00	50
187	**12**	1d. vermilion-red	2·00	15
		a. Imperf	23·00	23·00
		b. Oval broken by tip of bust (R. 10/3)		
188		2d. blue (old plate)	4·00	15
189		2d. pale blue (old plate)	3·75	15
190		2d. pale blue (retouched plate)	3·50	30
		a. "FWO" for "TWO" (R. 8/7)	—	20·00
191	**14**	2½d. carmine	10·00	55
192	**12**	3d. brown	8·50	1·40
193	**11**	4d. yellow	13·00	95
		a. "PENGE" for "PENCE" (R. 8/1)	60·00	
		b. "EN" joined in "PENCE" (R. 4/6)		
194		4d. orange	16·00	95
		a. "PENGE" for "PENCE" (R. 8/1)	70·00	22·00
		b. "EN" joined in "PENCE" (R. 4/6)		
195	**11**	4d. lemon	20·00	1·25
		a. "PENGE" for "PENCE" (R. 8/1)	80·00	28·00
		b. "EN" joined in "PENCE" (R. 4/6)		
196		6d. green	9·00	1·25
197	**12**	2s. red-brown	38·00	7·50
198		2s. pale brown	42·00	9·00

This issue is perforated by a new vertical comb machine, gauging about 12¾×12¾. The 3d. is from a plate similar to those of the last issue, No. 2 in each group of four types having "L" and "A" joined at the foot. The ½d. and 2½d. are likewise in groups of four types, but the differences are very minute. In the retouched plate of the 2d. the letters "L" and "A" no longer touch in No. 2 of each group and the "P" in No. 3 is normal.

1894–95. *A. Thick paper. W* **10**. (*a*) *P* 12½, 13.

202	**12**	1d. vermilion-red	2·50	15
		a. Oval broken by tip of bust (R. 10/3)		
203		1d. red-orange	2·50	15
		a. Oval broken by tip of bust (R. 10/3)		
204		2d. blue (retouched plate)	3·00	20
		a. "FWO" for "TWO" (R. 8/7)	—	20·00

(*b*) *P* 12

205	**11**	1s. mauve	12·00	2·75

B. *Unwmkd paper; with blue burelé band at back. P* 12½, 13

206	**12**	1d. deep vermilion-red	2·00	15
		a. Oval broken by tip of bust (R. 10/3)		
		b. "PE" of "PENNY" omitted (R. 1/2)	£100	75·00

C. *Thin paper. Crown and Q faintly impressed. P* 12½, 13

207	**12**	2d. blue (retouched plate)	6·00	
		a. "FWO" for "TWO" (R. 8/7)		

15 16

17 18

1895–96. A. *W* **6** (*sideways on* ½*d.*). (*a*) *P* 12½, 13.

208	**15**	½d. green	1·00	45
		a. Double impression		
209		½d. deep green	1·00	45
		a. Printed both sides	60·00	
210	**16**	1d. orange-red	2·25	20
211		1d. pale red	2·00	20
212		2d. blue	3·25	35
213	**17**	2½d. carmine	8·00	3·00
214		2½d. rose	9·00	3·00
215	**18**	5d. purple-brown	10·00	2·75

(*b*) *P* 12

217	**16**	1d. red	20·00	
218		2d. blue	—	12·00

B. *Thick paper. W* **10** (*sideways*) (*part only on each stamp*).

(*a*) *P* 12½, 13

219	**15**	½d. green	1·00	45
220		½d. deep green	1·00	45

(*b*) *P* 12

221	**15**	½d. green	12·00	
222		½d. deep green	12·00	

C. *No wmk; with blue burelé band at back.* (*a*) *P* 12½, 13

223	**15**	½d. green	1·00	50
		a. Without *burelé* band	40·00	
224		½d. deep green	1·00	

(*b*) *P* 12

225	**15**	½d. green	15·00	
		a. Without *burelé* band	50·00	

Nos. 223a and 225a are from the margins of the sheet.

D. *Thin paper, with Crown and Q faintly impressed. P* 12½, 13
227	**15**	½d. green		1·40	50
228	**16**	1d. orange-red		3·00	30

19

1896. *W* **6**. *P* 12½, 13.
229	**19**	1d. vermilion		7·50	40

Used examples of a 6d. green as Type **19** (figures in lower corners only) are known, mostly with readable 1902 postmark dates. It is believed that this 6d. was prepared, but not officially issued (*Price* £1000 *used*).

20   21   22

23   24   25

Die I   Die II
Two Dies of 4d.:

Die I. Serif of horizontal bar on lower right 4d. is clear of vertical frame line.
Die II. Serif joins vertical frame line.

1897–1907. *Figures in all corners. W* **6** (*sideways on* ½d.). *P* 12½, 13.
231	**20**	½d. deep green		3·50	2·00
		a. Perf 12		—	90·00
232	**21**	1d. orange-vermilion		1·00	15
233		1d. vermilion		1·00	15
234		2d. blue		1·25	15
		a. Cracked plate		50·00	20·00
235		2d. deep blue		1·25	15
		a. Cracked plate		50·00	20·00
236	**22**	2½d. rose		15·00	6·00
237		2½d. purple/*blue*		8·50	85
238		2½d. brown-purple/*blue*		8·50	85
239		2½d. slate/*blue*		11·00	2·75
240	**21**	3d. brown		10·00	1·00
241		3d. deep brown		8·00	80
242		3d. reddish brown (1906)		8·00	80
243		3d. grey-brown (1907)		9·50	80
244		4d. yellow (Die I)		8·00	80
		a. Die II		18·00	1·75
245		4d. yellow-buff (Die I)		8·00	80
		a. Die II		18·00	1·75
246	**23**	5d. purple-brown		7·00	80
247		5d. dull brown (1906)		8·00	1·50
248		5d. black-brown (1907)		9·00	1·75
249	**21**	6d. green		7·00	1·25
250		6d. yellow-green		6·00	1·25

251	**24**	1s. pale mauve		13·00	1·00
252		1s. dull mauve		13·00	1·00
253		1s. bright mauve		15·00	2·00
254	**25**	2s. turquoise-green		30·00	7·00

The 1d. perf 12×9½ was not an authorised issue.
The cracked plate variety on the 2d. developed during 1901 and shows as a white break on the Queen's head and neck.

1897–8. *W* **6** (*a*) *Zigzag roulette in black*. (*b*) *The same but plain*. (*c*) *Roulette* (*a*) *and also* (*b*). (*d*) *Roulette* (*b*) *and perf* 12½, 13. (*e*) *Roulette* (*a*) *and perf* 12½, 13. (*f*) *Compound of* (*a*), (*b*) *and perf* 12½, 13.
256	**21**	1d. vermilion (*a*)		5·00	4·00
257		1d. vermilion (*b*)		2·50	1·50
258		1d. vermilion (*c*)		4·75	
259		1d. vermilion (*d*)		3·00	2·50
260		1d. vermilion (*e*)		50·00	
261		1d. vermilion (*f*)		60·00	

26   27

1899–1906. *W* **6**. *P* 12½, 13.
262	**26**	½d. deep green		1·00	20
263		½d. grey-green		1·00	20
264		½d. pale green (1906)		1·00	20

Stamps of T **26** without wmk, are proofs.

(Des F. Elliott)

1900 (19 June). *Charity. T* **27** *and horiz design showing Queen Victoria in medallion inscr* "PATRIOTIC FUND 1900". *W* **6**. *P* 12.
264*a*		1d. (6d.) claret		80·00	90·00
264*b*		2d. (1s.) violet		£180	£200

These stamps, sold at 6d. and 1s. respectively, paid postage of 1d. and 2d. only, the difference being contributed to a Patriotic Fund.

28   A   B

TWO TYPES OF "QUEENSLAND". Three different duty plates, each 120 (12×10), were produced for Type **28**. The first contained country inscriptions as Type A and was only used for Nos. 265/6. The second duty plate, used for Nos. 265/6 and 282/5 contained 117 examples as Type A and 3 as Type B occurring on R. 1/6, R. 2/6 and R. 3/6. The third plate, also used for Nos. 265/6 and 282/5, had all inscriptions as Type B.

(Typo Victoria Govt Printer, Melbourne)

1903 (4 July). *W* **75** *of Victoria* (*double-lined V over Crown*). *P* 12½.
265	**28**	9d. brown and ultramarine (A)		10·00	1·75
266		9d. brown and ultramarine (B)		10·00	1·75

1903. *W* **6**. *P* 12.
267	**26**	½d. green		1·50	30
268	**21**	1d. vermilion		2·25	70
269		2d. blue		—	5·00

Nos. 267/9 can be found with rough or clean cut holes from this comb machine. A perf 12½ line machine was also used, but stamps from it are difficult to distinguish.

1905. *Recess. W* **6**. *P* 12½, 13 (*irregular line*).

270	**9**	2s. 6d. vermilion	60·00	32·00
271		£1 deep green	£450	£300
		a. Re-entry (R. 1/2)	—	£400
		b. Retouch (R. 6/4)	—	£400

29

1905–10. *Litho.* A. *W* **6**, *twice sideways.* (*a*) *P* 12 (1905–6).

272	**9**	5s. rose (7.06)	65·00	65·00
273		£1 deep green (7.11.05)	£250	90·00
		a. Re-entry (R. 1/2)	—	£150
		b. Retouch (R. 6/4)	—	£150

(*b*) *P* 12½, 13 (*irregular line*)

274	**9**	£1 deep green (7.06)	£350	£100
		a. Re-entry (R. 1/2)	—	£160
		b. Retouch (R. 6/4)	—	£160

B. *W* **29**, *twice sideways. P* 12½, 13 (*irregular line*) (1907–10)

275	**9**	2s. 6d. vermilion	40·00	26·00
276		2s. 6d. dull orange (1910)	55·00	32·00
277		5s. rose	45·00	26·00
278		5s. deep rose	55·00	38·00
279		10s. deep brown	£100	35·00
280		£1 bluish green	£170	80·00
		a. Re-entry (R. 1/2)	—	£130
		b. Retouch (R. 6/4)	—	£130
280c		£1 deep green	£325	£250
		ca. Re-entry (R. 1/2)	—	£350
		cb. Retouch (R. 6/4)	—	£350

The lithographic stone used for Nos. 272/80c took the full sheet of 30 so the varieties on the £1 recess-printed version also appear on the stamps printed by lithography.

30   32

Redrawn types of T **21**

T **30**. The head is redrawn, the top of the crown is higher and touches the frame, as do also the back of the chignon and the point of the bust. The forehead is filled in with lines of shading, and the figures in the corners appear to have been redrawn also.

T **32**. The forehead is plain (white instead of shaded), and though the top of the crown is made higher, it does not touch the frame; but the point of the bust and the chignon still touch. The figure in the right lower corner does not touch the line below, and has not the battered appearance of that in the first redrawn type. The stamps are very clearly printed, the lines of shading being distinct.

1906 (Sept). *W* **6**. *P* 12½, 13 (*comb*).

281	**30**	2d. dull blue (*shades*)	5·00	1·50

(Typo Victoria Govt Printer, Melbourne)

1906 (Sept)–10. *W* **93**a *of Victoria.* (*a*) *P* 12 × 12½.

282	**28**	9d. brown and ultramarine (A)	22·00	2·50
283		9d. brown and ultramarine (B)	11·00	2·00
283a		9d. pale brown and blue (A)		
284		9d. pale brown and blue (B)	11·00	2·25

(*b*) *P* 11 (1910)

285	**28**	9d. pale brown and blue (B)	—	£200

1907–09. *W* **29**. (*a*) *P* 12½, 13 (*comb*).

286	**26**	½d. deep green	1·00	20
287		½d. deep blue-green	1·00	20
288	**21**	1d. vermilion	1·00	15
		a. Imperf (pair)	£150	
289	**30**	2d. dull blue	1·40	15
289a		2d. bright blue (3.08)	7·50	2·00
290	**32**	2d. bright blue (4.08)	1·50	15
291	**21**	3d. pale brown (8.08)	10·00	70
292		3d. bistre-brown	10·00	80
293		4d. yellow (Die I)	10·00	1·25
		a. Die II	22·00	2·75
294		4d. grey-black (Die I) (4.09)	12·00	1·50
		a. Die II	27·00	3·50
295	**23**	5d. dull brown	7·50	1·25
295a		5d. sepia (12.09)	11·00	2·00
296	**21**	6d. yellow-green	8·50	1·25
297		6d. bright green	10·00	1·50
298	**24**	1s. violet (1908)	11·00	1·60
299		1s. bright mauve	12·00	1·50
300	**25**	2s. turquoise-green (8.08)	30·00	6·50

Stamps of this issue also exist with the irregular line perforation 12½, 13. This was used when the comb perforation was under repair.

(*b*) *P* 13 × 11 *to* 12½

301	**26**	½d. deep green		
302	**21**	1d. vermilion	2·50	50
303	**32**	2d. blue	4·00	1·00
304	**21**	3d. bistre-brown	8·00	2·00
305		4d. grey-black	20·00	
306	**23**	5d. dull brown	15·00	
307	**21**	6d. yellow-green	16·00	
308	**23**	1s. violet	25·00	

The perforation (*b*) is from a machine introduced to help cope with the demands caused by the introduction of penny postage. The three rows at top (or bottom) of the sheet show varieties gauging 13 × 11½. 13 × 11 and 13 × 12, respectively, are obtainable in strips of three showing the three variations.

Many values of the 1907–09 issue were subsequently produced by lithography.

1911. *W* **29**. *Perf irregular compound*, 10½ *to* 12½.

309	**21**	1d. vermilion	—	£120

This was from another converted machine, formerly used for perforating Railway stamps. The perforation was very unsatisfactory and only one or two sheets were sold.

POSTAL FISCALS

Authorised for use from 1 January 1880 until 1 July 1892

CANCELLATIONS. Beware of stamps which have had pen-cancellations cleaned off and then had faked postmarks applied. Used prices quoted are for postally used examples between the above dates.

F 1   F 2

1866–68. A. *No wmk. P* 13.

F 1	**F 1**	1d. blue	25·00	5·00
F 2		6d. deep violet	25·00	30·00
F 3		1s. blue-green	30·00	9·00
F 4		2s. brown	85·00	42·00
F 5		2s. 6d. dull red	85·00	30·00
F 6		5s. yellow	£200	60·00
F 7		10s. green	£350	£100
F 8		20s. rose	£425	£150

B. *Wmk* F **2**. *P* 13

F 9	**F 1**	1d. blue	10·00	20·00
F10		6d. deep violet	25·00	30·00
F11		6d. blue	25·00	14·00
F12		1s. blue-green	30·00	14·00

F13	F 1	2s. brown	85·00	30·00
F13a		5s. yellow	£200	65·00
F14		10s. green	£350	£100
F15		20s. rose	£425	£150

F 3   F 3a

1871–2. *P* 12 *or* 13. A. *Wmk* F **3**a.

F16	F **3**	1d. mauve	10·00	5·00
F17		6d. red-brown	20·00	10·00
F18		1s. green	30·00	12·00
F19		2s. blue	40·00	10·00
F20		2s. 6d. brick-red	60·00	25·00
F21		5s. orange-brown	£100	25·00
F22		10s. brown	£200	75·00
F23		20s. rose	£350	£120

B. *No wmk. Blue burelé band at back*

F24	F **3**	1d. mauve	14·00	6·50
F25		6d. red-brown	20·00	10·00
F26		6d. mauve	22·00	12·00
F27		1s. green	30·00	12·00
F28		2s. blue	45·00	50·00
F29		2s. 6d. vermilion	85·00	35·00
F30		5s. yellow-brown	£120	40·00
F31		10s. brown	£225	90·00
F32		20s. rose	£350	£110

F 4   F 5

1878–9. A. *No wmk. Lilac burelé band at back. P* 12.
F33   F **4**   1d. violet .... — 12·00

B. *Wmk Crown and Q, W* **5**. *P* 12
F34   F **4**   1d. violet .... 15·00   8·00
Stamps as Type F **5** were not issued until 1 July 1892. The existence of postal cancellations on such issues was unauthorised.

The six former colonies of New South Wales, Queensland, South Australia, Tasmania, Victoria and Western Australia united to form the Commonwealth of Australia on 1 January 1901.

On 1 March 1901 control of the postal service passed to the federal administration. The first national postage due stamps appeared in July 1902, but it was not until January 1913 that postage stamps inscribed "AUSTRALIA" were issued.

SOUTH AUSTRALIA

PRICES

First column = Mounted Mint
Second column = Used

PRICES FOR STAMPS ON COVER

Nos. 1/3	from ×3
No. 4	†
Nos. 5/12	from ×2
Nos. 13/18	from ×3
Nos. 19/43	from ×4
Nos. 44/9b	—
Nos. 50/110	from ×3
No. 111	—
Nos. 112/34	from ×6
Nos. 135/45	from ×3
Nos. 146/66	from ×5
Nos. 167/77	from ×10
Nos. 178/80	—
Nos. 181/94	from ×12
Nos. 195/208	—
Nos. 229/34	from ×12
No. 235	—
Nos. 236/44	from ×8
Nos. 245/60	from ×15
Nos. 262/7	from ×20
Nos. 268/75	from ×30
Nos. 276/9	—
Nos. 280/8	from ×30
Nos. 289/92	—
Nos. 293/304	from ×15
No. 305	—
Nos. O1/13	—
Nos. O14/36	from ×20
Nos. O37/42	from ×5
Nos. O43/6	from ×50
Nos. O47/9	—
Nos. O50/3	from ×30
No. O54	from ×15
Nos. O55/71	from ×50
Nos. O72/85	from ×75
Nos. O86/7	—

SPECIMEN OVERPRINTS. Those listed are from U.P.U. distributions between 1889 and 1895. Further "Specimen" overprints exist, but these were used for other purposes.

1   2 Large Star

(Eng Wm Humphrys. Recess P.B.)

1855. *Printed in London. W* **2**. *Imperf.*

1	**1**	1d. dark green (26.10.55)	£2500	£350
2		2d. rose-carmine (*shades*) (1.1.55)	£800	£125
3		6d. deep blue (26.10.55)	£2000	£150

Prepared and sent to the Colony, but not issued

4	**1**	1s. violet	£4500

A printing of 500,000 of these 1s. stamps was made and delivered, but as the colour was liable to be confused with that of the 6d. stamp, the stock was destroyed on 5 June 1857.

NOTE. Proofs of the 1d. and 6d. without wmk exist, and these are found with forged star watermarks added, and are sometimes offered as originals.

For reprints of the above and later issues, see note after No. 194.

1856–58. *Printed by Govt Ptr, Adelaide, from Perkins, Bacon plates.* W **2**.
Imperf.

5	1	1d. deep yellow-green (15.6.58)	£5000	£400
6		1d. yellow-green (11.10.58)	—	£475
7		2d. orange-red (23.4.56)	—	£110
8		2d. blood-red (14.11.56)	£1200	90·00
		a. Printed on both sides		
9		2d. red (*shades*) (29.10.57)	£650	55·00
		a. Printed on both sides	—	£600
10		6d. slate-blue (7.57)	£2000	£200
11		1s. red-orange (8.7.57)	—	£400
12		1s. orange (11.6.58)	£3750	£300

1858–59. W **2**. *Rouletted.* (*This first rouletted issue has the same colours as the local imperf issue*).

13	1	1d. yellow-green (8.1.59)	£475	45·00
14		1d. light yellow-green (18.3.59)	£475	50·00
		a. Imperf between (pair)		
15		2d. red (17.2.59)	£110	18·00
		a. Printed on both sides		
17		6d. slate-blue (12.12.58)	£375	25·00
18		1s. orange (18.3.59)	£800	35·00
		a. Printed on both sides	—	£1000

3　　　　　　　4　　　　　　(5)

1860–69. *Second rouletted issue, printed in colours only found rouletted or perforated. Surch with T* **5** (*Nos. 35/7*). W **2**.

19	1	1d. bright yellow-green (22.4.61)	45·00	25·00
20		1d. dull blue-green (17.12.63)	40·00	23·00
21		1d. sage-green	50·00	27·00
22		1d. pale sage-green (27.5.65)	40·00	
23		1d. deep green (1864)	£225	65·00
24		1d. deep yellow-green (1869)	90·00	
24a		2d. pale red	60·00	4·00
		b. Printed on both sides	—	£375
25		2d. pale vermilion (3.2.63)	48·00	4·00
26		2d. bright vermilion (19.8.64)	38·00	2·75
		a. Imperf between (horiz pair)	£700	£300
27	3	4d. dull violet (24.1.67)	48·00	17·00
28	1	6d. violet-blue (19.3.60)	£110	6·00
29		6d. greenish blue (11.2.63)	65·00	4·00
30		6d. dull ultramarine (25.4.64)	60·00	4·00
		a. Imperf between (horiz pair)	—	£300
31		6d. violet-ultramarine (11.4.68)	£150	6·00
32		6d. dull blue (26.8.65)	£100	6·50
		a. Imperf between (pair)	—	£600
33		6d. Prussian blue (7.9.69)	£550	50·00
33a		6d. indigo	—	55·00
34	4	9d. grey-lilac (24.12.60)	42·00	9·00
		a. Imperf between (horiz pair)		
35		10d. on 9d. orange-red (B.) (20.7.66)	90·00	24·00
36		10d. on 9d. yellow (25.7.67)	£140	20·00
37		10d. on 9d. yellow (Blk.) (14.8.69)	£1200	30·00
		a. Surch inverted at the top	—	£2500
		b. Printed on both sides	—	£800
		c. Roul × perf 10	†	
38	1	1s. yellow (25.10.61)	£450	28·00
		a. Imperf between (vert pair)	—	£1200
39		1s. grey-green (10.4.63)	£150	16·00
40		1s. dark grey-brown (26.5.63)	£130	16·00
41		1s. chestnut (25.8.63)	£150	11·00
42		1s. lake-brown (27.3.65)	£110	12·00
		a. Imperf between (horiz pair)	—	£400
43	3	2s. rose-carmine (24.1.67)	£160	25·00
		a. Imperf between (vert pair)	—	£750

1868–71. *Remainders of old stock subsequently perforated by the 11½–12½ machine.*

(*a*) *Imperf stamps.* P 11½–12½

44	1	2d. pale vermilion (Feb 1868)	—	£900
45		2d. vermilion (18.3.68)	—	£1000

(*b*) *Rouletted stamps.* P 11½–12½

46	1	1d. bright green (9.11.69)	—	£450
47		2d. pale vermilion (15.8.68)	—	£400
48		6d. Prussian blue (8.11.69)	—	£200
		aa. Horiz pair perf all round, roul between	. . .	
48a		6d. indigo		
49	4	9d. grey-lilac (29.3.71)	£1500	£160
		a. Perf × roulette	—	£150
49b	1	1s. lake-brown (23.5.70)		

1867–70. W **2**. P 11½–12½ × *roulette.*

50	1	1d. pale bright green (2.11.67)	£140	18·00
51		1d. bright green (1868)	£100	18·00
52		1d. grey-green (26.1.70)	£140	20·00
		a. Imperf between (horiz pair)		
53		1d. blue-green (29.11.67)	£175	30·00
54	3	4d. dull violet (July 1868)	£1400	£130
55		4d. dull purple (1869)	—	90·00
56	1	6d. bright pale blue (29.5.67)	£450	19·00
57		6d. Prussian blue (30.7.67)	£400	19·00
		a. Printed on both sides		
58		6d. indigo (1.8.69)	£500	24·00
59	4	10d. on 9d. yellow (B.) (2.2.69)	£600	30·00
		a. Printed on both sides	—	£550
60	1	1s. chestnut (April 1868)	£250	15·00
61		1s. lake-brown (3.3.69)	£250	15·00

NOTE. The stamps perf 11½, 12½, or compound of the two, are here combined in one list, as both perforations are on the one machine, and all the varieties *may* be found in each sheet of stamps. This method of classifying the perforations by the machines is by far the most simple and convenient.

3-PENCE

(6)

1868–79. *Surch with T* **6** (*Nos. 66/8*). W **2**. P 11½–12½.

62	1	1d. pale bright green (8.2.68)	£150	18·00
63		1d. grey-green (18.2.68)	£120	40·00
64		1d. dark green (20.3.68)	50·00	17·00
		a. Printed on both sides		
65		1d. deep yellow-green (28.6.72)	45·00	18·00
66	3	3d. on 4d. Prussian blue (7.2.71)	—	£700
67		3d. on 4d. sky-blue (Blk.) (12.8.70)	£275	10·00
		a. Imperf		
		b. Rouletted	—	£500
68		3d. on 4d. deep ultramarine (Blk.) (9.72) . . .	65·00	8·00
		a. Surch double (10.9.74)	—	£3250
		b. Additional surch on back	—	£2400
		c. Surch omitted (26.4.74)	£14000	£8000
70		4d. dull purple (1.2.68)	55·00	15·00
		a. Imperf between (horiz pair)		
71		4d. dull violet (1868)	50·00	8·00
72	1	6d. bright pale blue (23.2.68)	£300	11·00
73		6d. Prussian blue (29.9.69)	90·00	6·00
		a. Perf 11½ × imperf (horiz pair)		
74		6d. indigo (1869)	£120	17·00
75	4	9d. claret (7.72)	90·00	8·00
76		9d. bright mauve (1.11.72)	90·00	8·00
		a. Printed on both sides	—	£300
77		9d. red-purple (15.1.74)	40·00	8·00
78		10d. on 9d. yellow (B.) (15.8.68)	£1000	24·00
		a. Error. Wmk Crown and S A (1868)	—	£900
79		10d. on 9d. yellow (Blk.) (13.9.69)	£200	27·00
80	1	1s. lake-brown (9.68)	£150	11·00
81		1s. chestnut (8.10.72)	£110	16·00
82		1s. dark red-brown	90·00	11·00
83		1s. red-brown (6.1.69)	£100	11·00
84	3	2s. pale rose-pink (10.10.69)	£950	£150
85		2s. deep rose-pink (8.69)	—	£100
86		2s. crimson-carmine (16.10.69)	70·00	18·00
87		2s. carmine (1869)	60·00	10·00
		a. Printed on both sides	—	£300

1870–71. W **2**. P 10.

88	1	1d. grey-green (6.70)	£120	15·00
89		1d. pale bright green (9.8.70)	£120	15·00
90		1d. bright green (1871)	£100	15·00
91	3	3d. on 4d. dull ultramarine (R.) (6.8.70) . . .	£325	50·00

92	3	3d. on 4d. pale ultramarine (Blk.) (14.2.71)	£250	14·00
93		3d. on 4d. ultramarine (Blk.) (14.8.71)	£100	17·00
93a		3d. on 4d. Prussian blue (Blk.) (16.12.71)		
94		4d. dull lilac (1870)	£110	10·00
95		4d. dull purple (1871)	£100	10·00
96	1	6d. bright blue (19.6.70)	£180	17·00
97		6d. indigo (11.10.71)	£225	16·00
98		1s. chestnut (4.1.71)	£150	19·00

1870–73. *W* **2**. *P* 10 × 11½–12½, 11½–12½ × 10, *or compound.*

99	1	1d. pale bright green (11.10.70)	£140	14·00
		a. Printed on both sides		
100		1d. grey-green	£130	15·00
101		1d. deep green (19.6.71)	75·00	10·00
102	3	3d. on 4d. pale ultramarine (Blk.) (9.11.70)	£175	30·00
103		4d. dull lilac (11.5.72)	—	18·00
104		4d. slate-lilac (5.3.73)	£120	18·00
105	1	6d. Prussian blue (2.3.70)	£140	8·00
106		6d. bright Prussian blue (26.10.70)	£150	10·00
107	4	10d. on 9d. yellow (Blk.) (1.70)	£110	17·00
108	1	1s. chestnut (17.6.71)	—	32·00
109	3	2s. rose-pink (24.4.71)	—	£170
110		2s. carmine (2.3.72)	£120	25·00

1871 (17 July). *W* **20** *of Victoria* (*V over Crown*). *P* 10.

111	3	4d. dull lilac	£1500	£250
		a. Printed on both sides		

8 PENCE

8 Broad Star   (9)

1876–1900. *W* **8**. *Surch with T* **9** (*Nos.* 118/21). (*a*) *P* 11½–12½.

112	3	3d. on 4d. ultramarine (1.6.79)	50·00	15·00
		a. Surch double	—	£1000
113		4d. violet-slate (15.3.79)	90·00	11·00
114		4d. plum (16.4.80)	40·00	6·00
115		4d. deep mauve (8.6.82)	40·00	5·00
116	1	6d. indigo (2.12.76)	90·00	4·50
		a. Imperf between (horiz pair)		
117		6d. Prussian blue (7.78)	55·00	4·00
118	4	8d. on 9d brown-orange (7.76)	48·00	4·50
119		8d. on 9d. burnt umber (1880)	55·00	4·50
120		8d. on 9d. brown (9.3.80)	55·00	4·50
		a. Imperf between (vert pair)		£350
121		8d. on 9d. grey-brown (10.5.81)	48·00	6·00
		a. Surch double	—	£350
122		9d. purple (9.3.80)	30·00	6·00
		a. Printed on both sides	—	£200
123		9d. rose-lilac (21.8.80)	9·00	2·25
124		9d. rose-lilac (*large holes*) (26.5.00)	9·00	2·50
125	1	1s. red-brown (3.11.77)	42·00	2·75
		a. Imperf between (horiz pair)	—	£250
126		1s. reddish lake-brown (1880)	40·00	3·00
127		1s. lake-brown (9.1.83)	45·00	2·75
128		1s. Vandyke brown (1891)	60·00	8·00
129		1s. dull brown (1891)	38·00	2·75
130		1s. chocolate (*large holes*) (6.5.97)	24·00	3·00
		a. Imperf vert (horiz pair)		£200
131		1s. sepia (*large holes*) (22.5.00)	24·00	3·00
		a. Imperf between (vert pair)		£150
132	3	2s. carmine (15.2.77)	25·00	4·00
		a. Imperf between (horiz pair)	—	£400
		b. Imperf (pair)		
133		2s. rose-carmine (1885)	32·00	6·00
134		2s. rose-carmine (*large holes*) (6.12.98)	30·00	5·50

The perforation with larger, clean-cut holes resulted from the fitting of new pins to the machine.

(b) P 10

135	1	6d. Prussian blue (11.11.79)	80·00	12·00
136		6d. bright blue (1879)	£100	11·00
136a		1s. reddish lake-brown	£225	

		(c) P 10 × 11½–12½, 11½–12½ × 10, *or compound*		
137	3	4d. violet-slate (21.5.79)	£100	10·00
138		4d. dull purple (4.10.79)	25·00	2·00
139	1	6d. Prussian blue (29.12.77)	48·00	2·50
140		6d. bright blue	70·00	5·50
141		6d. bright ultramarine	35·00	1·75
142		1s. reddish lake-brown (9.2.85)	75·00	9·00
143		1s. dull brown (29.6.86)	90·00	10·00
144	3	2s. carmine (27.12.77)	40·00	5·00
145		2s. rose-carmine (1887)	35·00	4·50
		a. Imperf between (horiz pair)	—	£400

10   11   12

1901–2. *Wmk Crown SA* (*wide*), *W* **10**. *P* 11½–12½ (*large holes*).

146	4	9d. claret (1.2.02)	10·00	10·00
147	1	1s. dark brown (12.6.01)	20·00	9·00
148		1s. dark reddish brown (1902)	20·00	10·00
		a. Imperf between (vert pair)		
149		1s. red-brown (aniline) (18.7.02)	22·00	11·00
150	3	2s. crimson (29.8.01)	25·00	12·00
151		2s. carmine	19·00	8·00

(Plates and electrotypes by D.L.R. Printed in Adelaide)

1868–76. *W* **10**. (*a*) *Rouletted.*

152	12	2d. deep brick-red (8.68)	38·00	3·25
153		2d. pale orange-red (5.10.68)	35·00	2·75
		a. Printed on both sides	—	£200
		b. Imperf between (horiz pair)	—	£225

(b) P 11½–12½

154	11	1d. blue-green (10.1.75)	65·00	11·00
155	12	2d. pale orange-red (5.5.69)	£850	£190

(c) P 11½–12½ × *roulette*

156	12	2d. pale orange-red (20.8.69)	—	£120

(d) P 10 × *roulette*

157	12	2d. pale orange-red (7.5.70)	£200	20·00

(e) P 10

158	11	1d. blue-green (4.75)	18·00	3·50
159	12	2d. brick-red (4.70)	9·00	25
160		2d. orange-red (1.7.70)	8·00	20
		a. Printed on both sides	—	£160

(f) P 10 × 11½–12½, 11½–12½ × 10, *or compound*

161	11	1d. blue-green (27.8.75)	38·00	10·00
162	12	2d. brick-red (19.1.71)	£400	6·00
163		2d. orange-red (3.2.71)	£100	8·50
		a. Imperf (8.76)	£750	

1869. *Wmk Large Star, W* **2**. (*a*) *Rouletted.*

164	12	2d. orange-red (13.3.69)	38·00	11·00

(b) P 11½–12½ × *roulette*

165	12	2d. orange-red (1.8.69)	—	90·00

(c) P 11½–12½

165a	12	2d. orange-red (7.69)	—	£800

1871 (15 July). *W* **20** *of Victoria. P* 10.

166	12	2d. brick-red	40·00	12·00

A regular new issue supplement to this
catalogue appears each month in

GIBBONS STAMP MONTHLY

—from your newsagent or by postal subscription
—sample copy and details on request.

HALF-

PENNY

13　　　　　(14)

1876-85. *Wmk Crown SA (close), W* **13.** *(a) P* 10.
167	11	1d. blue-green (9.2.76)	4·50	1·25
168		1d. yellowish green (11.78)	4·75	1·25
169		1d. deep green (11.79)	5·00	1·25
		a. Imperf between (horiz pair)		
170	12	2d. orange-red (8.76)	4·50	10
171		2d. dull brick-red (21.5.77)	4·50	10
172		2d. blood-red (31.10.79)	£200	3·00
173		2d. pale red (4.85)	4·50	10

(b) P 10×11½–12½, *or* 11½–12½×10, *or compound*
174	11	1d. deep green (11.2.80)	18·00	2·25
175		1d. blue-green (2.3.80)	8·00	1·90
176	12	2d. orange-red (4.9.77)	£120	3·00
177		2d. brick-red (6.80)	£120	3·00

(c) P 11½–12½
178	11	1d. blue-green (2.84)	—	£110
179	12	2d. orange-red (14.9.77)	—	£110
180		2d. blood-red (4.80)	—	£110

For stamps perf 15, see Nos. 238/40.

1882 (1 Jan). *Surch with T* **14.** *W* **13.** *P* 10.
181	11	½d. on 1d. green	8·50	3·00

15 　　　　16

17 　　　　　18

1883-95. *W* **13** *(sideways on* ½d.). *(a) P* 10.
182	15	½d. chocolate (1.3.83)	2·25	40
		a. Imperf between (horiz pair)		
183		½d. Venetian red (4.4.89)	2·00	35
184		½d. brown (1895)	2·25	35
185	16	3d. sage-green (12.86) (Optd S. £25)	8·00	1·10
186		3d. olive-green (6.6.90)	8·00	1·50
187		3d. deep green (12.4.93)	5·50	60
188	17	4d. pale violet (3.90) (Optd S. £30)	7·00	95
189		4d. aniline violet (3.1.93)	9·00	1·00
190	18	6d. pale blue (4.87) (Optd S. £25)	7·00	1·40
191		6d. blue (5.5.87)	8·50	60

(b) P 10×11½–12½, 11½–12½×10, *or compound*
192	15	½d. pale brown (25.9.91)	11·00	1·25
193		½d. dark brown (9.9.92)	4·00	95
		a. Imperf between (horiz pair)	75·00	

(c) P 11½–12½
194	15	½d. Venetian red (12.10.90)	5·50	75

For stamps perf 15, see Nos. 236/7 and 242/4 and for those perf 13 Nos. 247/8, 254/6 and 259/60.

THE WORLD CENTRE FOR FINE STAMPS IS 399 STRAND

REPRINTS. In 1884, and in later years, reprints on paper wmkd Crown SA, W **10**, were made of Nos. 1, 2, 3, 4, 12, 13, 14, 15, 19, 24, 27, 28, 32, 33, 34, 35, 36, 37, 38, 40, 43, 44, 49a, 53, 65, 67, 67 with surcharge in red, 70, 71, 72, 73, 78, 79, 81, 83, 86, 90, 118, 119, 120, 121, 122, 155, 158, 159, 164, 181, 182. They are overprinted "REPRINT".
　In 1889 examples of the reprints for Nos. 1/3, 12, 15, 19, 27, 32/8, 44, 67, 67 surcharged in red, 70/1, 73, 83, 86, 118, 121/2, 158/9, 164 and 181/2, together with No. 141 overprinted "SPECIMEN" were supplied to the U.P.U. for distribution.

19 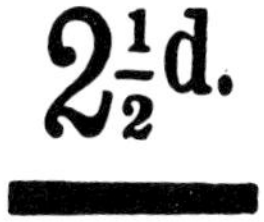　　　　　(20) 　　　　(21)

(Plates and electrotypes by D.L.R. Printed in Adelaide)

1886-96. *T* **19** *(inscr* "POSTAGE & REVENUE"). *W* **13.** *Parts of two or more wmks, on each stamp, sometimes sideways.* A. *Perf* 10. B. *Perf* 11½–12½ *(small or large holes).*

		A		B	
195	2s. 6d. mauve	25·00	8·00	†	
	a. Dull violet		†	24·00	6·00
	b. Bright aniline violet		†	25·00	7·00
196	5s. rose-pink	40·00	12·00	32·00	12·00
	a. Rose-carmine		†	35·00	14·00
197	10s. green	£110	35·00	80·00	35·00
198	15s. brownish yellow	£250	—	£275	£120
199	£1 blue	£200	90·00	£150	80·00
200	£2 Venetian red	£450	£200	£450	£200
201	50s. dull pink	£600	£250	£600	—
202	£3 sage green	£700	£200	£700	£200
203	£4 lemon	£900	—	£800	—
204	£5 grey	£1500	—	£1600	—
205	£5 brown (1896)		†	£1600	£1000
206	£10 bronze	£2250	£700	£1700	£700
207	£15 silver	£4500	—	£4500	—
208	£20 claret	£5000	—	£5000	—

Set of 14 (all perf 10 ex No. 205) optd "Specimen" . . . £500
Variations exist in the length of the words and shape of the letters of the value inscription.
　The 2s. 6d. dull violet, 5s. rose-pink, 10s., £1 and £5 brown exist perf 11½–12½ with either large or small holes; the 2s. 6d. aniline, 5s. rose-carmine, 15s., £2 and 50s. with large holes only and the remainder only with small holes.
　Stamps perforated 11½–12½ small holes, are, generally speaking, rather rarer than those with the 1895 (large holes) gauge.
　Stamps perf 10 were issued on 20 Dec 1886. Stamps perf 11½–12½ (small holes) are known with earliest dates covering the period from June 1890 to Feb 1896. Earliest dates of stamps with large holes range from July 1896 to May 1902.

1891 (1 Jan). *Colours changed and surch with T* **20/21.** *W* **13.**

(a) P 10
229	17	2½d. on 4d. pale green (Br.) (Optd S. £25)	5·50	2·50
		a. Fraction bar omitted	90·00	75·00
230		2½d. on 4d. deep green (Br.)	6·00	1·75
		a. "2" and "½" closer together	22·00	18·00
		b. Fraction bar omitted		
		c. Imperf between (horiz pair)		
		d. Imperf between (vert pair)	—	£325
231	18	5d. on 6d. pale brown (C.) (Optd S. £25)	14·00	3·50
232		5d. on 6d. dark brown (C.)	14·00	3·25
		a. No stop after "5D"	£150	

(b) P 10×11½–12½ *or* 11½–12½×10
233	17	2½d. on 4d. pale green (Br.)	7·00	3·00
234		2½d. on 4d. deep green (Br.)	7·00	3·00

(c) P 11½–12½
235	17	2½d. on 4d. green (Br.)	25·00	40·00

1893–4. *Surch with T* **20** *(No.* 241). *W* **13** *(sideways on ½d.). P* 15.

236	**15**	½d. pale brown (1.93)	2·50	30
237		½d. dark brown	2·50	30
		a. Perf 12½ between (pair)	£120	28·00
		b. Imperf between (horiz pair)	80·00	
238	**11**	1d. green (8.5.93)	3·00	1·25
239	**12**	2d. pale orange (9.2.93)	5·50	10
240		2d. orange-red	6·00	10
		a. Imperf between (vert pair)	£150	
241	**17**	2½d. on 4d. green (14.10.93)	8·00	2·50
		a. "2" and "½" closer	32·00	22·00
		b. Fraction bar omitted		
242		4d. purple (1.1.94)	10·00	2·00
243		4d. slate-violet	10·00	1·75
244	**18**	6d. blue (20.11.93)	19·00	3·50

22 Red Kangaroo

23

24 G.P.O., Adelaide

(Des Tannenberg, Melbourne; plates by D.L.R. Typo Sands and McDougall, Adelaide)

1894 (1 Mar). *W* **13**. *P* 15.

245	**22**	2½d. violet-blue	9·00	1·00
246	**23**	5d. brown-purple	10·00	1·25
		Set of 2 optd "Specimen"	50·00	

1895–99. *W* **13** *(sideways on ½d.). P* 13.

247	**15**	½d. pale brown (9.95)	2·50	30
248		½d. deep brown (19.3.97)	2·50	30
249	**11**	1d. pale green (11.1.95)	4·00	1·25
250		1d. green	4·00	1·25
		a. Imperf between (vert pair)		
251	**12**	2d. pale orange (19.1.95)	3·50	10
252		2d. orange-red (9.5.95)	3·50	10
253	**22**	2½d. violet-blue (11.2.95)	4·50	45
254	**16**	3d. pale olive-green (26.7.97)	5·00	55
255		3d. dark olive-green (27.11.99)	5·00	50
256	**17**	4d. violet (21.1.96)	6·00	40
257	**23**	5d. brown-purple (1.96)	6·50	50
258		5d. purple	6·50	45
259	**18**	6d. pale blue (3.96)	7·00	40
260		6d. blue	7·00	40

The 1d. in pale green, formerly listed under No. 261 as redrawn with slightly thicker lettering, is now accepted as resulting from a printing from a worn plate.

(½d. Typo D.L.R.)

1898–1906. *W* **13**.

A. *Perf* 13 (1898–1903). B. *Perf* 12 × 11½ *(comb)* (1904–6)

			A		B	
262	**24**	½d. yellow-green	1·25	20	1·50	15
263	**11**	1d. rosine	2·00	10	5·00	10
264		1d. scarlet	2·75	10	3·00	10
		a. Deep red	2·50	10	†	
265	**12**	2d. bright violet	2·00	10	2·75	10
266	**22**	2½d. indigo	4·50	30	5·50	30
267	**23**	5d. dull purple	†		7·00	85

Earliest dates: Perf 13. ½d., 27 Dec 1899; 1d. rosine, 8 August 1899; 1d. scarlet, 23 December 1903; 2d. 10 October 1899; 2½d. 25 March 1898.

Perf 12 × 11½. ½d. July 1905; 1d. rosine, 2 February 1904; 1d. scarlet, 25 July 1904; 2d. 11 October 1904; 2½d. 4 July 1906; 5d. January 1905.

25

The measurements given indicate the length of the value inscription in the bottom label. The dates are those of the earliest known postmarks.

1902–4. *As T* **19**, *but top tablet as T* **25** *(thin* "POSTAGE"). *W* **13**.

(a) P 11½–12½

268	3d. olive-green (18½ mm) (1.8.02)	3·25	45
269	4d. red-orange (17 mm) (29.11.02)	5·00	70
270	6d. blue-green (16–16½ mm) (29.11.02)	6·00	70
271	8d. ultramarine (19 mm) (25.4.02)	7·50	1·90
272	8d. ultramarine (16½ mm) (22.3.04)	7·50	1·90
	a. "EIGNT"	£1000	£1300
273	9d. rosy lake (19.9.02)	7·00	1·00
	a. Imperf between (vert pair)	£190	
	b. Imperf between (horiz pair)		
274	10d. dull yellow (29.11.02)	10·00	3·25
275	1s. brown (18.8.02)	11·00	1·75
	a. Imperf between (horiz pair)		
	b. Imperf between (vert pair)	£450	
	c. "POSTAGE" and value in red-brown	45·00	20·00
276	2s. 6d. pale violet (19.9.02)	27·00	9·00
	a. Bright violet (2.2.03)	20·00	7·00
277	5s. rose (17.10.02)	55·00	40·00
278	10s. green (1.11.02)	£100	60·00
279	£1 blue (1.11.02)	£225	£120

(b) P 12

280	3d. olive-green (20 mm) (15.4.04)	3·75	70
	a. "POSTAGE" omitted; value below "AUSTRALIA"	£350	
281	4d. orange-red (17½–18 mm) (18.2.03)	5·50	70
282	6d. blue-green (15 mm) (14.11.03)	15·00	2·25
283	9d. rosy lake (2.12.03)	15·00	3·00

26

V

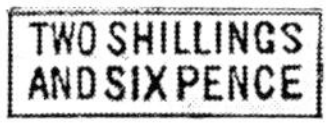

X

In Type X the letters in the bottom line are slightly larger than in Type V, especially the "A", "S" and "P".

Y

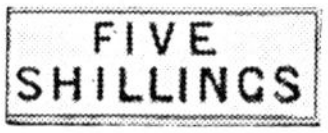

Z

In Type Z the letters "S" and "G" are more open than in Type Y. Nos. 196/*a* and 277 are similar to Type Y with all letters thick and regular and the last "S" has the top curve rounded instead of being slightly flattened.

1904–11. *As T* **19**, *but top tablet as T* **26** *(thick* "POSTAGE"). *W* **13**. *P* 12.

284	6d. blue-green (27.4.04)	5·50	70
285	8d. bright ultramarine (4.7.05)	7·00	2·00
	a. Value closer (15¼ mm)	15·00	
	b. Dull ultramarine (2.4.08)	8·00	2·25
	ba. Ditto. Value closer (15¼ mm)	21·00	
286	9d. rosy lake (17–17¼ mm) (18.7.04)	7·00	1·00
	a. Value 16½–16¾ mm (2.06)	15·00	3·50
	b. Brown-lake. Perf 12½ small holes (6.6.11)	10·00	
287	10d. dull yellow (8.07)	14·00	4·25
	a. Imperf between (horiz pair)	£225	£160
	b. Imperf between (vert pair)	£200	
288	1s. brown (12.4.04)	11·00	1·75
	a. Imperf between (vert pair)	£130	
	b. Imperf between (horiz pair)	£180	
289	2s. 6d. bright violet (V.) (14.7.05)	32·00	6·00
	a. Dull violet (X) (8.06)	32·00	6·00
290	5s. rose-scarlet (Y) (8.04)	40·00	20·00
	a. Scarlet (Z) (8.06)	40·00	20·00
	b. Pale rose. Perf 12½ (small holes) (Z) (7.10)	55·00	22·00
291	10s. green (26.8.08)	£100	£125
292	£1 blue (29.12.04)	£150	£100
	a. Perf 12½ (small holes) (7.10)	£130	80·00

The "value closer" variety on the 8d occurs six times in the sheet of 60. The value normally measure 16½ mm but in the variety it is 15¼ mm.

The 9d., 5s. and £1, perf 12½ (small holes), are late printings made in 1910–11 to use up the Crown SA paper.

No. 286*b* has the value as Type C of the 9d. on Crown over A paper.

27

1905–11. *W* **27**. *P* 12×11½ (*new comb machine*).

293	**24**	½d. pale green (4.07)	1·00	20
		a. Yellow-green	1·10	15
294	**11**	1d. rosine (2.12.05)	1·90	10
		a. Scarlet (4.11)	1·75	10
295	**12**	2d. bright violet (2.2.06)	2·50	10
		aa. Imperf between (pair)		
		a. Mauve (4.08)	1·60	10
296	**22**	2½d. indigo-blue (14.9.10)	7·00	95
297	**23**	5d. brown-purple (11.3.08)	7·50	1·40

Three types of the 9d., perf 12½, distinguishable by the distance between "NINE" and "PENCE".

A. Distance 1¾ mm. B. Distance 2¼ mm. C. Distance 2½ mm.

1906–12. *T* **19** ("POSTAGE" *thick as T* **26**). *W* **27**. *P* 12 *or* 12½ (*small holes*).

298	3d. sage-green (19 mm) (26.6.06)	4·25	70
	a. Imperf between (horiz pair)	—	£500
	b. Perf 12½. *Sage-green* (17 mm) (9.12.09)	4·75	70
	c. Perf 12½. *Deep olive* (20 mm) (7.10)	18·00	3·25
	d. Perf 12½. *Yellow-olive* (14 mm) (16.12.11)	8·50	80
	da. Perf 12½. *Bright olive-green* (19–19¾ mm) (5.12)	8·00	70
	e. Perf 11 (17 mm) (10.7.11)	£180	£180
299	4d. orange-red (10.9.06)	6·50	1·25
	a. Orange	8·00	1·10
	b. Perf 12½. *Orange* (27.10.09)	6·50	1·10
300	6d. blue-green (1.9.06)	8·00	75
	a. Perf 12½ (21.4.10)	6·50	55
	ab. Perf 12½. Imperf between (vert pair)	£275	£250
301	8d. bright ultramarine (*p* 12½) (8.09)	10·00	3·00
	a. Value closer (8.09)	28·00	24·00
302	9d. brown-lake (3.2.06)	10·00	1·50
	a. Imperf between (vert pair)	£190	
	aa. Imperf between (horiz pair)	£200	
	b. Deep lake (9.5.08)	24·00	3·00
	c. Perf 12½. *Lake* (A) (5.9.09)	11·00	3·00
	d. Perf 12½. *Lake* (B) (7.09)	12·00	3·00
	e. Perf 12½. *Brown-lake* (C)	17·00	5·00
	ea. Perf 12½. *Deep lake*. Thin paper (C)	14·00	3·00
	f. Perf 11 (1909)	—	£160
303	1s. brown (30.5.06)	12·00	2·50
	a. Imperf between (horiz pair)	£180	
	b. Perf 12½ (10.3.10)	10·00	1·00
304	2s. 6d. bright violet (X) (10.6.09)	30·00	6·00
	a. Perf 12½. *Pale violet* (X) (6.10)	30·00	7·00
	ab. Perf 12½. *Deep purple* (X) (5.11.12)	35·00	5·50
305	5s. bright rose (*p* 12½) (Z) (24.4.11)	55·00	

The "value closer" variety of the 8d. occurred 11 times in the sheet of 60 in the later printing only. On No. 301 the value measures 16½ mm while on No. 301a it is 15¾ mm.

The 1s. brown, perf compound of 11½ and 12½, formerly listed is now omitted, as it must have been perforated by the 12 machine, which in places varied from 11½ to 13. The 4d. has also been reported with a similar perforation.

OFFICIAL STAMPS

A. Departmentals

Following suspected abuses involving stamps supplied for official use it was decided by the South Australian authorities that such supplies were to be overprinted with a letter, or letters, indicating the department of the administration to which the stamps had been invoiced.

The system was introduced on 1 April 1868 using overprints struck in red. Later in the same year the colour of the overprints was amended to blue, and, during the latter months of 1869, to black.

In 1874 the Postmaster-General recommended that this somewhat cumbersome system be replaced by a general series of "O.S." overprints with the result that the separate accounting for the Departmentals ceased on 30 June of that year. Existing stocks continued to be used, however, and it is believed that much of the residue was passed to the Government Printer to pay postage on copies of the *Government Gazette*.

We are now able to provide a check list of these most interesting issues based on the definitive work, *The Departmental Stamps of South Australia* by A. R. Butler, FRPSL, RDP, published by the Royal Philatelic Society, London in 1978.

No attempt has been made to assign the various overprints to the catalogue numbers of the basic stamps, but each is clearly identified by both watermark and perforation. The colours are similar to those of the contemporary postage stamps, but there can be shade variations. Errors of overprint are recorded in footnotes, but not errors occurring on the basic stamps used.

Most departmental overprints are considered to be scarce to rare in used condition, with unused examples, used multiples and covers being regarded as considerable rarities.

Forgeries of a few items do exist, but most can be readily identified by comparison with genuine examples. A number of forged overprints on stamps not used for the genuine issues also occur.

A. (Architect)

Optd in red with stop. *W* **2**. 2d. (*roul*), 4d. (*p* 11½–12½), 6d. (*roul*), 1s. (*roul*)
Optd in red without stop. *W* **2**. *Roul*. 1d., 6d., 1s.
Optd in black. (*a*) *W* **2**. 4d. (*p* 11½–12½), 4d. (*p* 10), 4d. (*p* 10×11½–12½), 6d. (*p* 11½–12½), 2s. (*roul*)
(*b*) *W* **10**. 2d. D.L.R. (*roul*), 2d. D.L.R. (*p* 10)

A.G. (Attorney-General)

Optd in red. *W* **2**. *Roul*. 1d., 2d., 6d., 1s.
Optd in blue. (*a*) *W* **2**. *Roul*. 6d.
(*b*) *W* 10. *Roul*. 2d. D.L.R.
Optd in black. (*a*) *W* **2**. 1d. (*p* 11½–12½×*roul*), 4d. (*p* 11½–12½), 4d. (*p* 10), 6d. (*p* 11½–12½×*roul*), 6d. (*p* 11½–12½), 1s. (*p* 11½–12½×*roul*), 1s. (*p* 10)
(*b*) *W* **10**. 2d. D.L.R. (*roul*), 2d. D.L.R. (*p* 10)

A.O. (Audit Office)

Optd in red. *W* **2**. 2d. (*roul*), 4d. (*p* 11½–12½), 6d. (*roul*)
Optd in blue. (*a*) *W* **2**. *P* 11½–12½. 1d., 6d.
(*b*) *W* **10**. *Roul*. 2d. D.L.R.
Optd in black. (*a*) *W* **2**. 1d. (*p* 11½–12½), 1d. (*p* 10), 1d. (*p* 10×11½–12), 2d. D.L.R. (*roul*), 4d. (*p* 11½–12½), 4d. (*p* 10), 4d. (*p* 10×11½–12½), 6d. (*roul*), 6d. (*p* 11½–12½), 1s. (*p* 10), 1s. (*p* 11½–12½×*roul*)
(*b*) *W* **7**. *P* 10. 4d.
(*c*) *W* **10**. 2d. D.L.R. (*roul*), 2d. D.L.R. (*p* 10)

B.D. (Barracks Department)

Optd in red. *W* **2**. *Roul*. 2d., 6d., 1s.

B.G. (Botanic Garden)

Optd in black. (*a*) *W* **2**. 1d. (*p* 11½–12½×*roul*), 1d. (*p* 11½–12½), 1d. (*p* 10), 1d. (*p* 10×11½–12½), 2d. D.L.R. (*roul*), 6d. (*roul*), 6d. (*p* 11½–12½×*roul*), 6d. (*p* 11½–12½), 6d. (*p* 10), 1s. (*p* 11½–12½×*roul*), 1s. (*p* 11½–12½), 1s. (*p* 10×11½–12½)
(*b*) *W* **7**. *P* 10. 2d. D.L.R.
(*c*) *W* **10**. 2d. D.L.R. (*roul*), 2d. D.L.R. (*p* 10)

B.M. (Bench of Magistrates)

Optd in red. *W* **2**. *Roul*. 2d.
Optd in black. *W* **10**. *Roul*. 2d. D.L.R.

C. (Customs)

Optd in red. *W* **2**. 1d. (*roul*), 2d. (*roul*), 4d. (*p* 11½–12½), 6d. (*roul*), 1s. (*roul*)
Optd in blue. (*a*) *W* **2**. *Roul*. 1d., 4d., 6d., 1s., 2s.
(*b*) *W* **10**. *Roul*. 2d. D.L.R.
Optd in black. (*a*) *W* **2**. 1d. (*roul*), 1d. (*p* 10), 1d. (*p* 10×11½–12½), 2d. D.L.R. (*p* 10×11½–12½), 4d. (*p* 11½–12½), 4d. (*p* 10), 4d. (*p* 10×11½–12½), 6d. (*roul*), 6d. (*p* 11½–12½), 6d. (*p* 10), 1s. (*p* 11½–12½×*roul*), 1s. (*p* 11½–12½), 2s. (*roul*)
(*b*) *W* **7**. *P* 10. 2d. D.L.R.
(*c*) *W* **10**. 2d. D.L.R. (*roul*), 2d. D.L.R. (*p* 10×*roul*), 2d. D.L.R. (*p* 10), 2d. D.L.R. (*p* 10×11½–12½)

The 2d. (*W* **10**. *Roul*) with black overprint is known showing the error "G" for "C".

C.D. (Convict Department)

Optd in red. *W* **2**. 2d. (*roul*), 4d. (*p* 11½–12½), 6d. (*roul*), 1s. (*roul*)
Optd in black. (*a*) *W* **2**. 1d. (*p* 11½–12½×*roul*), 2d. D.L.R. (*roul*), 2d. D.L.R. (*p* 11½–12½), 2d. D.L.R. (*p* 11½–12½×*roul*), 4d. (*p* 11½–12½), 6d. (*p* 11½–12½×*roul*), 1s. (*p* 11½–12½×*roul*)
(*b*) *W* **10**. *Roul*. 2d. D.L.R.

C.L. (Crown Lands)

Optd in red. *W* **2**. 2d. (*roul*), 4d. (*p* 11½–12½), 6d. (*roul*), 1s. (*roul*)
Optd in blue. (*a*) *W* **2**. *Roul*. 4d., 6d.
(*b*) *W* **10**. *Roul*. 2d. D.L.R.

Optd in black. (a) W 2. 2d. D.L.R. (roul), 4d. (p 11½–12½), 4d. (p 10), 4d.
(p 10 × 11½–12½), 6d. (roul), 6d. (p 11½–12½), 1s. (p 11½–12½ × roul), 1s.
(p 11½–12½), 2s. (roul), 2s. (p 11½–12½)
(b) W 7. P 10. 2d. D.L.R., 4d.
(c) W 10. 2d. D.L.R. (roul), 2d. D.L.R. (p 10), 2d. D.L.R. (p 10 × 11½–12½)
    The 2s. (W 2. P 11½–12½) with black overprint is known showing the
stop omitted after "L".

C.O. (Commissariat Office)

Optd in red. W 2. 2d. (roul), 4d. (p 11½–12½), 6d. (roul), 1s. (roul)
Optd in black. (a) W 2. 4d. (p 11½–12½), 4d. (p 10), 4d. (p 10 × 11½–12½), 6d.
(p 11½–12½), 1s. (p 11½–12½), 2s. (p 11½–12½)
(b) W 10. 2d. D.L.R. (roul), 2d. D.L.R. (p 10)
    The 2s. (W 2. P 11½–12½) with black overprint is known showing the stop
omitted after "O".

C.P. (Commissioner of Police)

Optd in red. W 2. 2d. (roul), 4d. (p 11½–12½), 6d. (roul)

C.S. (Chief Secretary)

Optd in red. W 2. 2d. (roul), 4d. (p 11½–12½), 6d. (roul), 1s. (roul)
Optd in blue. (a) W 2. Roul. 4d., 6d.
(b) W 10. Roul. 2d. D.L.R.
Optd in black. (a) W 2. 2d. D.L.R. (roul), 4d. (roul), 4d. (p 11½–12½ × roul), 4d.
(p 11½ × 12½), 4d. (p 10), 4d. (p 10 × 11½–12½), 6d. (p 11½–12½ × roul), 6d.
(p 11½–12½), 6d. (p 10), 6d. (p 10 × 11½–12½), 1s. (p 11½–12½ × roul), 1s.
(p 11½–12½), 1s. (p 10), 1s. (p 10 × 11½–12½), 2s. (p 10 × 11½–12½)
(b) W 7. P 10. 4d.
(c) W 10. 2d. D.L.R. (roul), 2d. D.L.R. (p 10)

C.Sgn. (Colonial Surgeon)

Optd in red. W 2. 2d. (roul), 4d. (p 11½–12½), 6d. (roul)
Optd in black. (a) W 2. 2d. D.L.R. (roul), 4d. (p 11½–12½), 4d. (p 10), 4d.
(p 10 × 11½–12½), 6d. (roul), 6d. (p 11½–12½), 1s. (p 11½–12½ × roul)
(b) W 10. 2d. D.L.R. (roul), 2d. D.L.R. (p 11½–12½ × roul), 2d. D.L.R. (p 10)
    Two types of overprint exist on the 2d. D.L.R. (W 10. Roul), the second
type having block capitals instead of the serifed type used for the other
values.

D.B. (Destitute Board)

Optd in red. W 2. 1d. (roul), 2d. (roul), 4d. (p 11½–12½), 6d. (roul), 1s. (roul)
Optd in blue. (a) W 2. Roul. 2d. D.L.R., 6d.
(b) W 10. Roul. 2d. D.L.R.
Optd in black. (a) W 2. 1d. (p 11½–12½), 4d. (p 11½–12½), 4d. (p 10), 6d.
(p 10 × 11½–12½), 1s. (p 10)
(b) W 10. 2d. D.L.R. (roul), 2d. D.L.R. (p 10), 2d. D.L.R. (p 10 × 11½–12½)
    The 2d. D.L.R. (W 10. P 10) with black overprint is known showing the
stop omitted after "D".

D.R. (Deeds Registration)

Optd in red. W 2. Roul, 2d., 6d.

E. (Engineer)

Optd in red. W 2. 2d. (roul), 4d. (p 11½–12½), 6d. (roul), 1s. (roul)
Optd in blue. (a) W 2. Roul. 1s.
(b) W 10. Roul. 2d. D.L.R.
Optd in black. (a) W 2. 4d. (p 11½–12½ × roul), 4d. (p 11½–12½), 4d. (p 10), 4d.
(p 10 × 11½–12½), 6d. (p 11½–12½), 6d. (p 10 × 11½–12½), 1s.
(p 11½–12½ × roul). 1s. (p 11½–12½), 1s. (p 10 × 11½–12½), 2s.
(p 10 × 11½–12½)
(b) W 7. P 10. 4d.
(c) W 10. 2d. D.L.R. (roul), 2d. D.L.R. (p 10)

E.B. (Education Board)

Optd in red. W 2. 2d. (roul), 4d. (p 11½–12½), 6d. (roul)
Optd in blue. (a) W 2. Roul. 4d., 6d.
(b) W 10. Roul. 2d. D.L.R.
Optd in black. (a) W 2. 2d. D.L.R. (roul), 4d. (roul), 4d. (p 11½–12½), 4d.
(p 10), 4d. (p 10 × 11½–12½), 6d. (p 11½–12½ × roul), 6d. (p 11½–12½)
(b) W 7. P 10. 2d. D.L.R.
(c) W 10. 2d. D.L.R. (roul), 2d. D.L.R. (p 10), 2d. D.L.R. (p 10 × 11½–12½)

G.F. (Gold Fields)

Optd in black. (a) W 2. Roul. 6d.
(b) W 10. 2d. D.L.R. (p 10 × roul), 2d. D.L.R. (p 10)

G.P. (Government Printer)

Optd in red. W 2. Roul. 1d., 2d., 6d., 1s.
Optd in blue. (a) W 2. Roul. 1d., 6d., 1s., 2s.
(b) W 10. Roul. 2d. D.L.R.

Optd in black. (a) W 2. 1d. (roul), 1d. (p 11½–12½ × roul), 1d. (p 11½–12½), 1d.
(p 10), 1d. (p 10 × 11½–12½), 6d. (p 11½–12½ × roul), 1s. (p 10), 1s.
(p 10 × 11½–12½), 2s. (roul), 2s. (p 11½–12½), 2s. (p 10 × 11½–12½)
(b) W 10. 2d. D.L.R. (roul), 2d. D.L.R. (p 10)
    The 1d. (W 2. Roul) with red overprint is known showing "C.P."
instead of "G.P.".

G.S. (Government Storekeeper)

Optd in red. W 2. Roul. 2d., 6d., 1s.

G.T. (Goolwa Tramway)

Optd in red. W 2. 1d. (roul), 2d. (roul), 4d. (p 11½–12½), 6d. (roul), 1s. (roul)
Optd in black. (a) W 2. 2d. D.L.R. (roul), 4d. (p 11½–12½)
(b) W 10. 2d. D.L.R. (roul), 2d. D.L.R. (p 10)
    The 2d. and 6d. (both W 2. Roul) with red overprint are known
showing the stop omitted after "T". The 1s. (W 2. Roul) with red overprint
is known showing "C.T." instead of "G.T.".

H. (Hospitals)

Optd in black. (a) W 7. P 10. 2d. D.L.R.
(b) W 10. 2d. D.L.R. (p 10), 2d. D.L.R. (p 10 × 11½–12½)

H.A. (House of Assembly)

Optd in red. W 2. 1d. (roul), 2d. (roul), 4d. (p 11½–12½), 6d. (roul), 1s. (roul)
Optd in black. (a) W 2. 1d. (p 11½–12½), 1d. (p 10), 1d. (p 10 × 11½–12½), 4d.
(p 11½–12½), 4d. (p 10), 6d. (roul), 6d. (p 11½–12½), 1s. (p 11½–12½ × roul),
1s. (p 11½–12½)
(b) W 10. 2d. D.L.R. (roul), 2d. D.L.R. (p 10)

I.A. (Immigration Agent)

Optd in red. W 2. 1d. (roul), 2d. (roul), 4d. (p 11½–12½), 6d. (roul)

I.E. (Intestate Estates)

Optd in black. W 10. P 10. 2d. D.L.R.

I.S. (Inspector of Sheep)

Optd in red. W 2. Roul. 2d., 6d.
Optd in blue. W 2. P 11½–12½. 6d.
Optd in black. (a) W 2. 2d. D.L.R. (roul), 6d. (p 11½–12½ × roul)
(b) W 10. 2d. D.L.R. (roul), 2d. D.L.R. (p 10)

L.A. (Lunatic Asylum)

Optd in red. W 2. 1d. (roul), 2d. (roul), 4d. (p 11½–12½), 6d. (roul), 1s. (roul)
Optd in black. (a) W 2. 4d. (p 11½–12½), 4d. (p 10), 4d. (p 10 × 11½–12½), 6d.
(p 11½–12½ × roul), 6d. (p 11½–12½), 1s. (p 11½–12½), 2s. (roul)
(b) W 10. 2d. D.L.R. (roul), 2d. D.L.R. (p 10)

L.C. (Legislative Council)

Optd in red. W 2. Roul. 2d., 6d.
Optd in black. (a) W 2. Roul. 6d.
(b) W 10. 2d. D.L.R. (roul), 2d. D.L.R. (p 10 × roul)
    The 2d. and 6d. (both W 2. Roul) with red overprint are known showing
the stop omitted after "C".

L.L. (Legislative Librarian)

Optd in red. W 2. 2d. (roul), 4d. (p 11½–12½), 6d. (roul)
Optd in black. (a) W 2. P 11½–12½. 6d.
(b) W 10. P 10. 2d. D.L.R.
    The 2d. and 6d. (both W 2. Roul) with red overprint are known
showing the stop omitted from between the two letters.

L.T. (Land Titles)

Optd in red. W 2. 2d. (roul), 4d. (p 11½–12½), 6d. (roul), 1s. (roul)
Optd in blue. W 10. Roul. 2d. D.L.R.
Optd in black. (a) W 2. 4d. (p 11½–12½), 4d. (p 10), 4d. (p 10 × 11½–12½), 6d.
(p 11½–12½ × roul), 6d. (p 11½–12½), 6d. (p 10), 6d. (p 10 × 11½–12½)
(b) W 7. P 10. 2d. D.L.R.
(c) W 10. 2d. D.L.R. (roul), 2d. D.L.R. (p 10)
    The 2d. and 6d. (both W 2. Roul) with red overprint are known
showing the stop omitted after "T".

M. (Military)

Optd in red. W 2. Roul. 2d., 6d., 1s.
Optd in black. W 2. 6d. (p 11½–12½ × roul), 1s. (p 11½–12½ × roul), 2s. (roul)

M.B. (Marine Board)

Optd in red. W 2. 1d. (roul), 2d. (roul), 4d. (roul), 4d. (p 11½–12½), 6d. (roul),
1s. (roul)

Optd in black. (*a*) *W* **2**. 1d. (*roul*), 1d. (*p* 11½–12½), 2d. D.L.R. (*roul*), 4d. (*p* 11½–12½ × *roul*), 4d. (*p* 11½–12½), 4d. (*p* 10), 4d. (*p* 10 × 11½–12½), 6d. (*roul*), 6d. (*p* 11½–12½), 6d. (*p* 10), 6d. (*p* 10 × 11½–12½), 1s. (*p* 11½–12½ × *roul*), 1s. (*p* 11½–12½), 1s. (*p* 10), 1s. (*p* 10 × 11½–12½)
(*b*) *W* **7**. *P* 10. 2d. D.L.R., 4d.
(*c*) *W* **10**. 2d. D.L.R. (*roul*), 2d. D.L.R. (*p* 10)

M.R. (Manager of Railways)

Optd in red. *W* **2**. *Roul.* 2d., 6d.
Optd in black. (*a*) *W* **2**. 1d. (*p* 11½–12½), 1d. (*p* 10), 2d. D.L.R. (*roul*), 4d. (*roul*), 4d. (*p* 11½–12½), 6d. (*roul*), 6d. (*p* 11½–12½ × *roul*), 6d. (*p* 11½–12½), 10d. on 9d. (*roul*), 1s. (*roul*), 1s. (*p* 11½–12½ × *roul*), 2s. (*p* 11½–12½), 2s. (*p* 10 × 11½–12½)

M.R.G. (Main Roads Gambierton)

Optd in red without stops. *W* **2**. *Roul.* 2d., 6d.
Optd in blue without stops. *W* **10**. *Roul.* 2d. D.L.R.
Optd in black without stops. *W* **10**. 2d. D.L.R. (*roul*), 2d. D.L.R. (*p* 10)
Optd in black with stops. *W* **10**. 2d. D.L.R. (*roul*), 2d. D.L.R. (*p* 10)
The 2d. D.L.R. (*W* **10**. *P* 10) with black overprint is known showing the stops omitted after "M" and "R".

N.T. (Northern Territory)

Optd in black. (*a*) *W* **2**. *P* 11½–12½. 1d., 3d on 4d., 4d., 6d., 1s.
(*b*) *W* **10**. 2d. D.L.R. (*roul*), 2d. D.L.R. (*p* 10)

O.A. (Official Assignee)

Optd in red. *W* **2**. 2d. (*roul*), 4d. (*p* 11½–12½)
Optd in blue. *W* **10**. *Roul.* 2d. D.L.R.
Optd in black. (*a*) *W* **2**. 4d. (*roul*), 4d. (*p* 10)
(*b*) *W* **7**. *P* 10. 2d. D.L.R.
(*c*) *W* **10**. 2d. D.L.R. (*roul*), 2d. D.L.R. (*p* 10 × *roul*), 2d. D.L.R. (*p* 10)

P. (Police)

Optd in blue. (*a*) *W* **2**. *Roul.* 6d.
(*b*) *W* **10**. *Roul.* 2d. D.L.R.
Optd in black. (*a*) *W* **2**. 6d. (*p* 11½–12½ × *roul*), 6d. (*p* 11½–12½), 6d. (*p* 10)
(*b*) *W* **7**. *P* 10. 2d. D.L.R.
(*c*) *W* **10**. 2d. D.L.R. (*roul*), 2d. D.L.R. (*p* 11½–12½), 2d. D.L.R. (*p* 11½–12½ × *roul*), 2d. D.L.R. (*p* 10 × *roul*), 2d. D.L.R. (*p* 10), 2d. D.L.R. (*p* 10 × 11½–12½)

P.A. (Protector of Aborigines)

Optd in red. *W* **2**. *Roul.* 2d., 6d.
Optd. in black. (*a*) *W* **2**. *Roul.* 2d. D.L.R., 6d.
(*b*) *W* **10**. 2d. D.L.R. (*roul*), 2d. D.L.R. (*p* 10)

P.O. (Post Office)

Optd in red. *W* **2**. *Roul.* 1d., 2d., 6d., 1s.
Optd in blue. *W* **2**. *Roul.* 2d., 2d. D.L.R.
Optd in black. (*a*) *W* **2**. 1d. (*p* 10 × 11½–12½), 2d. D.L.R. (*roul*), 4d. (*p* 11½–12½), 6d. (*p* 11½–12½), 6d. (*roul*), 1s. (*p* 11½–12½ × *roul*), 1s. (*p* 11½–12½), 1s. (*p* 10), 1s. (*p* 10 × 11½–12½)
(*b*) *W* **10**. 2d. D.L.R. (*roul*), 2d. D.L.R. (*p* 10 × *roul*), 2d. D.L.R. (*p* 10)
The 6d. (*W* **2**. *Roul*) with red overprint is known showing the stop omitted after "O", but with two stops after "P".

P.S. (Private Secretary)

Optd in red. *W* **2**. 1d. (*roul*), 2d. (*roul*), 4d. (*p* 11½–12½), 6d. (*roul*), 1s. (*roul*)
Optd in black. (*a*) *W* **2**. 1d. (*p* 11½–12½ × *roul*), 1d. (*p* 11½–12½), 1d. (*p* 10), 3d. (*in black*) on 4d. (*p* 11½–12½), 3d. (*in red*) on 4d. (*p* 10), 3d. (*in black*) on 4d. (*p* 10), 4d. (*p* 11½–12½), 4d. (*p* 10), 4d. (*p* 10 × 11½–12½), 6d. (*roul*), 6d. (*p* 11½–12½ × *roul*), 6d. (*p* 11½–12½), 6d. (*p* 10), 9d. (*roul*), 9d. (*p* 11½–12½), 10d. on 9d. (*p* 10 × 11½–12½), 1s. (*p* 11½–12½ × *roul*), 2s. (*p* 11½–12½)
(*b*) *W* **7**. *P* 10. 2d. D.L.R.
(*c*) *W* **10**. 2d. D.L.R. (*roul*), 2d. D.L.R. (*p* 10)

P.W. (Public Works)

Optd in red without stop after "W". *W* **2**. *Roul.* 2d., 6d., 1s.
Optd in black. (*a*) *W* **2**. D.L.R. (*roul*), 4d. (*p* 10), 6d. (*roul*), 6d. (*p* 11½–12½), 6d. (*p* 11½–12½ × *roul*)
(*b*) *W* **10**. 2d. D.L.R. (*roul*), 2d. D.L.R. (*p* 10)

R.B. (Road Board)

Optd in red. *W* **2**. 1d. (*roul*), 2d. (*roul*), 4d. (*p* 11½–12½), 6d. (*roul*), 1s. (*roul*)
Optd in blue without stops. *W* **10**. *Roul.* 2d. D.L.R.
Optd in black. (*a*) *W* **2**. 1d. (*p* 11½–12½ × *roul*), 1d. (*p* 10), 4d. (*p* 10), 2s. (*roul*)
(*b*) *W* **7**. *P* 10. 2d. D.L.R.
(*c*) *W* **10**. 2d. D.L.R. (*roul*), 2d. D.L.R. (*p* 10)
The 6d. (*W* **2**. *Roul*) with red overprint is known showing the stop omitted after "B".

R.G. (Registrar-General)

Optd in red. *W* **2**. *Roul.* 2d., 6d., 1s.
Optd in blue. (*a*) *W* **2**. *P* 11½–12½ × *roul.* 6d.
(*b*) *W* **10**. 2d. D.L.R. (*roul*), 2d. D.L.R. (*p* 11½–12½ × *roul*)
Optd in black. (*a*) *W* **2**. 2d. D.L.R. (*roul*), 6d. (*p* 10), 6d. (*p* 10 × 11½–12½), 1s. (*p* 11½–12½ × *roul*), 1s. (*p* 10)
(*b*) *W* **7**. *P* 10. 2d. D.L.R.
(*c*) *W* **10**. 2d. D.L.R. (*roul*), 2d. D.L.R. (*p* 10 × *roul*), 2d. D.L.R. (*p* 10), 2d. D.L.R. (*p* 10 × 11½–12½)

S. (Sheriff)

Optd in red. *W* **2**. *Roul* 2d., 6d.
Optd in blue. (*a*) *W* **2**. *P* 11½–12½ × *roul.* 6d.
(*b*) *W* **10**. *Roul.* 2d. D.L.R.
Optd in black. (*a*) *W* **2**. 4d. (*p* 11½–12½), 4d. (*p* 10), 6d. (*roul*), 6d. (*p* 11½–12½), 6d. (*p* 10)
(*b*) *W* **10**. 2d. D.L.R. (*roul*), 2d. D.L.R. (*p* 10 × *roul*), 2d. D.L.R. (*p* 10), 2d. D.L.R. (*p* 10 × 11½–12½)

S.C. (Supreme Court)

Optd in red. *W* **2**. *Roul.* 2d., 6d.
Optd in black. *W* **10**. *P* 10. 2d. D.L.R.

S.G. (Surveyor-General)

Optd in red. *W* **2**. 2d. (*roul*), 4d. (*p* 11½–12½), 6d. (*roul*)
Optd in blue. (*a*) *W* **2**. *Roul.* 4d.
(*b*) *W* **10**. *Roul.* 2d. D.L.R.
Optd in black. (*a*) *W* **2**. 2d. D.L.R. (*roul*), 4d. (*p* 11½ × 12½), 4d. (*p* 10), 4d. (*p* 10 × 11½–12½), 6d. (*p* 11½–12½ × *roul*), 6d. (*p* 11½–12½), 6d. (*p* 10), 6d. (*p* 10 × 11½–12½)
(*b*) *W* **7**. *P* 10. 2d. D.L.R.
(*c*) *W* **10**. 2d. D.L.R. (*roul*), 2d. D.L.R. (*p* 10 × *roul*), 2d. D.L.R. (*p* 10)

S.M. (Stipendiary Magistrate)

Optd in red. *W* **2**. 2d. (*roul*), 4d. (*roul*), 4d. (*p* 11½–12½), 6d. (*roul*), 1s. (*roul*)
Optd in blue. (*a*) *W* **2**. *Roul.* 2d., 4d., 6d.
(*b*) *W* **10**. *Roul.* 2d. D.L.R.
Optd in black. (*a*) *W* **2**. 1d. (*p* 11½–12½), 1d. (*p* 10), 2d. D.L.R. (*roul*), 4d. (*roul*), 4d. (*p* 11½–12½ × *roul*), 4d. (*p* 11½–12½), 4d. (*p* 10), 4d. (*p* 10 × 11½–12½), 6d. (*p* 11½–12½ × *roul*), 6d. (*p* 11½–12½), 6d. (*p* 10), 1s. (*p* 11½–12½ × *roul*)
(*b*) *W* **7**. *P* 10. 2d. D.L.R.
(*c*) *W* **10**. 2d. D.L.R. (*roul*), 2d. D.L.R. (*p* 10 × *roul*), 2d. D.L.R. (*p* 10), 2d. D.L.R. (*p* 10 × 11½–12½)
The 2d. and 4d. (both *W* **2**. *Roul*) with red overprint are known showing the stop omitted after "M".

S.T. (Superintendent of Telegraphs)

Optd in red. *W* **2**. *Roul.* 2d., 6d.
Optd in blue. *W* **10**. 2d. D.L.R. (*roul*), 2d. D.L.R. (*p* 11½–12½)
Optd in black. (*a*) *W* **2**. *Roul.* 2d. D.L.R., 6d.
(*b*) *W* **7**. *P* 10. 2d. D.L.R.
(*c*) *W* **10**. 2d. D.L.R. (*roul*), 2d. D.L.R. (*p* 10 × *roul*), 2d. D.L.R. (*p* 10)
The 2d. and 6d. (both *W* **2**. *Roul*) with red overprint (2d., 6d.) or black overprint (6d.) are known showing the stop omitted after "T".

T. (Treasury)

Optd in red. *W* **2**. 1d. (*roul*), 2d. (*roul*), 4d. (*p* 11½–12½ × *roul*), 6d. (*roul*), 1s. (*roul*)
Optd in blue. *W* **10**. *Roul.* 2d. D.L.R.
Optd in black. (*a*) *W* **2**. 1d. (*p* 10), 2d. (*roul*), 4d. (*roul*), 4d. (*p* 11½–12½), 6d. (*p* 11½–12½ × *roul*), 6d. (*p* 11½–12½), 1s. (*p* 11½–12½ × *roul*), 1s. (*p* 10 × 11½–12½), 2s. (*roul*), 2s. (*p* 11½–12½), 2s. (*p* 10 × 11½–12½)
(*b*) *W* **7**. *P* 10. 2d. D.L.R.
(*c*) *W* **10**. 2d. D.L.R. (*roul*), 2d. D.L.R. (*p* 10)

T.R. (Titles Registration)

Optd in black. (*a*) *W* **2**. 4d. (*p* 11½–12½), 4d. (*p* 10 × 11½–12½), 6d. (*p* 11½–12½), 6d. (*p* 10 × 11½–12½), 1s. (*p* 11½–12½)
(*b*) *W* **10**. *P* 10. 2d. D.L.R.

V. (Volunteers)

Optd in red. *W* **2**. *Roul.* 2d., 6d., 1s.
Optd in black. *W* **2**. *Roul.* 6d.
(*b*) *W* **7**. *P* 10. 2d. D.L.R.
(*c*) *W* **10**. 2d. D.L.R. (*roul*), 2d. D.L.R. (*p* 10 × *roul*), 2d. D.L.R. (*p* 10)
The 2d. (*W* **10**. *P* 10 × *roul*) overprinted in black is only known showing the stop omitted after "V".

VA. (Valuator of Runs)

Optd in black without stop after "V". (*a*) *W* **2**. *P* 10. 4d.
(*b*) *W* **10**. *P* 10. 2d. D.L.R.

VN. (Vaccination)

Optd in black without stop after "V". *W* **2**. *P* 10. 4d.

W. (Waterworks)

Optd in red. *W* **2**. *Roul.* 2d.
Optd in black. (*a*) *W* **2**. *P* 11½–12½. 6d., 2s.
   (*b*) *W* **10**. 2d. D.L.R. (*roul*), 2d. D.L.R. (*p* 10)
    The 2d. (*W* **2**. *Roul*) with red overprint is known showing the stop omitted after "W".

B. General

O.S.   O.S.

   (O 1)   (O 2)

1874–77. *Optd with Type* O **1**. *W* **2**. (*a*) *P* 10.

O 1	3	4d. dull purple (18.2.74)	£950	£250

(*b*) *P* 11½–12½ × 10

O 2	1	1d. green (2.1.74)	—	75·00
O 3	3	4d. dull violet (12.2.75)	40·00	5·00
O 4	1	6d. Prussian blue (20.10.75)	—	8·00
O 4a	3	2s. rose-pink	—	
O 5		2s. carmine (3.12.76)	—	75·00

(*c*) *P* 11½–12½

O 6	1	1d. deep yellow-green (30.1.74)	—	16·00
		a. Printed on both sides	—	£250
O 7	3	3d. on 4d. ultramarine (26.6.77)	£900	£275
		a. No stop after "S"	—	£350
O 8		4d. dull violet (13.7.74)	32·00	5·50
		a. No stop after "S"	—	25·00
O 9	1	6d. bright blue (31.8.75)	55·00	11·00
		a. "O.S." double	—	40·00
O10		6d. Prussian blue (27.3.74)	45·00	6·00
		a. No stop after "S"	—	28·00
O11	4	9d. red-purple (22.3.76)	£225	90·00
		a. No stop after "S"	£275	
O12	1	1s. red-brown (5.8.74)	42·00	6·00
		a. "O.S." double	—	50·00
		b. No stop after "S"	60·00	25·00
O13	3	2s. crimson-carmine (13.7.75)	60·00	12·00
		a. No stop after "S"	—	
		b. No stops	—	60·00
		c. Stops at top of letters		

1876–85. *Optd with Type* O **1**. *W* **8**. (*a*) *P* 10.

O14	1	6d. bright blue (1879)	60·00	8·00

(*b*) *P* 10 × 11½–12½, 11½–12½ × 10, *or compound*

O15	3	4d. violet-slate (24.1.78)	60·00	6·50
O16		4d. plum (29.11.81)	35·00	2·75
O17		4d. deep mauve	25·00	2·50
		a. No stop after "S"	—	20·00
		b. No stop after "O"		
		c. "O.S." double		
		d. "O.S." inverted	—	85·00
O18	1	6d. bright blue (1877)	35·00	4·25
		a. "O.S." inverted		
		b. No stop after "O"		
O19		6d. bright ultramarine (27.3.85)	32·00	4·00
		a. "O.S." inverted		
		b. "O.S." double		
		c. "O.S." double, one inverted	—	£180
		d. No stop after "S"		
		e. No stops after "O" & "S"		
O20		1s. red-brown (27.3.83)	32·00	5·00
		a. "O.S." inverted		
		b. No stop after "O"		
		c. No stop after "S"		
O21	3	2s. carmine (16.3.81)	45·00	7·50
		a. "O.S." inverted	—	90·00
		b. No stop after "S"		

(*c*) *P* 11½–12½

O22	3	3d. on 4d. ultramarine	£600	
O23		4d. violet-slate (14.3.76)	£120	6·00
O24		4d. deep mauve (19.8.79)	38·00	2·50
		a. "O.S." inverted		
		b. "O.S." double, one inverted		
O25	1	6d. Prussian blue (6.77)	38·00	4·50
		a. "O.S." double	—	30·00
		b. "O.S." inverted		

O26	4	8d. on 9d. brown (9.11.76)	£325	£140
		a. "O.S." double	£500	
		b. "O" only	—	£200
O26c		9d. purple	£700	
O27	1	1s. red-brown (12.2.78)	24·00	3·50
		a. "O.S." inverted	£150	75·00
		b. No stop after "S"	£150	
O28		1s. lake-brown (8.11.83)	22·00	3·50
O29	3	2s. rose-carmine (12.8.85)	50·00	7·50
		a. "O.S." double	—	60·00
		b. "O.S." inverted	—	65·00
		c. No stop after "S"	—	30·00

1891–1903. *Optd with Type* O **2**. (*a*) *W* **8**. *P* 11½–12½.

O30	1	1s. lake-brown (18.4.91)	23·00	8·50
O31		1s. Vandyke brown	26·00	5·50
O32		1s. dull brown (2.7.96)	23·00	4·25
		a. No stop after "S"		
O33		1s. sepia (*large holes*) (4.1.02)	20·00	3·50
		a. "O.S." double		
		b. No stop after "S"		
O34	3	2s. carmine (26.6.00)	50·00	9·00
		a. No stop after "S"		

(*b*) *W* **8**. *P* 10 × 11½–12½

O35	3	2s. rose-carmine (9.11.95)	40·00	7·00
		a. No stop after "S"	75·00	
		b. "O.S." double		

(*c*) *W* **10**. *P* 11½–12½

O36	1	1s. dull brown (7.3.03)	22·00	3·50

1874–76. *Optd with Type* O **1**. *W* **10**. (*a*) *P* 10.

O37	11	1d. blue-green (30.9.75)	55·00	15·00
		a. "O.S." inverted		
		b. No stop after "S"		
O38	12	2d. orange-red (18.2.74)	10·00	30
		a. No stop after "S"		
		b. "O.S." double		

(*b*) *P* 10 × 11½–12½, 11½–12½ × 10, *or compound*

O39	11	1d. blue-green (16.9.75)	—	28·00
		a. No stop after "S"		
O40	12	2d. orange-red (27.9.76)	—	3·75

(*c*) *P* 11½–12½

O41	11	1d. blue-green (13.8.75)	—	12·00
		a. "O.S." inverted		
		b. No stop after "S"		
O42	12	2d. orange-red (20.5.74)	—	80·00

1876–80. *Optd with Type* O **1**. *W* **13**. (*a*) *P* 10.

O43	11	1d. blue-green (2.10.76)	5·50	25
		a. "O.S." inverted	—	30·00
		b. "O.S." double	32·00	25·00
		c. "O.S." double, one inverted		
		d. No stops	—	12·00
		e. No stop after "S"	—	7·00
		f. No stop after "O"		
O44		1d. deep green	6·00	25
		a. "O.S." double	—	28·00
O45	12	2d. orange-red (21.9.77)	6·00	25
		a. "O.S." double	35·00	22·00
		b. "O.S." inverted	—	14·00
		c. "O.S." double, both inverted	—	70·00
		d. "O.S." double, one inverted		
		e. No stop after "O"	—	12·00
		f. No stop after "S"		
		g. No stops after "O" & "S"		
O46		2d. brick-red	23·00	65

(*b*) *P* 10 × 11½–12½, 11½–12½ × 10, *or compound*

O47	11	1d. deep green (14.8.80)	—	18·00
		a. "O.S." double		
O48	12	2d. orange-red (6.4.78)	35·00	6·00
		a. "O.S." inverted		
		b. No stop after "S"		

(*c*) *P* 11½–12½

O49	12	2d. orange-red (15.7.80)	—	60·00

1882 (20 Feb). *No.* O43 *such with T* **14**. *W* **13**. *P* 10.

O50	11	½d. on 1d. blue-green	35·00	14·00
		a. "O.S." inverted		

1888–91. *Optd with Type* O **1**. *W* **13**. *P* 10.

O51	17	4d. violet (24.1.91)	20·00	2·75
O52	18	6d. blue (15.11.88)	9·50	1·25
		a. "O.S." double		
		b. No stop after "S"		

1891. *As No.* O51 *surch with T* **20.** *W* **13.** (*a*) *P* 10.

O53	**17**	2½d. on 4d. green (1.8.91)	32·00	6·00
		a. "2" and "½" closer	—	40·00
		b. No stop after "S"		
		c. "O.S." omitted (in pair with normal) . .		
		d. "O.S." inverted		
		e. "O.S." double		

(*b*) *P* 10 × 11½–12½, 11½–12½ × 10, *or compound*

O54	**17**	2½d. on 4d. green (1.10.91).	38·00	8·50

(*c*) *P* 11½–12½

O54*a*	**17**	2½d. on 4d. green (1.6.91)		

1891–95. *Optd with Type* O **2.** *W* **13.** (*a*) *P* 10.

O55	**15**	½d. brown (2.5.94)	6·00	3·00
		a. No stop after "S"		
O56	**11**	1d. green (24.4.91)	6·00	25
		a. "O.S." double	35·00	
		b. No stop after "S"		7·00
		c. "O.S." in blackish blue	£200	2·75
		d. "O.S." double, one inverted		
O57	**12**	2d. orange-red (22.4.91).	5·50	25
		a. No stop after "S"	—	8·00
		b. "O.S." double		
O58	**17**	2½d. on 4d. green (18.8.94).	28·00	4·00
		a. No stop after "S"	—	15·00
		b. "O.S." inverted	£110	
		c. "2" and "½" closer	65·00	20·00
		d. Fraction bar omitted		
O59		4d. pale violet (13.2.91)	18·00	2·75
		a. "O" only	—	40·00
		b. "O.S." double		
		c. No stop after "S"		
O60		4d. aniline violet (31.8.93)	23·00	2·50
		a. No stop after "S"		
		b. "O.S." double		
O61	**18**	5d. on 6d. brown (2.12.91)	35·00	11·00
		a. No stop after "S"	65·00	20·00
		b. No stop after "5D"	£150	
O62		6d. blue (4.4.93)	8·50	1·25
		a. No stop after "S"		
		b. "O.S." in blackish blue		

(*b*) *P* 10 × 11½–12½

O63	**15**	½d. pale brown (26.3.95)	6·50	3·00
O64	**17**	2½d. on 4d. green (17.9.95).	—	35·00
		a. "O.S." double		

(*c*) *P* 11½–12½

O65	**15**	½d. Venetian red (13.6.91)	17·00	3·50

1893–1901. *Optd with Type* O **2.** *W* **13.** *P* 15.

O66	**15**	½d. pale brown (8.6.95)	5·50	2·75
O67	**11**	1d. green (8.9.94)	5·00	25
		a. No stop after "S"		
		b. "O.S." double		
O68	**12**	2d. orange-red (16.6.94).	5·50	25
		a. "O.S." double	—	18·00
		b. "O.S." inverted	—	12·00
O68*c*	**22**	2½d. violet-blue	20·00	2·75
O69	**17**	4d. slate-violet (4.4.95)	26·00	2·75
		a. "O.S." double	—	20·00
O70	**23**	5d. purple (29.3.01).	45·00	4·00
O71	**18**	6d. blue (20.9.93)	9·50	1·25

1895–1901. *Optd with Type* O **2.** *W* **13.** *P* 13.

O72	**15**	½d. brown (17.5.98).	6·50	2·75
		a. Opt triple, twice sideways	£150	
O73	**11**	1d. green (20.5.95)	6·00	25
		a. No stop after "S"	25·00	7·00
O74	**12**	2d. orange (11.2.96)	5·00	25
		a. No stop after "S"	—	7·00
		b. "O.S." double		
O75	**22**	2½d. violet-blue (5.7.97).	20·00	2·25
		a. No stop after "S"		
O76	**17**	4d. violet (12.96).	20·00	2·25
		a. No stop after "S"	40·00	13·00
		b. "O.S." double	40·00	18·00
O77	**23**	5d. purple (29.9.01).	40·00	4·25
		a. No stop after "S"		
O78	**18**	6d. blue (13.9.99)	11·00	1·25
		a. No stop after "S"	25·00	

O. S.

(O 3)

1899–1901. *Optd with Type* O **3.** *W* **13.** *P* 13.

O80	**24**	½d. yellow-green (12.2.00)	6·00	2·75
		a. No stop after "S"		
		b. "O.S." inverted	35·00	
O81	**11**	1d. rosine (22.9.99)	4·75	50
		a. "O.S." inverted	—	25·00
		b. "O.S." double		
		c. No stop after "S"	—	12·00
O82	**12**	2d. bright violet (1.6.00).	7·00	50
		a. "O.S." inverted	26·00	26·00
		b. "O.S." double		
		c. No stop after "S"	22·00	
O83	**22**	2½d. indigo (2.10.01).	20·00	2·25
		a. "O.S." inverted	—	25·00
		b. No stop after "S"	50·00	
O84	**17**	4d. violet (18.11.00).	18·00	90
		a. "O.S." inverted	65·00	
		b. No stop after "S"	45·00	
O85	**18**	6d. blue (8.10.00).	9·50	1·00
		a. No stop after "S"	28·00	

1891 (May). *Optd as Type* O **3** *but wider.* *W* **13.** *P* 10.

O86	**19**	2s. 6d. pale violet	£2000	£1600
O87		5s. pale rose	£2000	£1600

Only one sheet (60) of each of these stamps was printed.

Stamps overprinted for Official use were withdrawn on 30 September 1903.

The six former colonies of New South Wales, Queensland, South Australia, Tasmania, Victoria and Western Australia united to form the Commonwealth of Australia on 1 January 1901.

On 1 March 1901 control of the postal service passed to the federal administration. The first national postage due stamps appeared in July 1902, but it was not until January 1913 that postage stamps inscribed "AUSTRALIA" were issued.

TASMANIA

PRICES FOR STAMPS ON COVER	
Nos. 1/4	from × 2
Nos. 5/12	from × 3
Nos. 14/23	from × 2
No. 24	—
Nos. 25/56	from × 3
Nos. 57/77	from × 6
Nos. 78/9	—
Nos. 80/90	from × 3
No. 91	—
Nos. 92/109	from × 3
No. 110	—
Nos. 111/23	from × 3
Nos. 124/6	—
Nos. 127/34	from × 4
Nos. 135/55	from × 3
Nos. 156/8	from × 20
Nos. 159/66	from × 10
Nos. 167/9	from × 15
Nos. 170/4	from × 6
Nos. 216/22	from × 15
Nos. 223/5	—
Nos. 226/7	from × 15
Nos. 229/36	from × 20
Nos. 237/57	from × 10
No. 258	—
Nos. 259/61	from × 10
Nos. F1/25	—
Nos. F26/9	from × 15
Nos. F30/9	—

SPECIMEN OVERPRINTS. Those listed are from U.P.U. distributions between 1892 and 1904. Further "Specimen" overprints exist, but these were used for other purposes.

   1   2   3

(Eng C. W. Coard. Recess H. and C. Best at the *Courier* newspaper, Hobart)

1853 (1 Nov). *No wmk. Imperf. Twenty-four varieties in four rows of six each.*

(*a*) *Medium soft yellowish paper with all lines clear and distinct*

1	**1**	1d. pale blue	£3250	£600
2		1d. blue	£3250	£600

(*b*) *Thin hard white paper with lines of the engraving blurred and worn*

3	**1**	1d. pale blue	£3000	£550
4		1d. blue	£3000	£550

1853—55. *No wmk. Imperf. In each plate there are twenty-four varieties in four rows of six each.*

(*a*) *Plate I. Finely engraved. All lines in network and background thin, clear, and well defined.* (1853)

(i) *First state of the plate, brilliant colours*

5	**2**	4d. bright red-orange	£2250	£500
		a. Double impression		
6		4d. bright brownish orange	—	£650

(ii) *Second state of plate, with blurred lines and worn condition of the central background*

7	**2**	4d. red-orange	£2000	£350
8		4d. orange	£1800	£325
9		4d. pale orange	—	£325

(*b*) *Plate II. Coarse engraving, lines in network and background thicker and blurred* (1855)

10	**2**	4d. orange	£2000	£300
		a. Double print, one albino		
11		4d. dull orange	£2000	£300
12		4d. yellowish orange	£2000	£300

In the 4d. Plate I, the outer frame-line is thin all round. In Plate II it is, by comparison with other parts, thicker in the lower left angle.

The 4d. is known on vertically laid paper from proof sheets. Examples from Plate I have the lines close together and those from Plate II wide apart (*Price* £5000 *unused*).

In 1879 reprints were made of the 1d. in blue and the 4d., Plate I, in brownish yellow, on thin, tough, white wove paper, and perforated 11½. In 1887, a reprint from the other plate of the 4d. was made in reddish brown and in black, and in 1889 of the 1d. in blue and in black, and of the 4d. (both plates) in yellow and in black on white card, imperforate. As these three plates were defaced after the stamps had been superseded, all these reprints show two, or three thick strokes across the Queen's head. All three plates were destroyed in July 1950.

(Eng. W. Humphrys, after water-colour sketch by E. Corbould. Recess P.B.)

1855 (17 Aug–16 Sept). *W* **2** *of Queensland* (*Large Star*). *Imperf.*

14	**3**	1d. carmine (16.9)	£4000	£750
15		2d. deep green (16.9)	£1500	£550
16		2d. green (16.9)	£1500	£500
17		4d. deep blue	£1200	85·00
18		4d. blue	£1200	95·00

Proofs of the 1d. and 4d. on thick paper, *without watermark*, are sometimes offered as the issued stamps.

(Recess H. and C. Best, Hobart, from P.B. plates)

1856 (Apr)–**57.** *No wmk. Imperf.* (*a*) *Thin white paper.*

19	**3**	1d. pale brick-red (4.56)	£4000	£550
20		2d. dull emerald-green (1.57)	£5000	£700
21		4d. deep blue (5.57)	£600	85·00
22		4d. blue (5.57)	£500	85·00
23		4d. pale blue (5.57)	—	£120

(*b*) *Pelure paper*

24	**3**	1d. deep red-brown (11.56)	£3000	£600

   4   7   8

(Recess H. Best (August 1857–May 1859), J. Davies (August 1859–March 1862), J. Birchall (March 1863), M. Hood (October 1863–April 1864), Govt Printer (from July 1864), all from P.B. plates)

1857 (Aug)–**69.** *Wmk double-lined numerals "1", "2" or "4" as W* **4** *on appropriate value. Imperf.*

25	**3**	1d. deep red-brown	£400	21·00
26		1d. pale red-brown	£275	16·00
27		1d. brick-red (1863)	£140	15·00
28		1d. dull vermilion (1865)	80·00	15·00
29		1d. carmine (1867)	80·00	15·00
		a. Double print	—	£120
		b. Error. Wmkd "2" (1869)		
30		2d. dull emerald-green	—	60·00
31		2d. green	—	27·00
		a. Double print	—	£150
32		2d. yellow-green	£200	55·00
33		2d. deep green (1858)	£170	30·00
34		2d. slate-green (1860)	£120	45·00
35		4d. deep blue	—	70·00
		a. Double print	—	£150
36		4d. pale blue	£100	11·00
37		4d. blue	£100	15·00
		a. Double print	—	£150
38		4d. bright blue	£100	15·00
		a. Printed on both sides	†	
		b. Double print	—	£120
39		4d. cobalt-blue	—	55·00

Printings before July 1864 were all carried out at the *Courier* printing works which changed hands several times during this period.

CANCELLATIONS. Beware of early Tasmanian stamps with pen-cancellations cleaned off and faked postmarks applied.

(Recess P.B.)

1858 (Jan). *Wmk double-lined numerals "6" or "12" as W* **4**. *Imperf.*

40	**7**	6d. dull lilac	£600	65·00
41	**8**	1s. bright vermilion	£500	70·00
42		1s. dull vermilion	—	55·00

Examples of the 6d. lilac on paper watermarked Large Star exist from a proof sheet (*Price* £650 *unused*).

(Recess J. Davies (March 1860), J. Birchall (April 1863), Govt Printer (from February 1865), all from P.B. plates)

1860 (Mar)–**67**. *Wmk double-lined "6" as W* **4**. *Imperf.*

44	**7**	6d. dull slate-grey	£275	50·00
45		6d. grey	—	55·00
46		6d. grey-violet (4.63)	£130	50·00
		a. Double print	—	£200
47		6d. dull bluish purple (2.65)	£130	40·00
48		6d. bluish purple (2.65)	£250	45·00
49		6d. reddish mauve (4.67)	£550	40·00

In 1871 reprints were made of the 6d. (in mauve) and the 1s. on white wove paper, and perforated 11½. They are found with or without "REPRINT". In 1889 they were again reprinted on white card, imperforate. These later impressions are also found overprinted "REPRINT" and perforated 11½.

PERFORATED ISSUES. From 1 October 1857 the Tasmania Post Office only supplied purchasers requiring five or more complete sheets of stamps. The public obtained their requirements, at face value, from licensed stamp vendors, who obtained their stocks at a discount from the Post Office.

From 1863 onwards a number of the stamp vendors applied their own roulettes or perforations. The Hobart firm of J. Walch & Sons achieved this so successfully that they were given an official contract in July 1869 to perforate sheets for the Post Office. The Government did not obtain a perforating machine until late in 1871.

1863–71. *Double-lined numeral watermarks. Various unofficial roulettes and perforations.*

(a) *By. J. Walch & Sons, Hobart*

(i) *Roulette about* 8, *often imperf×roul* (1863–68)

50	**3**	1d. brick-red	—	£150
51		1d. carmine	£300	£100
52		2d. yellow-green		
53		2d. slate-green		
54		4d. pale blue	—	£140
55	**7**	6d. dull lilac	—	£170
56	**8**	1s. vermilion	—	£500

(ii) *P* 10 (1864–69)

57	**3**	1d. brick-red	45·00	18·00
58		1d. dull vermilion	45·00	18·00
59		1d. carmine	42·00	18·00
60		2d. yellow-green	£225	70·00
61		2d. slate-green	£275	£120
62		4d. pale blue	90·00	9·50
63		4d. blue	90·00	9·50
		a. Double print	—	£110
64	**7**	6d. grey-violet	£150	13·00
65		6d. dull bluish purple	80·00	16·00
66		6d. bluish purple	—	18·00
67		6d. reddish mauve	£300	60·00
68	**8**	1s. vermilion	90·00	19·00
		a. Imperf vert (horiz)		

(iii) *P* 12 (1865–71—*from July* 1869 *under contract to the Post Office*)

69	**3**	1d. dull vermilion		45·00
70		1d. carmine	35·00	6·50
		a. Error. Wmkd "2" (*pen cancel* £75)	—	£1000
71		2d. yellow-green	£100	38·00
72		4d. deep blue	70·00	11·00
73		4d. blue	70·00	13·00
74		4d. cobalt-blue	—	28·00
75	**7**	6d. bluish purple	£120	18·00
		a. Imperf between (vert pair)		
76		6d. reddish mauve	70·00	32·00
		a. Imperf between (vert or horiz pair)		
77	**8**	1s. vermilion	95·00	28·00
		a. Double print	—	£150
		b. Imperf between (horiz pair)		

(iv) *Perf compound* 10 × 12 (1865–69)

78	**3**	1d. carmine	£1300	
79		4d. blue	—	£900

(b) *P* 12½ *by R. Harris, Launceston* (1864–68)

80	**3**	1d. brick-red	45·00	23·00
81		1d. dull vermilion	42·00	17·00

82	**3**	1d. carmine	25·00	6·50
83		2d. yellow-green	£225	80·00
84		2d. sage-green	£200	£100
85		4d. blue	£130	35·00
86		4d. bright blue	£130	35·00
87	**7**	6d. dull bluish purple	£160	40·00
88		6d. bluish purple	£170	40·00
89		6d. reddish mauve	£350	90·00
90	**8**	1s. vermilion	£180	65·00

(c) *Imperf×oblique roulette* 11½ *at Oatlands* (1866)

91	**3**	4d. blue		

(d) *Oblique roulette* 10–10½, *possibly at Deloraine* (1867)

92	**3**	1d. brick-red	—	£325
93		1d. carmine	£900	£275
94		2d. yellow-green	—	£425
95		4d. bright blue	—	£375
96	**7**	6d. grey-violet	—	£600

(e) *Oblique roulette* 14–15, *probably at Cleveland* (1867–69)

97	**3**	1d. brick-red	—	£375
98		1d. dull vermilion	—	£375
99		1d. carmine	—	£375
100		2d. yellow-green	—	£425
101		4d. pale blue	—	£325
102	**7**	6d. grey-violet	—	£600
103	**8**	1s. vermilion	—	£750

(f) *Pin-perf* 5½ *to* 9½ *at Longford* (1867)

104	**3**	1d. carmine	£300	70·00
105		2d. yellow-green		
106		4d. bright blue	—	£160
107	**7**	6d. grey-violet	—	£150
108		6d. reddish mauve	—	£425
109	**8**	1s. vermilion		

(g) *Pin-perf* 12 *at Oatlands* (1867)

110	**3**	4d. blue		

(h) *Pin-perf* 13½ *to* 14½ (1867)

111	**3**	1d. brick-red	—	£190
112		1d. dull vermilion	—	£190
113		1d. carmine		
114		2d. yellow-green	—	£275
115		4d. pale blue	—	£160
116	**7**	6d. grey-violet	—	£375
117	**8**	1s. vermilion		

(j) *Serrated perf* 19 *at Hobart* (1868–69)

118	**3**	1d. carmine (*pen-cancel* £9)	£225	£100
119		2d. yellow-green	—	£200
120		4d. deep blue	£550	95·00
121		4d. cobalt-blue	—	95·00
122	**7**	6d. bluish purple	—	£375
123	**8**	1s. vermilion		

(k) *Roul* 4½, *possibly at Macquarie River* (1868)

124	**3**	4d. blue		
125	**7**	6d. reddish mauve		
126	**8**	1s. vermilion		

For stamps perforated 11½ or 12 by the Post Office see Nos. 135/43.

11

12

13

14

(Typo Govt Printer, Hobart, from plates made by D.L.R.)

1870 (1 Nov)–**71**. *Wmk single-lined numerals W* **12** (2*d.*), **13** (1*d.*, 4*d.*) *or* **14** (1*d.*, 10*d.*). (*a*) *P* 12 *by J. Walch & Sons.*

127	**11**	1d. rose-red (*wmk* "10")	27·00	8·50
		a. Imperf (pair)	£190	£190
		b. *Deep rose-red*	45·00	6·50
128		1d. rose-red (*wmk* "4") (3.71)	40·00	8·50
		a. Imperf (pair)	—	£160
129		2d. yellow-green	38·00	4·50
		a. Imperf (pair)		
		b. *Blue-green*	42·00	4·50
130		4d. blue	£700	£400
131		10d. black	20·00	15·00
		a. Imperf (pair)	£110	

(*b*) *P* 11½ *by the Post Office* (1871)

132		1d. rose-red (*wmk* "10")	£900	
133		2d. yellow-green	80·00	6·50
		a. *Blue-green*	32·00	3·25
		ab. Double print		
134		10d. black	23·00	16·00

The above were printed on paper obtained from New South Wales.
See also Nos. 144/55, 156/8, 159/66, 170/4, 226/7, 242 and 255/6.

(Recess Govt Printer, Hobart)

1871–91. *Double-lined numeral watermarks as W* **4**. *Perforated by the Post Office.* (*a*) *P* 11½.

135	**7**	6d. dull mauve	70·00	19·00
136		6d. bright mauve	65·00	19·00
		a. Imperf between (pair)	—	£425
137		6d. dull purple (3.75)	65·00	19·00
		a. Imperf (pair)	—	£400
138		6d. bright purple (5.78)	65·00	28·00
		a. Double print	—	£110
		b. Imperf between (horiz pair)	£750	
139		6d. lilac-purple (10.79)	70·00	38·00
140	**8**	1s. dull vermilion (1.73)	80·00	38·00
		a. Imperf between (horiz pair)	—	
141		1s. brownish vermilion (1.73)	70·00	38·00

(*b*) *P* 12

142	**7**	6d. bright purple (1884)	80·00	16·00
143		6d. dull claret (7.91)	24·00	11·00

15	**16**

(Typo Govt Printer, Hobart, from plates made by D.L.R.)

1871 (25 Mar)–**78**. *W* **15**. (*a*) *P* 11½.

144	**11**	1d. rose (5.71)	3·25	50
		a. Imperf (pair) (*pen cancel* £25)		
		b. *Bright rose*	3·25	50
		c. *Carmine*	4·50	50
		d. *Pink*	4·50	1·50
		e. *Vermilion* (4.75)	£200	65·00
145		2d. deep green (11.72)	12·00	50
		a. *Blue-green*	20·00	50
		b. *Yellow-green* (12.75)	£110	1·50
146		3d. pale red-brown	30·00	3·25
		a. Imperf (pair)	£120	
		b. *Deep red-brown*	30·00	3·75
		ba. Imperf between (pair)		
		c. *Purple-brown* (1.78)	30·00	3·25
		ca. Imperf (pair)	—	£275
		d. *Brownish purple*	30·00	3·25
147		4d. pale yellow (8.8.76)	35·00	9·50
		a. *Ochre* (7.78)	42·00	5·50
		b. *Buff*	35·00	6·50
148		9d. blue (2.10.71)	13·00	5·00
		a. Imperf (pair)	£120	
		b. Double print		
149		5s. purple (*pen cancel* £3.75)	£130	30·00
		a. Imperf (pair)		
		b. *Mauve*	£110	30·00

(*b*) *P* 12

150	**11**	1d. rose	60·00	5·50
		a. *Carmine*	65·00	7·00
151		2d. green	£400	95·00
		a. Imperf (pair)	—	£150
152		3d. red-brown	60·00	14·00
		a. *Deep red-brown*	60·00	14·00
153		4d. buff	£225	15·00
154		9d. pale blue	28·00	
155		5s. purple	£225	
		a. *Mauve*	£150	

(Typo D.L.R.)

1878 (28 Oct). *W* **16**. *P* 14.

156	**11**	1d. carmine	2·75	25
		a. *Rose-carmine*	2·75	25
		b. *Scarlet*	2·75	25
157		2d. pale green	3·00	25
		a. *Green*	3·00	25
158		8d. dull purple-brown	14·00	3·25

(Typo Govt Printer, Hobart (some printings of 1d. in 1891 by *Mercury* Press) from plates made by Victoria Govt Printer, Melbourne (½d.) or D.L.R. (others))

1880 (Apr)–**91**. *W* **16** (*sideways on* 1*d.*). (*a*) *P* 11½.

159	**11**	½d. orange (8.3.89)	1·90	1·25
		a. *Deep orange*	1·90	1·25
160		1d. dull red (14.2.89)	3·50	1·10
		a. *Vermilion-red*	2·75	1·10
161		3d. red-brown	8·00	2·50
		a. Imperf (pair)	80·00	
162		4d. deep yellow (1.83)	25·00	9·00
		a. *Chrome-yellow*	25·00	10·00
		b. *Olive-yellow*	90·00	20·00
		c. *Buff*	26·00	6·50

(*b*) *P* 12

163	**11**	½d. orange	2·00	1·50
		a. *Deep orange*	1·90	1·25
164		1d. pink (1891)	11·00	2·50
		a. Imperf (pair)	90·00	£100
		b. *Rosine*	4·00	1·25
		c. *Dull rosine*	6·50	2·75
		ca. Imperf (pair)	65·00	
165		3d. red-brown	7·00	1·75
		a. Imperf between (pair)	£450	
166		4d. deep yellow	50·00	12·00
		a. *Chrome-yellow*	70·00	12·00
		ab. Printed both sides	£180	

SPECIMEN AND PRESENTATION REPRINTS OF TYPE 11. In 1871 the 1d., 2d., 3d., 4d. blue, 9d., 10d. and 5s. were reprinted on soft white wove paper to be followed, in 1879, by the 4d. yellow and 8d. on rough white wove. Both these reprintings were perforated 11½. In 1886 it was decided to overprint remaining stocks with the word "REPRINT".

In 1889 Tasmania commenced sending sample stamps to the U.P.U. in Berne and a further printing of the 4d. blue was made, imperforate, on white card. This, together with the 5d. on white card, both perforated 11½ and overprinted "REPRINT", were included in presentation sets supplied to members of the states' legislatures in 1901.

$$d. \qquad\qquad d.$$

$$\textbf{Halfpenny} \qquad 2\tfrac{1}{2} \qquad 2\tfrac{1}{2}$$

(**17**)	(**18**) (2¼ mm between "d" and "2")	(**19**) (3½ mm between "d" and "2")

1889 (1 Jan). *No.* 156*b surch locally with T* **17**.

167	**11**	½d. on 1d. scarlet	8·00	6·00
		a. "al" in "Half" printed sideways (R. 1/2)	£700	£450

No. 167a occurred in a second printing and was later corrected.

A reprint on white card, perforated 11½ or imperforate, overprinted "REPRINT" was produced in 1901.

1891 (1 Jan–June). *Surch locally. W* **16**. (*a*) *With T* **18**. *P* 11½.

168	**11**	2½d. on 9d. pale blue	5·50	2·50
		a. Surch double, one inverted	£250	£250
		b. *Deep blue* (May)	6·25	3·00

(b) With T **19**. *P* 12

169 **11** 2½d. on 9d. pale blue (June) . . . . 5·00 2·50
    a. Blue surch . . . .
A reprint, using a third setting, perforated 11½ and overprinted "REPRINT" was produced in 1901.

(Typo Govt Printer, Hobart)

1891 (Apr–Aug). W **15**. *(a) P* 11½.
170 **11** ½d. orange . . . . 12·00 4·00
    a. *Brown-orange* . . . . 10·00 3·75
171   1d. rosine . . . . 10·00 4·00

(b) P 12

172 **11** ½d. orange . . . . 12·00 6·00
    a. Imperf (pair) . . . . 60·00
173   1d. dull rosine . . . . 14·00 6·00
    a. *Rosine* . . . . 25·00 10·00
174   4d. bistre (Aug) . . . . 13·00 4·75

    20   21   21*a*

1892 (12 Feb)–99. W **16**. *P* 14.
216 **20** ½d. orange and mauve (11.92) . . . . 1·25 40
217 **21** 2½d. purple. . . . . 2·50 1·00
218 **20** 5d. pale blue and brown . . . . 4·50 1·40
219   6d. violet and black (11.92) . . . . 5·50 1·75
220 **21***a* 10d. purple-lake & deep green (30.1.99) . . . . 9·00 6·50
221 **20** 1s. rose and green (11.92) . . . . 6·00 1·75
222   2s. 6d. brown and blue (11.92) . . . . 20·00 8·50
223   5s. lilac and red (3.2.97) . . . . 38·00 18·00
224   10s. mauve and brown (11.92) . . . . 75·00 45·00
225   £1 green and yellow (2.97) £500 £150
    Set of 10 . . . . £600 £200
    Set of 10 optd *"Specimen"* £250
See also Nos. 243 and 257/8.

(Typo Govt Printer, Hobart)

1896. W **16**. *P* 12.
226 **11** 4d. pale bistre . . . . 12·00 5·50
227   9d. pale blue . . . . 7·50 2·00
    a. *Blue* . . . . 8·00 3·00

    22 Lake Marion   23 Mount Wellington

    24 Hobart   25 Tasman's Arch

26 Spring River, Port Davey   27 Russell Falls

28 Mount Gould, Lake   29 Dilston Falls
    St. Clair

30

(Eng L. Phillips. Recess D.L.R.)

1899 (Dec)–**1900**. W **30**. *P* 14.
229 **22** ½d. deep green (31.3.00) . . . . 3·00 55
230 **23** 1d. bright lake . . . . 3·00 25
231 **24** 2d. deep violet . . . . 3·25 15
232 **25** 2½d. indigo (1900) . . . . 10·00 4·50
233 **26** 3d. sepia (1900) . . . . 7·50 1·00
234 **27** 4d. deep orange-buff (1900) . . . . 13·00 1·75
235 **28** 5d. bright blue (31.3.00) . . . . 14·00 4·50
236 **29** 6d. lake (31.3.00) . . . . 18·00 4·00
    Set of 8 . . . . 65·00 15·00
    Set of 8 optd *"Specimen"* £225
See also Nos. 237/9, 240/1, 245/8, 249/54 and 260/1.

DIFFERENCES BETWEEN LITHOGRAPHED AND TYPOGRAPHED PRINTINGS OF TYPES 22/9

Lithographed	Typographed
General appearance fine.	*Comparatively crude and coarse appearance.*
½**d.** All "V over Crown" wmk.	All "Crown over A" wmk.
1d. The shading on the path on the right bank of the river consists of very fine dots. In printings from worn stones the dots hardly show.	The shading on the path is coarser, consisting of large dots and small patches of colour.
The shading on the white mountain is fine (or almost absent in many stamps).	The shading on the mountain is coarse, and clearly defined.
2d. Three rows of windows in large building on shore, at extreme left, against inner frame.	Two rows of windows.
3d. Clouds very white.	Clouds dark.
Stars in corner ornaments have long points.	Stars have short points.
Shading of corner ornaments is defined by a coloured outer line.	Shading of ornaments terminates against white background.
4d. Lithographed only.	—

6d. No coloured dots at base of waterfall.

Outer frame of value tablets is formed by outer line of design.

Coloured dots at base of waterfall.

Thick line of colour between value tablets and outer line.

Small break in inner frame below second "A" of "TASMANIA".

(Litho, using transfers from D.L.R. plates, Federal Government Printing Office, Melbourne)

1902 (Jan)–03. *W* **75** *of Victoria* (*V over Crown*) (*sideways on ½d., 2d.*). *P* 12½.

237	**22**	½d. green		1·25	25
		a. Wmk upright			
		b. Perf 11		3·25	45
		c. Perf comp of 12½ and 11		50·00	35·00
238	**23**	1d. carmine-red		3·00	25
239	**24**	2d. violet		1·50	10
		a. Perf 11		1·50	30
		b. Perf comp of 12½ and 11		55·00	35·00
		c. Purple		1·50	10
		ca. Perf 11		3·25	15
		d. Wmk upright			
		Set of 3 optd "Specimen"		£120	

As the V and Crown paper was originally prepared for stamps of smaller size, portions of two or more watermarks appear on each stamp.

We only list the main groups of shades in this and the following issues. There are variations of shade in all values, particularly in the 2d. where there is a wide range, also in the 1d. in some issues.

(Typo, using electrotyped plates, Federal Govt Ptg Office, Melbourne)

1902 (Oct)–03. *W* **75** *of Victoria. P* 12½.

240	**23**	1d. pale red (*wmk sideways*)		2·50	20
		a. Perf 11		18·00	20
		b. Perf comp of 12½ and 11		£160	35·00
		c. Wmk upright (1.03)			
241		1d. rose-red (*wmk upright*) (4.03) (Optd S. £40)			
		a. Perf 11		2·00	15
		b. Perf comp of 12½ and 11		11·00	20
		c. Deep carmine-red		£150	35·00
		ca. Perf 11		50·00	75
		cb. Perf comp of 12½ and 11		—	15·00

(Typo Federal Govt Ptg Office, Melbourne)

1903–05. *W* **75** *of Victoria. P* 12½.

242	**11**	9d. blue (1905)		7·00	2·50
		a. Perf 11		7·50	2·75
		b. Perf comp of 12½ and 11		—	£375
		c. Pale blue		8·50	2·75
		d. Bright blue		8·50	3·00
		e. Ultramarine		£350	
		f. Indigo		£130	
243	**20**	1s. rose and green		8·50	3·00
		a. Perf 11		20·00	
		Set of 2 optd "Specimen"		£100	

1½**d.**

ONE PENNY

(31)   (32)

1904 (29 Dec). *No. 218 surch with T* **31**.

244	**20**	1½d. on 5d pale blue and brown (Optd S. £28)		1·25	90

Stamps with inverted surcharge or without surcharge se-tenant with stamps with normal surcharge were obtained irregularly and were not issued for postal use.

(Litho, using transfers from D.L.R. plates, Federal Govt Ptg Office, Melbourne)

1905 (Sept)–12. *W* **93***a of Victoria* (*Crown over A*) (*sideways on horiz stamps*). *P* 12½.

245	**24**	2d. purple		3·25	15
		a. Perf 11		7·00	15
		b. Perf comp of 12½ and 11		14·00	2·75
		c. Perf comp of 12½ and 12		—	42·00
		d. Perf comp of 11 and 12			
		e. Dull purple		2·25	
		ea. Perf 11		11·00	25
246	**26**	3d. brown		7·50	85
		a. Perf 11		11·00	1·75
		b. Perf comp of 12½ and 11		48·00	

247	**27**	4d. orange-buff (3.07)		12·00	1·75
		a. Perf 11		11·00	1·75
		b. Perf comp of 12½ and 11		£160	
		c. Brown-ochre (wmk sideways). Perf 11 (6.11)		24·00	8·50
		d. Orange-yellow (3.12)		15·00	3·75
		da. Perf 11		17·00	
248	**29**	6d. lake (7.08)		24·00	3·50
		a. Perf 11		30·00	4·00
		b. Perf comp of 12½ and 11		£130	

Stamps with perf compound of 12½ and 12 or 11 and 12 are found on sheets which were sent from Melbourne incompletely perforated. The line of perforation gauging 12 was done at the Government Printing Office, Hobart.

(Typo, using electrotyped, plates, Federal Govt Ptg Office, Melbourne)

1905 (Sept)–11. *W* **93***a of Victoria* (*sideways on horiz designs*). *P* 12½.

249	**22**	½d. yellow-green (10.12.08)		1·25	20
		a. Perf 11		1·25	20
		b. Perf comp of 12½ and 11		35·00	
		c. Perf comp of 11 and 12		55·00	
		d. Wmk upright (1909)			
		da. Perf 11			
250	**23**	1d. rose-red		1·50	10
		a. Perf 11		1·50	10
		b. Perf comp of 12½ and 11		2·00	70
		c. Perf comp of 12½ and 12		40·00	5·50
		d. Perf comp of 11 and 12		45·00	
		e. Bright rose		—	15
		ea. Perf 11		3·00	15
		f. Wmk sideways (1908)			
		g. Crimson (3.10)			
		ga. Perf 11		—	30
		gb. Perf comp of 12½ and 12			
251	**24**	2d. purple (8.07)		3·00	30
		a. Wmk upright			
		b. Perf 11		2·50	10
		ba. Wmk upright			
		c. Perf comp of 12½ and 11		18·00	6·00
		d. Perf comp of 12½ and 12			
		e. Perf comp of 11 and 12		70·00	38·00
252		2d. bright violet (*new plate*)* (1.11)		2·50	20
		a. Wmk upright			
		b. Perf 11		2·75	20
		c. Perf comp of 12½ and 11		70·00	
253	**26**	3d. brown (3.09)		6·50	1·25
		a. Perf 11		8·50	1·50
		b. Perf comp of 12½ and 11		£130	
254	**29**	6d. dull lake (12.10)		15·00	4·75
		a. Perf 11		15·00	4·50
		b. Perf comp of 12½ and 11		£130	

*Stamps from this stereotyped plate differ from Nos. 251c and 251ca in the width of the design (33 to 33¾ mm, against just over 32 mm), in the taller, bolder letters of "TASMANIA", in the slope of the mountain in the left background, which is clearly outlined in white, and in the outer vertical frame-line at left, which appears "wavy". Compare Nos. 259, etc, which are always from this plate.

The note after No. 248 re perfs compound with perf 12 also applies here.

(Typo Federal Govt Printing Office, Melbourne)

1906–13. *W* **93***a of Victoria. P* 12½.

255	**11**	8d. purple-brown (1907)		17·00	4·00
		a. Perf 11		15·00	3·00
256		9d. blue (1907)		7·00	2·25
		a. Perf 11		7·00	2·25
		b. Perf comp of 12½ and 11 (1909)		48·00	
		c. Perf comp of 12½ and 12 (1909)		90·00	
		d. Perf comp of 11 and 12		£180	
257	**20**	1s. rose and green (1907)		9·00	1·50
		a. Perf 11 (1907)		9·50	4·50
		b. Perf comp of 12½ and 11		14·00	
		c. Perf comp of 12½ and 12		45·00	
258		10s. mauve and brown (1906)		£100	60·00
		a. Perf 11		£150	
		b. Perf comp of 12½ and 12		£140	

The note after No. 248 re perfs compound with perf 12, also applies here.

1912 (Oct). *No. 252 surch with T* **32**. *P* 12½.

259	**24**	1d. on 2d. bright violet (R.)		90	25
		a. Perf 11		1·50	35
		b. Perf comp of 12½ and 11		85·00	85·00

(Typo, using electrotyped plates, Federal Govt Ptg Office, Melbourne)

1912 (Dec). *Thin paper, white gum (as Victoria, 1912). W 93a of Victoria (sideways on 3d.). P 12½.*

260	**23**	1d. crimson		6·00	40
		a. Perf 11		6·50	40
		b. Perf comp of 12½ and 11			
261	**26**	3d. brown		24·00	28·00

POSTAL FISCAL STAMPS

VALIDITY. Nos. F1/29 were authorised for postal purposes on 1 November 1882.

CLEANED STAMPS. Beware of postal fiscal stamps with pen-cancellations removed.

F 1

F 2

F 3

F 4

(Recess Alfred Bock, Hobart)

1863–80. *Wmk double-lined "1", W 4. (a) Imperf.*

F 1	F **1**	3d. green (1.65)		45·00	35·00
F 2	F **2**	2s. 6d. carmine (11.63)		50·00	35·00
F 3		2s. 6d. lake (1880)		55·00	
F 4	F **3**	5s. brown (1.64)		£130	£110
F 5		5s. sage-green (1880)		50·00	42·00
F 6	F **4**	10s. orange (1.64)		£170	£110
F 7		10s. salmon (1880)		£120	£110

(b) P 10

F 8	F **1**	3d. green		28·00	16·00
F 9	F **2**	2s. 6d. carmine		30·00	
F10	F **3**	5s. brown		45·00	
F11	F **4**	10s. orange		30·00	

(c) P 12

F12	F **1**	3d. green		32·00	20·00
F13	F **2**	2s. 6d. carmine		32·00	27·00
F14	F **3**	5s. brown		55·00	
F15		5s. sage-green		22·00	19·00
F16	F **4**	10s. orange		30·00	27·00
F17		10s. salmon		22·00	20·00

(d) P 12½

F18	F **1**	3d. green		55·00
F19	F **2**	2s. 6d. carmine		55·00
F20	F **3**	5s. brown		70·00
F21	F **4**	10s. orange-brown		45·00

(e) P 11½

F22	F **1**	3d. green			
F23	F **2**	2s. 6d. lake		28·00	25·00

F24	F **3**	5s. sage-green		22·00	16·00
F25	F **4**	10s. salmon		38·00	30·00

See also No. F30.

In 1879, the 3d., 2s. 6d., 5s. (brown), and 10s. (orange) were reprinted on thin, tough, white paper, and are found with or without "REPRINT". In 1889 another reprint was made on white card, imperforate and perforated 12. These are also found with or without "REPRINT".

REVENUE

F **5** Duck-billed Platypus

(F **6**)

(Typo D.L.R.)

1880 (19 Apr). *W **16** (sideways). P 14.*

F26	F **5**	1d. slate		8·50	3·25
F27		3d. chestnut		9·00	2·25
F28		6d. mauve		40·00	2·00
F29		1s. rose-pink		48·00	4·00

All values are known imperf, but not used.

Reprints are known of the 1d. in *deep blue* and the 6d. in lilac. The former is on yellowish white, the latter on white card. Both values also exist on wove paper, perf 12, with the word "REPRINT".

1888. *W **16**. P 12.*

F30	F **2**	2s. 6d. lake		15·00	11·00
		a. Imperf between (horiz pair)		£450	

1900 (Nov). *Optd with Type F **6**. (a) On Types F **2** and F **4**. W **16**. P 12.*

F31	F **2**	2s. 6d. carmine		£160
		a. "REVFNUE"		
		b. Opt inverted		
		c. Imperf		£170
		ca. "REVFNUE"		£250
F32	F **4**	10s. salmon		
		a. "REVFNUE"		
		b. On No. F 17 (wmk W **4**)		
		ba. "REVFNUE"		

(b) On No. F27

F33	F **5**	3d. chestnut		15·00	
		a. Double opt, one vertical		75·00	£100

*(c) On stamps as Nos. F26/9, but litho locally. W **15** (No. F34) or W **16** (others). P 12*

F34	F **5**	1d. blue		65·00	
F35		1d. blue		15·00	
		a. Imperf between (horiz pair)		£300	
		b. "REVENUE" inverted		£100	
		c. "REVENUE" double		£160	
		d. *Pale blue*		15·00	
F36		2d. chestnut		16·00	
		a. Value omitted		£180	£150
		b. Value double		£225	£150
		c. Imperf between (horiz pair)		£200	
F37		6d. mauve		50·00	
		a. Double print		£200	
F38		1s. pink		75·00	

(d) On No. 225

F39	**20**	£1 green and yellow		£150	£125
		a. Opt double, one vertical		£275	

It was not intended that stamps overprinted with Type F **6** should be used for postal purposes, but an ambiguity in regulations permitted such usage until corrected on 1 December 1900. All postal fiscal stamps were invalidated for postal purposes after 30 June 1901.

The six former colonies of New South Wales, Queensland, South Australia, Tasmania, Victoria and Western Australia united to form the Commonwealth of Australia on 1 January 1901.

On 1 March 1901 control of the postal service passed to the federal administration. The first national postage due stamps appeared in July 1902, but it was not until January 1913 that postage stamps inscribed "AUSTRALIA" were issued.

VICTORIA

PRICES FOR STAMPS ON COVER

Nos. 1/29	*from* ×	2
Nos. 30/8	*from* ×	4
Nos. 39/43	*from* ×	3
Nos. 44/8	*from* ×	2
Nos. 49/51	*from* ×	4
No. 52	*from* ×	8
No. 53		—
No. 54	*from* ×	6
Nos. 55/90	*from* ×	2
No. 91		—
Nos. 92/186	*from* ×	3
Nos. 187/220	*from* ×	4
Nos. 221/2	*from* ×	10
Nos. 223/38	*from* ×	5
Nos. 239/67	*from* ×	10
Nos. 268/82		—
Nos. 283/91	*from* ×	10
Nos. 292/6		—
Nos. 297/303	*from* ×	12
Nos. 304/22	*from* ×	8
Nos. 323/4		—
Nos. 325/6	*from* ×	4
Nos. 327/9	*from* ×	10
Nos. 330/45	*from* ×	15
Nos. 346/7	*from* ×	2
Nos. 348/75	*from* ×	10
Nos. 376/7		—
Nos. 378/87	*from* ×	10
Nos. 388/98		—
Nos. 399/409	*from* ×	10
Nos. 410/12		—
Nos. 413/23	*from* ×	4
Nos. 424/33		—
Nos. 434/43	*from* ×	10
No. 444		—
No. 445	*from* ×	10
Nos. 446/52	*from* ×	6
No. 453		—
No. 454	*from* ×	6
Nos. F1/6		—
Nos. F7/15	*from* ×	20
Nos. F16/22		—
Nos. F23/5	*from* ×	20
Nos. F26/40		—
Nos. F41/5	*from* ×	20
Nos. F46/50		—
Nos. F51/2	*from* ×	20
Nos. F53/9		—
Nos. D1/8	*from* ×	30
Nos. D9/10		—
Nos. D11/67	*from* ×	30

SPECIMEN OVERPRINTS. Those listed are from U.P.U. distributions in 1892 and 1897. Further "Specimen" overprints exist, but these were used for other purposes.

Unlike many British colonies, Victoria, with three exceptions only, produced her own dies, plates and stamps. The exceptions were the 1d. and 6d. "Queen-on-Throne" (the dies and plates for which were produced and the stamps printed by Perkins, Bacon) and the 2d. of 1870 for which though it was printed throughout in Victoria, the die and plates were produced by De La Rue. Being the products of local endeavour in a remote country, the stamps of Victoria possess great technical interest for students although its issues are too complicated for many collectors. The present list is an attempt alike to demonstrate their interest and to clarify their complications, particularly by the inclusion of carefully written notes on various aspects of their production.

A. THE PRIVATE CONTRACT PERIOD. 1850–59 (Ham, Campbell & Co, Campbell and Fergusson, Calvert, Robinson)

1 Queen Victoria ("Half Length")

(Dies engraved on a single piece of steel by Thomas Ham, Melbourne)

I. Lithographed by Thomas Ham, Melbourne

1850 (3 Jan). *T* **1.** *Imperf except groups* (9) *and* (10).

1d. Thin line at top

2d. Fine border and background

3d. White area to left of orb

(1) Original state of dies: 1*d.* (*tops of letters of* "VICTORIA" *reach to top of stamp*); 2*d.* (*fine border and background*); 3*d.* (*thicker white outline around left of orb, central band of orb does not protrude at left*). No frame-lines on dies.

1	1d. orange-vermilion	—	£1000
	a. Orange-brown	—	£550
	b. Dull chocolate-brown	—	£500
2	2d. lilac-mauve (*shades*)	—	£400
3	2d. brown-lilac (*shades*)	£2250	£250
	a. Grey-lilac	—	£250
4	3d. bright blue (*shades*)	—	£275
	a. Blue (*shades*)	—	£170
	ab. Retouched (Nos. 10 and 11 in transfer-group only)	—	£275

Periods of use: 1d., 2d. and 3d. No. 4 (January 1850); 3d. No. 4*a* (March 1850 to October 1851).

Note on Group (1). With the exception of No. 4*a* all the above were printed from a small stone of 30 (5×6), laid down without the use of an Intermediate stone. The 3d. No. 4*a* was the first "Half Length" to appear in sheets of 120, which was the case for all subsequent Ham printings. It was produced from an Intermediate stone of 15 (5×3). The 2d. No. 2 was the first printing (from Stone "A") and Nos. 3 and 3*a* the second (from Stone "B"). Impressions clear and fine.

Note on margins found in the Ham printings: These stamps divide into two groups—Nos. 1 to 7—which were from 5-wide groups (or sheets) and Nos. 8 to 17— which were from 6-wide groups. The spacing between stamps horizontally is greater for Nos. 1 to 7 than Nos. 8 to 17 (and see later notes).

1d. Thick line at top

2d. Coarse background

3d. White area small and band
protruding to left of orb

(2) Second state of dies: 1d. (more colour over top of letters of "VICTORIA"); 2d. (fine border as in (1) but with coarse background); 3d. (thinner white outline around left of orb, central band of orb protrudes at left).

5	1d. red-brown (shades)	£2750	£275
	a. Pale dull red-brown	—	£275
6	2d. grey-lilac (shades)	£1000	80·00
	a. Dull grey	—	80·00
7	3d. blue (shades)	—	£110
	a. Retouched (22 varieties) ....from	—	£225

Periods of use: 1d. (Feb–Sept 1850); 2d. (Jan–April 1850); 3d. (June 1851 to Dec 1852).

Note on Group (2). These were all printed in sheets of 120 (10×12), the Printing stones for the 1d. and 2d. being produced from an Intermediate stone of 30 (5×6), and that for the 3d. from one of 10 (5×2). Impressions are clear and fine.

Frame-lines added

(3) Third state of dies: As in (2) but with frame-lines added, very close up, on all four sides.

8	1d. dull orange-vermilion	—	£120
	a. Dull red (shades)	—	£120
9	1d. deep red-brown	—	£400
	a. Brownish red (shades)	—	£110
	b. Dull rose (shades)	—	£110
10	2d. grey (shades)	—	£120
	a. Olive-grey (shades)	—	£120
11	3d. blue (shades)	—	50·00
	a. Deep blue (shades)	—	50·00
	b. Pale greenish blue (shades)	—	£100

Periods of use: 1d. No. 8 (Oct 1850 to April 1851); 1d. No. 9 (April 1851 to March 1854); 2d. (Aug–Oct 1850); 3d. (Dec 1852 to April 1854).

Note on Group (3). Although the above were all printed in sheets of 120 the format was 12×10—and continued so—and not 10×12 as in Group (2). For No. 8 (i.e. third 1d. printing) an Intermediate stone of 30 (6×5) was used, but for all the others (i.e. fourth printings) one of 12 (6×2) was employed. These stamps (and those under Group (4) following) are very closely spaced as compared with the (1) and (2) groups. Group (3) represented the last state of the 1d. and 3d. dies but not of the 2d. Impressions vary from medium to fine.

White veil

(4) As (3) but altered to give, for the 1d. and 3d., the so-called "white veils", and for the 2d., the effect of vertical drapes to the veil.

12	1d. reddish brown	—	£100
	a. Bright pinky red (shades)	£475	£100
13	2d. drab	—	£110
	a. Grey-drab	—	£110
	b. Lilac-drab	—	£110
	c. Red-lilac	—	£500
	d. Void S.W. corner	—	£1200
14	3d. blue (shades)	—	45·00
	a. Deep blue (shades)	—	45·00
	b. Greenish blue (shades)	—	50·00
	c. Retouched (9 varieties)	—	£120

Periods of use: 1d. (April 1851–March 1854); 2d. (Aug–Oct 1850); 3d. (April–June 1854).

Note on Group (4): The alterations to the veils were made to each of the 12 impressions on the Intermediate Stones used for Group (3), and there are therefore 12 varieties of the veil in each value. Impressions are relatively coarse, particularly of the 2d. (save for No. 13c). Spacing of stamps is very close as in (3). In the 1d. and 2d. the shades found in Group (4) differ considerably from those met in (3).

2d. Coarse border and background

(5) Fourth state of die. 2d. value only: Coarse border and background. Veil details as in original die.

15	2d. red-lilac (shades)	—	£180
	a. Lilac	—	£180
	b. Grey	—	£275
	c. Dull brownish lilac	—	£100
	d. Retouched lower label—value omitted. (Nos. 15 to 15c)	—	£1800
	e. Other retouches (Nos. 15 to 15c) (17 varieties) from	—	£225

Period of use: May–August 1850.

Note on Group (5): This comprised the sixth printing of this value and was printed from Stone "A". Ham utilized an Intermediate Stone of 30 (6×5). This was the only printing of the 2d. value in which retouches were made to the printing stone. Impressions (save for No. 15a) are generally good, sometimes fine.

No. 15b can generally, and No. 15c can always be readily distinguished as they are on thin wove paper of good quality, not found elsewhere.

(6) 2d. only: As (5) but with veils altered to give effect of vertical drapes.

16	2d. lilac-grey	—	£110
	a. Deep grey	—	£110
	b. Brown-lilac (shades)	—	60·00
17	2d. cinnamon (shades)	£450	95·00
	a. Drab (shades)	—	60·00
	b. Pale dull brown (shades)	—	70·00
	c. Greenish grey	—	60·00
	d. Olive-drab (shades)	—	£110
	e. Buff	—	£110

Periods of use: No. 16 etc. (Nov 1850—March 1851), No. 17 etc. (March 1851–Dec 1852).

Note on Group (6): The 2d. Stone "B" (No. 16, etc.) and Stone "C" (No. 17, etc.) constituted Ham's seventh and eight printings respectively. Two shades in the Stone "B" printings do not differ greatly from stones in the Stone "A" printings, but all those listed under No. 17 are entirely and peculiarly distinctive. The veil alterations were again made to each of the impressions on the Intermediate Stones so that there are 30 varieties of these.

General note on Ham printings. Ham's contract was completed in May 1850 but his 1d. and 3d. stamps remained in use up till March and June 1854 respectively. The 2d. "Half Length" design was, however, as the result of an injury to the die, superseded by Ham's "Queen-on-Throne" design in December 1852. In all Ham made five printings of each of the 1d. and 3d. and eight of the 2d. The paper employed by the three contractors was distinctive. For instance, for the whole of the Campbell and Fergusson printings (1d. and 3d. only) a coarse wove paper of poor quality, easily thinned and with a marked "mesh" (horizontal or vertical) was used. This paper is nothing like any paper used for the Ham or Campbell printings, and affords the best preliminary test for all 1d. and 3d. "Half Lengths".

II. Lithographed by J. S. Campbell & Co, Melbourne

(7) *Wide settings. Stamps 2½–3 mm apart (1d.) or 1½–2 mm apart (3d.).*
18   1d. orange-red *(shades)* £425   £110
    a. Rose . . . .   —   £250
19   3d. blue *(shades)* . . . .   £450   32·00
    a. Retouched (No. 17 in group) . . . .   —   £120
  Periods of use: 1d. (Mar 1854–Jan 1855); 3d. (June 1854–April 1855, also 1858/9).
  Note on Group (7): The Campbell 1d. was printed from a stone of 192 impressions (96 × 2), and the 3d. from a stone of 320 (160 × 2). For each value an intermediate stone of 24 (6 × 4) was used. Impressions are generally good.

III. Lithographed by Campbell and Fergusson, Melbourne

(8) *Wide settings as* (7). *Impressions medium to poor, depending on state of printing stones. Paper used is distinctive (see final note after Ham printings).*

  (a) Same intermediate stones as had been employed for Group (7)
20   1d. brown *(shades)* . . . .   £350   95·00
    a. Brick-red *(shades)* . . . .   —   75·00
    b. Dull red *(shades)* . . . .   —   75·00
21   1d. orange-brown *(shades)* . . . .   —   £100
    a. Dull rose-red *(shades)* . . . .   —   60·00
    b. Bright rose-pink . . . .   —   £100
    c. Retouched (4 varieties) . . . .   —   £400
22   1d. pink *(shades)* . . . .   £325   32·00
    a. Rose *(shades)* . . . .   £325   32·00
    b. Lilac-rose *(shades)* . . . .   —   32·00
    c. Dull brown-red *(shades)* . . . .   —   £100
    d. Retouched (9 varieties) . . . .   —   £325
23   3d. bright blue *(shades)* . . . .   £425   48·00
    a. Greenish blue *(shades)* . . . .   £375   40·00
    b. Retouched (No. 17 in group) . . . .   —   95·00
24   3d. Prussian blue *(shades)* . . . .   —   70·00
    a. Milky blue . . . .   —   £110
    b. Retouched (No. 17 in group) . . . .   —   £225
  Periods of use: 1d. No. 20, etc. (Stone 2, July 1854 and December 1855–May 1856); 1d. No. 21, etc. (Stone 3, Aug–Nov 1855); 1d. No. 22, etc. (Stones 4, 5, Feb–Aug 1855 and May–Oct 1856); 3d. No. 23, etc. (Stone "B", July 1857–Dec 1858); 3d. No. 24 etc. (Stone "C", Nov 1856–June 1857).

  (b) New intermediate stone of similar size (6 × 4) and spacing 2½–3 mm apart horizontally. (Stone "D")
25   3d. steel-blue *(shades)* . . . .   —   42·00
    a. Greenish blue *(shades)* . . . .   £350   30·00
    b. Blue *(shades)* . . . .   £350   30·00
    c. Deep blue *(shades)* . . . .   £350   30·00
    d. Indigo *(shades)* . . . .   —   38·00
  Period of use: May 1855 to November 1856. Impressions generally heavier than previous 3d.
  Note on Group (8): All printing stones were of 400 impressions, consisting of an upper and lower pane of 200 (20 × 10) save in two cases, viz.: the 3d. No. 23 which was of 320 (160 × 2) and No. 24 which was probably of 200 (20 × 10) impressions. The 3d. No. 24, etc., presents a considerably worn appearance. No. 25 (steel-blue) comprised the earlier part of the printing and is, comparatively, of good appearance and impression.
  No. 21*b* is only found with barred oval cancellations and as these were not used after the end of 1855 they are of assistance in identification.

IV. 3d. stamps rouletted and perforated in 1857 and 1859 respectively

(9) *Rouletted 7 to 8½ at G.P.O., Melbourne (see later notes).*

  (a) Campbell printing (No. 19)
26   3d. blue (shades) . . . .   —   £150
    a. Retouched (No. 17 in group) . . . .

  (b) Campbell & Fergusson printing (No. 23)
27   3d. bright blue *(shades)* . . . .   —   £160
    a. Greenish blue *(shades)* . . . .   —   £140
    b. Retouched (No. 17 in group) . . . .
  Period of use: Sept–Dec 1858.

(10) *Perforated 12 by Robinson. (a) Campbell printing (No. 19).*
28   3d. blue *(shades)* . . . .   —   £110
    a. Retouched (No. 17 in group) . . . .   —   £250

  (b) Campbell & Fergusson printing (No. 23)
29   3d. greenish blue *(shades)* . . . .   —   £350
    a. Retouched (No. 17 in group) . . . .
  Period of use: Jan 1859 to Jan 1860.
  Note on Groups (9) *and* (10): The roulettes are seldom found on all four sides. The great majority of the perforated stamps are badly off-centre.
  Lithographic Reprints of the three values (the 2d. die then being in a defaced condition) were made in 1891, on paper wmk V over Crown (Type V2) W **23**, perf 12½. The 1891 Reprints of all issues were the direct result of

Victoria, in that year, joining the Universal Postal Union. As a member she was expected to supply specimens of her old issues to other countries. None of these being available and most of the old plates having been destroyed she was, in the majority of cases, compelled to make new plates for which, fortunately, all the original dies (save the "Emblems" (3) and the "Woodblocks" (4)) were available.
  FURTHER INFORMATION on these interesting issues, including the details of the numbers printed, the plating of the Transfer Groups, the papers used, the retouches, creased transfers, "abnormal" combinations, "stitch" watermarks, etc., etc., will be found in "The Half-Lengths of Victoria", the work by J. R. W. Purves, F.R.P.S.L., on which the above list is based.

2 Queen on Throne

1852–54. *T* **2.** *Imperf.*
  Corner letters: Each of the fifty subjects of the original plate show different letter combinations of A to Z, except J.

I. Dec 1852. *Recess-printed by Thomas Ham from a steel plate of* 50 (10 × 5) *impressions, engraved by him by hand.*
30   2d. reddish brown . . . .   £120   22·00
    a. Chestnut . . . .   —   £110
    b. Purple-brown . . . .   £120   22·00
  Reprints were made in 1891 (and later) using the original plate, on paper wmk V over Crown Type V2, both imperf and perf 12½.

II. Dec 1853–May 1854. *Lithographed by Campbell & Co, transfers for the stones being taken from Ham's steel plate. Period of issue:* Dec 1853–April 1855 and May 1856–May 1857. *On various types of good quality paper, hand-made and machine-wove.*

  (i) Early printings: full impression, detail around back of throne generally complete. Impressions fine and clear; colours rich
31   2d. brownish purple . . . .   £160   22·00
    a. Grey-brown . . . .   —   22·00
    b. Purple-black . . . .   —   22·00
    c. Dull lilac-brown (spotty print on toned) . . . . .   —   40·00
  Papers: The papers used for (i) and (ii) were, save in the two cases indicated, distinguished by their *whiteness*, as compared with the toned (yellowish) character of all that follow. This toning is due in part to the type of gum used but also to the larger proportion of wood pulp used in manufacture. The *hand-made* paper, which is always *white*, is found in (i) and (ii) only.

  (ii) Intermediate printings. Impressions not so full or sharp, background round top of throne not so fully defined
32   2d. violet-black . . . .   —   22·00
    a. Grey-black . . . .   —   24·00
    b. Grey-lilac . . . .   —   24·00
    c. Dull brown (on toned) . . . .   —   24·00
    d. Substituted transfer (in pair) . . . .   —   £2000

  (iii) Later printings, on toned paper only. Background round top of throne generally whiter. Stamps lack the detail of (i) *and* (ii) *although impression is reasonably good*
33   2d. grey-black . . . .   £120   20·00
    a. Purple-black . . . .   £120   20·00

  (iv) Last printing; on toned paper only. Background generally full as (i) *but impression is singularly flat, and lacking in fineness and sharpness. Normal colour is distinctive*
34   2d. grey-drab *(shades)* . . . .   —   19·00
    a. Black . . . .   —   £100

Notes on the Campbell & Co Printings
  (a) Stones: In all, 2,000,000 stamps were printed (and issued) under this contract. They were not printed on the one occasion but on several. A total of 22 transfers were taken from the steel plate, *nine* printing stones being used. Of these the first eight were of 100 impressions (one "fifty" over another "fifty") and the ninth was of 300 impressions (three "fifties" over three "fifties"). Only three of these stones were used to a point where they showed wear and in those cases the wear was nothing like that found in the Campbell & Fergusson printings. Whiteness in the background around the throne, where it occurs, is more often the result of weak pressure in the taking of the transfers.
  (b) Shades: These should be readily distinguishable from the C. & F.

printings, with the possible exception of No. 32*b* which has a pinkish element.

(*c*) *Papers*: At least *six* varieties, all of good quality (comprising both hand and machine made papers) were used but they were all so different (and of so much better quality) to that employed for the C. & F. contract that, once a C. & F. stamp is acquired, no difficulty should be encountered in identifying a Campbell.

(*d*) *Vertical pairs* (they are rare) have been met from four of the Campbell stones, with *wide* distances (up to 199 mm) between the stamps. In such cases the top stamp is from the lower row of a top transfer of fifty and the bottom stamp from the top row of a similar lower transfer.

(*e*) *"Substituted Transfers"*. These (a block of four in the S.W. corner of a sheet) occurred on one out of the 22 transfers on printing stone 5. The horizontal pairs read WA–HN and GM–SX respectively and the vertical pairs VZ over VZ and WA over WA respectively. They are all of the greatest rarity.

(*f*) No *"Creased Transfer"* varieties are to be met in the Campbell printings where the method followed for laying down the printing stones differed from that employed for the Campbell & Fergussons. The same is true of the "Half-Lengths" printed by these two contractors.

Some instances of *retouching* (they are rare) may be met. One stone only was affected.

III. June 1854. *Lithographed by Campbell & Fergusson; transfers for the stones again being taken from Ham's steel plate. Period of issue: March 1855–May 1856. Printed, like the Campbell & Fergusson Half-Lengths, on a machine-wove paper of poor quality (easily thinned and torn). This factor alone provides an unfailing guide for distinguishing the products of the two contractors.*

(i) *Printings from stones which were not over-used; background around top of throne generally full and detail good*

35	2d. lilac (*shades*)	£130	19·00
	a. Purple (*shades*)	—	19·00
	b. Variety "TVO"	—	£550

(ii) *Early printings from stones which were over-used. Similar characteristics to (i) above, though detail is not quite so full. Distinctive shades*

36	2d. brown	—	70·00
	a. Brown-purple	£160	22·00
	b. Warm purple	—	22·00
	c. Rose-lilac	—	22·00
	d. Substituted transfer (pair)	—	£600

(iii) *Later printings from the same stones used for (ii) when in a worn condition. Impressions heavy, coarse and overcoloured; details blurred; generally white background around top of throne*

37	2d. dull lilac-mauve	£110	22·00
	a. Dull mauve	£110	22·00
	b. Grey-violet	—	22·00
	c. Red-lilac	—	24·00
	d. Substituted transfer (pair)	—	£600

(iv) *Printings from a stone giving (from the start) blotchy and unpleasing results, with poor definition. Mainly shows in extra colour patches found on most stamps*

38	2d. dull purple	—	40·00
	a. Dull grey-lilac	£160	40·00
	b. On thick card paper	—	£500

Notes on the Campbell & Fergusson Printings

(*a*) *Stones*: 3,000,000 stamps in all were printed under this contract, of which, however, 1,500,000 (deemed to be in excess of requirements) were destroyed. A total of four printing stones (comprising 16 transfers from the steel plate) were used. The greater size of the printing and the smaller number taken of transfers of fifty (and hence of printing impressions) explains the *over-use* of certain stones, and the badly-worn prints (with filled-in colour, finer details missing, etc.) that are often met.

(*b*) *Shades*: At least 95 per cent of these printings, whatever their actual shade names, have—by comparison with the Campbell stamps—a *pink* quality. Only about 2 per cent of the Campbells, a proportion of the stamps printed from one stone only, have such a quality, but in that case the paper used was wholly different.

(*c*) *Paper* is invariably of vertical mesh. *Both* horizontal and vertical meshes are found in the Campbells.

(*d*) *Vertical pairs* with *wide* spacing have been found. They are rare: See note above on similar Campbell pairs.

(*e*) *"Substituted Transfers"*: Here the entire *five* impressions comprising the left vertical row of a sheet were affected. The *horizontal* pairs (starting at the top and going down) are as follows: UY-BF, TX-MQ, DI-WA, SW-GM and CH-RW. The *vertical* pairs are UY over TX and DI over SW. They occur in various shades and stages of wear.

(*f*) *"Creased Transfer"* varieties. As in the C. & F. "Half-Length" printings, various major instances are met, including the "TVO" variety. At least two transfer groups of 50 were affected.

No retouching has been met in any printing.

3   4 Queen on Throne

(Die engraved and stamps lithographed by Campbell & Fergusson)

1854–65. *T* 3. (*a*) *Imperf.*

39	1s. blue (*shades*) (6.7.54)	£650	22·00
	a. Greenish blue	£750	22·00
	b. Indigo-blue	—	£110

(*b*) *Rouletted 7–7½ at G.P.O., Melbourne (see later notes)*

40	1s. greenish blue (27.8.57)	—	80·00
	a. Blue	—	80·00

(*c*) *Perf 12 by Robinson, early in 1859*

41	1s. blue (*shades*) (13.4.59)	£120	15·00
	a. Greenish blue	£110	12·00
	b. Indigo-blue	—	22·00

For this stamp four printing stones, each of 400 impressions (in four panes of 100), were used. These were built up from an "intermediate" stone of 40 (8 × 5) impressions. Retouches and "creased transfer" varieties also exist. At least two classes of paper were used.

This stamp was reprinted (by lithography) in 1891, wmk V over Crown, Type V2, perf 12½. The transfers were taken from the original die.

(Recess P.B.)

1856–58. *W* 2 of Queensland (Large Star). (*a*) *Imperf.*

42	4	1d. yellow-green (23.10.56)	£110	19·00

(*b*) *Rouletted 5½–6½ by F. W. Robinson, in Melbourne*

43	4	6d. bright blue (1.11.58)	95·00	12·00
		a. Light blue	£160	24·00

The gumming for the 6d. was deemed unsatisfactory and it was not used until the exhaustion of Nos. 44–48. The stock was imperf and was rouletted by Robinson before issue. It only exists imperf, obliterated "CANCELLED" in London, in 1861.

Re-entries and re-cuts occur in both values.

These stamps were reprinted in 1891. Wmk V over Crown, Type V2, imperf using the original steel plates. The 1d. is found in two colours—a dull yellow-green and a bright blue-green. The 6d. has an indigo quality and can be found in two shades.

5   6   7

1854–59. *T* 5 *to* 7 (the *"Woodblocks"*). Typo.

I. *T* 5. 6*d.*: *Printed in sheets of* 100 *stamps, representing two impressions from a plate of* 50 *woodblocks* (*in two panes of* 25—5 × 5), *engraved individually by S. Calvert. These all differ but are of two main types:—*

A. *Small white mark after* "VICTORIA" *like an apostrophe.*
B. *No white mark after* "VICTORIA".

(*a*) *Imperf*

44	6d. reddish brown (13.9.54)	85·00	22·00
	a. Dull orange	75·00	18·00
	b. Orange-yellow	75·00	19·00

(*b*) *Rouletted 7–9*

45	6d. reddish brown (12.8.57)	—	42·00
	a. Dull orange (3.12.57)	—	35·00
	b. Orange-yellow	—	42·00

These stamps may be met rouletted on two sides only, and also (with finer points) on all four sides. The first class emanates from some "rouletters" used by the window-clerks at the G.P.O., Melbourne (see note after No. 62). The latter class were "perforated" by Calvert, and this gauge was also used for the Rouletted "emblems" of early 1858.

(*c*) *Serpentine Roulette 10½*

46	6d. orange-yellow (5.12.57)	—	55·00

(d) *Serrated 18–19 × serpentine 10½; also serrated compound on one side with serpentine*

47	6d. orange-yellow (19.10.57)	—	55·00

(e) *Serrated 18–19*

48	6d. orange-yellow	—	55·00

Part of (b) and all of (c), (d) and (e) were "perforated" by Calvert under his contract of 14.10.57, a total of 163,000 stamps being so treated. The "pin-perf about 10" variety previously listed belongs to 1856 and is clearly not of official origin.

II. *T* **5**. 2*s.*: For this value Calvert employed a plate of 25 (5 × 5) *separately engraved wood-blocks, two impressions of which made up the sheet of 50. (a) Imperf.*

49	2s. dull bluish green (1.9.54)	£900	£110

(b) *Rouletted 7–7½*

50	2s. dull bluish green	—	£350

(c) *Perf 12 by Robinson (1859)*

51	2s. dull bluish green	£200	30·00
	a. *Pale bluish green*	£200	25·00

Nos. 49–51 were printed on a printed *yellow* background which is usually faint. For the blue-on-green printings of 1864–81 see Nos. 127, 130, 140 and 147. These latter were printed in sheets of 30, in two panes of 15 (3 × 5). The plate comprised 18 of the original woodblocks and 12 electros.

III. *T* **6**. REGISTRATION *stamp. (a) Imperf.*

52	1s. rose-pink and blue (1.12.54)	£600	75·00

(b) *Rouletted 7–7½*

53	1s. rose-pink and blue	£3000	£180

IV. *T* **7**. "TOO LATE" *stamp. Imperf.*

54	6d. lilac and green (1.1.55)	£450	£120

The *same* main plate of 25 woodblock impressions (5 × 5 printed four times make up a sheet of 100) was originally used for both the "Registered" and "Too Late" stamps. For the portions printed in blue and green respectively separate stereotype plates were used of each stamp.

A second woodblock plate of 25 (5 × 5) impressions from a different model was used (with the first plate) for later printings of the "Registered" only. Die 2 is distinguished by the longer head "R" of "VICTORIA" and the absence of the small white letters "V" and "R" etc. The "Registered" stamp ceased to be used from 5.1.58 although Postmasters were then instructed to use up remaining stocks for normal postal purposes. The "Too Late" stamp was withdrawn from issue as from 1.7.57. A very few used multiples of both these stamps are known. They all represent abnormal usage.

8

1857–60. *T* **8** ("Emblems"). *Typo.*

For these stamps the dies were "wood-blocks" engraved by Calvert, and the "plates" consisted of 120 individual electrotypes clamped together. In all, six settings were employed for the 4d. value and three each for the 1d. and 2d. values.

I. 1857: Printed by Calvert

(i) *W* **2** of Queensland (*Large Star*). (a) *Imperf*

55	1d. yellow-green (18.2.57)	95·00	13·00
	a. *Deep green*	£110	26·00
	b. Printed on both sides	—	£700
56	4d. vermilion (26.1.57)	£250	10·00
	a. *Brown-vermilion*	£225	9·00
	b. Printed on both sides	—	£550
57	4d. dull red (20.7.57)	£160	7·50
58	4d. dull rose (6.9.57)	£180	7·50

(b) *Rouletted 7–9 (often on two sides only)*

59	1d. yellow-green	£275	65·00
60	4d. vermilion	—	£100
61	4d. dull red (1.8.57)	—	38·00
62	4d. dull rose	—	26·00

Nos. 59–62 were not rouletted by Calvert, but by one or other of three "rouletters" used by the clerks at the selling windows of the G.P.O., Melbourne. One of these "rouletters" gauged 6½–7½ and another 7¾–9. The most effective of them was purchased from one Raymond early in August 1857.

(c) *P* 12

63	1d. yellow-green	—	£275

This stamp and Nos. 66, 66a, 72 and 77 were the result of the perforating (by Robinson), probably in 1860, of a few sheets of old stock.

(ii) *No wmk. On good quality medium-woven paper. (a) Imperf*

64	2d. pale lilac (25.5.57)	£160	10·00
	a. *Grey-lilac*	£160	10·00

(b) *Rouletted 7–9 (often on two sides only)*

65	2d. pale lilac	—	23·00
	a. *Grey-lilac*	£1500	23·00

See note following No. 62.

(c) *P* 12

66	2d. pale lilac	—	£225
	a. *Grey-lilac*	—	£225

See note following No. 63.

(d) *Serrated 18–19*

67	2d. grey-lilac	£500	£350

This variety is probably the result of an experiment by Calvert. Most of the copies seen are unused.

II. 1858: Printed by Calvert on white wove paper of good quality

(a) *Rouletted all round 8–9 (usually fine points)*

68	1d. pale emerald (19.1.58)	£300	14·00
	a. *Emerald-green*	£300	14·00
	b. Roulette horiz only	—	£325
69	4d. rose-pink (10.1.58)	£200	5·50
	a. *Bright rose*	£200	5·50
	b. *Reddish pink*	—	11·00
	c. Roulette horiz only	—	£300
	d. Roulette vert only	—	£300

(b) *Imperf* (April 1858)

70	1d. pale emerald	£190	10·00
	a. *Emerald-green*	—	13·00
71	4d. rose-pink	£250	23·00
	a. *Bright rose*	—	23·00
	b. *Reddish pink*	—	30·00

The imperf varieties above were stamps which *should* have been rouletted by Calvert. On the cancellation of his contract they were taken over from him but since supplies were urgently required (and Robinson not having then commenced his contract) the stamps were put into use as they were. They *follow* and do not precede the roulettes.

(c) *P* 12

72	1d. emerald-green	—	£275
	a. Imperf between (horiz pair)		

III. 1858–9: Printed under contract by F. W. Robinson, first outside and later (1859) inside the Post Office Establishment

(i) *On wove paper of a somewhat poorer quality than Calvert's. Imperf*

73	4d. dull rose (5.58)	—	60·00

(ii) *On smooth vertically laid paper of good quality. (a) Imperf*

74	4d. dull rose (8.5.58)	—	23·00
	a. *Dull rose-red*	—	23·00
	b. *Dull rose-red (normal ink)*	£400	15·00

The imperforate stamps Nos. 73, 74 and 74a can be easily distinguished by their distinctive *heavy, coarse* impression and the *oily* nature of the ink employed. They were the *first* stamps printed by Robinson and because of the demand were rushed into circulation without being rouletted, as also was No. 74b which was the first stamp printed by him using a more satisfactory quality of ink.

(b) *Rouletted 5½–6½*

75	2d. brown-lilac (*shades*) (9.58)	£200	9·50
76	4d. pale dull rose (5.58)	£150	3·50
	a. *Dull rose-red*	£120	3·50
	b. *Rose-red*	£120	3·25

(c) *P* 12

77	4d. dull rose	—	£300

See note following No. 63.

(d) *Serrated 19*

78	4d. rose-red	—	£350

(iii) *On Smooth horizontally laid paper of same quality as* (ii) *above*

(a) *Rouletted 5½–6½*

79	2d. brown-lilac (*shades*) (7.58)	£120	5·50
	a. *Violet (shades)* (27.11.58)	£150	5·50
	b. *Dull violet*	—	18·00
80	4d. pale dull rose	—	£800

(iv) *On good quality wove paper. (a) Rouletted 5½–6½*

81	1d. yellow-green (25.12.58)	£275	23·00
82	4d. dull rose	—	£325

(b) Perf 12 (the first perforated stamps to be issued in Victoria)
83 1d. yellow-green (shades) (11.1.59) . . . . £160 11·00
  a. Imperf × perf (vert pair) . . . . — £250
84 4d. dull rose (16.2.59) . . . . £150 2·75
  Note: No. 83 is found on two classes of paper.

(v) P 12. On poorer quality wove paper of coarser mesh
85 1d. dull green (7.59) . . . . £120 7·50
  a. Green (11.59) . . . . £120 7·50
86 4d. dull rose (19.4.59) . . . . — 5·00
  a. Rose-carmine (6.59) . . . . £150 5·00
  b. Rose-pink (12.59) . . . . — 9·00
Save in the rouletted 1d. (where a second paper of vertical mesh was also employed) all the paper used for (iv) above was of horizontal mesh, whereas under (v) except for No. 86b (which was printed on a tough, thick, handmade paper) it is always of vertical mesh. In two printings of the 1d. both wove and laid papers were included.

(vi) P 12. On horizontally laid papers, of coarser quality and not so smooth as those previously employed by Robinson
(a) Laid lines closer together
87 1d. dull green (July 1859) . . . . — 15·00
88 4d. rose-pink (23.12.59) . . . . — 7·00
(b) Laid lines further apart
89 1d. green (shades) (October 1859) . . . . £130 9·50
90 4d. rose-pink (shades) (January 1860) . . . . £120 7·50

(vii) P 12. On thin glazed paper, emanating from Bordeaux
91 1d. deep yellow-green (July 1859) . . . . — £150
This stamp must have been printed before the "dull greens" of July 1859.

PLATES: 1857–68

The plates prepared for use between January 1857 and December 1867 (with one exception, see note after No. 51 on 2s. value) consisted of a number of individual electros (usually 120) clamped together in a "forme" and spaced and arranged to fit the pattern of the watermarked paper. Five such schemes are to be found, viz.: (a) from 1857 to Sept 1863 when (save for the 2d. of May 1857) the forme comprised 4 blocks of 30 (6×5) electros; (b) for the 2d. of May 1857 only, the sheet consisted of 20 blocks of 6 (2×3); (c) from Sept 1863 to Feb 1866 when three separate arrangements, constant for any one value, are found. These were based on the face value of the stamps in the unit group and were as follows:—(i) For the 1d., 2d. and 4d. values the forme was composed of 4 blocks of 15 (3×5) separated by "gutters"; (ii) for the 3d., 6d. and 1s. values of 6 blocks (or 3, in the case of the 1s.) of 20 (4×5) separated by "gutters" and (iii) in the case of the 10d. of 20 blocks of 6 (3×2) separated by "gutters"; (d) over and following the period Jan–July 1866, in anticipation of the introduction of the V over Crown watermarked paper, the old formes (with the exception of the 10d.) were reset and the new formes (e.g. 3d. and 6d.) arranged to give one block of 120 (12×10) evenly spaced units without "gutters". For various values, therefore, two "settings" were employed of the same electrotypes. Those interested in this subject should consult an article in Philately from Australia for March 1954. From 1869 to 1874 new printing plates consisted of 4 electrotypes each of 30 impressions (6×5) clamped together. These were produced via one (or two) "master" electrotypes of the same size. From 1875 (with four exceptions in the 1885 issues) all new printing plates consisted of a continuous surface electrotype of 120 (12×10) impressions. The foregoing remarks apply to normal size stamps only and require modification for other sizes.

B. GOVERNMENT STAMP PRINTING. THE FIRST PERIOD, 1860–1884

Robinson was employed, in April 1858, to finish Calvert's uncompleted Contracts of 1857. Subsequently, under further Contracts, he printed more stamps. The work being satisfactory the Government (on 12.4.59) undertook to continue his employment and at the same time purchased the whole of his equipment, paper stocks, etc. As from 1.1.60 a Government Stamp Printing Branch was set up, Robinson was appointed its Chief Officer and there was no more Stamp Printing in terms of Private Contract. He was succeeded in 1867 by James Atkinson, and from 1883 to 1906 the same work was performed by William Bond. In December 1885 printing operations were transferred from the Post Office to the Government Printing Office and the Stamp Printer then joined the staff of the Government Printer. The Stamp Printers after Bond were J. Kemp and J. B. Cooke (1909–12), the latter being also appointed the first Commonwealth Stamp Printer.
Note: All issues of this period, 1860–84, were printed by typography from electrotypes.

THE WORLD CENTRE FOR FINE STAMPS IS 399 STRAND

9   10

11   12

(Dies for 3d., 4d. and 6d. (T 9) designed and engraved by Frederick Grosse. The die for the 6d. T 11 consisted of a frame die engraved by Grosse into which was plugged a head portion, cut out of his die for the 6d. T 9. The design, die and plate for the 1d. T 10 were all supplied by Messrs. De Gruchy and Leigh of Melbourne)

1860–66. T 5, 8, 9, 10 and 11. P 12.
(i) No wmk. On horizontally laid paper (lines further apart, as (vi) (b) above)
92 9 3d. deep blue (31.1.60) . . . . £300 23·00
  a. Light blue £1200 £110

(ii) No wmk. On thin glazed paper emanating from Bordeaux (see also under (vii) above)
93 8 1d. bright green (25.5.60) . . . . — 22·00
94 9 4d. rose (21.4.60) . . . . £275 12·00
  a. Rose-pink . . . . — 7·50

(iii) No wmk. On a thicker coarser paper
95 9 4d. rose-pink (7.60) . . . . £275 7·50

(iv) 1860–66: Watermarked with the appropriate words of value as W 12. The paper, which was hand-made, was supplied by T. H. Saunders of London)
96 8 1d. pale yellowish green (8.7.60) . . . . 65·00 4·50
  a. Yellow-green . . . . 75·00 4·75
  b. Wmk "FOUR PENCE" . . . . — £1200
97 10 1d. pale green (1.10.61) . . . . 75·00 5·50
  a. Olive-green . . . . — 6·00
  b. Pale green (deep brown gum) (2.63) . . . . . 75·00 6·00
98 8 2d. brown-lilac (7.7.61) . . . . — 15·00
99 2d. bluish slate (8.61, 6.62) . . . . £100 4·75
  a. Greyish lilac (9.61) . . . . £110 4·75
  b. Slate-grey (1.62) . . . . — 4·75
100 9 3d. pale blue (1.61) . . . . £120 7·00
  a. Bright blue (8.61) . . . . £120 8·00
  b. Blue (deep brown gum) (2.63) . . . . £130 6·00
  ba. "TRREE" for "THREE" in wmk . . . .
  c. Deep blue (1864) . . . . £130 6·00
101 3d. maroon (13.2.66) . . . . £100 25·00
  a. Perf 13 . . . . £120 28·00
102 4d. rose-pink (1.8.60) . . . . — 4·75
  a. Rose-red (shades) (9.60) . . . . 80·00 3·00
  b. Rose-carmine (12.60) . . . . — 7·50
  c. Dull rose (shades) (1861) . . . . 80·00 3·00
103 6d. orange (18.10.60) £1600 £200
104 5 6d. black (22.6.61) . . . . £150 35·00
105 9 6d. black (20.8.61) . . . . 95·00 5·50
  a. Grey-black . . . . 95·00 5·50
106 11 6d. grey (26.4.62) . . . . 80·00 5·50
  a. Grey-black . . . . 80·00 6·50
  b. Jet black (deep brown gum) (3.63) . . . . 85·00 7·50
Reprints on paper wmkd V over Crown (W 23), perf 12½, were made in 1891 of the 1d. Type 10, 3d. and 4d. Type 9 and 6d. Type 11. In all cases new plates were used, and certain "die flaws" are found on the "Reprints" which are not met on the originals.

                    13   14

1862–63. *Emergency printings owing to supplies of the appropriate paper not being available.*

(a) On paper wmkd "FIVE SHILLINGS", W **13**

107	**9**	4d. dull rose-pink (11.9.62)	£1500	20·00
		a. Dull rose	—	20·00

(b) On paper wmkd "THREE PENCE", W **12**

108	**8**	2d. pale slate (27.12.62)	£110	10·00
		a. Bluish grey (deep brown gum) (2.63) . . .	£120	12·00

Note: Certain stamps are to be met on the "words of value" papers with wmk *reversed* under Nos. 99, 100, 102, also 173 and 176. *Inverted* wmks may also be found in several cases. All these wmk varieties are scarce to rare.

(v) 1862–64: *Same types as before but wmkd with the appropriate single-lined numeral of value, as W* **14**, *the paper being supplied by De La Rue. P* 12 *unless otherwise described*

109	**10**	1d. olive-green (1.2.63).	55·00	4·50
		a. Pale green (9.63)	55·00	4·50
		b. Apple-green (4.64)	55·00	4·50
110	**8**	2d. dull reddish lilac (21.4.63)	£160	5·50
111		2d. grey-lilac (10.63)	£150	12·00
		a. Wmk "6" (10.63)	—	£4000
		b. Grey-violet (shades) (11.63)	£100	9·00
		c. Slate (12.63)	£150	18·00
112	**9**	4d. dull rose-pink (9.10.62)	90·00	4·50
		a. Dull rose (deep brown gum) (2.63)	95·00	4·75
		b. Rose-red	—	4·50
113	**11**	6d. grey (18.6.63)	70·00	4·50
		a. Grey-black (2.64)	70·00	4·75
		b. Intense black	—	5·50
114		6d. jet-black (p 13) (12.64).	80·00	5·00
		a. Grey-black	80·00	5·50

July–Aug 1863: *Varieties due to a temporary break-down of the perforating machine.*

115	**9**	4d. dull rose-pink (imperf)	—	60·00
116		4d. dull rose-pink (roul)	—	£250

Notes on plate varieties found on stamps printed from plates made by Robinson.

The electros prepared by Robinson over the period 1860–66 (many, e.g. the 4d., which lasted until 1881, remaining in use for a long time after) furnish perhaps the most interesting varieties found in typographed stamps. Since the lead moulds for these were struck by hand, on semifused metal, and without the aid of a "collar", the stamps present us with certain constant abnormalities, viz *partial strikes, double strikes* and *internal distortion* varieties of a nature and extent not found in any other issues, as well as also providing all the more usual types of flaw found in typographed stamps. The whole of the Robinson "Beaded Ovals" and "Laureates" are plateable since the process used made it *impossible* for any stamp to be a perfect reproduction of the die. The 6d. black (Type **11**) is the most interesting of all since the die here was in two parts. This meant the adherence of lead along the line of junction, etc, and gave rise to yet further classes of plate variety. For information on this stamp see various articles in the *London Philatelist*.

Notes on the two single-line numeral watermark papers.

Two different English firms supplied the single-line numeral wmk papers used from October 1862 onwards. The two classes of paper supplied are so distinct that they have now been given separate listing. Their characteristics are as follows:—

1. *De La Rue papers* (several consignments). Comprised *white* paper wmkd "1", "2", "4", "6" and "8" respectively, *blue* paper wmkd "1" and *green* paper wmkd "2". In certain printings particularly in the 1d., 2d. and 4d. Laureates and the 6d. black (1863–65) on this paper, a *pelure* type—thin, hard and semi-transparent—may be found. This variety has not been separately listed as it is worthy of the specialist's attention. Generally the quality of these De La Rue papers varied considerably among the different consignments.

2. *T. H. Saunders papers* (one consignment only). Comprised *white* paper wmkd "1", "4" and "6" respectively, *blue* paper wmkd "1", *green* paper wmkd "2", and *pink* paper wmkd "10". It was first used in

December 1865 and the white papers were exhausted by August 1867. The paper was (apart from the *blue* variety, which was rather thinner than the rest) of even quality throughout and was smoother, thicker, more brittle and (in the white variety) not so white as the De La Rue product. It will be noted that the "2" and "8" papers were supplied by De La Rue only, whereas the "10" paper (pink) was supplied by Saunders only. Comparison of these should assist collectors in accurate classification. The *coloured* papers lasted much longer than the white, as will be seen from the listings. The *blue* lasted until 1875, and the *green* and *pink* until 1879.

In both papers, in practically all cases, *reversed* and/or *inverted* wmks may be met. *Sideways* wmks have been found under Nos. 113, 124 and 200. Stamps showing little or no wmk are from the left or right sides of badly cut sheets.

          15   16   17

            18   19

(The *"Laureated"* series: Dies engraved by Frederick Grosse. Printing plates (see previous note) made by F. W. Robinson until late in 1867)

Note. Since various printings of the 2s. Calvert (Type **5**) were also made between 1864 and 1881 these have been included where appropriate.

1863–80.

(i) 1863–64. *Early printings. Wmkd with appropriate single-lined numeral as W* **14**, *on paper supplied by De La Rue. P* 12

117	**15**	1d. pale green (8.9.64)	75·00	7·00
118		2d. violet (4.64)	65·00	4·75
		a. Dull violet (10.64)	70·00	5·00
119		4d. deep rose (4.9.63)	—	3·50
		a. Doubly printed	—	£500
		b. Rose-pink (9.63)	85·00	2·50
		c. Pink (4.64)	85·00	2·50

Emergency printings on Perkins, Bacon paper wmkd double-lined numerals "1" *and* "4" *respectively, supplied by Tasmania. P* 12.

120	**10**	1d. yellow-green (10.12.63)	£110	7·00
		a. Dull green (4.64)	—	7·00
		b. Imperf between (pair)	—	
121	**15**	4d. deep rose (7.1.64)	£110	3·75
		a. Pale rose	—	3·75

Like the 1d. and 4d. Perkins, Bacon types of Van Diemen's Land most of the Victorian stamps printed on the above two papers may occasionally be found with wmk *inverted*. This applies both to the 1d. and 4d. above and also the various "Laureates" of the 1867–68 printings. Instances are also known where the wmk is *reversed* and one (in No. 132) where it is *sideways*. Most of these varieties are rare.

(ii) *Printings of October 1864 onwards. As* (i) *but P* 13

122	**15**	1d. pale green (10.10.64)	70·00	3·50
		a. Bluish green (12.64)	65·00	2·75
		aa. Doubly printed	—	£550
		b. Green (shades) (8.65)	65·00	3·50
		c. Deep green (12.65)	—	3·00
123		2d. dull violet (10.64)	55·00	3·75
		a. Dull lilac (shades) (4.65)	55·00	3·50
		b. Reddish mauve (11.65)	60·00	3·50
124		4d. rose (10.64)	75·00	2·50
		a. Dull rose-red (2.65)	75·00	2·50
125		8d. orange (22.2.65)	£300	50·00
126	**18**	1s. blue/blue (10.4.65)	£100	3·50
127	**5**	2s. light blue green (22.11.64)	£150	5·00
		a. Deep blue green (1865)	£150	5·00

The above 1s. stamp can be immediately identified by the white patches (comprising an *albino* impression) due to the lack of a *make-ready* which are found on all stamps. The 8d. was withdrawn from issue on 11.6.69.

(iii) *July–August* 1865. *As before but P* 12 *or* 12 × 13 *from repaired state of* 12 *machine, with larger holes and sharper teeth than previously.* (a) *Perf* 12

128	**15**	1d. green (*shades*)	70·00	3·00
		a. *Deep green*	70·00	3·00
129		4d. dull rose-red (8.65)	£120	7·50
130	**5**	2s. dark blue/*green*	£170	8·50

(b) *Perf* 12 × 13

131	**15**	1d. deep green	—	6·00

August and December 1865. *Emergency printings* (2) *on Perkins Bacon paper wmkd double-lined "4" supplied by Tasmania.*

132	**15**	4d. dull reddish rose (*p* 13) (11.8.65)	£110	3·50
		a. Perf 12	—	3·75
		b. Perf 12 × 13	—	11·00
133		4d. red (*p* 13) (16.12.65)	£120	3·50

October 1865. *Emergency printing on De La Rue paper wmkd single-lined "8", no "10" paper having arrived. P* 13.

134	**17**	10d. grey (21.10.65).	£450	£100
		a. *Grey-black*	£450	£100

(iv) *December* 1865–66 *printings. These, in general, were of finer impression than the previous* 1865 *printings*

A. *On Saunders paper, wmkd with the appropriate single-line numerals as* W **14**.

135	**15**	1d. deep yellow-green (*p* 13) (1.66)	65·00	2·75
		a. Perf 12	—	6·50
		b. Perf 12 × 13	—	5·50
136		4d. rose-red (*p* 13) (12.12.65).	75·00	3·00
		a. Perf 12	—	4·75
		b. Perf 12 × 13	—	5·50
137	**17**	6d. blue (*p* 13) (28.5.66)	21·00	1·50
		a. Perf 12	23·00	3·00
		b. Perf 12 × 13	21·00	1·75
		ba. Imperf between (pair)	—	£550
138		10d. dull purple/*pink* (*p* 13) (22.3.66).	65·00	5·00
		a. Perf 12 × 13	70·00	5·50
		b. *Blackish brown/pink* (*p* 13) (1869)	75·00	5·50
139	**18**	1s. indigo-blue/*blue* (*p* 13) (1870).	55·00	3·25
		a. Perf 12 (1873)	—	5·00
		b. *Bright blue/blue* (*p* 13) (1.71)	55·00	2·50
		ba. Perf 12	—	3·25
		c. *Pale dull blue/blue* (*p* 13) (1.75)	—	7·00
		ca. Perf 12	—	3·25
140	**5**	2s. dark blue/*green* (12.67)	£160	5·50
		a. Perf 12 (1875)	£180	5·50
		b. *Blue/green* (1872, 1878)	£160	4·25
		c. *Greenish blue/green* (*p* 12) (1875)	£180	5·50
		d. *Deep greenish blue/green* (*p* 12½) (1880)	£160	7·50

The 1s. on Saunders paper was issued later than 1866 but it and the 2s. printing are included here for the sake of convenience. The Saunders green paper is distinctly *deeper* in shade and more apparently *green* than the De La Rue variety.

B. *On De La Rue paper wmkd with the appropriate single-line numerals as* W **14**. *P* 13.

141	**15**	1d. bright yellow-green (1.67)	—	15·00
142		2d. rosy lilac (1.66)	55·00	4·75
		a. Perf 12 × 13	55·00	4·75
143		2d. dull lilac (6.66)	—	4·75
		a. Perf 12	—	6·00
		b. Perf 12 × 13	—	7·50
144		2d. grey (25.7.66)	55·00	3·00
		a. Perf 12	85·00	6·00
145	**17**	6d. blue (16.2.66)	23·00	2·50
		a. Perf 12	23·00	4·00
		b. Perf 12 × 13	21·00	1·75
146	**18**	1s. blue/*blue* (1866, 1869).	55·00	3·00
		a. Perf 12 × 13 (1866)	55·00	3·50
		b. *Bright blue/blue* (*p* 13) (1867, 1871) . . .	—	3·00
		ba. Perf 12 (1871)	—	3·50
		c. *Indigo/blue* (*p* 13)	—	2·75
		d. *Dull blue/blue* (*p* 12) (1874)	—	3·50
		e. *Imperf between (vert pair)* (*p* 12 × 13) . .	—	£550
147	**5**	2s. blue/*green* (1868).	£140	4·25
		a. *Greenish blue/green* (1873)	£140	4·25
		aa. Perf 12	£160	5·50
		b. *Dark blue/green* (*p* 12½) (1880)	£140	4·25

The 1d. of 1867 on De La Rue, distinguishable only by its shade, was presumably the result of the discovery of a small quantity of old stock. The 2d. and 4d. of 1866 may also be found 13 × 12 but are rare in *this* condition. The 10d. was withdrawn from issue on 21.6.71. There were, between 1864 and 1881, no less than 21 different printings of the 2s. blue on green. Only the main schools of colour have been listed.

1866 (Sept)–**67**. *Various Emergency printings, all the results of the non-arrival of the first shipment of "V over Crown" paper.*

1. *Printings on De La Rue paper wmkd single-lined "8". P* 13.

148	**15**	1d. bright yellow-green (27.12.66)	£120	9·50
149		2d. grey (18.1.67)	£110	4·50
150	**16**	3d. lilac (29.9.66).	£160	20·00
151	**15**	4d. rose-red (?date)	†	£2000

2. *Printings on Saunders paper wmkd single-lined "4". P* 13.

152	**15**	1d. bright yellow-green (6.3.67)	85·00	6·50
153		2d. grey (21.2.67)	75·00	4·75

3. *Printings on paper wmkd single-lined "6". P* 13.

(a) *On De La Rue paper*

154	**15**	1d. bright yellow-green (6.67)	—	14·00

(b) *On Saunders paper*

155	**15**	1d. bright yellow-green (6.67)	£120	11·00
156		2d. grey (13.5.67)	££130	6·00

9 **9**

NINEPENCE

20 (*V*1) (21)

WATERMARKS. Many stamps watermarked V and Crown may be found with watermark inverted or sideways.

1867–68. *Printings on first consignment of paper wmkd "V over Crown", W* **20**, *received in April* 1867. *P* 13.

157	**15**	1d. bright yellow-green (10.8.67)	85·00	3·50
158		2d. slate-grey (*shades*) (26.8.67)	70·00	3·50
		a. *Grey-lilac* (1.68)	—	4·75
159	**16**	3d. lilac (8.67).	£200	24·00
		a. *Grey-lilac* (8.68)	£225	26·00
160	**15**	4d. dull rose (11.67).	75·00	5·00
161	**17**	6d. dark blue (12.67)	—	3·00
162	**19**	5s. blue/*yellow* (26.12.67).	£1600	£300
		a. Wmk reversed	—	£500

The above shades (there are also paper differences) are sufficiently distinctive to enable separation of the five lower values from *later* "V over Crown" printings. The 5s. was printed from the first electros prepared by Atkinson. There were two printings, both in sheets of 25 (5 × 5). The first (1200) was from a single vertical column of 5 electros clamped together. The second (2000) was from a plate of 25 impressions, comprising a different "5 vertical", repeated 5 times (i.e. giving 5 types). The reversed wmk variety belongs to the first printing and was created *deliberately* to avoid the appearance of the "page number" on the front of one stamp in every four sheets of 25.

1867 (Sept)–**68** and **1870**. *Various Emergency printings due first to the* 1867 *shipment of white "V over Crown" paper being so small, later to its exhaustion and the non-arrival of the second shipment ordered, later still* (1870) *to a further shortage of this paper*

1. *Printings on the Perkins, Bacon paper wmkd double-lined "1" received from Tasmania in* 1863. *P* 13.

163	**15**	1d. pale yellowish green (24.9.67)	65·00	3·50
		a. *Deep yellow-green* (6.68)	65·00	3·50
164		2d. slate (5.68)	£110	5·50
		a. *Mauve* (30.6.68)	£110	6·50
165	**16**	3d. grey-lilac (8.68)	£150	35·00
166	**17**	6d. blue (28.7.68)	55·00	4·25

2. *Printings on the Perkins, Bacon paper wmkd double-lined "4" received from Tasmania in* 1863.

167	**15**	1d. pale yellow-green (27.5.68)	£750	80·00
168		2d. grey-lilac (3.2.68)	£110	4·25
		a. *Slate* (28.3.68)	£110	3·50
		b. *Mauve* (3.7.68)	—	4·50
169		4d. dull rose-red (5.68)	£110	5·00
170	**17**	6d. blue (5.68)	£150	13·00
		a. *Indigo-blue*	—	15·00

3. *Printing on Saunders paper wmkd* "SIX PENCE" *as W* **12**. *P* 13.

171	**15**	1d. pale yellow-green (5.6.68)	£325	15·00	
172		2d. slate-grey		£1100	
173	**17**	6d. blue (23.5.68)	£150	11·00	
		a. Indigo-blue	—	15·00	

Only one copy is apparently known of No. 172. From its shade it would appear to belong to an 1867–68 printing. No. 171 is known with the wmk *sideways*.

4. *Printings on lilac paper wmkd V over Crown from* 1867 *consignment. P* 13.

174	**15**	2d. mauve/*lilac* (12.8.68)	55·00	6·50
		a. Lilac/lilac	55·00	6·00

5. 1869–70. 6d. *value only. Printings on various wmkd papers as indicated. P* 13.

175	**17**	6d. dull blue (THREE PENCE) (6.12.69)	£130	6·00
		a. Deep blue	—	7·00
176		6d. dull blue (FOUR PENCE) (18.6.70)	£250	22·00
		a. Deep blue	—	23·00
177		6d. dull blue ("4") (21.5.70)	—	£1200
178		6d. dull blue ("2") (1870)	—	£1200

Of the six or seven copies known of No. 177 all but one have the watermark reversed.

1868 (Aug)–**71**. *Printings on second and later consignments of V over Crown paper. W* **20**. *P* 13 *only*. (i) *Printed from Robinson plates.*

179	**15**	2d. lilac (26.8.68)	50·00	3·25
		a. Dull mauve (shades) (10.68)	50·00	3·25
		b. Lilac-grey (1.69)	—	3·50
		c. Lilac-rose (2.70)	—	3·00
180	**16**	3d. yellow-orange (12.6.69)	15·00	3·00
181	**15**	4d. pale red (aniline) (21.4.69)	—	6·50
		a. Deep red (aniline) (16.7.69)	—	6·50
		b. Rose-pink (2.70)	—	5·00
182	**17**	6d. blue (shades) (7.11.68)	14·00	1·10
		a. Indigo-blue (1869)	14·00	1·10
183	**19**	5s. indigo-blue and carmine (I) (8.10.68)	£200	15·00
		a. Blue and carmine (1869)	£170	11·00

Nos. 179*b/c* were printed from badly worn plates. For the frame-plate of the 5s. (I) the electros of the 1867 plate, with the Crown, "VICTORIA" and "FIVE SHILLINGS" cut out were employed. A new plate, also produced via cut-out portions of the 1867 plate, was brought into use for the red portion. The 1868 printing of the 5s. was produced, in April of that year, using the residue of the first consignment.

(ii) *Printed from new plates made by Atkinson*

184	**15**	1d. bright yellow-green (10.68)	65·00	2·50
		a. Bright olive-green (1.69)	—	14·00
		b. Dull yellow-green (4.69)	—	2·10
		c. Dull green (3.70)	65·00	2·10
		d. Very pale green (10.70)	—	2·10
185		2d. lilac-grey (15.1.69)	—	3·75
		a. Lilac-rose (shades) (24.2.69)	55·00	3·75
		b. Mauve (20.4.69)	—	3·25
		c. Red-lilac (shades) (5.69)	55·00	3·00
		d. Dull lilac (shades) (6.69)	55·00	2·50
		e. Silver-grey (2.9.69)	£110	7·00

The Atkinson plates, produced by an improved technique; do not show the *double* and *partial strikes* and *internal distortion* varieties met on a large proportion of the stamps from the Robinson plates. The later printings from the 2d. and 6d. Robinson plates show obvious signs of wear. These factors and the differing shades should make classification relatively easy. For the first two printings of the 2d. in 1869 the first of the new Atkinson plates was used in conjunction with the old Robinson plate, following which the latter was replaced by a second Atkinson plate. The dates of introduction of the Atkinson plates were 1d., October 1868; 2d., January 1869 and 6d., December 1875.

1871. *Provisional. Surch with T* **21**, *in blue. On Saunders paper wmkd single-lined* "10". *P* 13.

186	**17**	9d. on 10d. purple-brown/*pink* (22.4.71)	£180	10·00
		a. Blackish purple/pink	—	12·00
		b. Surch double	—	£700

PERFORATIONS (TO 1883)

The perforations of Victoria, particularly those of the period October 1864–80, form a complex study for specialists. We have adopted in this listing a simplified classification based on *three* descriptions—Perf 12, Perf 13 and Perf 12½ respectively, the latter being substituted for Perf 13 for the period 1881 on. The position can be concisely put as follows:—

A. "*Perf* 12": Here the gauge is *never* quite 12 and nearer 11½. It is not found after 1883. There were two machines (both single-line), the first introduced by Robinson in January 1859 and the second purchased in 1871. No "perf 12" are found in the period mid 1866–mid 1871. At various periods, more particularly in 1865 and 1880, one or both of the machines was repaired, to give larger holes and sharper teeth over a succeeding period.

B. "*Perf* 13": Here the gauge is invariably *over* 12 and with a sole exception (covering a section of the pins on one machine over the period 1876–80) invariably *under* 13. Generally speaking up to the end of 1880, these machines gauged 12½ to 12¾. Two classes of machine are found:

(i) *Single-line* machines. These were three in number—purchased in October 1864, 1866 and 1873 respectively. Two of them were converted into combs in 1873. The other was repaired on several occasions, particularly in 1879–80, to give larger holes and sharper teeth.

(ii) *Comb* machines. First introduced in 1873 (see above). Over the period of use they gave various gauges, depending on the machine and its state of repair. They were all *vertical* combs adapted only for normal size stamps of either dimension as likewise (until 1913) were all other comb-machines used in Victoria for perforating stamps.

C. "*Perf* 12½": Found from late 1876 onwards, in both single-line (used mainly for the larger-size stamps) and vertical comb machines. Gradually superseded the A and B gauges. Certain stamps of the 1879–80 period are found in both B and C gauges but these are no longer differentiated as separate varieties, being only listed under the one or the other gauge. This applies also to the Postal Fiscal section.

"*Compound*" *perforations*: In previous editions certain 12 × 13 perforations were listed which were not true compounds of A and B but simply the product of one or other of the *comb* machines. Such varieties have now been eliminated. The "Compounds" now listed are all true compounds (or "mixeds") of A and B. They generally fall into two categories: (i) those of the 1865–66 period where the two machines were both used for the original perforating, one in the one direction (top to bottom) and the other in the other (sides); (ii) isolated examples, better termed "mixed" perfs, from 1873 on, where one gauge machine was used to correct off-centre perforating done by the other gauge machine. Such cases are almost invariably associated with "mends", viz the pasting of gummed strips down the back of the faulty line of perforations.

1871–84 PRINTINGS

These are listed separately from the 1868–71 printings because of the perforation changes made in the period, viz the reintroduction of the 12 gauge (1871), the introduction of comb machines (1873), the repairs of various 12 and 13 machines (1879), and the introduction of the 12½ gauge (1879–80). Many stamps issued in the latter period are found both perf 13 and 12½ but no distinction is made. The 13 gauge disappears in 1880–81.

Papers: All printings on white paper made after April 1878 and also the last 8d. printing were on the "*glazed*" variety of paper and this furnishes another means of identification. Some shades, e.g. 6d. blue of 1878–79 are found on *both* papers.

Shades are different from those found in the 1868–71 printings.

1871–84.

(i) *Printed from Robinson plates; W* **20**; *P* 13, 12½ *unless otherwise described*

187	**16**	3d. dull orange (1871)	14·00	1·90
		a. Perf 12 (1872)	14·00	20·00
		b. Orange (1874)	—	2·25
		ba. Perf 12		2·10
		c. Bright orange	20·00	2·50
		ca. Perf 12		2·50
188		3d. orange-brown (1878)	20·00	5·50
189		3d. dull orange-yellow (1881)	22·00	2·50
		a. Perf 12		
190	**15**	4d. rose (shades) (1871–78)	70·00	3·00
		a. Perf 12	70·00	3·00
		b. Dull rose (5.3.79)	70·00	3·00
		ba. Perf 12	—	3·00
		c. Dull rose-red (23.12.79)	—	3·00
		ca. Perf 12	—	3·00
		d. Bright lilac-rose (aniline) (3.3.80)	75·00	3·75
		da. Perf 12	—	6·50
191		4d. rosine (aniline) (22.9.80)	75·00	5·00
		a. Perf 12	80·00	4·75
		b. Compound perf 12 with 12½	—	£325
192	**17**	6d. Prussian blue (1872, 1874)	12·00	90
		a. Perf 12	14·00	1·10
		b. Indigo (1873)	14·00	1·40
		ba. Perf 12	18·00	1·75
		c. Dull blue (worn plate)	—	90
193	**15**	8d. lilac-brown/*pink* (24.1.77)	75·00	5·50
		a. Purple-brown/pink (21.3.78)	75·00	5·50
		b. Chocolate/pink (6.8.78)	80·00	5·00
		bb. Compound perf 13 × 12	—	£325
194		8d. red-brown/pink (20.5.78)	75·00	5·00
195		8d. dark red-brown/*pink* (*p* 12) (*glazed*) (30.11.80)	75·00	5·50
		a. ½ Perf 12½		

196	**18**	1s. light blue/*blue* (5.75)	75·00	6·50
		a. Perf 12	—	6·50
197	**19**	5s. pale bright blue and carmine (I) (7.77) . .	—	15·00
		a. *Grey-blue and carmine* (8.78)	£160	13·00
		b. *Deep lavender-blue and carmine* (5.80) .	£160	13·00
198		5s. bright blue and red (II) (12.5.81)	£140	11·00
		a. Perf 12	£130	12·00
		b. *Indigo-blue and red*	—	15·00
		ba. Perf 12	—	16·00
		c. Second "I" in "SHILLINGS" short at foot	—	90·00

The 4d. "pink" previously listed is a *faded* rosine. For the 5s. (Type II) new dies were made for *each* portion of the design. All Type I stamps have a blue line under the Crown, which is missing in Type II. The latter were printed in sheets of 100 (10 × 10), as compared with 25 (5 × 5) for Type I.

No. 197*b* has the watermark sideways.

1877–79. *Printings of the 8d. value on Saunders paper wmkd single-lined "10". P 13, 12½ unless otherwise stated.*

199	**15**	8d. lilac-brown/*pink* (12.77)	—	£500
		a. *Purple-brown/pink* (20.2.78)	£100	6·00
200		8d. red-brown/*pink* (8.8.79)	85·00	5·00
		a. Perf 12	—	8·00

The 8d. printings (save that of 1880) were *mixed* and comprised stamps on *both* V over Crown and "10" papers.

HALF

(22)

(ii) *Printed from plates made by Atkinson. The ½d. made by surch with* T **22**, *in red*

201	**15**	½d. on 1d. green (25.6.73)	38·00	10·00
		a. Perf 12	45·00	12·00
		b. *Grass-green*	40·00	10·00
		ba. Perf 12	45·00	12·00
		c. Short "1" at right	—	70·00
202		1d. pale green (1871)	60·00	2·25
		a. Perf 12 (10.71)	70·00	2·40
		b. *Green (shades)*	60·00	2·25
		ba. Perf 12	60·00	2·25
		c. *Grass-green*	—	2·40
		ca. Perf 12	60·00	2·40
		d. *Bluish green (shades)*	60·00	2·40
		da. Perf 12	—	2·40
203	**17**	6d. dull ultramarine (2.12.75)	19·00	1·25
		a. *Light Prussian-blue* (29.12.75)	—	1·25
		b. *Dull violet-blue* (4.78)	—	5·50
		c. *Blue* (13.5.78)	20·00	90
		ca. Perf 12	—	90
		d. *Dull milky blue* (7.3.79)	19·00	1·10
		da. Perf 12	—	1·10
		e. *Blue (light ink)* (8.80)	—	90
		f. *Light blue* (10.5.81)	20·00	1·10
		fa. Perf 12	—	2·40
		g. *Deep blue* (15.1.82)	19·00	90

23 (*V*2)

24

The types of V over Crown watermark (1867–1912)

In all, *five* types were employed.

The first two types (*V*1 and *V*2) belong to the contracts made with De La Rue to supply postage stamp paper. That firm lost the contract in 1895 to Waterlow and Sons, who held it until 1912. The third and fourth types are therefore products of the Waterlow contracts. The fifth type (found only in 1912) was supplied by James Spicer & Sons. The change in the pattern from *V*1 to *V*2 is explained by the dandyroll (which was the property of De

La Rue) requiring replacement. Since *all* the changes in pattern are also associated with changes in the nature and texture of the paper supplied, little difficulty should be encountered, with the new descriptions, in identifying the various types. Each pattern (save in a few cases of "left over" stock) succeeded the previous pattern.

Types *V*1 and *V*2 are mainly to be distinguished from one another by the four "points" around the top of the Crown which are found in *V*1 but not in *V*2. Also, as compared with *V*2, the shapes of the top ornaments in *V*1 resemble diamonds, and not ovals. It must be remembered that *V*1 *coloured* papers continued in use long after the exhaustion of the *V*1 white paper, the earliest date met for the *V*2 white paper being 15.8.82. The first *V*2 coloured papers (blue and green) were not used until February 1890. In general the papers supplied by De La Rue were whiter than their successors. The quality found with the *V*1 wmk varied greatly both with and without a pronounced mesh. The quality of the *V*2 papers on the other hand varied little. It is generally more "loaded" and opaque than any of the *V*1 papers and the wmk clearer when held to the light.

(iii) 1882–4. *As* (ii) *above but on paper wmkd V over Crown* (*V*2), W **23**. *P 12½*

204	**16**	3d. yellow-orange (13.4.83)	18·00	4·50
		a. *Dull brownish orange*	22·00	6·50
205	**17**	6d. dull violet-blue (10.11.82)	12·00	1·00
		a. *Indigo-blue* (11.83)	12·00	1·10
		b. *Light ultramarine* (9.84)	12·00	1·25

The above 3d. was printed from two new plates made by Atkinson. For the 6d. the same Atkinson plates introduced in December 1875 were employed.

Reprints were made, in 1891, on V over Crown paper, Type **23**, perf 12½, of the 1d., 2d., 3d., 4d., 6d., 8d., 10d., 1s. and 5s. "Laureates". The shades are distinctive and a number of values show "die flaws" not found in the originals. The 3d. was printed in yellow, the 8d. in orange-yellow, the 10d. in greenish slate and the 5s. in blue and red.

(Printed in Melbourne from a double electrotyped plate of 240 subjects supplied by D.L.R.)

1870 (28 Jan). *Wmk V over Crown* (*V*1), *W* **20**. *P* 13.

206	**24**	2d. brown-lilac	48·00	1·50
		a. *Dull lilac-mauve* (9.70)	38·00	1·00
		aa. Perf 12 (1871)	48·00	1·50
		b. *Mauve* (worn plate, 3.73)	38·00	1·25
		ba. Perf 12	48·00	1·00

25   26   27

8d.   8d.

EIGHTPENCE

(28)

29   30

31 (Die I)   32 (Die II)

(Des and dies eng by William Bell and stamps printed from electrotyped plates)

1873–84. *Two dies of 2d.: I, single-lined outer oval; II, double-lined Outer oval. The 8d. is made by surch with T 28 in blue. P 13 unless otherwise described.*

(a) On Saunders paper, wmkd single-lined "10"

207	29	9d. pale brown/*pink* (25.3.73).	60·00	7·00
		a. Perf 12	65·00	10·00
		b. Red-brown/*pink* (8.74)	55·00	7·50

(b) Wmk V over Crown (V1) (sideways on T 25), W 20

208	25	½d. rose-red (10.2.74).	4·50	50
		a. Perf 12	5·00	70
		b. Lilac-rose (1874)	5·00	70
		ba. Perf 12	4·50	70
		c. Rosine (shades) (12.80)	3·75	50
		ca. Perf 12	4·50	35
		d. Pale red (1882)	4·50	35
		da. Perf 12	4·50	40
		e. Mixed perf 13 and 12		£110
209	26	1d. dull bluish green (14.12.75).	13·00	75
		a. Perf 12	15·00	75
		b. Green (shades) (1877)	13·00	70
		ba. Perf 12	14·00	4·50
		c. Yellow-green (1878 and 1880)	13·00	55
		ca. Perf 12	—	1·75
210	27	2d. deep lilac-mauve, Die I (1.10.73)	13·00	35
		a. Perf 12	—	1·50
		b. Dull violet-mauve	13·00	35
		ba. Perf 12	—	1·40
		c. Dull mauve	13·00	35
		ca. Perf 12	15·00	50
		d. Pale mauve (worn plate) (1.79)	14·00	50
		da. Perf 12		65
		e. Mixed perf 13 and 12	£130	£100
211		2d. lilac-mauve, Die II (17.12.78)	10·00	35
		a. Perf 12	14·00	35
		b. Grey-mauve (1.80)	—	40
		ba. Perf 12	—	80
		c. Pale mauve (6.80)	20·00	40
		ca. Perf 12	—	1·25
		e. Vert pair, lower stamp imperf horiz . . .		
212	29	8d. on 9d. lilac-brown/*pink* (p 12) (1.7.76). . .	£120	15·00
		a. "F.IGHT" (broken "E")	—	£150
213		9d. lilac-brown (p 12) (1.12.75)	£100	11·00
214	30	1s. indigo-blue/*blue* (16.8.76).	30·00	3·00
		a. Deep blue/*blue* (1877)	32·00	3·00
		aa. Perf 12 (10.80)	—	7·50
		b. Blue/*blue* (1878)	35·00	3·00
		ba. Perf 12	—	7·50
		c. Ultramarine/*blue* (1879)	45·00	7·50
		d. Bright blue/*blue* (11.83)	45·00	5·00

(c) 18 February–April 1878. Emergency printings on various coloured papers, due to the exhaustion of white V1 paper. W 20 (V1) (sideways on T 25). P 13 only.

215	25	½d. rose-red/*pink* (1.3.78)	20·00	8·00
216	26	1d. yellow-green/*yellow* (25.2.78).	50·00	11·00
217		1d. yellow-green/*drab* (4.78)	£100	40·00
218	27	2d. violet-mauve/*green* (18.2.78)	£120	10·00
219		2d. violet-mauve/*lilac* (21.2.78)	£1000	£400
220		2d. violet-mauve/*brown* (21.3.78).	£120	10·00

Two shades of yellow paper, termed *pale canary* and *deep canary* respectively, are found.

All supplies of V1 paper received in Victoria after 15.3.78 were, as compared with previous supplies, highly surfaced on the printing side. An experimental printing was made on the new paper in July 1877 (1d., 2d., 6d. and 5s.) and all printings on white V1 paper from April 1878 on were made on this glazed paper. The glazed V1 coloured papers, with few exceptions, made their appearance later.

(d) 1882–83. On white paper wmkd V over Crown (V2), W 23 (sideways on T 25). P 13

221	25	½d. rosine (4.83)	5·00	65
		a. Perf 12	50·00	15·00
222	26	1d. yellow-green (9.82).	14·00	1·00
		a. Perf 12		

Reprints: The ½d., 1d., 2d. (Die II), 9d. and 1s. were reprinted in 1891, perf 12½. The first four from new plates, made from Dies containing *die flaws* not found in the originals. The 9d. was on V1 and the others on V2 paper.

33	**34**	**35**

(Des and eng by Charles Naish (T **33** & **34**) and William Bell (T **35**). Typo from electrotyped plates)

1880–84. *P 12½ unless otherwise described, this description including the P 13 varieties found in 1880. (a) W 20 (V1).*

223	33	2d. sepia (3.11.80).	15·00	45
		a. Perf 12	—	38·00
		b. Sepia-brown (2.81)	12·50	45
		ba. Perf 12	£130	38·00
		c. Brown (aniline) (5.81)	16·00	45
		ca. Perf 12	—	38·00
		d. Dull black-brown (10.81)	—	45
		e. Dull grey-brown (3.82)	12·00	45
		f. Mixed perf 13 and 12	—	£190
224		2d. mauve (worn plate) (2.84)	—	4·50
225	34	4d. rose-carmine (10.81).	35·00	4·00
		a. Rosine (8.82)	35·00	3·50
226	35	2s. dark blue (shades) (8.7.81).	£110	18·00
		a. Light blue/green (wmk sideways) (8.83)	£120	22·00
		b. Ultramarine/green (7.84)	—	28·00
		ba. Wmk sideways	—	48·00

(b) W 23 (V2)

227	33	2d. dull grey-brown (15.8.82).	12·00	30
228		2d. chocolate (3.83)	12·00	30
		a. Perf 12	—	19·00
229		2d. mauve (20.12.83)	7·00	20
		a. Worn plate	7·50	20
		b. Perf 12	—	£180
		c. Mixed perfs 12½ and 12	—	£180
230	34	4d. rose-red (3.83).	40·00	4·50

For the scarce perf 12 stamps listed above the holes are large and the teeth sharp. See also the note about perf 12 stamps after No. 186b.

The first printings of the 2d. in mauve were from the two plates used for the browns. Later printings were from two new plates. Reprints were made in 1891 of the 2d. (brown), 4d. (in pale red) and 2s., all on V2 paper.

36

(Des and die eng Charles Naish. Typo)

1883 (29 Oct)**–84.** *P 12½. (a) W 20 (V1).*

231	36	1d. green (2.84)	90·00	6·00

(b) W 23 (V2)

232	36	1d. yellow-green (29.10.83).	14·00	1·25
		a. Green	12·00	1·25
		b. Pale green (5.84)	12·00	1·25

Nos. 224 and 231 represent a printing on old stocks of paper.

C. THE "POSTAGE AND REVENUE" PERIOD, 1884–1901

Under the provisions of the Postage Act 1883 the stamps of the three series then in use (Postage, Duty, Fee) became, as from 1.1.84, mutually interchangeable. It was, at the same time, decided to issue (as soon as possible) the *one* stamp only, for any value, to serve *all* purposes. Since there were available many more dies (and plates) inscribed "Stamp Duty" than there were of either the "Postage" or "Fee" (Stamp Statute) series it was agreed that all values should be inscribed "Stamp Duty" by the beginning of 1885. All stamps *printed* after 1.1.84 are therefore true "Postage and Revenue" stamps whereas all Stamp Duty and Fee stamps printed before that date are Postal Fiscals, since they were originally printed solely for fiscal purposes. These principles have been strictly adhered to in our listing. Little difficulty should however be met in distinguishing between the printings of the one stamp found respectively in the main list and in the "Postal Fiscal" section since there are many major differences of printing, watermark, perforation and shade. On 1.1.84 there were no "Stamp Duty" designs for the ½d., 2d., 4d., 8d. and 2s. 6d. values. Also the existing "Stamp Duty" designs for the 1d., 6d., 1s. and 2s. were deemed to be too large to be convenient for general and extensive use. For all these values it was therefore necessary to produce new and smaller designs inscribed "Stamp Duty". Pending the preparation of new dies and plates, printings were made in 1884 (for the ½d., 1d., 2d., 4d., 6d., 1s. and 2s. values) from the existing "Postage" plates. These printings are also "Postage and Revenue" stamps but have naturally been included, for the sake of convenience, in the previous period. By the beginning of 1885 printings were available, in the new designs, of all values save the 1s. and 2s., and these latter appeared later.

(37)

I. **1885.** *Postage Stamps optd with T **37**. The 1s. and 2s. appeared in February 1885, 3d. and 4d. in November 1885. P 12½.*

*(a) W **20** (V1)*

233	**16**	3d. dull orange-yellow (Pl 1) (**B.**)	—	£130
234	**30**	1s. ultramarine/*blue*	95·00	20·00
		a. *Dull blue/blue*	—	22·00
235		1s. deep ultramarine/*blue* (**B.**) (F.C. £14) . . .	—	£400
236	**35**	2s. ultramarine/*green*	80·00	18·00
		a. Wmk sideways	90·00	20·00

*(b) W **23** (V2)*

237	**16**	3d. yellow-orange (Pl 2) (**B.**)	60·00	22·00
		a. *Dull brownish orange* (**B.**)	65·00	24·00
238	**34**	4d. rose-carmine (**B.**)	55·00	20·00

The overprinted 1s. was replaced by the 1s. Type **44** on lemon. Collectors should beware of faded black overprints purporting to be the "blue". In genuine examples the blue of the overprint is difficult to distinguish in the blue of the stamp.

Reprints of the 4d. and 1s. (with and without overprint) were made in 1895–6. The 1s. is wmkd V2 and the 4d. (from a new plate) is a pale red. Examples of the latter genuinely postally used are sometimes met.

44 45 46 47

48 49 50 51

(Typo. Dies for ½d., 2d., 3d., 4d., 8d. and 2s. 6d. eng by Charles Naish, the other values being derived from these)

II. **1884–95.** *New designs inscr "STAMP DUTY". P 12½.*

*(a) W **20** (V1)*

239	**42**	8d. rose/*pink* (shades) (1.1.85)	19·00	5·50
		a. *Rose-red/pink*	20·00	5·50
240	**40**	1s. deep dull blue/*lemon* (11.85)	35·00	6·00
		a. *Dull blue/yellow* (6.86)	35·00	6·50
241	**42**	2s. olive/*bluish green* (shades) (6.86)	25·00	3·00

*(b) W **23** (V2)*

243	**38**	½d. pale rosine (1.1.85)	4·50	65
		a. *Deep rosine* (7.85)	5·00	1·00
		b. *Salmon* (9.85)	5·50	1·25

244	**39**	1d. yellowish green (*shades*((1.1.85)	5·25	30
		a. *Dull pea-green* (2.85)	8·00	1·75
245	**40**	2d. lilac (*shades*) (1.1.85)	3·75	25
		a. *Mauve* (1.86)	4·00	25
		b. *Rosy-mauve* (1.86)	5·50	50
246	**39**	3d. yellowish brown (1.1.85)	7·00	60
		a. *Pale ochre* (11.86)	6·50	60
		b. *Bistre-yellow* (12.92)	7·00	60
247	**41**	4d. magenta (1.1.85)	27·00	3·00
		a. *Bright mauve-rose* (1.87)	30·00	3·50
248		4d. dull lilac (*error*) (12.86)	£2250	£400
249	**39**	6d. chalky blue (1.1.85)	30·00	2·50
		a. *Bright blue* (2.85)	24·00	2·10
		b. *Cobalt* (9.85)	24·00	2·10
250	**42**	8d. bright scarlet/*pink* (1892)	22·00	7·50
251		2s. olive-green/*pale green* (shades) (3.90) . . .	25·00	3·00
252		2s. apple-green (12.8.95)	25·00	15·00
253		2s. blue-green (29.10.95)	18·00	4·75
254	**43**	2s. 6d. brown-orange (23.4.84)	80·00	11·00
		a. *Yellow* (1885)	75·00	10·00
		b. *Lemon-yellow* (1.93)	75·00	10·00

In each of the 1d., 6d., 1s. and 2s. values six types are to be found differing, *inter alia*, in the engraving of the words of value.

In the 2d. two die states are found: the *original* (1) which occurs on all but seven stamps in the Plate 1 sheet and the *damaged* (1a) which occurs on seven stamps in the Plate 1 sheet and on all 120 stamps in the Plate 2 sheet. The damage consists of a clear break in the top frame just in from the top right corner.

4d. "*error*": This comprised a printing of 6000 stamps, 1886, in a *dull lilac* shade. It is true that only seven unused specimens are known but it is not true (as previously stated) that it is unknown used, since a leading authority has himself seen upwards of 30 undoubted used copies, all of which have certain characteristics which distinguish them from certain colour changelings, accidental or deliberate. The records show that the whole printing of 6000 was issued which confirms the findings of so many used copies.

The 8d. value was withdrawn from sale on 24.8.95.

Reprints were made in 1891, using one of the original plates in each case, of the ½d., 1d., 2d., 4d., 6d. and 1s. values. In the three lower values the shades are fairly distinctive. The 1s. was wmkd V1. In all cases the wmk is equally common normal and inverted and this applies to *all* the Reprints made in 1891 or later.

52 53 54 55

38 39 40

41 42 43

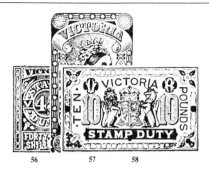

56   57   58

III. **1884–96**. *New printings, all typographed from electrotypes, of "STAMP DUTY" designs first issued in 1879. (Des Charles Jackson and Ludwig Lang. Dies eng by Charles Jackson, Arthur Williams, Charles Evans and possibly others, supplied (1879) by Messrs Sands and McDougall of Melbourne). P 12½. Wmk sideways save where shown as upright (U). (a) W **20** (V1).*

255	44	1s. ultramarine/*blue* (11.84)	80·00	5·00
256		1s. chalky blue/*lemon* (3.3.85)	75·00	20·00
257	46	3s. maroon/*blue* (8.84)	50·00	10·00
258	48	5s. reddish purple/*lemon* (6.87)	30·00	10·00
		a. Brown-red/*yellow* (1.94)	75·00	20·00
259	52	£1 orange/*yellow* (9.84)	—	45·00
		a. Reddish orange/*yellow* (12.90)	£325	45·00

*(b) W **23** (V2)*

260	45	1s. 6d. pink (2.85)	£100	19·00
		a. Bright rose-carmine (5.86)	£120	15·00
261	46	3s. drab (11.85)	70·00	15·00
		a. Olive-drab (10.93)	65·00	15·00
262	47	4s. red-orange (27.5.86)	75·00	12·00
		a. Yellow-orange (S, U)	£100	8·50
263	48	5s. rosine (8.5.96)	75·00	19·00
264	49	6s. pea-green (12.11.91)	£110	30·00
		a. Apple-green (U) (4.96)	£100	30·00
265	50	10s. dull bluish green (10.85)	£120	28·00
		a. Grey-green (9.87)	£100	25·00
266	51	15s. purple-brown (12.85)	£250	35·00
267		15s. brown (U) (5.95)	£400	55·00
268	53	£1 5s. pink† (U) (6.8.90)	£700	60·00
269	54	£1 10s. pale olive† (10.88)	£500	50·00
270	55	£2 blue† (8.88)	£700	60·00
271	56	45s. lilac† (15.8.90)	—	60·00
272	57	£5 pink (10.85)	—	£170
273	58	£10 lilac (7.85)	—	70·00
		a. Mauve† (7.93)	—	60·00

Stamps of the above designs printed by lithography or line-engraving, or similar designs not found in the above list should be looked for among the Postal Fiscals.

---

†Both here and later indicates that prices quoted are for stamps postmarked to order by the Victorian postal authorities for sale in sets.

59

IV. **1896–1900**. *T **59** and similar types. W **23** (V2) sideways (S) or upright (U). The line-engraved stamps were all printed singly direct from the dies and both the lithographed and typographed stamps were in sheets of 10 (2 × 5). (i) Lithographed. Printings of 1886 to 1889.*

274		£25 dull yellowish green (S, U) (1.86)	F.C.	45·00
		a. Dull blue-green (10.88)	F.C.	45·00
275		£50 bright violet (U) (2.86)	F.C.	55·00
		a. Dull purple (U) (10.87)	F.C.	55·00
276		£100 rosine (S, U) (1.86)	F.C.	65·00

(ii) Recess-printed. Printings of November 1890 *to April* 1897

277	£25 bright blue-green (S, U) (11.90)	F.C.	45·00
278	£50 black-violet (S) (11.90)	F.C.	55·00
279	£100 crimson (aniline) (S, U) (11.90)	F.C.	55·00
	a. Scarlet-red† (1897)	—	£130

For earlier recess-printed printings, see under "POSTAL FISCALS".

(iii) Typographed from electrotyped plates. Printings of November 1897 *on*

280	£25 dull blue-green† (U)	—	60·00
281	£50 bright mauve† (U)	—	85·00
282	£100 pink-red† (U) (10.00)	—	£110

Collectors should beware of stamps with cleaned fiscal markings particularly in the higher values. Some of these bear forged cancellations but others, in fraud of the revenue, did genuine postal service.

60   61   62

63   64   65

66   67

(Typo. Previous 2d. and 4d. dies "lined" by Charles Naish; 1s. 6d. des and eng Charles Naish; rest des Philip Astley, probably eng Samuel Reading and supplied by Fergusson and Mitchell)

1886–96. *W **23** (V2) upright save in ½d., 1s. and high values (excepting the £6) where it is sideways. P 12½.*

283	60	½d. lilac-grey (20.8.86)	15·00	3·00
		a. Grey-black	—	35·00
284		½d. pink (15.2.87)	5·00	25
		a. Rosine (aniline) (12.89)	4·75	25
		b. Rose-red (5.91)	4·50	20
		c. Vermilion (3.96)	4·75	35
285	61	1d. green (26.7.86)	5·25	20
		a. Yellow-green (7.87)	5·25	20
286	62	2d. pale lilac (17.12.86)	2·75	20
		a. Pale mauve (1887)	2·50	20
		b. Deep lilac (1888, 1892)	2·50	20
		c. Purple (5.94)	2·75	25
		d. Violet (5.95)	2·50	20
		e. Imperforate (1890)	—	£700
287	63	4d. rose-red (1.4.87)	6·50	1·00
		a. Red (1893)	5·75	90
288	64	6d. bright ultramarine (27.8.86)	7·50	65
		a. Pale ultramarine (10.87)	7·00	50
		b. Dull blue (2.91)	6·50	50
289	65	1s. dull purple-brown (14.3.87)	20·00	2·00
		a. Lake (2.90)	15·00	1·50
		b. Carmine-lake (5.92)	14·00	1·00
		c. Brownish red (1.96)	15·00	1·25

290	66	1s. 6d. pale blue (6.88)	£100	65·00
291		1s. 6d. orange (18.9.89)	15·00	4·50
		a. Red-orange	15·00	5·00
292	67	£5 pale blue and maroon† (7.2.88)	£950	55·00
293		£6 yellow and pale blue† (1.10.87)	£1100	70·00
294		£7 rosine and black† (17.10.89)	£1300	£100
295		£8 mauve and brown-orange† (U) (2.8.90)	£1400	£125
296		£9 apple-green and rosine† (21.8.88)	£1700	£140

Reprints of the ½d. grey and 1s. 6d. blue were made in 1894–5. They differ from the originals in shade. A £10 (T **67**) was prepared for use, but not issued.

An imperforate sheet of the 2d. was on sale at the Mortlake Post Office in 1890 and a pair was noted in 1902.

68  69  70

(1d. die supplied, des and eng by Samuel Reading; 2½d. and 5d. des by M. Tannenberg; 9d. first printed from the new Reprint plate of 1891. Typo)

1890–96. *New designs and values.* P 12½. (a) W **20** (V1).
297	68	1d. orange-brown/pink (16.6.91)	3·50	1·25

This was an emergency printing, caused by a temporary shortage of white V2 paper.

(b) W **23** (V2)
298	68	1d. dull chestnut (1.1.90)	2·10	15
		a. Deep red-brown (1.90)	2·10	30
		b. Orange-brown (4.90)	2·10	15
		c. Yellow-brown (4.91)	1·90	15
		d. Brown-red (8.90)	1·90	15
		e. Bright yellow-orange (9.93)	50·00	12·00
		f. Brownish orange (6.94)	1·75	15
299	69	2½d. red-brown/lemon (18.12.90)	6·00	80
300		2½d. brown-red/yellow (1892)	5·50	80
		a. Red/yellow (1893)	5·50	70
301	70	5d. purple-brown	6·50	85
		a. Pale reddish brown (1892)	6·00	80
302	29	9d. apple-green (18.10.92)	20·00	9·00
303		9d. carmine-rose (18.10.95)	12·00	2·50
		a. Rosine (aniline) (1896)	13·00	2·75

The yellow papers used for the 2½d. value differed considerably in tint.

71  72 (V3)

(Eng A. Williams (1½d.))

1896 (June)–**1899** (Aug). W **72** (V3). *Paper supplied by Waterlow and Sons. This paper differs noticeably from the previous De La Rue products. It is less white, softer and generally thicker, and has a coarser grain or mesh than any previous V over Crown paper. It will be noted that some coloured V2 papers of earlier manufacture were utilised during this period. T* **60**, **65**, **71** *and the larger size stamps have the wmk sideways unless marked U (upright). P* 12½.
304	60	½d. light scarlet (1.7.96)	2·75	15
		a. Carmine-rose (11.97)	3·25	15
		b. Deep carmine-red (coarse impression) (1899)	—	75
305	68	1d. brown-red (13.6.96)	2·00	10
		a. Brownish orange (11.97)	1·90	10
306	71	1½d. apple-green (8.10.97)	4·00	1·50
307	62	2d. violet (shades) (12.6.96)	2·10	10
308	39	3d. ochre (11.96)	7·00	55
		a. Buff (2.98)	6·50	50
309	63	4d. red (6.97)	5·00	90

310	70	5d. red-brown (7.97)	8·00	95
311	64	6d. dull blue (9.96)	6·50	55
312	29	9d. rosine (10.96)	15·00	2·00
		a. Rose-carmine (4.98)	—	2·00
		b. Dull rose (6.98)	12·00	2·00
313	65	1s. brownish red (3.97)	11·00	1·25
314	66	1s. 6d. brown-orange (8.98)	23·00	7·50
315	42	2s. blue-green (4.97)	21·00	5·00
316	43	2s. 6d. yellow (9.96)	90·00	11·00
		a. Yellow (U) (9.98)	£100	11·00
317	46	3s. olive-drab (12.96)	50·00	11·00
		a. Olive-drab (U) (10.98)	50·00	10·00
318	47	4s. orange (9.97)	75·00	4·50
319	48	5s. rosine (2.97)	75·00	5·00
		a. Rose-carmine (11.97)	75·00	5·00
		b. Rosine (U) (3.99)	75·00	5·50
320	49	6s. pale yellow-green† (4.99)	75·00	20·00
321	50	10s. grey-green (4.97)	75·00	15·00
		a. Blue-green (7.98)	75·00	15·00
322	51	15s. brown† (4.97)	£200	25·00
323	59	£25 dull bluish green† (U) (1899)	—	80·00
324		£50 dull purple† (U) (11.97)	—	80·00

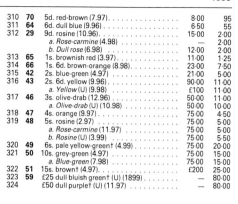

73 74

(Des M. Tannenberg. Eng A. Mitchelhill)

1897 (7 Oct). *Charity.* W **72** (V3) *sideways.* P 12½.
325	73	1d. (1s.) blue	18·00	18·00
326	74	2½d. (2s. 6d.) red-brown	80·00	60·00
		Set of 2 optd "Specimen"	£140	

These stamps, sold at 1s. and 2s. 6d. respectively, paid postage of 1d. and 2½d. only, the difference being given to a Hospital Fund.

1899 (1 Aug)–**1900.** *Colours changed for ½d., 1d., 1½d. and 2½d. P 12½.*

(a) W **23** (V2)
327	71	1½d. brown-red/yellow (1.8.99)	3·00	1·75

(b) W **72** (V3)
328	60	½d. emerald (8.99)	5·00	40
329	69	2½d. blue (1.8.99)	5·00	1·75

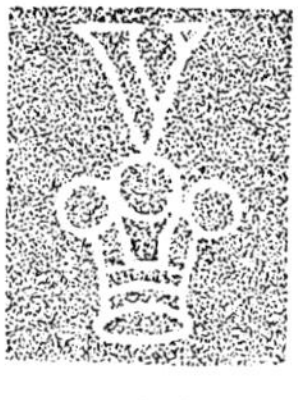

75 (V4)

(c) W **75** (V4)

This wmk and paper, like V3, was supplied by Waterlow and Sons and it continued in use until 1905. It was the result of an amended specification. Like the V3 paper it has a marked mesh but is whiter, smoother and harder. The 1s. and the four higher values have the wmk sideways, the ½d. being found with both positions.
330	60	½d. emerald (1.8.99)	4·75	40
		a. Deep blue-green	5·00	40
331	68	1d. rosine (1.8.99)	3·75	10
		a. Rose-red (6.00)	3·75	15
332	62	2d. violet (shades) (1.8.99)	2·50	10
333	69	2½d. blue (2.00)	4·50	1·50
334	39	3d. bistre-yellow (9.99)	5·25	55
335	63	4d. rose-red (12.99)	4·75	95
336	70	5d. red-brown (10.99)	5·50	95
337	64	6d. dull ultramarine (2.00)	7·00	55

338	29	9d. rose-red (8.99)		8·00	1·75
339	65	1s. brown-red (5.00).		10·00	1·40
340	66	1s. 6d. orange (12.99)		14·00	4·75
341	42	2s. blue-green (6.00).		15·00	4·25
342	43	2s. 6d. yellow (1.00)		90·00	10·00
343	46	3s. pale olivet (5.00)		£130	12·00
344	48	5s. rose-red (4.00)		£100	12·00
345	50	10s. green† (3.00)		£130	12·00

76   77

(Eng S. Reading)

1900 (23 May). *Charity. W* **75** (*V4*) *sideways. P* 12½.

346	76	1d. (1s.) olive-brown		35·00	25·00
347	77	2d. (2s.) emerald-green		£100	80·00
		Set of 2		£130	£100

These stamps were sold for a Boer War Patriotic Fund, on a similar basis to the issue of 1897.

V over Crown Wmks: A Note on "Abnormal" Watermark Positions

It should always be remembered that the block of 120 wmks (12 × 10) in the sheet was designed to fit the normal size stamp in an upright position. *Other* sizes, larger and smaller, were printed, at various times, with the wmk *both* upright and sideways. The following note concerns only varieties as they are found on stamps of normal size.

Inverted Wmks: This description also embraces cases of wmks lying sideways with V at right found on stamps of Type **60** etc. which are of the same dimensions (but reversed) as the usual size stamps. In printings before 1882 all inverted wmks may be regarded as "abnormals". In this period all sheets of 240 wmks were, where necessary, cut into two before printing. From 1882 to mid-1896 the *only* inverted "abnormals" are found in certain of the common values where the area of the printing surface (i.e. 2 plates of 120) more or less equalled the area of the complete sheet of watermarked paper as it was supplied by De La Rue's. This was of 240 wmks, consisting of one pane of 120 wmks over another pane of 120. In this period the sheet of 240 wmks was not cut up before printing from single plates as had been done previously. Where only one plate was employed the sheet was fed in in one direction, removed, dried, and fed in the other direction, giving in the result of 120 normal and 120 inverted wmks. (This fact is of assistance when distinguishing certain Reprints.) From 1896 the same principle applied save that the complete sheets supplied were of 480 wmks so that the only "abnormal" inverteds found are in those cases, e.g. 1d. and 2d. where the stamps were printed from a block of similar size viz. of 4 plates of 120 impressions clamped together. However, in 1901 to 1912, following a change in postal rates, resulting in a smaller demand for the 1d. value, some plates are printed from two plates so that inverted watermarks in this period are always normal.

Sideways Wmks: This description includes upright wmks on stamps of the dimensions of Type **60** etc. They usually arose through the suppliers placing the paper in the wrong direction in the bound books (and later unbound reams) of paper supplied. *Three* periods concern us in this regard.

(i) 1867–1882: Before 1867 paper was supplied in single sheets of 120 wmks and from 1867 in double sheets of 240 wmks. From 1867 to 1882 wherever it was necessary (i.e. where only one plate was used) the double sheets were cut into half before printing. The variety may be found under the following numbers. All are extremely rare—viz. 174, 180, 190, 192, 193, 202, 214, 225.

(ii) 1882–1896. In this period no "abnormal" sideways wmks are met since the paper supplied was not cut up before printing and since the complete sheet supplied was rectangular and *not square* in shape.

(iii) 1896–1912: Here the wmkd paper supplied was of 480 (120 × 4) wmks and such sheets were practically square. One meets "abnormals" under the following numbers, many of these being extremely rare—viz. 304, 305, 307, 308, 312, 313, 328, 330, 331, 332, 334, 338, 356, 357, 359, 366, 367, 368, 371, 373, 386, 400, 405, 407, 414, 417, 445, 447, 451.

Reversed Wmks: These involved a printing on the wrong side of the paper. Since the side which should have been printed was usually "surfaced" to some degree these varieties almost invariably show the impression of the stamp coarser than normally and the back of the stamp smoother and glossier. From 1878 to 1896 the back of the paper supplied by De La Rue was treated with a special preparation to prevent the gum soaking through to the front. This preparation was susceptible to moisture and when printed upon and subsequently exposed to moisture occasionally shed portions of the design, so that in this period such varieties often bear the superficial appearance of having been printed on the gum, whereas in fact, up to July 1912, all gumming was done after printing. Reversed wmks, many of them very rare, have been found under the following Nos.—158, 162, 179, 181, 183, 184, 185, 187, 190, 192, 193, 197, 198, 206, 207 (inverted and reversed), 210, 211, 214, 228, 243, 244, 245, 263, 283, 284, 285, 286, 287, 288, 289, 298, 305, 307, 310, 331, 332, 356, 357, 366, 373, 400, 401, 403, 406, 407, 408, 447, 448—also in certain of the £25, £50 and £100 stamps (in both sections) and in various items in the Postal Fiscal list. In the reversed V over Crown cases—looking through the front of the stamp in a normal upright position—the double side of the "V" will appear on the *right* and not on the left as it should do.

D. THE COMMONWEALTH PERIOD, 1901–12

All postage stamps issued by the States in this period were in reality COMMONWEALTH stamps. This viewpoint has now received official endorsement ("Commonwealth of Australia Philatelic Bulletin" No. 2, October 1953). Prior to the actual coming into being of the Commonwealth it had been agreed between the States that the Postal Services were to be the concern of the Commonwealth and that the postal revenue was to go to it. This decision meant, for Victoria, the separation of the Postal and the Fiscal systems. So long, however, as the Commonwealth lacked printing facilities and a Postal administration of its own the work had to be done by each State on its behalf. Separate series of Postage stamps (for which the State was obliged to account to the Commonwealth) and of Duty stamps (which were to continue as a State concern) therefore became necessary. The first Kangaroo stamps were not issued by the Commonwealth until January 1913, but in the intervening period a long chain of philatelic events had contributed to make this issue possible. From the beginning of 1902 all the stamps of Tasmania and Western Australia were printed in Melbourne, on Victorian paper. Later Papua (1907) and later again South Australia (1909) were added to these. In the same year (1902) the first Commonwealth Postage Dues, printed in Sydney on New South Wales paper, appeared. In 1903 a 9d. stamp of the same "Commonwealth" design was issued in New South Wales and Queensland. In 1905 all States commenced using one or other of four types of Crown over A paper, marginally wmkd "COMMONWEALTH OF AUSTRALIA". In 1909, printed in Melbourne, appeared new bi-coloured Postage Dues, the first stamps to be inscribed "AUSTRALIA". This followed the appointment of J. B. Cooke, the South Australian stamp printer, as Commonwealth Stamp Printer. As from 13.10.10 the stamps of any State could legally be used in any other State, and in April 1911 the first Commonwealth Postal Stationery was issued. In short, in the period 1901 to 1912, although certain States printed and issued postage stamps, this was a privilege, subject at all times to Commonwealth control and direction and conducted, in respect of the nett revenue received, solely for the Commonwealth's benefit.

The Commonwealth was proclaimed as from 1 January 1901. In only three cases in the first issue, viz. the 1d., 2½d. and 5d. values was there sufficient time to alter the dies and produce new plates. In all the other cases the same plates were used as had been employed to produce the 1891 Reprints.

1901 (29 Jan)–**1905**. *P* 12½ *or* 12 × 12½.

(a) Without the word "POSTAGE" *in the design.* (i) W **72** (*V3*)

348	35	2s. blue/*pink*		35·00	10·00

(ii) W **75** (*V4*) (*sideways on T* **25**)

349	25	½d. bluish green		2·00	85
		a. "VICTCRIA"		23·00	19·00
350	33	2d. reddish violet		4·00	20
351	16	3d. dull orange		10·00	1·25
352	34	4d. bistre-yellow		25·00	6·50
353	17	6d. emerald		9·00	5·00
354	30	1s. yellow		30·00	15·00
355	19	5s. pale red and deep blue		45·00	18·00

78   79   80

(b) With the word "POSTAGE" in the design. W **75** (*V*4)

356	**78**	1d. rose (Die I)	1·25	15
		a. *Dull red* (12.01)	1·25	15
357		1d. rose (Die II) (2.4.01)	1·25	15
		a. *Dull red* (12.01)	1·25	15
358		1d. pale rose-red (Die III) (3.5.05)	2·00	15
359	**79**	2½d. dull blue (1901)	2·75	25
		a. *Deep blue* (1902)	2·75	20
360	**80**	5d. reddish brown	4·75	40
		a. *Purple-brown* (1903)	4·00	40

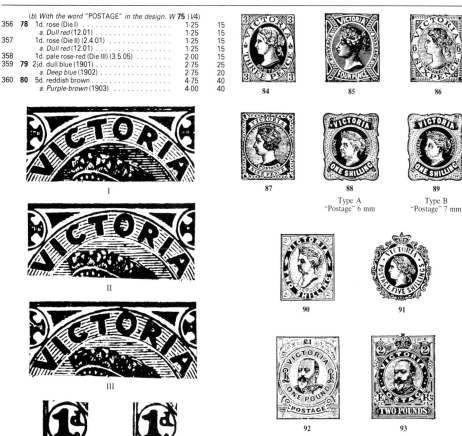

I

II

III

I and II   III

Three dies of the 1d.: Principal differences are:

I. Horizontal lines over Queen's head fill oval surround under "VIC-TORIA". Found in two plates employed January 1901–February 1903.

II. Practically all the lines of shading to the left of and on top of the head have been "thinned", giving a lighter appearance. Some lines at the top have been cut away, leaving small white patches, particularly under the "OR". Found in ten plates in use between April 1901 and April 1905.

III. As II but with stop at lower left clearly separated from circle line at its right; spot of colour in shading between "O" and "R"; two lines of shading meet in lower left portion of "P" of "PENNY". Found in twelve plates in use between May 1905 and the end of 1912.

1901 (June). W **75** (*V*4). P 12 × 12½.

361	**68**	1d. olive (6.6.01)	5·00	3·50
362	**39**	3d. slate-green (20.6.01)	21·00	5·00

These stamps were available for postal purposes to 30 June 1901, afterwards for fiscal purposes only.

81

82

83

84

85

86

87

88

89

Type A
"Postage" 6 mm

Type B
"Postage" 7 mm

90

91

92

93

1901 (June)–**10**. *Similar to former types but "POSTAGE" inserted in design.* W **75** (*V*4) (*sideways on* ½d., 1½d., £1, £2). (*a*) P 12½ *or* 12 × 12½.

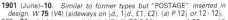

363	**81**	½d. blue-green (*shades*) (Die I) (26.6.01)	1·90	15
		a. *Blue-green* (U)	1·90	15
364		½d. pale blue-green (Die II) (6.04)	2·50	15
365		½d. pale bluish green (Die III) (6.05)	5·00	50
366	**82**	1½d. maroon/*yellow* (9.7.01)	3·00	85
		a. *Brown-red/yellow* (1901)	2·10	55
		b. *Dull red/yellow* (1906)	2·10	55
367	**83**	2d. lilac (16.7.01)	1·90	30
		a. *Reddish violet* (1902)	1·90	30
		b. *Violet* (1904)	3·00	30
		c. *Bright purple* (1905)	3·00	50
368	**84**	3d. dull orange-brown (2.7.01)	4·75	55
		a. *Chestnut* (1901)	4·75	55
		b. *Yellowish brown* (1903)	4·75	55
369	**85**	4d. bistre-yellow (26.6.01)	4·75	55
		a. *Brownish bistre* (1905)	5·25	70
370	**86**	6d. emerald (5.7.01)	7·50	85
		a. *Dull green* (1904)	9·00	85
371	**87**	9d. dull rose-red (5.7.01)	9·50	1·40
		a. *Pale red* (1901)	10·00	1·25
		b. *Dull brownish red* (1905)	10·00	1·75
372	**88**	1s. yellow-orange (Type A) (5.7.01)	9·50	1·75
		a. *Yellow* (1902)	12·00	1·75
373	**89**	1s. yellow (Type B) (4.03)	12·00	3·00
		a. *Yellow-orange* (1903)	10·00	2·50
374	**90**	2s. blue/*rose* (5.7.01)	22·00	3·00
375	**91**	5s. rose-red and pale blue (5.7.01)	70·00	11·00
		a. *Scarlet and deep blue* (1902)	65·00	9·00
		b. *Rosine and blue* (1905)	65·00	9·00
376	**92**	£1 carmine-rose (18.11.01)	£275	£100
377	**93**	£2 deep blue (2.6.02)	£550	£250

(b) P 11

378	**81**	½d. blue-green (Die I) (9.02)	4·00	75
		a. Blue-green (U)	3·00	20
379		½d. blue-green (Die II)	3·00	25
380		½d. bluish green (Die III)	3·50	50
381	**78**	1d. dull red (Die I)	—	22·00
382		1d. dull red (Die II)	40·00	18·00
		a. Pale red (aniline) (3.03)	3·50	75
		b. Pale rose (aniline) (1904)	—	3·00
383		1d. pale rose-red (Die III)	38·00	23·00
384	**82**	1½d. dull red/*yellow* (1910)	28·00	28·00
385	**83**	2d. violet (1904)	—	£140
		a. Bright purple (1905)	—	£140
386	**84**	3d. orange-brown (1903)	5·25	3·00
387	**86**	6d. emerald (1903)	9·50	3·75
		a. Dull green (1906)	£250	£160
388	**92**	£1 carmine-red (1905)	£325	£130
389	**93**	£2 deep blue (1905)	£750	£650

(c) Compound or mixed perf 12½ *and* 11

390	**81**	½d. blue-green (Die I)	15·00	4·00
		a. Blue-green (U) (1903)	—	4·00
391		½d. blue-green (Die II) (1904)	14·00	11·00
392	**78**	1d. dull red (Die I)	—	£150
393		1d. dull red (Die II)	—	£110
394	**82**	1½d. dull red/*yellow*	—	£200
395	**83**	2d. reddish violet	—	£250
396	**84**	3d. orange-brown	—	£200
397	**86**	6d. emerald	—	£200
398	**91**	5s. rose and blue	£800	

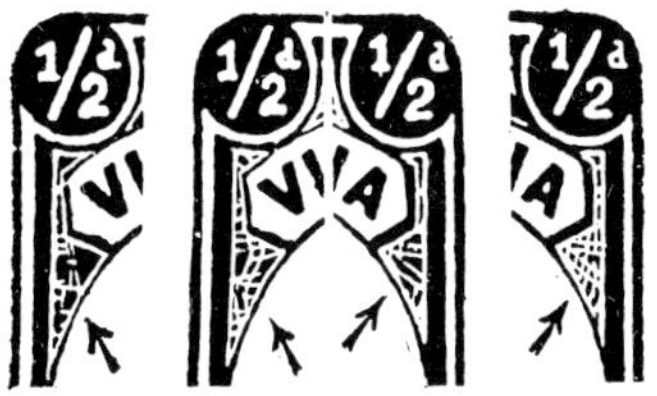

I II III

Three dies of the ½d.; Principal differences are:

I. Outer of two vertical lines of colour to left of "V" is continuous save for a marked break opposite top of "V". Found in two plates in use 1901–May 1904.

II. Outer vertical line to left of "V" is broken in three places; the triangular space S.W. of "V" has also been "opened up" and shows more white lines than in I. Found in two plates in use June 1904–June 1905.

III. As II but the vertical coloured line to right of the "A" of "VICTORIA" (previously broken in the middle) is now broken in four or five places. The triangular ornament to S.E. of the same "A" has also been "opened up", the white cross-hatching now being stronger than in I and II. Found in two plates introduced in June 1905 and in two subsequent plates introduced late in 1909.

The paper used for the 1½d. value for two printings in 1908–9 was yellow-buff in colour but in used copies the difference is not so marked as to warrant separate description.

There were two main states of the 2d. Die, the original showing the S.E. corner correctly squared and the later showing it damaged and blunter. There are other differences. The original state is found in all printings before April 1904 but not after, and the later state to a small extent (5 per cent) in the printings before April 1904 and *solely* in the printings from that date.

For the 1s. Type A the same plate was used as for the 1s. "No Postage" of 1901, the words "POSTAGE" being separately punched on. For Type B two new plates, prepared via an etched line-block, were introduced.

Certain *unlisted shades* (due to their being unsatisfactory) are found *only* punctured O.S. Marked instances of this are found in the 2d., 3d. and 4d. values.

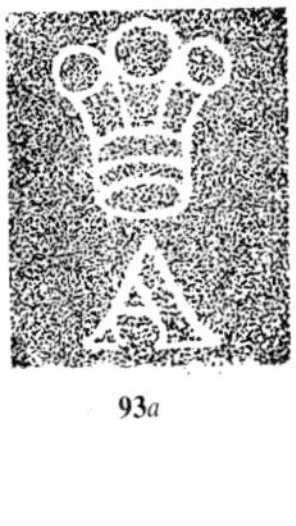

93*a*

1905–13. *Wmk Crown over A, W* **93***a.* I. *Medium paper, supplied, like the V4 paper, by Waterlow & Sons.*

(a) P 12½ *or* 12 × 12½

399	**81**	½d. blue green (21.10.05)	1·60	15
		a. Light bluish green	1·60	15
400	**78**	1d. rose-red (*shades*) (16.7.05)	80	10
		a. Pale rose (1907)	1·25	10
		b. Rose-carmine (9.11)	2·50	15
401	**83**	2d. dull mauve (13.9.05)	3·00	30
		a. Bright mauve (1906)	3·00	25
		b. Reddish violet (1907)	3·00	25
		c. Lilac (1910)	2·40	40
402	**79**	2½d. blue (*shades*) (4.08)	3·00	40
		a. Indigo (1909)	3·00	40
403	**84**	3d. orange-brown (11.11.05)	4·00	55
		a. Yellow-orange (1908)	5·00	30
		b. Dull orange-buff (1909)	4·75	30
		c. Ochre (1912)	4·75	30
404	**85**	4d. yellow-bistre (15.1.06)	6·00	65
		a. Bistre (1908)	6·00	65
		b. Yellow-olive (1912)	6·00	70
405	**80**	5d. chocolate (14.8.06)	5·00	90
		a. Dull reddish brown (1908)	5·00	65
406	**86**	6d. dull green (25.10.05)	8·00	80
		a. Dull yellow-green (1907)	7·50	80
		b. Emerald (1909)	7·50	1·10
		c. Yellowish green (1911)	7·50	1·00
407	**87**	9d. rose-red (11.12.05)	9·50	1·25
		a. Pale salmon-red (1906)	9·50	1·25
		b. Brown-red (1908)	10·00	1·25
		c. Pale dull rose (worn plate)	11·00	2·40
		d. Rose-carmine (new plate) (12.09)	9·50	1·25
408	**89**	1s. yellow-orange (13.2.06)	8·00	2·00
		a. Yellow (1906)	10·00	2·00
		b. Lemon (1908)	12·00	2·00
409	**91**	5s. rose-red and ultramarine (U) (11.07)	70·00	13·00
		a. Rose-red and blue (U) (1912)	80·00	13·00
		b. Rose-red and blue (S)	80·00	16·00
410	**92**	£1 salmon (12.2.07)	£275	£100
411		£1 dull rose (5.10)	£275	£100
		a. Deep dull rose (U) (10.11)	£275	£120
412	**93**	£2 dull blue (18.7.06)	£600	£250

Perforations of period 1901–12

In general, up to 1910, five machines were available at any one time—three single-line (two "11" and one "12½") and two vertical combs (12 × 12½). Only single-line machines were used for the 5s., £1 and £2 values. The "12½" single line was used on many occasions for the ½d. and occasionally for other values. The "11" machines were primarily employed for larger size stamps, e.g. Victorian Duty Stamps, Tasmanian Pictorials and Papua, and their use for the normal size Victorian postage stamps was in the main restricted to emergencies. At certain periods, e.g. 1909–10 one encounters the true "compounds" i.e. the products of two single-line machines, 12½ and 11 respectively. For the ½d. the vertical comb 12 × 12½ was also used, particularly in the earlier period, on the sheet turned sideways. In the result the alternate vertical margins between stamps were left imperforate and a single-line machine (either 12½ or 11) was often used to complete the perforating, in the latter case (11) giving us a variety for separate listing. "Mixed" perforations in this period are, like their predecessors of the 70s, the result of the correction—with another machine—of faultily centred lines of perforation (either single-line or comb), the back of these faulty lines being usually pasted over with gummed strips to assist in tearing down the corrected lines.

The rotary-comb machines gauging 11½ × 12¼ were brought over from South Australia by J. B. Cooke when he moved to Melbourne in 1909.

The ½d. perf 11 and the 2½d. and 5s. first printings (all perforated with single line machines) may be met with *full imperforate base margins.* Likewise in the Crown over A issues the ½d. perf 12½ and the 5s. perf 12½ (1912) have been similarly found. Such varieties are, of course, rare.

(b) P 11

413	**81**	½d. light bluish green	1·60	15
		a. Blue-green	1·60	15
414	**78**	1d. rose-red (1905)	1·60	75
		a. Pale rose (1907)	1·75	75
		b. Rose-carmine (1911)	5·00	2·75
415	**83**	2d. mauve (1906)	—	£150
		a. Reddish violet (1908)	65·00	15·00
		b. Lilac (1910)	19·00	7·50
416	**79**	2½d. blue (1909)	15·00	7·50
		a. Indigo (1909)	5·50	3·25
417	**84**	3d. brown (1908)	7·00	5·00
		a. Orange-buff (1909)	14·00	9·50
		b. Dull orange-yellow (1911)	—	£125
		c. Ochre (1912)	6·50	1·50
418	**85**	4d. yellow-bistre (1908)	7·00	
		a. Yellow-olive (1912)	6·50	3·00

419	80	5d. reddish brown	—	£300
420	86	6d. emerald (1910)	8·50	2·40
		a. Yellowish green (1911)	11·00	2·40
421	87	9d. rose-carmine	—	£325
422	89	1s. yellow-orange	£275	
		a. Yellow	—	£225
423	91	5s. rose-red and ultramarine	70·00	9·50
424	92	£1 salmon (12.2.07)	£325	£100
425	93	£2 dull blue (1.07)	£650	£250

(c) Compound or mixed perfs 12½ and 11

426	81	½d. light bluish green (6.09)	15·00	14·00
427	78	1d. rose-red	32·00	,32·00
428	83	2d. mauve	—	£200
429	84	3d. brown (1908).	£190	£225
		a. Ochre (1912)	—	£190
430	85	4d. bistre	—	£275
431	86	6d. yellowish green	—	£300
432	87	9d. dull rose-red	—	£375
433	89	1s. yellow-orange	—	£400

(d) Rotary comb perf 11½ × 12¼

434	78	1d. pale scarlet-red (2.10)	3·00	20
		a. Rose-red (3.10)	2·25	60
435	83	2d. lilac (shades)	3·50	75

II. On thinner paper, ready gummed with white gum. (July–Nov 1912).

(a) P 12½ or 12 × 12½

436	81	½d. blue-green	3·00	25
437	78	1d. rose-red	4·50	25
438	83	2d. lilac	20·00	2·25
439	80	5d. brown	6·50	1·75
440	86	6d. emerald	9·50	2·25
441	89	1s. dull yellow (11.12)	15·00	6·00
		a. Pale orange (1.13)	15·00	6·00

(b) P 11

442	81	½d. blue-green	12·00	7·50
443	78	1d. rose-red	5·00	2·25

(c) P 11 × 12½

444	81	½d. blue-green	£100	80·00

(d) Rotary comb perf 11½ × 12¼

445	78	1d. rose-carmine (2.7.12)	2·25	15
		a. Rose-red (10.12)	2·40	15

Two qualities of the "thin" paper were supplied, the first supply (earliest date 2.7.12) being thicker and with a less obvious mesh than the second (earliest date 2.10.12). The ½d. and 1d. are found on both classes of paper, the 2d. on the first only, and the 5d., 6d. and 1s. on the second only. There was a shortage pending the arrival of the second supply, and this gap was filled by the use of the "Stamp Duty" paper next described and the ONE PENNY overprint of 1.7.12. The 5d. perforated O.S. on the thin paper may be met in dull red-brown.

ONE PENNY

(95)

III. Printed on "Stamp Duty" paper, W 94 (V5). This paper is rather softer and of a more pronounced mesh than the V4 paper. (Aug–Oct 1912).

(a) P 12½ or 12 × 12½.

446	81	½d. bluish green	2·50	35
447	78	1d. rose-carmine (7.8.12)	2·25	20
448	83	2d. reddish violet	2·50	50
		a. Lilac	3·75	1·40
449	87	9d. carmine-red	9·50	2·10

(b) P 11

450	81	½d. bluish green	12·00	9·00
451	78	1d. rose-carmine (8.12)	20·00	6·50
452	87	9d. carmine-red	13·00	3·50

(c) Compound perf 11 with 12½

453	87	9d. carmine-red	—	£350

This paper was supplied by Spicer Bros at the beginning of 1911 and continued to be used for many years in the production of Duty Stamps for this State.

1912 (1 July). *Surch with T 95 in red. W 93a. P 11½ × 12¼.*

454	83	1d. on 2d. lilac	70	45

Late in June 1912 the first consignment of "thin" paper was exhausted and the second had not arrived. A further supply of the 1d. value was urgently required, and the expedient of overprinting current 2d. stock was employed to fill the gap. The same reason also produced the 1d. and 2d. overprints of Tasmania and Western Australia, respectively.

POSTAL FISCALS

This section embraces those printings of Duty and Fee stamps made before 1.1.84. These were made available for postal purposes as from 1.1.84. The two series were in concurrent use between December 1879 and 1884.

A. The "STAMP STATUTE" series

This series was first issued on 26 April 1871 and it was in the main used to record the payment of various Court fees. The issue of the series ceased in April 1884.

F 1   F 2   F 3

F 4

1870–83. *Large rectangular stamps of various designs as Types F 1 to F 4. All save the 3d. and 2s. 6d. (eng by James Turner) have the Queen's head included in the design (eng by William Bell). Typo at the Stamp Printing Office, Melbourne.*

(a) Wmk single-lined numerals (1, 2 and 10) as used for Postage Stamps (1863–67). On Saunders paper unless otherwise noted. Both sideways and upright wmks are found in certain cases.

F 1	1s. blue/blue (p 13)	25·00	15·00
	a. Perf 12	40·00	15·00
F 2	2s. blue/green (D.L.R.) (p 13)	50·00	45·00
	a. Perf 12	50·00	45·00
F 3	2s. deep blue/green (S) (p 13)	50·00	
	a. Perf 12	—	45·00
F 4	10s. brown-olive/pink (p 13) (6.71)		
F 5	10s. red-brown/pink (p 13) (1879)	f250	£100

(b) Wmk V over Crown, W 20 (V1)

The wmk is usually sideways but in certain cases the whole of a printing was upright. One also meets "abnormal" upright wmks.

F 7	½d. on 1d. pale green (R.) (p 13)	12·50	25·00
F 8	1d. pale green (p 13)	12·50	15·00
	a. Green (p 12½) (U) (1880)	40·00	35·00
F 9	3d. mauve (p 13) (9.79)	45·00	75·00
F10	4d. rose (p 13)	40·00	55·00
F11	6d. blue (p 13) (1871)	30·00	15·00
	a. Dull ultramarine (p 13) (1876)	18·00	10·00
	aa. Perf 12	35·00	12·50

F12   1s. blue/*blue* (*p* 13) (6.76) .... 25·00
    a. Perf 12 .... 40·00   18·00
    b. *Ultramarine/blue* (*p* 12½) (1882) .... —   25·00
    ba. Perf 12 .... —   20·00
    c. *Deep blue/blue* (*p* 12½) (1883) .... 25·00   15·00
    ca. Perf 12 .... —   15·00
F13   2s. blue/*green* (*p* 13) (7.76) .... 50·00   35·00
    a. Perf 12 .... 50·00
    b. *Deep blue/blue-green* (*p* 13) (1883) ...... 50·00   40·00
    ba. Perf 12 .... 50·00   45·00
F15   2s. 6d. orange (*p* 13) (7.76) .... —   50·00
    a. Perf 12 .... £100
    b. *Yellow* (*p* 13) (11.78) £100
    ba. Perf 12 .... £100   55·00
    c. *Orange-yellow* (*p* 12½) (1882) .... —   60·00
    ca. Perf 12 ....
F16   5s. blue/*yellow* (*p* 13) .... £120   40·00
    a. Perf 12 .... £130
    b. *Ultramarine/lemon* (*p* 12½) (1881) .... £120   40·00
F17   10s. brown/*pink* (*p* 13) (8.76) £250   £100
    a. *Purple-brown/pink* (*p* 12½) (1882) £250   £100
    aa. Perf 12 ....
F18   £1 slate-violet (S, U) (*p* 13) (1871) £250
    a. Perf 12 (1880) £250
    b. *Mauve/yellow* (*p* 13) (1873) £250
    ba. Perf 12 (1881) £250
    bb. Perf 12½ (1882) .... £250   80·00
F19   £5 black and yellow-green (*p* 12) (11.71) ....
    a. Perf 13 ....
    b. Perf 12½ (U) ....

(c) 1882-3: *Wmk V over Crown, W* **23** (*V* 2)

F20   1d. yellowish green (*p* 12½) .... 20·00   25·00
F21   2s. 6d. pale orange-yellow (*p* 12½) .... 75·00
F22   £5 black and yellow-green (*p* 12) .... —   £400

Reversed watermarks, all rare, have been found under Nos. F12, F15, F18 and F19.

All the values of the "Stamp Statute" series were reprinted in 1891 on paper wmkd V1 (5s., 10s. and £1) and V2 (the rest). The colours used, in all cases, differed radically from the originals. Except for the £5, for which the old electrotypes were used, new plates were made for the Reprints, from dies which showed "die flaws" not to be found on the originals. In 1877 a 12s. 6d. value was prepared for use but although it was placed on sale at the Law Courts and was available there for some months not a single copy was sold, and it was withdrawn. Proofs are known.

B. The "STAMP DUTY" series

This series was used mainly to record the payment of duties on the sale of land, receipts and numerous other documents.

F 5   F 6   F 7   F 8

F 9   F 10   F 11

(Dies for these issues (except 1d. of 1880) supplied by Messrs. Sands and McDougall. Des Charles Jackson and Ludwig Lang. Eng Charles Jackson, Arthur Williams and others (See previously). The 1d. of 1880 was eng by Charles Naish)

1879 (Dec)—**1883** (Dec). I. *December 1879. Litho Stamp Printing Office, Melbourne. Wmk V over Crown, W* **20** (*V*1). *Sideways unless otherwise indicated* (U). P 13.

F23   F **5**   1d. blue-green .... 10·00   7·50
        a. Perf 12 .... 12·00   7·50
F24   **45**   1s. 6d. rosine .... 45·00   15·00
        a. Perf 12 .... —   20·00
F25   **46**   3s. purple/*blue* .... 40·00   15·00
        a. Perf 12 .... —   20·00
F26   **47**   4s. orange-red .... 50·00   15·00
        a. Perf 12 .... 50·00   15·00
F27   **40**   6s. apple-green (U) .... 60·00   20·00
        a. Perf 12 (U) ....
F28   **50**   10s. brown/*rose* (S, U) .... £250   50·00
        a. Perf 12 (S, U) ....
F29   **51**   15s. mauve .... —   £100
F30   **52**   £1 red-orange .... —   25·00
F31   **53**   £1 5s. dull rose (U) .... —   50·00
F32   **54**   £1 10s. deep grey-olive (S, U) ... —   40·00
F33   35s. grey-violet (U) .... .F.C. £150
F34   **55**   £2 blue .... —   50·00
F35   **56**   45s. dull brown-lilac (U) .... —   60·00
F36   **57**   £5 rose-red (U) .... —   £120
F37   F **9**   £6 blue/*pink* (U) .... —   £350
F38   F **10**   £7 violet/*blue* (U) .... —   £350
F39   F **11**   £8 brownish red/*yellow* (U) .... —   £350
F40   –   £9 yellow-green/*green* (U) .... .F.C. £100   £1500

Apart from the "Half-Lengths", the 2d. Queen-on-Throne, the first 1s. Octagonal and the £25, £50 and £100 of 1886–89 these were the only stamps of Victoria to be printed by lithography and its adoption on this occasion was dictated by the necessity for speed of production. All the lithographed stamps can be distinguished from the typographed stamps of the same design by their colours which are highly distinctive. Other differences, of wmk and perf, will be found Some values, e.g. the 6s., 25s. and 30s. (1884–91) were available for postage over a considerable period. No F32 occurs with *reversed* watermark (rare).

II. Dec 1879–1882: *Typographed from electrotypes at Stamp Printing Office, Melbourne*

(i) *Wmk V over Crown, W* **20** (*V*1)

F41   F **5**   1d. yellowish green (*p* 13) (12.79) .... 10·00   7·00
        a. Perf 12 .... 12·00   7·50
F42   F **6**   1d. pale bistre (*p* 12½) (6.80) .... 5·00   1·00
        a. Perf 12 .... 5·00   2·00
F43   F **7**   6d. dull blue (*p* 13) (12.79) .... 20·00   5·00
        a. Perf 12 .... 25·00   12·00
F44   **44**   1s. deep blue/*blue* (*p* 13) (12.79) .... 20·00   2·00
        a. Perf 12 .... 20·00   3·00
        b. *Bright blue/blue* (*p* 12½) (1882) .. 20·00   2·50
        ba. Perf 12 .... —   3·00
F45   F **8**   2s. deep blue/*green* (*p* 13) (12.79) ... 40·00   10·00
        a. Perf 12 .... —   12·00
        b. *Indigo/green* .... 30·00   15·00
        ba. Perf 12 .... 50·00   15·00
F46   **48**   5s. claret/*yellow* (*p* 13) (12.79) ...... 30·00   3·00
        a. Perf 12 .... 30·00   7·50
        b. *Pale claret/yellow* (*p* 12½) (1880) 30·00   7·50
        ba. Perf 12 .... 50·00   7·50
F47   **50**   10s. chocolate/*rose* (*p* 13) (S, U) (12.79) .... —   50·00
        a. Perf 12 (S, U) ....
F48   **52**   £1 yellow-orange/*yellow* (*p* 12) (1882)....
F49   **55**   £2 deep blue (*p* 12½) (1881) .... —   60·00
F50   **58**   £10 dull mauve (*p* 12) (1879) ....
        a. *Deep red-lilac* (1882) .... —   50·00

(ii) 1882-3: *Wmk V over Crown, W* **23** (*V2*)

F51   F **6**   1d. ochre (*shades*) (*p* 12½) .... 10·00   2·00
        a. Perf 12 .... 10·00   2·00
F52   F **7**   6d. ultramarine (*p* 12½) .... 20·00   3·00
        a. Perf 12 .... 20·00   3·00
F53   **55**   £2 blue (*p* 12) .... —   60·00
F54   **57**   £5 rose-pink (*p* 12) .... —   £120

III. 1879-80: *Recess-printed direct from the die*

(i) *Wmk V over Crown, W* **20** (*V1*). P 13

F55   **59**   £25 yellow-green (1879) .... F.C.   40·00
        a. *Deep green* (1880) .... F.C.   40·00
F56   £50 bright mauve (1879) .... F.C.   65·00
F57   £100 crimson-lake (1879) .... F.C.   65·00

(ii) 1882–3: *Wmk V over Crown, W* **23** (*V2*). *P* 12½

F58	**59**	£50 dull lilac-mauve	F.C.	80·00
F59		£100 crimson	F.C.	95·00
		a. Perf 12	F.C.	95·00

Nos. F44 and F45 occur with *reversed* watermark (both rare).

Reprints of Stamp Duty Series: The only stamps in this series to be reprinted in 1891 (on wmk *V2*) were the two types of 1d. which by then had become obsolete. Again the colours are distinctive from the originals.

In 1879 certain other values inscribed "STAMP DUTY" (of varying heraldic designs) viz; 7s., 8s., 9s., 11s., 12s., 13s., 14s., 16s., 17s., 18s. and 19s. were prepared for use but were not issued. Proofs are known.

POSTAGE DUE STAMPS

D 1

(Dies eng Arthur Williams (values) and John McWilliams (frame). Typo)

1890–1908. *Type D* **1**. A. *Wmk V over Crown, W* **23** (*V2*). *P* 12 × 12½.

(i) 1 Nov 1890 (½d., 24.12.90).

D 1	½d. dull blue and brown-lake		2·50	2·00
D 2	1d. dull blue and brown-lake		3·75	1·40
D 3	2d. dull blue and brown-lake		6·00	1·10
D 4	4d. dull blue and brown-lake		7·00	1·50
D 5	5d. dull blue and brown-lake		6·00	2·00
D 6	6d. dull blue and brown-lake		7·50	1·75
D 7	10d. dull blue and brown-lake		70·00	35·00
D 8	1s. dull blue and brown-lake		35·00	6·50
D 9	2s. dull blue and brown-lake		£110	45·00
D10	5s. dull blue and brown-lake		£160	90·00

The blue shades vary considerably.

(ii) 1890–94

D11	½d. dull blue and deep claret (1890)		2·25	1·90
D12	1d. dull blue and brownish red (20.1.93)		4·00	1·10
D13	2d. dull blue and brownish red (28.3.93)		6·00	90
D14	4d. dull blue and pale claret (28.5.94)		6·00	6·00

Set of 10 (*Nos. D2/11*) optd "Specimen" .. £300

Nos. D1 and D11 were separate printings, both made in December 1890.

(iii) 17 Jan 1895. *Colours changed*

D15	½d. rosine and bluish green		2·10	1·60
D16	1d. rosine and bluish green		1·60	40
D17	2d. rosine and bluish green		2·25	30
D18	4d. rosine and bluish green		4·50	1·50
D19	5d. rosine and bluish green		4·75	2·75
D20	6d. rosine and bluish green		4·50	2·75
D21	10d. rosine and bluish green		12·00	10·00
D22	1s. rosine and bluish green		7·50	3·25

(iv) 28 March 1895

D23	2s. pale red and yellowish green		60·00	20·00
D24	5s. pale red and yellowish green		£100	40·00

(v) March 1896 onwards

D25	½d. pale scarlet and yellow-green		2·25	1·50
D26	1d. pale scarlet and yellow-green		1·75	35
D27	2d. pale scarlet and yellow-green		2·50	30
D28	4d. pale scarlet and yellow-green		5·50	1·00
D29	5d. pale scarlet and yellow-green		5·00	2·50

B. *W* **72** (*V3*). *P* 12½ *or* 12 × 12½. (i) July 1897 onwards

D30	1d. pale scarlet and yellow-green		2·00	30
D31	2d. pale scarlet and yellow-green		3·00	30
D32	4d. pale scarlet and yellow-green		4·50	1·25
D33	5d. pale scarlet and yellow-green		5·00	2·50
D34	6d. pale scarlet and yellow-green		5·00	2·75

(ii) July–Sept 1899

D35	1d. dull red and bluish green		2·50	30
D36	2d. dull red and bluish green		3·00	35
D37	4d. dull red and bluish green		5·50	1·10

C. *W* **75** (*V4*). *P* 12½ *or* 12 × 12½. (i) 1900–1

D38	½d. rose-red and pale green		2·50	1·50
D39	1d. rose-red and pale green		2·00	35
D40	2d. rose-red and pale green		2·50	30
D41	4d. rose-red and pale green		6·00	1·75

(ii) 1901–2

D42	½d. pale red and deep green		1·50	1·50
D43	1d. pale red and deep green		1·50	35
D44	2d. pale red and deep green		2·75	35
D45	4d. pale red and deep green		5·00	1·40

(iii) 1902–3

D45a	½d. scarlet and deep green		–	20·00
D46	1d. scarlet and deep green		2·50	30
D47	2d. scarlet and deep green		2·75	30
D48	4d. scarlet and deep green		5·50	1·00
D49	5d. scarlet and deep green		4·50	2·50
D50	1s. scarlet and deep green		8·00	2·75
D51	2s. scarlet and deep green		£100	60·00
D52	5s. scarlet and deep green		£120	60·00

The deep green of Nos. D45a–52 has more "yellow" than that of D42–45.

(iv) 1904

D53	½d. rosine (*aniline*) and green		2·75	2·00
D54	1d. rosine (*aniline*) and green		2·00	40
D55	2d. rosine (*aniline*) and green		2·50	45
D56	4d. rosine (*aniline*) and green		6·00	1·50

D. *Wmk Crown over A, W* **93a**. *P* 12½ *or* 12 × 12½.

(i) Jan 1906

D57	½d. rosine (*aniline*) and pale green		3·25	3·00
D58	1d. rosine (*aniline*) and pale green		22·00	2·75

(ii) March 1906

D59	½d. scarlet and pale yellow-green		2·00	1·50
D60	1d. scarlet and pale yellow-green		2·00	30

(iii) Dec 1906

D61	1d. scarlet (*aniline*) and deep yellow-green		2·25	30
D62	2d. scarlet (*aniline*) and deep yellow-green		3·00	45

(iv) 1907–8

D63	½d. dull scarlet and pea-green		2·25	1·50
D64	1d. dull scarlet and pea-green		2·50	35
D65	2d. dull scarlet and pea-green		3·75	35
D66	4d. dull scarlet and pea-green		7·00	3·75

Perf compound 12 × 12½ *with* 11

D67	½d. dull scarlet and pea-green		£110	65·00

In D59 and D60 the centre is more clearly printed than in the later printings. A 5d. value was prepared and printed on Crown over A paper but was not issued. A few copies are known, some postmarked to order from presentation sets. (*Price,* £1500 *mint,* £750 *used c.t.o.*).

The six former colonies of New South Wales, Queensland, South Australia, Tasmania, Victoria and Western Australia united to form the Commonwealth of Australia on 1 January 1901.

On 1 March 1901 control of the postal service passed to the federal administration. The first national postage due stamps appeared in July 1902, but it was not until January 1913 that postage stamps inscribed "AUSTRALIA" were issued.

WESTERN AUSTRALIA

<table>
<tr><td colspan="4" align="center">**PRICES**</td></tr>
<tr><td colspan="4">First column = Mounted Mint
Second column = Used</td></tr>
</table>

PRICES FOR STAMPS ON COVER

Nos. 1/6	from × 4
Nos. 15/32	from × 3
Nos. 33/46	from × 4
Nos. 49/51	from × 5
Nos. 52/62	from × 8
Nos. 63/a	from × 6
No. 67	from × 5
Nos. 68/92a	from × 8
Nos. 94/102	from × 30
Nos. 103/5	from × 6
Nos. 107/10a	from × 10
Nos. 111a/b	—
Nos. 112/16	from × 20
Nos. 117/25	from × 10
Nos. 126/8	—
Nos. 129/34	from × 8
Nos. 135/6	—
Nos. 138/48	from × 12
Nos. 151/63	from × 4
Nos. 168/9	from × 20
Nos. 170/1	from × 4
Nos. 172/3	from × 40
Nos. F11/22	from × 10
Nos. T1/2	—

SPECIMEN OVERPRINTS. Those listed are from U.P.U. distributions between 1889 and 1892. Further "Specimen" overprints exist, but these were used for other purposes.

1

2

3

4

GUM. The 1854 issues are hardly ever seen with gum and so the unused prices quoted are for examples without gum.

(Eng W. Humphrys. Recess P.B.)

1854 (1 Aug). *W 4 (sideways).* (a) *Imperf*

1	1	1d. black	£800	£180

(b) *Rouletted 7½ to 14 and compound*

2	1	1d. black	£1100	£350

In addition to the supplies received from London a further printing, using the original plate and watermarked paper from Perkins, Bacon, was made in the colony before the date of issue.

The 1d. is also known pin-perforated.

(Litho H. Samson (later A. Hillman), Government Lithographer)

1854 (1 Aug)–**55.** *W 4 (sideways).* (a) *Imperf.*

3	2	4d. pale blue	£225	£150
		a. Blue	£225	£150
		b. Deep dull blue	£1200	£600
		c. Slate-blue (1855)	£1100	£600

4	3	1s. salmon	—	£1200
		a. Deep red-brown	£525	£350
		b. Grey-brown (1.55)	£425	£300
		c. Pale brown (10.55)	£300	£250

(b) *Rouletted 7½ to 14 and compound*

5	2	4d. pale blue	£1100	£375
		a. Blue	—	£375
		b. Slate-blue (1855)	—	£1100
6	3	1s. grey-brown (1.55)	£1300	£600
		a. Pale brown (10.55)	£1300	£600

The 1s. is also known pin-perforated.

The 4d. value was prepared from the Perkins, Bacon 1d. plate. A block of 60 (5 × 12) was taken as a transfer from this plate, the frames painted out and then individually replaced by transfers taken from a single impression master plate of the frame. Four transfers were than taken from this completed intermediate stone to construct the printing stone of 240 impressions. This first printing stone was used by H. Samson to print the initial supplies in July 1854.

The intermediate stone had carried several transfer errors, the most prominent of which was the "T" of "POSTAGE" sliced at foot, which appeared on four positions of the printing stone.

3d. "T" of "POSTAGE" shaved off to a point at foot (R.7/5, 7/10, 7/15, 7/20)	£600	£475

The original printing stone also contained three scarce creased transfers, whose exact positions in the sheet have yet to be established.

3e. Top of letters of "AUSTRALIA" cut off so that they are barely 1 mm high	—	£6000
f. "PEICE" instead of "PENCE"	—	£6000
g. "CE" of "Pence" close together	—	£8000

Further supplies were required in January 1855 and Samson's successor, A. Hillman, used the original printing stone to produce three further sheets, after which this first stone was discarded. He then returned to the intermediate stone to produce a second printing stone. On inspection it was found that two of the impressions on the intermediate stone were defective so two new transfers of the frame, for use in these positions, were prepared. Unfortunately when these frames were replaced one was inverted and the other tilted. Each error occurs in four positions on the second printing stone, as do the transfer errors shown on the intermediate stone.

3h. Frame inverted (R.8/1, 8/6, 8/11, 8/16)	—	£60000
i. Tilted border (R.7/4, 7/9, 7/14, 7/19)	£650	£500

None of the creased transfers from the first printing stone appear on the second, which exhibits its own range of similar varieties.

3j. "WEST" in squeezed-down letters and "F" of "FOUR" with pointed foot (R.2/17)	£700	£550
k. "ESTERN" in squeezed-down letters and "U" of "FOUR" squeezed-up (R.3/17)	£1200	£1000
l. Small "S" in "POSTAGE" (R.4/17)	£700	£550
m. "EN" of "PENCE" shorter (R.6/4)	£650	£500
n. "N" of "PENCE" tilted to right with thin first down-stroke (R.6/16)	£600	£475
o. Swan and water above "ENCE" damaged (R.6/20)	£650	£500
p. "F" of "FOUR" slanting to left (R.7/17)	£650	£500
q. "WESTERN" in squeezed-down letters only 1½ mm high (R.8/17)	£750	£600
r. "P" of "PENCE" with small head (R.9/15)	£650	£500
s. "RALIA" in squeezed-down letters only 1½ mm high (R.9/16)	£700	£550
t. "PE" of "PENCE" close together (R.10/15)	£650	£500
u. "N" of "PENCE" narrow (R.10/16)	£650	£500
v. Part of right cross-stroke and down-stroke of "T" of "POSTAGE" cut off (R.11/15)	£650	£500
w. "A" in "POSTAGE" with thin right limb (R.11/16)	£600	£475

For the third printing in October 1855 the impressions showing the inverted frame were replaced on the printing stone with fresh individual transfers of the frame. On two of the positions traces of the original frame transfer remained visible.

3x. Coloured line above "AGE" of "POSTAGE" (R.8/6)	£650	£500
y. No outer line above "GE" of "POSTAGE" and coloured line under "FOU" of "FOUR" (R.10/16)	£700	£550

The same stone was used for a further printing in December 1855 and it is believed that the slate-blue shade occurred from one of the 1855 printings.

The above varieties, with the exception of Nos. 3e/g, also occur on the rouletted stamps.

The 1s. value was produced in much the same way, based on a transfer from the Perkins, Bacon 1d. plate.

5

(Litho A. Hillman, Government Lithographer)

1857 (7 Aug)–**59**. *W* **4** (*sideways*) (*a*) *Imperf.*
15	**5**	2d. brown-black/*red* (26.2.58)		£1700	£500
		a. Printed both sides		£1900	£800
16		2d. brown-black/*Indian red* (26.2.58)		—	£800
		a. Printed both sides		£1700	£850
17		6d. golden bronze		£2750	£1300
18		6d. black-bronze		£1600	£600
19		6d. grey-black (1859)		£1700	£500

(*b*) *Rouletted 7½ to* **14** *and compound*
20	**5**	2d. brown-black/*red*	£2500	£1000
		a. Printed both sides		
21		2d. brown-black/*Indian red*	—	£1200
22		6d. black-bronze	£2250	£700
23		6d. grey-black	—	£750

The 2d. and 6d. are known pin-perforated.
Prices quoted for Nos. 15/23 are for "cut-square" examples. Collectors are warned against "cut-round" copies with corners added.

(Recess in the colony from P.B. plates)

1860 (11 Aug)–**64**. *W* **4** (*sideways*). (*a*) *Imperf*
24	**1**	2d. pale orange	65·00	50·00
25		2d. orange-vermilion	60·00	45·00
25a		2d. deep vermilion	£200	£275
26		4d. blue (21.6.64)	£170	£700
27		4d. deep blue	£170	£800
28		6d. sage-green (27.7.61)	£850	£400
28a		6d. deep sage-green	—	£475

(*b*) *Rouletted 7½ to* **14**
29	**1**	2d. pale orange	£300	£130
30		2d. orange-vermilion	£375	£140
31		4d. deep blue	£1500	
32		6d. sage-green	£1000	£375

(Recess P.B.)

1861. *W* **4** (*sideways*). (*a*) *Intermediate perf* 14–16.
33	**1**	1d. rose	£200	70·00
34		2d. blue	£100	38·00
35		4d. vermilion	£275	£150
36		6d. purple-brown	£250	50·00
37		1s. yellow-green	£300	75·00

(*b*) *P* **14** *at Somerset House*
38	**1**	1d. rose	£110	35·00
39		2d. blue	55·00	25·00
40		4d. vermilion	£120	95·00

(*c*) *Perf clean-cut* 14–16
41	**1**	2d. blue	60·00	24·00
		a. Imperf between (pair)		
42		6d. purple-brown	£140	32·00
43		1s. yellow-green	£250	42·00

(*d*) *P* 14–16 *very rough* (July)
44	**1**	1d. rose-carmine	£150	24·00
45		6d. purple/*blue*	£500	95·00
46		1s. deep green	£700	£160

Perkins, Bacon experienced considerable problems with their perforating machine during the production of these stamps.

The initial printing showed intermediate perforation 14–16. Further supplies were then sent, in late December 1860, to Somerset House to be perforated on their comb 14 machine. The Inland Revenue Board were only able to process the three lower values, although the 6d. purple-brown and 1s. yellow-green are known from this perforation overprinted "SPECIMEN".

The Perkins, Bacon machine was repaired the following month and the 6d., 1s. and a further supply of the 2d. were perforated on it to give a clean-cut 14–16 gauge.

A final printing was produced in July 1861, but by this time the machine had deteriorated so that it produced a very rough 14–16.

(Recess D.L.R. from P.B. plates)

1863 (16 Dec)–**64**. *No wmk. P* 13.
49	**1**	1d. carmine-rose	40·00	8·00
50		1d. lake	40·00	7·00
51		6d. deep lilac (15.4.64)	75·00	30·00
51a		6d. dull violet (15.4.64)	95·00	35·00

Both values exist on thin and on thick papers, the former being the scarcer.

Both grades of paper show a marginal sheet watermark, "T H SAUNDERS 1860" in double-lined large and small capitals, but parts of this watermark rarely occur on the stamps.

(Recess D.L.R. from P.B. plates)

1864 (27 Dec)–**79**. *W w* **4** (*sideways on* 1d.). *P* 12½.
52	**1**	1d. bistre	40·00	1·40
53		1d. yellow-ochre (16.10.74)	48·00	5·50
54		2d. chrome-yellow (18.1.65)	42·00	90
55		2d. yellow	40·00	90
		a. Wmk sideways (5.79)		
		b. Error. Mauve (1879)	£5000	£2500
56		4d. carmine (18.1.65)	50·00	7·50
		a. Doubly printed	£5000	
57		6d. violet (18.1.65)	60·00	9·00
		a. Doubly printed	†	—
		b. Wmk sideways		
58		6d. indigo-violet	£225	28·00
59		6d. lilac (1872)	£120	9·00
60		6d. mauve (12.5.75)	£110	9·00
61		1s. bright green (18.1.65) (H/S S. £85)	80·00	12·00
62		1s. sage-green (10.68)	£200	20·00

Beware of fakes of No. 55b made by altering the value tablet of No. 60.

7

ONE PENNY

(8)

(Typo D.L.R.)

1871 (29 Oct)–**73**. *W w* **4** (*sideways*). *P* 14.
63	**7**	3d. pale brown (H/S S. £75)	22·00	4·00
		a. Cinnamon (1873)	22·00	3·50

1874 (10 Dec). *No. 55 surch with T* **8** *by Govt Printer.*
67	**1**	1d. on 2d. yellow (G.)	£130	45·00
		a. Pair, one without surch		
		b. Surch triple	—	£900
		c. "O" of "ONE" omitted		

Forged surcharges of T **8** are known on stamps wmk Crown CC perf 14, and on Crown CA, perf 12 and 14.

(Recess D.L.R. from P.B. plates)

1876–81. *W w* **4** (*sideways*). *P* 14.
68	**1**	1d. ochre	32·00	70
69		1d. bistre (1878)	38·00	2·75
70		1d. yellow-ochre (1879)	32·00	70
71		2d. chrome-yellow	35·00	50
		a. Wmk upright (1877)	48·00	85
74		4d. carmine (1881)	£200	75·00
75		6d. lilac (1877)	75·00	4·50
		a. Wmk upright (1879)	£450	15·00
75b		6d. reddish lilac (1879)	75·00	5·50

(Recess D.L.R. from P.B. plates)

1882 (Mar)–**85**. *W w* **6** (*sideways*). (*a*) *P* 14.
76	**1**	1d. yellow-ochre	12·00	50
77		2d. chrome-yellow	15·00	50
		a. Wmk upright	†	—
78		4d. carmine (8.82)	70·00	10·00
		a. Wmk upright (1885)		
79		6d. reddish lilac (1882)	70·00	3·50
80		6d. lilac (1884) (H/S S. £75)	70·00	4·00

(*b*) *P* 12 × 14
81	**1**	1d. yellow-ochre (2.83)	£1000	£150

(*c*) *P* 12
82	**1**	1d. yellow-ochre (2.83)	55·00	1·25
83		2d. chrome-yellow (6.83)	65·00	1·25
		a. Imperf between (pair)		
84		4d. carmine (5.83)	£110	25·00
85		6d. lilac (6.83)	£170	19·00

(Typo D.L.R.)

1882 (July)–**95**. W w **6** (*sideways*). *P* 14.

86	**7**	3d. pale brown		8·00	70
87		3d. red-brown (12.95)		8·50	70

The 3d. stamps in other colours, watermark Crown CA and perforated 12, are colour trials dating from 1883.

$$\frac{1}{2} \quad \textbf{1d.} \quad \textbf{1d.}$$

  (9)   (10)   (11)

1884 (19 Feb). *Surch with T* **9**, *in red, by Govt Printer*.

89	**1**	½d. on 1d. yellow-ochre (No. 76)		13·00	12·00
		a. Thin bar		70·00	48·00
90		½d. on 1d. yellow-ochre (No. 82)		9·00	7·50

Inverted or double surcharges are forgeries made in London about 1886.

The "Thin bar" varieties occur on R12/3, R12/8, R12/13 and R12/18, and show the bar only 0.2 mm thick.

1885 (May). *Nos. 63/a surch, in green, by Govt Printer*.

(a) Thick "1" with slanting top, T **10** *(Horizontal Rows 1/5)*

91	1d. on 3d. pale brown		27·00	9·00
	a. Cinnamon		18·00	7·00
	b. Vert pair. Nos. 91/2			

(b) Thin "1" with straight top, T **11** *(Horizontal Row 6)*

92	1d. on 3d. pale brown		42·00	9·00
	a. Cinnamon		28·00	10·00

12

13

14

15

(Typo D.L.R.)

1885 (May)–**93**. W w **6** (*sideways*). *P* 14.

94	**12**	½d. yellow-green		1·50	10
94a		½d. green		1·50	10
95	**13**	1d. carmine (2.90)		3·50	10
96	**14**	2d. bluish grey (6.90)		7·00	25
96a		2d. grey		6·00	25
97	**15**	2½d. deep blue (1.5.92)		5·50	35
97a		2½d. blue		6·00	35
98		4d. chestnut (7.90)		6·00	35
99		5d. bistre (1.5.92)		8·00	1·25
100		6d. bright violet (1.93)		14·00	1·00
101		1s. pale olive-green (4.90)		22·00	2·50
102		1s. olive-green		17·00	2·00
		Set of 6 (*Nos.* 94, 96a, 97a/99, 101) *optd*			
		H/S "*Specimen*"		£200	

(Recess D.L.R. from P.B. plates)

1888 (Mar–Apr). W w **6** (*sideways*). *P* 14.

103	**1**	1d. carmine-pink		12·00	60
104		2d. grey		25·00	1·00
105		4d. red-brown (April)		80·00	18·00
		Set of 3 H/S "*Specimen*"		90·00	

ONE PENNY   **Half-penny**

  (16)   (17)

1893 (Feb). *Surch with T* **16**, *in green, by Govt Printer*

107	**7**	1d. on 3d. pale brown (No. 63)		8·50	2·75
108		1d. on 3d. cinnamon (No. 63a)		8·50	3·00
		a. Double surcharge		£450	
109		1d. on 3d. pale brown (No. 86)		26·00	4·25

1895 (21 Nov). *Surch with T* **17** *by Govt Printer*. (*a*) *In green*.

110	**7**	½d. on 3d. pale brown (No. 63)		7·50	13·00
110a		½d. on 3d. cinnamon (No. 63a)		5·50	7·50
		b. Surcharge double		£350	

(b) In red and in green

111a	**7**	½d. on 3d. cinnamon (No. 63a)		90·00
111b		½d. on 3d. red-brown (No. 87)		50·00

Green was the adopted surcharge colour but a trial had earlier been made in red on stamps watermarked Crown CC. As they proved unsatisfactory they were given another surcharge in green. The trial stamps were inadvertently issued and, to prevent speculation, a further printing of the duplicated surcharge was made, but on both papers, Crown CC (No. 111a) and Crown CA (No. 111b).

18

19

20   21

(Typo D.L.R.)

1898 (Dec)–**1907**. Wmk W Crown A, W **18**. *P* 14.

112	**13**	1d. carmine		2·50	10
113	**14**	2d. bright yellow (1.99)		5·50	25
114	**19**	2½d. blue (1.01)		5·00	30
115	**20**	6d. bright violet (10.06)		12·00	50
116	**21**	1s. olive-green (4.07)		18·00	3·50

22

23

24

25

26

27

28

29

30

| 31 | 32 |

(Typo Victorian Govt Printer, Melbourne)

1902 (Oct)–**12**. W 75 *of Victoria* (V *over Crown*) (*sideways on horiz designs*).

(a) P 12½ *or* 12½ × 12 (*horiz*), 12 × 12½ (*vert*)

117	22	1d. carmine-rose (1.03)	2·75	10
		a. Wmk upright (10.02)	5·00	30
118	23	2d. yellow (4.1.03)	2·75	20
		a. Wmk upright (12.7.04)	—	65
119	24	4d. chesnut (4.03)	5·50	90
		a. Wmk upright		
120	15	5d. bistre (4.9.05)	60·00	38·00
121	25	8d. apple-green (3.03)	20·00	2·50
122	26	9d. yellow-orange (5.03)	26·00	4·75
		a. Wmk upright (11.03)	35·00	14·00
123	27	10d. red (3.03)	28·00	4·50
124	28	2s. bright red/yellow	65·00	14·00
		a. Wmk sideways		10·00
		b. Orange/yellow (1.06)	48·00	8·50
		c. Brown-red/yellow (5.11)	48·00	8·50
125	29	2s. 6d. deep blue/rose	40·00	10·00
126	30	5s. emerald-green	80·00	18·00
127	31	10s. deep mauve	£180	48·00
		a. Bright purple (1910)	£200	60·00
128	32	£1 orange-brown (1.11.02)	£350	£150
		a. Orange (10.7.09)	£700	£300

(b) P 11

129	22	1d. carmine-rose	80·00	5·50
		a. Wmk upright		
130	23	2d. yellow	£100	6·00
		a. Wmk upright		
131	24	4d. chestnut	£300	£100
132	15	5d. bistre	42·00	18·00
133	26	9d. yellow-orange	60·00	35·00
134	28	2s. bright red/yellow	£100	55·00
		a. Orange/yellow	£200	£100

(c) Perf compound of 12½ or 12 and 11

135	22	1d. carmine-rose	—	£160
136	23	2d. yellow	—	£200
137	24	4d. chestnut		

Type **22** is similar to Type **13** but larger.

1905–12. W 93a *of Victoria* (*double-lined* A *and Crown*) (*sideways*).

(a) P 12½ *or* 12½ × 12 (*horiz*), 12 × 12½ (*vert*)

138	12	½d. green (6.10)	1·25	30
139	22	1d. rose-pink (10.05)	2·75	10
		a. Wmk upright (1.06)	2·25	10
		b. Carmine (1909)	3·00	15
		c. Carmine-red (1912)	3·50	35
140	23	2d. yellow (15.11.05)	1·50	15
		a. Wmk upright (4.10)		
141	7	3d. brown (2.06)	4·50	50
142	24	4d. bistre-brown (12.06)	5·50	90
		a. Pale chestnut (1908)	8·50	70
		b. Bright brown-red (14.10.10)	7·50	60
143	15	5d. pale olive-bistre (8.05)	11·00	1·25
		a. Olive-green (1.09)	11·00	1·25
		b. Pale greenish yellow (5.12)	48·00	32·00
144	25	8d. apple-green (22.4.12)	17·00	8·50
145	26	9d. orange (11.5.06)	18·00	3·50
		a. Red-orange (6.10)	27·00	3·50
		b. Wmk upright (7.12)	35·00	10·00
146	27	10d. rose-orange (16.2.10)	18·00	7·00
148	30	5s. emerald-green (wmk upright) (9.07)	60·00	35·00

(b) P 11

150	12	½d. green		
151	22	1d. rose-pink	8·50	1·75
		a. Carmine-red	8·00	90
		b. Wmk upright	8·00	2·50
152	23	2d. yellow	10·00	3·00
153	7	3d. brown	8·50	2·00
154	24	4d. yellow-brown	£350	85·00
		a. Pale chestnut		

155	15	5d. pale olive-bistre	28·00	10·00
		a. Olive-green	16·00	4·00
157	26	9d. orange	70·00	75·00
		a. Red-orange	—	65·00
		b. Wmk upright (inverted)		

(c) Perf compound of 12½ or 12 and 11

161	22	1d. rose-pink	£150	75·00
162	23	2d. yellow	£170	80·00
163	7	3d. brown	£190	85·00
164	26	9d. red-orange		

Only six examples are known of No. 157b, all used in 1912 or 1913.

1912 (Mar). W 27 *of South Australia* (*Crown and* A) (*sideways*). P 11½ × 12.

168	20	6d. bright violet	9·50	2·50
169	21	1s. sage-green	20·00	4·50
		a. Perf 12½ (single line)		

1912 (7 Aug). W 93a *of Victoria* (*sideways*). *Thin paper and white gum* (*as Victoria*).

170	7	3d. brown (p 12½)	23·00	23·00
		a. Wmk upright	23·00	23·00
171		3d. brown (p 11)		
		a. Wmk upright		

ONE PENNY

(36)

1912 (6 Nov). Nos. 140 *and* 162 *surch with* T 36 *in Melbourne.*

(a) P 12½ *or* 12 × 12½

172	23	1d. on 2d. yellow	80	30
		a. Wmk upright	1·00	45

(b) Perf compound of 12½ and 11

173	23	1d. on 2d. yellow	£275	

POSTAL FISCAL STAMPS

By the Post and Telegraph Act of 5 September 1893 the current issue of fiscal stamps up to and including the 1s. value, Nos. F11/15, was authorised for postal use.

These stamps had been initially supplied, for fiscal purposes, in February 1882 and had been preceded by a series of "I R" surcharges and overprints on postage stamps which were in use for a period of about six months. Examples of these 1881–82 provisionals can be found postally used under the terms of the 1893 Act but, as they had not been current for fiscal purposes for over eleven years, we no longer list them.

F 3

(Typo D.L.R.)

1893 (5 Sept). *Definitive fiscal stamps of Feb* 1882. W w 7. P 14.

F11	F 3	1d. dull purple	4·50	55
F12		2d. dull purple	60·00	30·00
F13		3d. dull purple	17·00	1·75
F14		6d. dull purple	20·00	2·75
F15	—	1s. dull purple	28·00	3·25

The 1s. value is as Type F 3 but with rectangular outer frame and circular frame surrounding swan.

Higher values in this series were not validated by the Act for postal use.

Two varieties of watermark exist on these stamps. Initial supplies showed an indistinct watermark with the base of the "A" 4 mm wide. From 1896 the paper used showed a clearer watermark on which the base of the "A" was 5 mm wide.

1897. *Wmk W Crown A, W* **18.** *P* 14.

F19	F **3**	1d. dull purple	3·50	65
F20		3d. dull purple	8·50	85
F21		6d. dull purple	9·50	1·25
F22	–	1s. dull purple	20·00	3·00

TELEGRAPH STAMPS USED FOR POSTAGE

The 1d. Telegraph stamps were authorised for postal purposes from 25 October 1886.

T **1**

1886 (25 Oct). *W* w **4**.

T1	T **1**	1d. bistre (*p* 12½)	16·00	2·50
T2		1d. bistre (*p* 14)	18·00	4·00

Copies of a similar 6d. value are known postally used, but such use was unauthorised.

OFFICIAL STAMPS

Stamps of the various issues from 1854–85 are found with a circular hole punched out, the earlier size being about 3 mm. in diameter and the later 4 mm. These were used on official correspondence by the Commissariat and Convict Department, branches of the Imperial administration separate from the colonial government. This system of punching ceased by 1886. Subsequently many stamps between Nos. 94 and 148 may be found punctured, "PWD", "WA" or "OS".

The six former colonies of New South Wales, Queensland, South Australia, Tasmania, Victoria and Western Australia united to form the Commonwealth of Australia on 1 January 1901.

On 1 March 1901 control of the postal service passed to the federal administration. The first national postage due stamps appeared in July 1902, but it was not until January 1913 that postage stamps inscribed "AUSTRALIA" were issued.

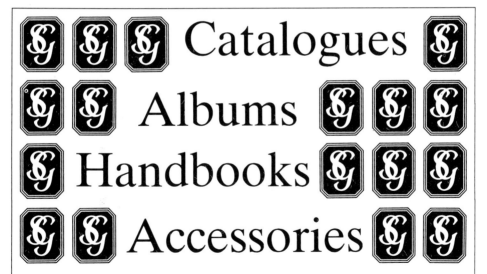

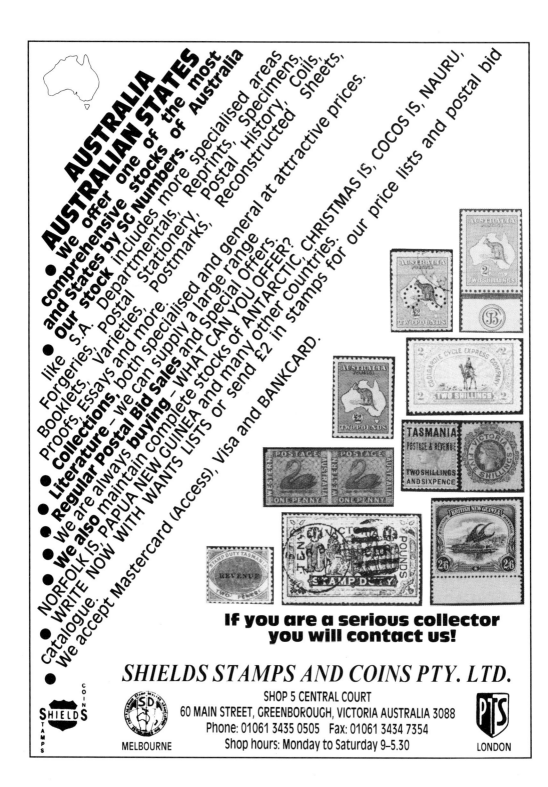

Australia

1913 12 Pence = 1 Shilling
20 Shillings = 1 Australian Pound
1966 100 Cents = 1 Australian Dollar

COMMONWEALTH

An island continent to the S.E. of Asia. Incorporating the previous stamp-issuing states of New South Wales, Queensland, South Australia, Tasmania, Victoria and Western Australia.

PRICES FOR STAMPS ON COVER TO 1945		
Nos. 1/27	from×	4
Nos. 29/34	from×	2
Nos. 35/50d	from×	3
Nos. 51/3	from×	4
Nos. 56/75	from×	3
Nos. 76/84	from×	4
Nos. 85/104	from×	3
Nos. 105/6	from×	4
Nos. 107/15	from×	3
No. 116	from×	5
Nos. 117/20	from×	4
Nos. 121/39a	from×	2
Nos. 140/a	from×	5
Nos. 141/4	from×	3
No. 146	from×	6
Nos. 147/53	from×	3
Nos. 153a/b	from×	2
Nos. 154/63	from×	3
Nos. 164/211	from×	2
Nos. D1/118	from×	8
Nos. O1/18	from×	5

PRICES
George V issues (1913–1936)
First column = Mounted Mint
Second column = Used

PRINTERS. Except where otherwise stated, all Commonwealth stamps to No. 581 were printed under Government authority at Melbourne. Until 1918 there were two establishments (both of the Treasury Dept)—the Note Printing Branch and the Stamp Printing Branch. The former printed T **3** and **4**.

In 1918 the Stamp Printing Branch was closed and all stamps were printed by the Note Printing Branch. In 1926 control was transferred from the Treasury to the Commonwealth Bank of Australia, and on 14 January 1960 the branch was attached to the newly established Reserve Bank of Australia.

Until 1942 stamps bore in the sheet margin the initials or names of successive managers and from 1942 to March 1952 the imprint "Printed by the Authority of the Government of the Commonwealth of Australia". After November 1952 (or Nos. D129/31 for Postage Dues) imprints were discontinued.

SPECIMEN OVERPRINTS. These come from Specimen sets, first produced in 1913. In these sets the lower values were cancelled-to-order, but stamps with a face value of 7s. 6d. or 75 c. were overprinted "Specimen" in different types. These overprints are listed as they could be purchased from the Australian Post Office.

It is, however believed that examples of No. 112 overprinted "SPECIMEN" were distributed by the U.P.U. in 1929. Supplies of the 1902 and 1902–04 postage due stamps overprinted "Specimen" were supplied to the U.P.U. by some of the states.

The sale of the cancelled-to-order sets ceased after 1966, but high value "Specimen" overprints were retained to support philatelic funds.

1

2

Die I

Die II

Dies of Type **1** (mono-coloured values only):—

Die I.   Break in inner frame line at lower left level with top of words of value.
Die II.   Die repaired showing no break.

Die I was only used for the ½d., 1d., 2d. and 3d. Several plates were produced for each except the 3d. When the second plate of the 3d. was being prepared the damage became aggravated after making 105 out of the 120 units when the die was returned for repair. This gave rise to the *se-tenant* pairs showing the two states of the die.

Die II was used until 1945 and deteriorated progressively with damage to the frame lines and rounding of the corners.

Specialists recognise seven states of this die, but we only list the two most major of the later versions.

Die IIA. This state is as Die II, but, in addition, shows a break in the inner left-hand frame line, 9 mm from the top of the design.

Die IIB. As Die IIA, but now also showing break in outer frame line above "ST", and (not illustrated) an incomplete corner to the inner frame line at top right.

(Des B. Young. Eng S. Reading. Typo J. B. Cooke)

1913 (Jan–Apr).   W **2**. P 12.

1	**1**	½d. green (Die I) (16 Jan)	5·00	1·50
		a. Wmk sideways		†
		Wi. Wmk inverted	22·00	5·00
2		1d. red (Die I) (2 Jan)	6·50	40
		a. Wmk sideways	£700	£100
		b. Carmine	6·50	40
		c. Die II. Red	6·50	40
		ca. Wmk sideways	£750	£100
		cb. Carmine	6·50	40
		d. Die IIA. Red	7·00	40
		da. Wmk sideways	£700	£100
		db. Carmine	7·00	40
		Wi. Wmk inverted	20·00	1·25
3		2d. grey (Die I) (11 Jan)	24·00	2·75
		Wi. Wmk inverted	35·00	3·75
4		2½d. indigo (Die II) (27 Jan)	26·00	10·00
5		3d. olive (Die I) (22 Jan)	40·00	5·50
		a. Imperf three sides (pair)	£10000	
		b. In pair with Die II	£375	£130
		c. Yellow-olive	40·00	6·00
		ca. In pair with Die II	£375	£130
		d. Die II. Olive	£140	40·00
		da. Yellow-olive	£140	40·00
		Wi. Wmk inverted	60·00	8·00
6		4d. orange (Die II) (12 Feb)	48·00	22·00
		a. Orange-yellow	£170	48·00
8		5d. chestnut (Die II) (16 Jan)	40·00	28·00
9		6d. ultramarine (Die II) (11 Jan)	48·00	22·00
		a. Retouched "E"	£1500	£500
		b. Die IIA	£850	£225
		Wi. Wmk inverted	65·00	22·00
10		9d. violet (Die II) (29 Jan)	45·00	45·00
11		1s. emerald (Die II) (21 Jan)	45·00	11·00
		a. Blue-green	45·00	11·00
		Wi. Wmk inverted	60·00	18·00
12		2s. brown (Die II) (25 Jan)	£140	50·00
13		5s. grey and yellow (20 March)	£250	£110
14		10s. grey and pink (20 March)	£500	£350
15		£1 brown and blue (20 March)	£1100	£1000
16		£2 black and rose (8 April)	£2100	£1500
		Set of 15	£4000	£2750
		Set of 3 (Nos. 14/16) optd "Specimen"	£550	

No. 9a shows a badly distorted second "E" in "PENCE", which is unmistakable. It occurs on the last stamp in the sheet and was replaced by a substitute cliché in Type IIA (No. 9b).

For the previous No. 12a see No. O11a.

See also Nos. 20/27 (W **5**), 35/45b (W **6**), 73/5 (W **6**, new colours), 107/14 (W **7**), 132/8 (W **15**), 212 (2s. re-engraved).

3   4 Laughing Kookaburra

(Des R. A. Harrison. Eng and recess T. S. Harrison)

1913 (8 Dec)–**14**.   No wmk. P 11.

17	**3**	1d. red	1·75	4·00
		a. Pale rose-red	6·50	10·00
		b. Imperf horiz (vert pair)	£1500	
19	**4**	6d. claret (26.8.14)	70·00	38·00
		Set of 2	70·00	42·00

All printing from Plate 1 of the 1d. were in the shade of No. 17a. This plate shows many retouches.

5   5a

(Typo J. B. Cooke)

1915.   W **5**. P 12.

20	**1**	2d. grey (Die I) (2 Jan)	50·00	10·00
		Wi. Wmk inverted		—
21		2½d. indigo (Die I) (July)	50·00	25·00
23		6d. ultramarine (Die I) (April)	£130	22·00
		a. Bright blue	£170	45·00
		b. Die IIA. Ultramarine	£900	£200
		ba. Bright blue	£1100	£250
		Wi. Wmk inverted	£170	40·00
24		9d. violet (Die II) (9 July)	£130	28·00
		Wi. Wmk inverted	£750	£190
25		1s. blue-green (Die II) (Aug)	£140	20·00
26		2s. brown (Die II) (April)	£400	80·00
27		5s. grey and yellow (12 Feb)	£600	£200
		a. Yellow portion doubly printed	£5500	£1000
		Wi. Wmk inverted	£800	£200
		Set of 7	£1400	£325

The watermark in this issue is often misplaced as the paper was made for the portrait stamps.

Die II   Die III

Die II. The flaw distinguishing the so-called Die II is now known to be due to a defective roller-die and occurs in 18 impressions on one of the plates. It appears as a white upward projection to right of the base of figure "1" in the shield containing value at left, as shown in the illustration.

Die III. In 1918 a printing (in sheets of 120) was made on paper prepared for printing War Savings Stamps, with wmk T **5**. A special plate was made for this printing, differing in detail from those previously used. The shading round the head is even; the solid background of the words "ONE PENNY" is bounded at each end by a *white* vertical line; and there is a horizontal white line cutting the vertical shading lines at left on the King's neck. See Nos. 55b/c.

(Dies eng P. B. Typo J. B. Cooke until 1918, then T. S. Harrison)

1914–21.   W **5**. P 14.

29	**5a**	½d. bright green (22.2.15)	3·00	60
		a. Green (13.5.16)	2·75	50
		b. Yellow-green (8.16)	20·00	5·00
		c. Thin "1" in fraction at right	£1000	£500
		Wi. Wmk inverted	9·00	1·50
30		1d. carmine-red (shades) (I) (17.7.14)	6·00	20
		a. Rusted cliché (2 vars)*	£4000	£400
		b. Substituted cliché	£1300	50·00
		c. Pale carmine (shades)	14·00	20
		d. Carmine-pink (1.18)	90·00	2·50
		e. Rose-red (3.18)	10·00	1·50
		f. Carmine (aniline) (1921)	15·00	1·75
		Wi. Wmk inverted	8·00	25
31		1d. carmine-red (shades) (III) (1914)	£400	6·00
		a. Substituted cliché	£1300	50·00
		b. Pale red (shades)	£350	6·00
		Wi. Wmk inverted	£450	8·00
32		4d. orange (6.1.15)	38·00	2·25
		a. Yellow-orange	38·00	3·25
		b. Pale orange-yellow (10.15)	65·00	9·00
		c. Lemon-yellow (1916)	£120	14·00
		d. Dull orange	42·00	3·25
		e. Line through "FOUR PENCE" (all shades) .... From	£550	£110
		Wi. Wmk inverted	50·00	12·00
34		5d. brown (22.2.15)	15·00	1·25
		a. Yellow-brown (1920)	25·00	1·75
		Wi. Wmk inverted	45·00	6·50

The variety No. 29c was caused by the engraving of a new fraction in a defective electro.

*The two varieties listed under No. 30a were caused by rusting of the steel plate and show as white patches on the back of King's neck and on, and beside, the top of the right frame (upper left pane, No. 34); and on the left frame, wattles, head and ears of kangaroo (upper left pane, No. 35). These were noticed in late 1916 when the damaged impressions were removed and replaced by a pair of copper electros (Die II for No. 34 and Die I for No. 35), showing rounded corners and some frame damage, the former also showing a white spot under tail of emu. In time the tops of the crown quickly wore away. These substituted clichés (Nos. 30b and 31a) were formerly described as "Top of crown missing".

The 5d. is known printed on the gummed side of the paper.

Two machines were used for the 14 perforation, one an old single line, converted to that gauge, the other a new comb-machine. The former was used mainly for early printings of the 1d. and 5d. and very rarely for later printings of the ½d. and 1d.

See also Nos. 47/50b (W 5, rough paper), 55b/c (1d. Die III), 51/5a (W 6a), 56/66b and 76/84 (W 5, new colours), 85/104 (W 7), 124/31 (W 15).

6   6a

Nos. 38ca and 73a
(R. 1/6, lower plate)

(Typo J. B. Cooke (to May 1918), T. S. Harrison (to February 1926), A. J. Mullett (to January 1927) and thereafter J. Ash)

1915–28. W 6 (narrow Crown). P 12.

35	1	2d. grey (Die I) (11.15)	28·00	3·75
		a. In pair with Die IIA (1917)*	£650	£300
		b. Silver-grey (shiny paper) (2.18)	28·00	4·00
		c. Die II. Grey (1918)	32·00	5·50
		ca. Silver-grey (shiny paper) (2.18)	30·00	5·50
		Wi. Wmk inverted	42·00	6·00
36		2½d. deep blue (Die II) (9.17)	22·00	6·50
		a. Deep indigo (1920)	26·00	8·00
		ab. "1" of fraction omitted	£9000	£3000
		Wi. Wmk inverted	42·00	6·00
37		3d. yellow-olive (Die I) (12.10.15)	27·00	3·00
		a. In pair with Die II	£225	75·00
		b. Olive-green (1917)	30·00	3·00
		ba. In pair with Die II	£225	75·00
		c. Die II. Yellow-olive	90·00	22·00
		ca. Olive-green	90·00	22·00
		d. Die IIB. Light olive (1923)	38·00	11·00
		Wi. Wmk inverted	45·00	7·00
38		6d. ultramarine (Die II) (15.12.15)	48·00	6·00
		a. Die IIA (substituted cliché)	£650	£150
		b. Dull blue	55·00	7·00
		ba. Die IIA (substituted cliché)	£750	£150
		c. Die IIB. Bright ultramarine (23.7.21)	48·00	6·00
		ca. Leg of kangaroo broken	£2500	£500
		Wi. Wmk inverted	60·00	10·00
39		9d. violet (Die II) (29.7.16)	38·00	4·75
		a. Die IIB. Violet (16.4.19)	35·00	4·25
		Wi. Wmk inverted	50·00	11·00
40		1s. blue-green (Die II) (6.16)	35·00	2·75
		a. Die IIB (9.12.20)	35·00	2·50
		b. Wmk sideways (1927)	80·00	£100
		Wi. Wmk inverted	70·00	11·00
41		2s. brown (Die II) (6.16)	£150	9·00
		a. Imperf three sides (pair)	£12000	
		b. Red-brown (aniline)	£400	38·00
		Wi. Wmk inverted	£200	30·00
42		5s. grey and yellow (4.18)	£175	60·00
		a. Grey and orange (1920)	£175	60·00
		b. Grey and deep yellow	£175	60·00
		ba. Wmk sideways	£2250	£1600
		c. Grey and pale yellow (1928)	£175	60·00
		Wi. Wmk inverted	£250	70·00
43		10s. grey and pink (5.2.17)	£400	£140
		a. Grey and bright aniline pink	£400	£140
		ab. Wmk sideways	£2750	£1500
		b. Grey and pale aniline pink (1928)	£425	£140
		Wi. Wmk inverted	£850	£160
44	1	£1 chocolate and dull blue (7.16)	£1300	£650
		a. Chestnut and bright blue (1917)	£1400	£700
		b. Bistre-brown and bright blue	£1300	£650
		ba. Wmk sideways	£4500	£1800
		Wi. Wmk inverted	£1600	£800
45		£2 black and rose (12.19)	£2100	£1100
		a. Grey and crimson (1920)	£2000	£1100
		b. Purple-black and pale rose (1924)	£1800	£1100
		Set of 11 (Nos. 35/45b)	£3500	£1700
		Set of 3 (Nos. 43/5) optd "Specimen"	£500	

*The Die II of No. 35a is a substituted cliché introduced to replace a cracked plate which occurred on No. 55 of the upper left pane (Row 10, No. 1). The Die IIA characteristics are more pronounced in this cliché than on the sheet stamps from this die. The break at left, for instance, extends to the outer, in addition to the inner, frame line.

All values were printed by both Cooke and Harrison, and the 9d., 1s. and 5s. were also printed by Mullett and Ash.

1916–18. W 5. Rough paper, locally gummed. P 14.

47	5a	1d. scarlet (I) (14.12.16)	22·00	1·25
		Wi. Wmk inverted	26·00	1·25
48		1d. deep red (I) (1917)	22·00	1·00
		Wi. Wmk inverted	26·00	1·25
49		1d. rose-red (I) (1918)	35·00	1·50
		a. Substituted cliché	£1300	75·00
		Wi. Wmk inverted	40·00	1·75
49b		1d. rosine (I) (1918)	85·00	8·00
		c. Substituted cliché	£1600	£110
50		1d. rose-red (II) (1918)	£275	20·00
		aa. Substituted cliché	£1300	75·00
		Wi. Wmk inverted	£450	25·00
50a		1d. rosine (II) (1918)	£600	50·00
		ab. Substituted cliché	£1600	£110

For explanations of substituted cliché varieties, see 2nd paragraph of note below No. 34a.

For illustrations and descriptions of Dies II and III, see after T 5a.

For the previous No. 50b see No. O60.

(Typo J. B. Cooke or T. S. Harrison)

1918–20. W 6a (Mult). P 14.

51	5a	½d. green (shades) ((8.1.18)	4·00	1·50
		a. "1" in fraction at right thinner	£100	40·00
		b. Wmk sideways	†	£1500
		Wi. Wmk inverted	15·00	3·50
52		1d. carmine-pink (I) (23.1.18)	£120	40·00
		a. Deep red (I) (1918)	£750	£140
		Wi. Wmk inverted	£600	£120
53		1d. carmine (I) (10.12.19)	32·00	5·00
		a. Deep red (aniline) (I) (1920)	£140	35·00
		Wi. Wmk inverted	£180	60·00
54		1½d. black-brown (30.1.19)	5·00	1·50
		a. Very thin paper (3.19)	28·00	13·00
		Wi. Wmk inverted	15·00	1·75
55		1½d. red-brown (4.19)	9·00	1·25
		a. Chocolate	9·00	1·25
		Wi. Wmk inverted	24·00	2·00

No. 51 was printed by Cooke and Harrison, Nos. 52/a by Cooke only and Nos. 53/55a by Harrison only. Nos. 52/a have rather yellowish gum, that of No. 53 being pure white.

1918 (June). Printed from a new plate (Die III) on white unsurfaced paper, locally gummed. W 5. P 14.

55b	5a	1d. rose-red (III)	60·00	24·00
55c		1d. rose-carmine (III)	60·00	24·00
		Wi. Wmk inverted	90·00	26·00

(Typo T. S. Harrison and also A. J. Mullett for 1s. 4d. from March 1926)

1918–23. W 5. P 14.

56	5a	½d. orange (9.11.23)	2·50	90
		Wi. Wmk inverted	4·75	1·50
57		1d. violet (shades) (13.2.22)	4·50	60
		a. Imperf three sides (pair)	£7000	
		b. Red-violet	5·50	70
58		1½d. black-brown (9.11.18)	7·00	55
		Wi. Wmk inverted	15·00	1·00
59		1½d. deep red-brown (4.19)	4·50	25
		a. Chocolate	4·75	30
		Wi. Wmk inverted	15·00	90
60		1½d. bright red-brown (20.1.22)	10·00	1·50
61		1½d. green (7.3.23)	2·00	25
		a. Rough unsurfaced paper	90·00	50·00
		Wi. Wmk inverted		
62		2d. dull orange (5.10.20)	14·00	30
		a. Brown-orange	14·00	30
		Wi. Wmk inverted	£130	45·00

63	5a	2d. bright rose-scarlet (17.2.22)	6·50	40
		a. Dull rose-scarlet	6·50	40
		Wi. Wmk inverted	15·00	2·50
64		4d. violet (21.6.21)	9·00	10·00
		a. Line through "FOUR PENCE"	£7000	£3500
		b. "FOUR PENCE" in thinner letters	£600	£225
65		4d. ultramarine (shades) (23.3.22)	48·00	5·00
		a. "FOUR PENCE" in thinner letters	£750	£150
		b. Pale milky blue	55·00	8·00
		Wi. Wmk inverted	70·00	30·00
66		1s. 4d. pale blue (2.12.20)	65·00	18·00
		a. Dull greenish blue (1923)	65·00	18·00
		b. Deep turquoise	£550	80·00
		Set of 11	£160	40·00

In addition to a number of mint pairs a single used example of No. 57 imperforate on three sides is known.

The 4d. ultramarine was originally printed by Cooke but the plates were worn in mid-1923 and Harrison prepared a new pair of plates. Stamps from these plates can be distinguished by the minor flaws which are peculiar to them.

The variety of Nos. 64 and 65 with "FOUR PENCE" thinner, was caused by the correction of a defective cliché (No. 6, 2nd row, right-hand pane), which showed a line running through these words.

No. 61a was printed on a small residue of paper which had been employed for Nos. 47/50d.

(Typo T. S. Harrison (to February 1926), A. J. Mullet (to June 1927), thereafter J. Ash)

1923-24. W 6. P 12.

73	1	6d. chestnut (Die IIB) (6.12.23)	20·00	1·00
		a. Leg of kangaroo broken	£100	£100
74		2s. maroon (Die II) (1.5.24)	50·00	15·00
		Wi. Wmk inverted	80·00	23·00
75		£1 grey (Die IIB) (1.5.24) (Optd S. £75)	£500	£175

The 6d. and 2s. were printed by all three printers, but the £1 only by Harrison.

(Typo T. S. Harrison (to February 1926), thereafter A. J. Mullett)

1924. P 14. (a) W 5 (1 May).

76	5a	1d. sage-green	2·25	25
		Wi. Wmk inverted	6·50	1·25
77		1½d. scarlet (shades)	2·00	20
		a. Very thin paper	40·00	12·00
		b. "HALEPENCE"	35·00	15·00
		c. "RAL" of "AUSTRALIA" thin	35·00	15·00
		d. Curved "1" and thin fraction at left	32·00	15·00
		Wi. Wmk inverted	18·00	6·00
78		2d. red-brown	18·00	5·00
		a. Bright red-brown	26·00	7·50
79		3d. dull ultramarine	24·00	1·25
		a. Imperf three sides (pair)	£6500	
80		4d. olive-yellow	26·00	2·00
		a. Olive-green	28·00	2·00
		Wi. Wmk inverted		
81		4½d. violet	23·00	2·00

(b) W 6a

82	5a	1d. sage-green (20 May)	8·50	6·00
		Wi. Wmk inverted		

(c) No wmk

83	5a	1d. sage-green (18 August)	4·75	8·00
84		1½d. scarlet (14 August)	9·50	9·00
		Set of 9	£100	30·00

Nos. 78·a and 82·4 were printed by Harrison only but the remainder were printed by both Harrison and Mullett.

In the semi-transparent paper of Nos. 54a and 77a the watermark is almost indistinguishable. Nos. 77b, 77c and 77d are typical examples of retouching of which there are many others in these issues. In No. 77c the letters "RAL" differ markedly from the normal. There is a white stroke cutting the oval frame-line above the "L", and the right-hand outer line of the Crown does not cut the white frame-line above the "A". No. 77b occurs on the row above No. 77c in the sheet, so that the varieties may be found se-tenant.

I

II

New Dies

1d. For differences see note after No. 27a.

1½d. From new steel plates made from a new die. Nos. 88 and 98 are the Ash printings, the ink of which is shiny.

2d. Die I. Height of frame 25.6 mm. Left-hand frame-line thick and uneven behind Kangaroo. Pearls in Crown vary in size.
Die II. Height of frame 25.6 mm. Left-hand frame-line thin and even. Pearls in Crown are all the same size.
Die III. Height 25.1 mm; lettering and figures of value bolder than Die I.

3d. Die II has bolder letters and figures than Die I, as illustrated above.

5d. Die II has a bolder figure "5" with flat top compared with Die I of the earlier issues.

(Typo by A. J. Mullet or J. Ash)

1926-30. W 7. (a) P 14.

85	5a	½d. orange (10.3.27)	7·50	6·00
		Wi. Wmk inverted	22·00	8·50
86		1d. sage-green (23.10.26)	3·75	75
		Wi. Wmk inverted	10·00	2·50
87		1½d. scarlet (5.11.26)	5·50	70
		Wi. Wmk inverted	16·00	2·00
88		1½d. golden scarlet (1927)	8·00	1·75
		Wi. Wmk inverted	22·00	2·75
89		2d. red-brown (Die I) (17.8.27)	28·00	26·00
90		3d. dull ultramarine (12.26)	22·00	4·00
		Wi. Wmk inverted		
91		4d. yellow-olive (17.1.28)	48·00	26·00
92		4½d. violet (26.10.27)	15·00	3·00
93		1s. 4d. pale greenish blue (6.9.27)	£150	75·00
		Wi. Wmk inverted		
		Set of 8	£250	£120

(b) P 13½ × 12½

94	5a	½d. orange (21.11.28)	1·50	75
95		1d. sage-green (Die I) (23.12.26)	1·60	20
		Wi. Wmk inverted	5·00	90
96		1d. sage-green (Die II)	60·00	70·00
		Wi. Wmk inverted	£160	£160
97		1½d. scarlet (14.1.27)	1·50	25
		Wi. Wmk inverted	7·00	1·25
98		1½d. golden scarlet	2·00	35
		Wi. Wmk inverted	8·50	1·40
98a		1½d. red-brown (16.9.30)	4·50	5·50
99		2d. red-brown (Die II) (28.4.28)	7·00	7·00
99a		2d. golden scarlet (Die II) (2.8.30)	8·00	90
99b		2d. golden scarlet (Die III) (9.9.30)	7·50	40
		c. No wmk	£950	£400
		d. Tête-bêche (pair)	£28000	
		Wi. Wmk inverted	10·00	80
100		3d. dull ultramarine (Die I) (23.2.28)	45·00	4·25
		Wi. Wmk inverted	£130	50·00
101		3d. deep ultramarine (Die II) (28.9.29)	23·00	1·25
		Wi. Wmk inverted	£120	
102		4d. yellow-olive (4.29)	23·00	2·00
		Wi. Wmk inverted		
103		4½d. violet (11.28)	48·00	18·00
103a		5d. orange-brown (Die II) (27.8.30)	17·00	2·25
104		1s. 4d. turquoise (30.9.28)	80·00	20·00
		Set of 11	£190	50·00

Owing to defective manufacture, part of a sheet of the 2d. (Die III) escaped unwatermarked; while the watermark in other parts of the same sheet was faint or normal.

Only one example of No. 99d is known.

8 Parliament House, Canberra   9 "DH66" Biplane and Pastoral Scene

TWO

PENCE
(12)

13 The *Southern Cross* above hemispheres

(Des R. A. Harrison. Die eng by Waterlow. Plates and printing by A. J. Mullett)

1927 (9 May). *Opening of Parliament House, Canberra. No wmk. P* 11.
105   **8**   1½d. brownish lake 50   50
     a. Imperf between (pair) £2750   £1900

(Eng T. S. Harrison. Recess J. Ash)

1928 (29 Oct). *National Stamp Exhibition, Melbourne. As T* **4**. *No. wmk. P* 11.
106   3d. blue . . . . 4·25   4·00
     a. Pane of four with margins £175   £225
     ab. Imperf (pane of four) £15000
No. 106a comes from special sheets of 60 stamps divided into 15 blocks of 4 (5×3) and separated by wide gutters perforated down the middle, printed and sold at the Exhibition.

(Typo J. Ash)

1929–30. *W* **7**. *P* 12.
107   **1**   6d. chestnut (Die IIB) (25.9.29) . . . . 22·00   4·00
108   9d. violet (Die IIB) (2.29) . . . . 30·00   8·50
109   1s. blue-green (Die IIB) (12.6.29) . . . . 40·00   4·75
     Wi. Wmk inverted £225   £140
110   2s. maroon (Die II) (3.29) . . . . 50·00   14·00
111   5s. grey and yellow (30.11.29) . . . . £190   75·00
112   10s. grey and pink (2.29) £350   £250
114   £2 black and rose (11.30) £1800   £350
     Set of 7 . . . . £2250   £650
     Set of 2 (*Nos.* 112, 114) *optd "Specimen"*   £300

(Des R. A. Harrison and H. Herbert. Eng A. Taylor. Recess J. Ash)

1929 (20 May). *Air. No wmk. P* 11.
115   **9**   3d. green (*shades*) . . . . 10·00   3·25
Variations of up to ¾ mm in the design size of No. 115 are due to paper shrinkage; the stamps having been printed by a "wet" process.

10 Black Swan   11 Capt. Charles Sturt

(Des Pitt Morison. Eng F. D. Manley. Recess J. Ash)

1929 (28 Sept). *Centenary of Western Australia. No wmk. P* 11.
116   **10**   1½d. dull scarlet . . . . 1·00   1·00
     a. Re-entry ("T" of "AUSTRALIA" clearly double) . . . . 55·00   40·00

(Des R. A. Harrison. Eng F. D. Manley. Recess J. Ash)

1930 (2 June). *Centenary of Exploration of River Murray by Capt. Sturt. No wmk. P* 11.
117   **11**   1½d. scarlet . . . . 1·00   45
118   3d. blue . . . . 3·75   5·00
     Set of 2 . . . . 4·75   5·25
No. 117 with manuscript surcharge of "2d, paid P M L H I" was issued by the Postmaster of Lord Howe Island during a shortage of 2d. stamps between August and October 1930. A few copies of the 1½d. value No. 98 were also endorsed. These provisionals are not recognized by the Australian postal authorities. (*Price* £550 *un. or us., either stamp.*)

1930 (1 Aug). *T* **5***a surch at T* **12**. *W* **7**. *P* 13½ × 12½.
119   2d. on 1½d. golden scarlet . . . . 1·00   40
120   5d. on 4½d. violet . . . . 7·00   7·50
     Set of 2 . . . . 8·00   7·50
No. 120 is from a redrawn die in which the words "FOURPENCE HALFPENNY" are noticeably thicker than in the original die and the figure "4" has square instead of tapering serifs.
Stamps from the redrawn die without the surcharge were printed, but not issued thus. Some stamps, *cancelled to order*, were included in sets supplied by the post office. A few mint copies, which escaped the cancellation, were found and some may have been used postally. (*Price* £38 *used c.t.o.*)

(Des and eng F. D. Manley. Recess John Ash)

1931 (19 Mar). *Kingsford Smith's flights. No wmk. P* 11. (*a*) *Postage.*
121   **13**   2d. rose-red 75   35
122   3d. blue . . . . 5·00   4·00

(*b*) *Air. Inscr* "AIR MAIL SERVICE"
123   **13**   6d. violet . . . . 10·00   10·00
     a. Re-entry ("FO" and "LD" double) . . . . . 80·00   65·00
     Set of 3 . . . . 14·00   13·00

15   17 Superb Lyrebird

(Typo John Ash)

1931–36. *W* **15**. (*a*) *P* 13½ × 12½.
124   **5***a*   ½d. orange (2.33) . . . . 3·00   4·00
125   1d. green (Die I) (10.31) . . . . 1·25   10
     Wi. Wmk inverted . . . . 5·00   90
126   1½d. red-brown (10.36) . . . . 5·00   7·00
127   2d. golden scarlet (Die III) (18.12.31) . . . . . 1·75   10
     Wi. Wmk inverted . . . . 2·50   30
128   3d. ultramarine (Die II) (30.9.32) . . . . 16·00   55
     Wi. Wmk inverted . . . . £160   55·00
129   4d. yellow-olive (2.33) . . . . 16·00   70
     Wi. Wmk inverted . . . .
130   5d. orange-brown (Die II) (25.2.32) . . . . . . 14·00   15
     Wi. Wmk inverted . . . .
131   1s. 4d. turquoise (18.8.32) . . . . 70·00   3·25
     Wi. Wmk inverted . . . .
     Set of 8 . . . . £110   14·00

(*b*) *P* 12
132   **1**   6d. chestnut (Die IIB) (20.4.32) . . . . 20·00   24·00
133   9d. violet (Die IIB) (20.4.32) . . . . 18·00   75
134   2s. maroon (Die II) (6.8.35) . . . . 5·00   45
135   5s. grey and yellow (12.32) . . . . £100   9·50
136   10s. grey and pink (31.7.32) . . . . £250   90·00
137   £1 grey (Die IIB) (11.35) £425   £140
138   £2 black and rose (6.34) £1500   £225
     Set of 7 . . . . £2000   £450
     Set of 3 (*Nos.* 136-8) *optd "Specimen"* . . 85·00
Stamps as No. 127, without wmk and perf 11 are forgeries made in 1932 to defraud the P.O.
For re-engraved type of No. 134, see No. 212.

(Recess John Ash)

1931 (4 Nov). *Air Stamp. As T* **13** *but inscr* "AIR MAIL SERVICE" *in bottom tablet. No wmk. P* 11.
139   6d. sepia . . . . 16·00   12·00

1931 (17 Nov). *Air. No.* 139 *optd with Type* O **4**.
139a 6d. sepia . . . . 40·00 40·00
This stamp was not restricted to official use but was on general sale to the public.

(Des F. D. Manley. Recess John Ash)

1932 (15 Feb). *No wmk. P* 11.
140 **17** 1s. green . . . . 60·00 1·00
140a 1s. yellow-green . . . . 65·00 1·40

18 Sydney Harbour Bridge   19 Laughing Kookaburra

(Des R. A. Harrison. Eng F. D. Manley. Printed John Ash)

1932 (14 Mar). (*a*) *Recess. No. wmk. P* 11.
141 **18** 2d. scarlet . . . . 2·25 2·50
142 3d. blue . . . . 4·00 6·50
143 5s. blue-green £375 £180

(*b*) *Typo. W* **15**. *P* 10½.
144 **18** 2d. scarlet . . . . 2·50 85
Set of 4 . . . . £375 £180
Stamps as No. 144 without wmk and perf 11 are forgeries made in 1932 to defraud the P.O.

(Typo John Ash)

1932 (1 June). *W* **15**. *P* 13½ × 12½.
146 **19** 6d. red-brown . . . . 25·00 45
Wi. Wmk inverted . . . . — £100

20 Melbourne and R. Yarra   21 Merino Ram

(Des and eng F. D. Manley. Recess John Ash)

1934 (2 July). *Centenary of Victoria. W* **15**.

			I. *P* 10½.		II. *P* 11½.	
147	**20**	2d. orange-vermilion	2·00	1·00	4·00	1·25
148		3d. blue	6·00	5·50	7·00	7·00
149		1s. black	42·00	12·00	42·00	12·00
		Set of 3	45·00	17·00	48·00	18·00

(Des and eng F. D. Manley. Recess John Ash)

1934 (1 Nov). *Death Centenary of Capt. John Macarthur. W* **15**. *P* 11½.
150 **21** 2d. carmine-red (A) . . . . 3·25 1·00
150a 2d. carmine-red (B) . . . . 32·00 2·75
151 3d. blue . . . . 8·00 8·00
152 9d. bright purple . . . . 35·00 30·00
Set of 3 . . . . 42·00 35·00
Type A of the 2d. shows shading on the hill in the background varying from light to dark (as illustrated). Type B has the shading almost uniformly dark.

22 Hermes   23 Cenotaph, Whitehall

(Des F. D. Manley. Eng E. Broad and F. D. Manley. Recess John Ash until April 1940; W. C. G. McCracken thereafter)

1934–48. (*a*) *No wmk. P* 11.
153 **22** 1s. 6d. dull purple (1.12.34) . . . . 32·00 90

(*b*) *W* **15**. *P* 13½ × 14
153a **22** 1s. 6d. dull purple (22.10.37) . . . . 7·50 30
b. Thin rough paper (12.2.48) . . . . 7·00 40

(Des B. Cottier; adapted and eng F. D. Manley. Recess John Ash)

1935 (18 Mar). *20th Anniv of Gallipoli Landing. W* **15**. *P* 13½ × 12½ *or* 11 (1s.).
154 **23** 2d. scarlet 80 25
155 1s. black (*chalk-surfaced*) . . . . 48·00 38·00
a. Perf 13½ × 12½ £1500
Set of 2 . . . . 48·00 38·00

24 King George V   25 Amphitrite and Telephone
on "Anzac"   Cable

(Des and eng F. D. Manley. Recess John Ash)

1935 (2 May). *Silver Jubilee. Chalk-surfaced paper. W* **15** (*sideways*). *P* 11½.
156 **24** 2d. scarlet . . . . 1·00 30
157 3d. blue . . . . 6·00 6·00
158 2s. bright violet . . . . 45·00 38·00
Set of 3 . . . . 48·00 40·00

(Des and eng F. D. Manley. Recess John Ash)

1936 (1 Apr). *Opening of Submarine Telephone Link to Tasmania. W* **15**. *P* 11½.
159 **25** 2d. scarlet 60 35
160 3d. blue . . . . 2·50 3·25
Set of 2 . . . . 3·00 3·50

26 Site of Adelaide, 1836; Old Gum Tree,
Glenelg; King William St., Adelaide

(Des and eng F. D. Manley. Recess John Ash)

1936 (3 Aug). *Centenary of South Australia. W* **15**. *P* 11½.
161 **26** 2d. carmine 90 25
162 3d. blue . . . . 5·00 4·00
163 1s. green . . . . 10·00 7·00
Set of 3 . . . . 14·00 10·00

PRICES
George VI issues (1937–1952)

First column = Unmounted Mint
Second column = Mounted Mint
Third column = Used

27 Kangaroo   28 Queen Elizabeth   29 King George
VI

30   King George VI   31   32 Koala

Die I   Die Ia   Die II

33 Merino Ram   34 Laughing Kookaburra   35 Platypus

36 Superb Lyrebird   38 Queen Elizabeth   39 King George VI

40 King George VI and   40a   40b
    Queen Elizabeth   (Background evenly shaded,
                          lettering strengthened)

(Des R. A. Harrison (T **28/30**), F. D. Manley (T **27, 31/6**), H. Barr (T **38/9**), H. Barr and F. D. Manley (T **40**). Eng F. D. Manley and T. C. Duffell (T **34**), T. C. Duffell (revised lettering for T **40a/b**), F. D. Manley (others). All recess with John Ash, W. C. G. McCracken or "By Authority . . ." imprints)

1937–49. W **15** (sideways on 5d., 9d., 5s. and 10s.).

(a) P 13½ × 14 (vert designs) or 14 × 13½ (horiz)

164	27	½d. orange (3.10.38)	2·00	90	45
165	28	1d. emerald-green (10.5.37)	30	15	10
166	29	1½d. maroon (20.4.38)	9·00	4·25	2·50
167	30	2d. scarlet (10.5.37)	30	15	10
167a	31	3d. blue (Die I, 1st ptg) (2.8.37) . .	£110	50·00	65·00
168		3d. blue (Die I) (2.8.37)	45·00	15·00	7·50
168a		3d. blue (Die Ia) (1937)	£110	38·00	6·50
168b		3d. blue (Die II) (1938)	45·00	15·00	2·75
169		3d. bright blue, thin paper (Die II)			
		(21.12.38)	42·00	15·00	2·00
170	32	4d. green (1.2.38)	9·00	4·00	30
171	33	5d. purple (1.12.38)	4·00	1·50	40
172	34	6d. purple-brown (2.8.37)	24·00	8·00	80
173	35	9d. chocolate (1.9.38)	9·00	3·50	90
174	36	1s. grey-green (2.8.37)	55·00	18·00	1·90
175	31	1s. 4d. deep magenta (3.10.38) . .	2·50	1·00	1·75
		a. Pale magenta	1·50	65	1·50

(b) P 13½

176	38	5s. claret **C** (1.4.38)	10·00	3·50	75
		a. Thin rough paper **O** (4.2.48) . .	7·00	3·50	1·50
177	39	10s. dull purple **C** (1.4.38) (Optd S.			
		£30 unmounted £12 mount-			
		ed)	28·00	12·50	10·00
		a. Thin rough paper **O** (11.48) . .	55·00	22·00	20·00
178	40	£1 blue-slate **C** (1.11.38) (Optd S.			
		£400 unmounted £200 moun-			
		ted)	60·00	25·00	28·00
		a. Thin rough paper **O** (4.4.9) . .	£110	50·00	60·00
		Set of 14	£225	90·00	45·00

(c) P 15 × 14 (vert designs) or 14 × 15 (horiz)

179	27	½d. orange (28.1.42).	45	15	10
		a. Coil pair	10·00	4·25	12·00
180	40a	1d. emerald-green (1.8.38)	1·25	35	10
181		1d. maroon (10.12.41)	1·25	35	10
		a. Coil pair	12·00	5·00	14·00
182	29	1½d. maroon (21.11.41)	4·50	2·25	7·50
183		1½d. emerald-green (10.12.41). . . .	1·00	35	25
184	40b	2d. scarlet (11.7.38)	2·25	70	10
		a. Coil pair	£275	£150	£275
		Wi. Wmk inverted (from booklets)	6·00	3·00	
185		2d. bright purple (10.12.41)	50	20	40
		a. Coil pair	25·00	11·00	26·00
		Wi. Wmk inverted (from coils) . . .	30·00	15·00	
186	31	3d. bright blue (10.40)	38·00	12·00	2·00
187		3d. purple-brown (10.1.42)	20	10	10
188	32	4d. green (10.42)	1·50	45	10
		Wi. Wmk inverted	†	†	—
188a	33	5d. purple (5.46)	45	20	1·50
189	34	6d. red-brown (5.42)	2·00	75	10
		a. Purple-brown (1944)	1·75	65	10
190	35	9d. chocolate (1943).	80	40	10
191	36	1s. grey-green (3.41)	1·00	55	10
		Wi. Wmk inverted	£275	£120	
		Set of 14	50·00	17·00	11·00

For unwmkd issue, see Nos. 228/30d.

Dies of the 3d. In Die I the letters "TA" of "POSTAGE" at right are joined by a white flaw; the outline of the chin consists of separate strokes.

Die Ia is similar, but "T" and "A" have been clearly separated by retouches made on the plate.

In Die II "T" and "A" are separate and a continuous line has been added to the chin. The outline of the cheek extends to about 1 mm above the lobe of the King's right ear.

No. 167a is a preliminary printing made with unsuitable ink and may be detected by the absence of finer details; the King's face appears whitish and the wattles are blank. The greater part of this printing was distributed to the Press with advance notices of the issue.

No. 186 is re-engraved and differs from Nos. 167a to 169 in the King's left eyebrow which is shaded downwards from left to right instead of from right to left.

Thin paper. Nos. 176a, 177a, 178a. In these varieties the watermark is more clearly visible on the back and the design is much less sharp. Early printings of No. 176a have tinted paper.

SPECIAL COIL PERFORATION. This special perforation of large and small holes on the narrow sides of the stamps is intended for stamps issued in coils, to facilitate separation. When they exist we list them as "Coil pairs".

The following with "special coil" perforation were placed on sale in sheets: Nos. 204ba, 222a (1952), 228, 230, 237, 262 (1953), 309, 311 and 314. These are listed as "Coil blocks of four".

Coils with "normal" perforations also exist for some values.

PUZZLED ?

Then you need
PHILATELIC TERMS ILLUSTRATED
to tell you all you need to know about printing methods, papers, errors, varieties, watermarks, perforations, etc. 192 pages, almost half in full colour, soft cover. Second Edition.

41 "Governor Phillip at Sydney Cove" (J. Allcot)

"Tail" flaw

(Des and eng E. Broad and F. D. Manley. Recess J. Ash)

1937 (1 Oct). *150th Anniv of Foundation of New South Wales. W* **15**. *P* 13½ × 14.

193	41	2d. scarlet	1·50	60	10
		a. "Tail" flaw (Left pane R. 7/1)	£170	80·00	40·00
194		3d. bright blue	10·00	4·00	1·75
195		9d. purple	22·00	10·00	7·00
		Set of 3	30·00	13·00	8·00
		First Day Cover			11·00

42 A.I.F. and Nurse

(Des and eng F. D. Manley from drawing by Virgil Reilly. Recess W. C. G. McCracken)

1940 (15 July). *Australian Imperial Forces. W* **15** *(sideways). P* 14 × 13½.

196	42	1d. green	1·50	60	60
197		2d. scarlet	1·50	60	15
198		3d. blue	7·00	3·00	5·00
199		6d. brown-purple	20·00	6·00	9·00
		Set of 4	27·00	10·00	13·50
		First Day Cover			18·00

(43) (44) (45)

(Opts designed by F. D. Manley)

1941 (10 Dec). *Nos. 184, 186 and 171 surch with T* **43/5**.

200	40b	2½d. on 2d. (V.)	1·25	40	20
201	31	3½d. on 3d. (Y. on Black)	1·50	60	1·25
202	33	5½d. on 5d. (V.)	7·50	3·00	2·75
		Set of 3	9·00	3·50	3·75

46 Queen Elizabeth 46a

48 King George VI **49** King George VI **50** Emu

(Des and eng F. D. Manley)

1942–44. *Recess. W* **15**. *P* 15 × 14.

203	46	1d. brown-purple (1.1.43)	20	10	10
		a. Coil pair	10·00	3·75	13·00
204	46a	1½d. green (1.12.42)	20	10	10
204a	47	2d. bright purple (4.12.44)	40	15	25
		b. Coil pair	40·00	19·00	45·00
		ba. Coil block of four			
205	48	2½d. scarlet (7.1.42)	20	10	10
		a. Imperf (pair)*	—	£1300	
		Wi. Wmk inverted (from booklets)	1·00	50	
206	49	3½d. bright blue (3.42)	25	10	10
		a. Deep blue	50	20	15
207	50	5½d. slate-blue (12.2.42)	65	25	10
		Set of 6	1·75	65	35

*No. 205a is in pair with stamp which only has the right-hand side imperf.

For stamps as Nos. 204/a but without watermark see Nos. 229/30.

52 Duke and Duchess of Gloucester

(Des and eng F. D. Manley. Recess)

1945 (19 Feb). *Arrival of Duke and Duchess of Gloucester in Australia. W* **15**. *P* 14½.

209	52	2½d. lake	10	10	10
210		3½d. ultramarine	15	10	25
211		5½d. indigo	20	10	30
		Set of 3	40	15	55
		First Day Cover			1·75

A B

1946 (3 Jan). *Kangaroo type, re-engraved as B. W* **15**. *P* 12.

| 212 | 1 | 2s. maroon | 3·25 | 1·75 | 3·75 |
| | | Wi. Wmk inverted | † | † | — |

Earlier version (No. 134) has two background lines between the value circle and "TWO SHILLINGS"; No. 212 has only one line in this position. There are also differences in the shape of the letters.

47 King George VI **53** Star and Wreath **56** Sir Thos. Mitchell and Queensland

(Des F. D. Manley (2½d.), F. D. Manley and G. Lissenden (3½d.),
G. Lissenden (5½d.). Eng F. D. Manley. Recess)

1946 (18 Feb). *Victory Commemoration. T* **53** *and similar designs.*
W **15** *(sideways on* 5½d.). *P* 14½.

213	2½d. scarlet		10	10	10
214	3½d. blue		25	10	65
215	5½d. green		30	15	45
	Set of 3		60	30	1·10
	First Day Cover				2·00

Designs: *Horiz*—3½d. Flag and dove. *Vert*—5½d. Angel.

(Des and eng F. D. Manley. Recess)

1946 (14 Oct). *Centenary of Mitchell's Exploration of Central Queensland.* W **15**. *P* 14½.

216	**56**	2½d. scarlet		10	10	10
217		3½d. blue		15	10	50
218		1s. grey-olive		20	10	20
		Set of 3		40	20	65
		First Day Cover				2·00

57 Lt John   58 Steel Foundry   59 Coal Carrier Cranes
Shortland R.N.

(Des G. Lissenden, eng G. Lissenden and F. D. Manley (5½d.); des and eng
F. D. Manley (others). Recess)

1947 (8 Sept). *Sesquicentenary of City of Newcastle, New South Wales.*
W **15** *(sideways on* 3½d.). *P* 14½ *or* 15 × 14 (2½d.).

219	**57**	2½d. lake		10	10	10
		a. Imperf three sides		£700		
220	**58**	3½d. blue		15	10	40
221	**59**	5½d. green		15	10	30
		Set of 3		35	15	65
		First Day Cover				1·75

The following items are understood to have been the subject of
unauthorised leakages from the Commonwealth Note and Stamp
Printing Branch and are therefore not listed by us.
It is certain that none of this material was distributed to post offices
for issue to the public.
Imperforate all round. 1d. Princess Elizabeth; 1½d. Queen; 2½d.
King; 4d. Koala; 6d. Kookaburra; 9d. Platypus; 1s. Lyre-bird (small);
1s. 6d. Air Mail (Type **22**); 2½d. Newcastle.
Also 2½d. Peace, unwatermarked; 2½d. King, *tête-bêche*; 3½d.
Newcastle, in dull ultramarine; 2½d. King on "toned" paper.

60 Queen Elizabeth II when Princess

(Des R. A. Harrison. Eng F. D. Manley. Recess)

1947 (20 Nov)–**48**. *Marriage of Princess Elizabeth. P* 14 × 15.

(a) W **15** *(sideways)*

222	**60**	1d. purple		10	10	10

(b) No wmk

222a	**60**	1d. purple		10	10	10
		b. Coil pair		2·00	1·00	4·50
		c. Coil block of four		4·00	2·00	
		First Day Cover				75

61 Hereford Bull   61a Hermes and Globe

62 Aboriginal Art   62a Commonwealth
Coat of Arms

(Des G. Sellheim (T **62**), F. D. Manley (others), eng F. D. Manley and
G. Lissenden (T **62**), F. D. Manley (others). Recess)

1948 (16 Feb)–**56**. *(a)* W **15** *(sideways). P* 14½.

223	**61**	1s. 3d. brown-purple		1·75	70	75
223a	**61a**	1s. 6d. blackish brown (1.9.49)		1·75	80	10
224	**62**	2s. chocolate		2·00	90	10

(b) W **15**. *P* 14½ × 13½

224a	**62a**	5s. claret (11.4.49)		7·00	3·50	15
		ab. Thin paper		20·00	9·00	65
224b		10s. purple (3.10.49)		30·00	14·00	65
224c		£1 blue (28.11.49)		48·00	20·00	2·75
224d		£2 green (16.1.50)		£100	50·00	13·00
		Set of 3 (*Nos. 224b/d*)				
		"*Specimen*"		£150	80·00	

(c) No wmk. P 14½

224e	**61a**	1s. 6d. blackish brown (6.12.56)		18·00	8·00	60
224f	**62**	2s. chocolate (21.7.56)		20·00	9·50	45
		Set of 9 (*Nos. 223/224f*)		£200	95·00	16·00

No. 224ab is an emergency printing on white Harrison paper instead of
the toned paper used for No. 224a.

63 William J.   64 F. von Mueller   65 Boy Scout
Farrer

(Des and eng F. D. Manley. Recess)

1948 (12 July). *William J. Farrer (wheat research).* W **15**. *P* 15 × 14.

225	**63**	2½d. scarlet		10	10	10
		First Day Cover				1·25

(Des and eng F. D. Manley. Recess)

1948 (13 Sept). *Sir Ferdinand von Mueller (botanist).* W **15**. *P* 15 × 14.

226	**64**	2½d. lake		10	10	10
		First Day Cover				1·25

(Des and eng F. D. Manley. Recess)

1948 (15 Nov). *Pan-Pacific Scout Jamboree, Wonga Park.* W **15** *(sideways). P* 14 × 15.

227	**65**	2½d. lake		10	10	10
		First Day Cover				1·25

See also No. 254.

Sky retouch (normally unshaded near hill)

No. 230da. Major retouch consisting of repair to weak entry over a large area at left of bird's feathers (Upper plate left pane Row 9/3).

1948–56. No wmk. P 15 × 14 or 14 × 15 (9d.).

228	27	½d. orange (9.49)	20	10	10
		aa. Sky retouch (Rt. pane, R. 6/8)	6·00	3·00	
		a. Coil pair	75	35	2·00
		ab. Sky retouch (in pair)	70·00	30·00	
		b. Coil block of four	2·00	90	
229	46a	1½d. green (29.8.49)	90	30	45
230	47	2d. bright purple (12.48)	70	30	35
		aa. Coil pair	3·00	1·50	4·50
		ab. Coil block of four	£150	£100	
230a	32	4d. green (18.8.56)	2·00	90	40
230b	34	6d. purple-brown (18.8.56)	3·50	1·25	30
230c	35	9d. chocolate (13.12.56)	16·00	6·50	1·00
230d	36	1s. grey-green (13.12.56)	12·00	5·00	40
		da. "Green mist" retouch	—	£550	
		Set of 7	32·00	13·00	2·75

66 "Henry Lawson"
(Sir Lionel Lindsay)

67 Mounted Postman and
Aeroplane

(Des F. D. Manley. Eng E. R. M. Jones. Recess)

1949 (17 June). *Anniv of Birth of Henry Lawson (poet).* P 15 × 14.

231	66	2½d. maroon	15	10	10
		First Day Cover			1·25

(Des Sir Daryl Lindsay and F. D. Manley. Eng F. D. Manley. Recess)

1949 (10 Oct). *75th Anniv of Founding of U.P.U.* P 15 × 14.

232	67	3½d. ultramarine	20	10	25
		First Day Cover			1·25

68 Lord Forrest of   69 King George VI   70 Queen
Bunbury   Elizabeth

(Des and eng F. D. Manley. Recess)

1949 (28 Nov). *Lord Forrest of Bunbury (explorer and politician).* W **15**. P 15 × 14.

233	68	2½d. lake	15	10	10
		First Day Cover			1·25

(Des and eng F. D. Manley. Recess)

1950–51. P 15 × 14. (a) W **15**.

234	69	2½d. scarlet (12.4.50)	10	10	10
235		3d. scarlet (28.2.51)	15	10	10
		aa. Coil pair	9·00	4·25	12·00
		Set of 2	25	15	15

(b) No wmk

235a	69	2½d. purple-brown (23.5.51)	15	10	15
235b		3d. grey-green (14.11.51)	15	10	10
		c. Coil pair	16·00	8·00	24·00
		Set of 2	30	15	20

On 1 December 1951 No. 235 was placed on sale in sheets of 144 originally intended for use in stamp booklets. These sheets contain 3 panes of 48 (16 × 3) with horizontal gutter margin between.

(Des and eng F. D. Manley. Recess)

1950–51. P 15 × 14.

236	70	1½d. green (19.6.50)	15	10	10
237		2d. yellow-green (28.3.51)	15	10	10
		a. Coil pair	3·75	1·90	6·00
		b. Coil block of four	8·00	4·00	
		Set of 2	30	15	20

71 Aborigine

72
73
Reproductions of First Stamps of New
South Wales and Victoria

(Des F. D. Manley. Eng E. R. M. Jones. Recess)

1950 (14 Aug). W **15**. P 15 × 14.

238	71	8½d. brown	15	10	40

For T **71** in a larger size, see Nos. 253/b.

(Des and eng E. R. M. Jones (T **72**); des and eng G. Lissenden (T **73**). Recess)

1950 (27 Sept). *Centenary of First Adhesive Postage Stamps in Australia.* P 15 × 14.

239	72	2½d. maroon	10	10	10
		a. Horiz pair. Nos. 239/40	20	15	55
240	73	2½d. maroon	10	10	10
		Set of 2	20	15	10
		First Day Cover			1·25

Nos. 239/40 were printed alternately in vertical columns throughout the sheet.

74 Sir Edmund
Barton

75 Sir Henry
Parkes

76 "Opening First Federal Parliament" (T. Roberts)

77 Federal Parliament House, Canberra

(Des and eng F. D. Manley. Recess)

1951 (1 May). *Golden Jubilee of Commonwealth of Australia. P* 15 × 14.

241	74	3d. lake	30	10	10
		a. Horiz pair. Nos 241/2	1·50	55	1·75
242	75	3d. lake	30	10	10
243	76	5½d. blue	20	15	1·50
244	77	1s. 6d. purple-brown	35	25	50
		Set of 4	1·75	85	2·00
		First Day Cover			3·00

Nos. 241/2 are printed alternately in vertical columns throughout the sheet.

78
E. H. Hargraves

79
C. J. Latrobe

80
King George VI

(Des and eng F. D. Manley. Recess)

1951 (2 July). *Centenary of Discovery of Gold in Australia. P* 15 × 14.

245	78	3d. maroon	30	10	10
		a. Horiz pair. Nos. 245/6	60	25	95

(Des and eng F. D. Manley. Recess)

1951 (2 July). *Centenary of Responsible Government in Victoria. P* 15 × 14.

246	79	3d. maroon	30	10	10
		First Day Cover (Nos. 245/6)			1·75

Nos. 245/6 were printed alternately in vertical columns throughout the sheet.

(Des and eng. E. R. M. Jones. Recess)

1951 (31 Oct). *W* 15. *P* 15 × 14.

247	80	7½d. blue	15	10	40
		a. Imperf 3 sides (vert pr)	—	£1500	

81 King George VI

(Des F. D. Manley. Eng G. Lissenden. Recess)

1951–52. *W* 15. *P* 15 × 14.

248	81	3½d. brown-purple (28.11.51)	10	10	10
249		4½d. scarlet (20.2.52)	15	10	50
250		6½d. brown (20.2.52)	15	10	45
251		6½d. emerald-green (9.4.52)	10	10	15
		Set of 4	45	25	1·10

82 King George VI

(Des F. D. Manley. Eng D. Cameron (No. 252), E. R. M. Jones (Nos. 253/b). Recess)

1952 (19 Mar)–**65.** *P* 14½. *(a) W* 15 *(sideways).*

252	82	1s. 0½d. indigo	35	15	30
253	–	2s. 6d. deep brown	2·50	1·25	25
		Wi. Wmk Crown to left of C of A*	†	†	—
		Set of 2	2·75	1·40	55

(b) No wmk

253a	–	2s. 6d. deep brown (30.1.57)	5·00	2·00	30
		b. *Sepia* (10.65)	10·00	3·50	8·50

Design:—2s. 6d. As T **71** but larger (21 × 25½ mm).

*The normal sideways watermark on No. 253 shows Crown to right of C of A, *as seen from the back of the stamp.*

No. 253b was an emergency printing and can easily be distinguished from No. 253a as it is on white Harrison paper, No. 253a being on toned paper.

(Des and eng F. D. Manley. Recess)

1952 (19 Nov). *Pan-Pacific Scout Jamboree, Greystanes. As T* **65,** *but inscr* "1952–53" *W* 15 *(sideways). P* 14 × 15.

254		3½d. brown-lake	10	10	10
		First Day Cover			1·25

83 Butter   84 Wheat   85 Beef

(Des P.O. artists; adapted G. Lissenden. Typo)

1953 (11 Feb). *Food Production. P* 14½.

255	83	3d. emerald	30	10
		a. Strip of 3. Nos. 255/7	2·75	
256	84	3d. emerald	30	10
257	85	3d. emerald	30	10
258	83	3½d. scarlet	30	10
		a. Strip of 3. Nos. 258/60	2·75	
259	84	3½d. scarlet	30	10
260	85	3½d. scarlet	30	40
		Set of 6	5·00	40
		First Day Cover		12·00

The three designs in each denomination appear in rotation, both horizontally and vertically, throughout the sheet.

86 Queen
Elizabeth II

87 Queen Elizabeth II

(Des F. D. Manley from photograph by Dorothy Wilding Ltd. Eng D. Cameron. Recess)

1953–56. *P* 15 × 14. *(a) No wmk.*

261	86	1d. purple (19.8.53)	15	10
261a		2½d. blue (23.6.54)	20	10
262		3d. deep green (17.6.53)	20	10
		aa. Coil pair	4·50	5·50
		ab. Coil block of four	9·00	
262a		3½d. brown-red (2.7.56)	2·25	10
262b		6½d. orange (9.56)	2·75	70
		Set of 5	5·00	80

(b) W **15**

263	**86**	3½d. brown-red (21.4.53)		20	10
263a		6½d. orange (23.6.54)		1·50	10
		Set of 2		1·60	15

(Des and eng F. D. Manley. Recess)

1953 (25 May). *Coronation.* P 15 × 14.

264	**87**	3½d. scarlet	35	10
265		7½d. violet	1·50	55
266		2s. dull bluish green	5·50	30
		Set of 3	6·50	75
		First Day Cover		3·00

88 Young Farmers and Calf

(Des P.O. artist; adapted P. E. Morriss. Eng E. R. M. Jones. Recess)

1953 (3 Sept). *25th Anniv of Australian Young Farmers' Clubs.* P 14½.

267	**88**	3½d. red-brown and deep green	10	10
		First Day Cover		50

89 Lt.-Gov. D Collins	**90** Lt.-Gov. W. Paterson

91 Sullivan Cove, Hobart, 1804

(Des E. R. M. Jones, eng D. Cameron (T **89/90**); des and eng G. Lissenden (T **91**). Recess)

1953 (23 Sept). *150th Anniv of Settlement in Tasmania.* P 15 × 14.

268	**89**	3½d. brown-purple	30	10
		a. Horiz pair. Nos. 268/9	80	1·25
269	**90**	3½d. brown-purple	30	10
270	**91**	2s. green	2·00	2·50
		Set of 3	2·50	2·50
		First Day Cover		4·50

Nos. 268/9 are printed alternately in vertical columns throughout the sheet.

92 Stamp of 1853

(Des R. L. Beck; eng G. Lissenden. Recess)

1953 (11 Nov). *Tasmanian Postage Stamp Centenary.* P 14½.

271	**92**	3d. rose-red	10	10
		First Day Cover		75

93 Queen Elizabeth II and Duke of Edinburgh

94 Queen Elizabeth II	Re-entry (R. 8/2)

(Des and eng F. D. Manley; border and lettering on 7½d. des by R. M. Warner. Recess)

1954 (2 Feb). *Royal Visit.* P 14.

272	**93**	3½d. scarlet	20	10
		a. Re-entry	25·00	5·00
273	**94**	7½d. purple	35	50
274	**93**	2s. dull bluish green	85	30
		Set of 3	1·25	75
		First Day Cover		1·75

95 "Telegraphic Communications"	**96** Red Cross and Globe

(Des R. M. Warner. Eng P. E. Morriss. Recess)

1954 (7 Apr). *Australian Telegraph System Centenary.* P 14.

275	**95**	3½d. brown-red	10	10
		First Day Cover		50

(Des B. Stewart. Eng P. E. Morriss. Design recess; cross typo)

1954 (9 June). *40th Anniv of Australian Red Cross Society.* P 14½.

276	**96**	3½d. ultramarine and scarlet	10	10
		First Day Cover		50

97 Black Swan	**98** Locomotives of 1854 and 1954

(Des R. L. Beck. Eng G. Lissenden. Recess)

1954 (2 Aug). *Western Australian Postage Stamp Centenary.* P 14½.

277	**97**	3½d. black	15	10
		First Day Cover		60

(Des R. M. Warner. Eng G. Lissenden. Recess)

1954 (13 Sept). *Australian Railways Centenary.* P 14.

278	**98**	3½d. purple-brown	15	10
		First Day Cover		60

99 Territory Badge   100 Olympic Games Symbol

(Des F. D. Manley. Eng G. Lissenden. Recess)

1954 (17 Nov).   *Australian Antarctic Research. P* 14½ × 13½.
279 **99**   3½d. grey-black   15   10
              First Day Cover   70

(Des R. L. Beck. Eng P. E. Morriss. Recess)

1954–55.   *Olympic Games Propaganda. P* 14.
280 **100**   2s. deep bright blue (1.12.54)   70   40
280a   2s. deep bluish green (30.11.55) ...... 2·00 70
               Set of 2 .... 2·50 1·10
               First Day Covers (2) ....   4·00

101 Rotary Symbol,   102 Queen Elizabeth II
     Globe and Flags

(Des and eng D. Cameron. Recess)

1955 (23 Feb).   *50th Anniv of Rotary International. P* 14 × 14½.
281 **101**   3½d. carmine   10   10
               First Day Cover   50

(Des F. D. Manley from bas-relief by W. L. Bowles. Eng G. Lissenden.
Recess)

1955 (9 Mar)–**57.**   *P* 14½. (*a*) *W* **15** (*sideways*).
282 **102**   1s. 0½d. deep blue ....   3·00   30

               (*b*) *No wmk*
282a **102**   1s. 7d. red-brown (13.3.57) .... 3·50   10

103 American Memorial,   104 Cobb & Co. Coach (from
     Canberra   dry-print by Sir Lionel Lindsay)

(Des R. L. Beck (head by F. D. Manley). Eng F. D. Manley. Recess)

1955 (4 May).   *Australian-American Friendship. P* 14 × 14½.
283 **103**   3½d. violet-blue   10   10
               First Day Cover   50

(Design adapted and eng by F. D. Manley. Recess)

1955 (6 July).   *Mail-coach Pioneers Commemoration. P* 14½ × 14.
284 **104**   3½d. blackish brown   25   10
285   2s. reddish brown   75   1·25
               Set of 2 .... 1·00   1·25
               First Day Cover ....   3·00

105 Y.M.C.A. Emblem and Map   106 Florence Nightingale
     of the World   and Young Nurse

(Des E. Thake. Eng P. E. Morriss. Design recess; emblem typo)

1955 (10 Aug).   *World Centenary of Y.M.C.A P* 14½ × 14.
286 **105**   3½d. deep bluish green and red   10   10
               a. Red (emblem) omitted £4000
               First Day Cover   50

(Des and eng F. D. Manley. Recess)

1955 (21 Sept).   *Nursing Profession Commemoration. P* 14 × 14½.
287 **106**   3½d. reddish violet   10   10
               First Day Cover   50

107 Queen Victoria   108 Badges of New South Wales,
                                  Victoria and Tasmania

(Des and eng D. Cameron. Recess)

1955 (17 Oct).   *Centenary of First South Australian Postage Stamps.
P* 14½.
288 **107**   3½d. green   10   10
               First Day Cover   50

(Des and eng F. D. Manley. Recess)

1956 (26 Sept).   *Centenary of Responsible Government in New South
Wales, Victoria and Tasmania. P* 14½ × 14.
289 **108**   3½d. brown-lake   10   10
               First Day Cover   50

109 Arms of   110 Olympic Torch and
     Melbourne   Symbol

111 Collins Street, Melbourne   112 Melbourne across R. Yarra

(Des P. E. Morriss; eng F. D. Manley (4d.). Des and eng F. D. Manley (7½d.). Recess. Des and photo Harrison from photographs by M. Murphy and sketches by L. Coles (1s.). Des and photo Courvoisier from photographs by M. Murphy (2s.))

1956 (31 Oct). *Olympic Games, Melbourne. P* 14½ (4d.), 14 × 14½ (7½d., 1s.) *or* 11½ (2s.).

290	109	4d.	carmine-red	25	10
291	110	7½d.	deep bright blue	40	60
292	111	1s.	multicoloured	40	20
293	112	2s.	multicoloured	50	60
			Set of 4	1·40	1·25
			First Day Cover	3·00	

113	114	115 South Australia
Queen Elizabeth II	Queen Elizabeth II	Coat of Arms

(Des F. D. Manley from bas-relief by W. L. Bowles. Eng G. Lissenden. Recess.)

1957 (6 Mar–13 Nov). *P* 15 × 14.

294	113	4d.	lake (13 Mar)	30	10
294a	114	7½d.	violet (13 Nov)	1·25	85
			ab. Double print	£550	
295	113	10d.	deep grey-blue	1·50	30
			Set of 3	2·75	1·10

The 4d. exists in booklet panes of six stamps, with imperf outer edges, producing single stamps with one or two adjacent sides imperf.

(Des and eng P. E. Morriss. Recess)

1957 (17 Apr) *Centenary of Responsible Government in South Australia. P* 14½.

296	115	4d.	red-brown	10	10
			First Day Cover	50	

116 Map of Australia and Caduceus

(Des J. E. Lyle; adapted B. Stewart. Eng D. Cameron. Recess)

1957 (21 Aug). *Flying Doctor Service. P* 14½ × 14.

297	116	7d.	ultramarine	15	10
			First Day Cover	1·00	

117 "The Spirit of Christmas"

Re-entry (Row 10/1)

(Des and eng D. Cameron from a painting by Sir Joshua Reynolds. Recess)

1957 (6 Nov). *Christmas. P* 14½ × 14.

298	117	3½d.	scarlet	10	10
			a. Re-entry	7·00	4·00
299		4d.	purple	10	10
			Set of 2	20	10
			First Day Cover	90	

118
Super-Constellation Airliner

(Des and eng P. E. Morriss. Recess)

1958 (6 Jan). *Inauguration of Australian "Round the World" Air Service. P* 14½ × 14.

301	118	2s.	deep blue	50	75
			First Day Cover	1·50	

119 Hall of Memory, Sailor	120 Sir Charles
and Airman	Kingsford Smith
	and *Southern Cross*

(Des and eng G. Lissenden. Recess)

1958 (10 Feb). *Australian War Memorial, Canberra. T* **119** *and similar horiz design. P* 14½ × 14.

302	119	5½d.	brown-red	55	25
			a. Horiz pair. Nos. 302/3	1·10	5·00
303	–	5½d.	brown-red	55	25
			Set of 2	1·10	50
			First Day Cover	5·50	

No. 303 shows a soldier and service-woman respectively in place of the sailor and airman. Nos. 302/3 are printed alternately in vertical columns throughout the sheet.

(Des J. E. Lyle. Eng F. D. Manley. Recess)

1958 (27 Aug). *30th Anniv of First Air Crossing of the Tasman Sea. P* 14 × 14½.

304	120	8d.	deep ultramarine	60	70
			First Day Cover	1·40	

121 Silver Mine, Broken Hill	122 The Nativity

(Des R. H. Evans; adapted and eng F. D. Manley. Recess)

1958 (10 Sept). *75th Anniv of Founding of Broken Hill*. P 14½ × 14.

305	**121**	4d. chocolate	15	10
		First Day Cover		50

(Des D. Cameron. Eng P. E. Morriss. Recess)

1958 (5 Nov). *Christmas*. P 14½ × 15.

306	**122**	3½d. deep scarlet	10	10
307		4d. deep violet	10	10
		Set of 2	20	10
		First Day Cover		75

PHOSPHOR STAMPS ("Helecon").

Experiments, which had been going on since 1963, were based on a substance known commercially as "helecon", one of the zinc sulphide group. Helecon becomes luminescent in the orange-red spectrum when subjected to ultra-violet rays and has the property of "residual phosphorescence", i.e. it retains the luminescence for a brief period after the UV light is removed, enabling the "tagged" stamp to be detected by the scanners during the instant of lamp black-out. The point of this is that envelope paper, often treated by the manufacturer with a whitening agent, may also react under UV light but would cease to do so when the light source is removed. The success of the operation therefore depends on the UV lamp using a rapid on-off cycle, while the adjoining sensing mechanism is on "continuous alert".

Helecon has been incorporated in stamps in two different ways, either in the ink with which the stamps are printed, or included in the surface coating of the stamp paper.

The only certain method of positively identifying stamps containing helecon in ink or paper is to subject them to ultra-violet light within the 3,000–4,000 Angstrom range, preferably viewing through a suitable filter to retard visible blue light, when the helecon stamps should fluoresce brightly in orange-red colours.

Owing to the difficulty of identification without the use of a UV lamp we do not list the helecon stamps separately but when in stock can supply them after testing under the lamp.

The first stamp to be issued was the 11d. Bandicoot from an experimental printing of four million on helecon paper released to the public in December 1963. The next printing on ordinary paper was released in September 1964. The experimental printing was coarse, showing a lot of white dots and the colour is slate-blue, differing from both the ordinary and the later helecon paper.

The following helecon printings have been reported: 2d. and 3d. (sheets, coils and coil sheets), and 5d. (No. 354) Queen Elizabeth II; 8d. Tiger Cat; 11d. Bandicoot; 1s. Colombo Plan; 1s. 2d. Tasmanian Tiger; 2s. 3d. Wattle (No. 324a); and 6d. (No. 363a), 9d. and 1s. 6d. Birds (the 2s., 2s. 6d. and 3s. Birds were only issued on helecon paper). The 5d. Queen Elizabeth II in red (No. 354b) exists ordinary and with helecon ink. The coil pair was only issued with helecon ink; the booklet is normally with helecon ink, but some were printed with ordinary ink by mistake. The Churchill stamp was printed on ordinary and helecon paper. The I.T.U. Centenary and Monash and later commemorative stamps were printed on helecon paper and all issues from No. 382 onwards were on helecon paper or on paper coated with Derby luminescence.

There were initially two kinds of helecon paper:

(*a*) for Photogravure. Greyish cream, slight dulling of colours, which are generally paler. The normal stamps have a very white paper.

(*b*) for Recess. Cream paper, smooth surface, heavy coating looking like "chalk-surfaced". The normal stamps have white paper, rough and virtually unsurfaced. In both types of printing the helecon prints appear slightly sharper.

The above descriptions may serve as a general guide but are not likely to be very helpful for distinguishing used stamps.

In 1982 a series of booklet stamps, Nos. 870/4, were printed by Enschedé on Harrison paper which gives a bluish white reaction under U.V. light.

For developments in 1971 and 1986 see notes after Nos. 465 and 1038.

    127   128   129

Queen Elizabeth II

DIE I	DIE II
Short break in outer line to bottom right of "4"	Line unbroken

DIE A	DIE B
Four short lines inside "5"	Five short lines inside "5"

(Des G. Lissenden from photographs by Baron Studios. Eng F. D. Manley (2d.). D. Cameron (3d.). P. E. Morriss (others). Recess)

1959–62. P 14 × 15 (*horiz*), 15 × 14 (*vert*).

308	**123**	1d. deep slate-purple (2.2.59)	10	10
		a. Deep slate-lilac	40	20
309	**124**	2d. brown (21.3.62)	30	10
		a. Coil pair (1962)	3·75	4·25
		b. Coil block of four	7·50	
311	**126**	3d. blue-green (20.5.59)	15	10
		a. Coil pair (8.60)	3·50	4·00
		b. Coil block of four	7·00	
312	**127**	3½d. deep green (18.3.59)	15	10
313	**128**	4d. carmine-lake (Die I) (2.2.59)	1·25	10
		b. Die II	1·25	10
		ba. Carmine-red	1·25	10
314	**129**	5d. deep blue (Die A or B) (1.10.59)	60	10
		a. Vert se-tenant pair (A and B)	1·25	2·00
		b. Coil pair (early 1960)	6·00	8·00
		c. Coil block of four	15·00	
		Set of 6	2·25	25

No. 313. Die I occurs in the upper pane and Die II in the lower pane of the sheet.

No. 314. Both dies occur in alternate horizontal rows in the sheet (Die A in Row 1, Die B in Row 2, and so on), and their value is identical.

Nos. 309a/b, 311a/b and 314b/c have horizontal coil perforations as described after No. 191.

The Note after No. 295 also applies to Nos. 313/14.

  123   124   126

131 Banded Ant-eater   132 Tiger Cat (Dasyure)   133 Kangaroos

134 Rabbit Bandicoot

135 Platypus

136 Tasmanian Tiger

137 Christmas Bells

138 Flannel Flower

139 Wattle

140 Banksia

141 Waratah

142 Aboriginal Stockman

(Des Eileen Mayo (6d., 8d., 9d., 11d., 1s., 1s. 2d.), B. Stewart (5s.), Margaret Stones (others). Eng P. Morriss (11d.), F. D. Manley (1s.), B. Stewart (others). Recess)

1959-64. *W* 15 (5s.), *no wmk* (others). *P* 14 × 15 (*T* 136), 15 × 14 (*T* 131/5), 14½ × 14 (5s.) or 14½ (others).

316	131	6d. brown (30.9.60)	1·75	10
317	132	8d. red-brown (shades) (11.5.60)	75	10
		a. Pale red-brown (1961)	75	10
318	133	9d. deep sepia (21.10.59)	2·50	30
319	134	11d. deep blue (3.5.61)	1·00	10
320	135	1s. deep green (9.9.59)	3·50	20
321	136	1s. 2d. deep purple (21.3.62)	1·10	10
322	137	1s. 6d. crimson/yellow (3.2.60)	2·25	70
323	138	2s. grey-blue (8.4.59)	1·25	10
324	139	2s. 3d. green/maize (9.9.59)	1·75	10
324a		2s. 3d. yellow-green (28.10.64)	7·50	1·50
325	140	2s. 5d. brown/yellow (16.3.60)	6·50	35
326	141	3s. scarlet (15.7.59)	1·75	10
327	142	5s. red-brown (26.7.61)	25·00	75
		a. White paper. Brown-red (17.6.64) . .	£160	5·00
		Set of 13	50·00	4·00

No. 327 is on toned paper. No. 327a was a late printing on the white paper referred to in the note below No. 360.

See notes after No. 307 re helecon ink.

143 Postmaster Isaac Nichols boarding the brig *Experiment*

144 Parliament House, Brisbane, and Arms of Queensland

(Des R. Shackel; adapted and eng F. D. Manley. Recess)

1959 (22 Apr). *150th Anniv of the Australian Post Office. P* 14½ × 14.

331	143	4d. slate	15	10
		First Day Cover		50

(Des and eng G. Lissenden. Recess and typo)

1959 (5 June). *Centenary of Self-Government in Queensland. P* 14 × 14½.

332	144	4d. lilac and green	10	10
		First Day Cover		60

145 "The Approach of the Magi"

146 Girl Guide and Lord Baden-Powell

(Des and eng F. D. Manley. Recess)

1959 (4 Nov). *Christmas. P* 15 × 14.

333	145	5d. deep reddish violet	10	10
		First Day Cover		60

(Des and eng B. Stewart. Recess)

1960 (18 Aug). *Golden Jubilee of Girl Guide Movement. P* 14½ × 14.

334	146	5d. deep ultramarine	30	10
		First Day Cover		75

147 "The Overlanders" (Sir Daryl Lindsay)

148 "Archer" and Melbourne Cup

I Mane is rough   II Mane is smooth

Type II occurs on Pane A, Row 2 Nos. 8 and 9, Row 4 Nos. 1 to 12, Row 5 Nos. 10 to 12, and on Pane C, Row 4 Nos. 5 to 12, Row 5 Nos. 1 to 9, and Rows 6 to 10 inclusive; the stamps in Row 4 Nos. 5 to 12 and Row 5 Nos. 1 to 9 are considered to be of an intermediate type with the mane as in Type II but the ear and rein being as in Type I. All the rest are Type I.

(Adapted and eng P. E. Morriss. Recess)

1960 (21 Sept). *Centenary of Northern Territory Exploration. P* 15 × 14½.

335	147	5d. magenta (I)	15	10
		a. Type II	80	15
		First Day Cover		60

(Des F. D. Manley. Eng G. Lissenden. Recess)

1960 (12 Oct). *100th Melbourne Cup Race Commemoration. P* 14½.

336	148	5d. sepia	15	10
		First Day Cover		60

149 Queen Victoria   150 Open Bible and Candle

(Des F. D. Manley. Eng B. Stewart. Recess)

1960 (2 Nov). *Centenary of First Queensland Postage Stamp.* P 14½ × 15.

337	149	5d. deep myrtle-green	. . . .	25	10
		First Day Cover	. . . .		60

(Des K. McKay. Adapted and eng B. Stewart. Recess)

1960 (9 Nov). *Christmas.* P 15 × 14½.

338	150	5d. carmine-red	. . . .	10	10
		First Day Cover	. . . .		60

151 Colombo Plan   152 Melba (after bust by
Bureau Emblem   Sir Bertram Mackennal)

(Des and eng G. Lissenden. Recess)

1961 (30 June). *Colombo Plan.* P 14 × 14½.

339	151	1s. red-brown	. . . .	10	10
		First Day Cover	. . . .		95

See notes after No. 307 *re* helecon ink.

(Des and eng B. Stewart. Recess)

1961 (20 Sept). *Centenary of Birth of Dame Nellie Melba (singer).* P 14½ × 15.

340	152	5d. blue	. . . .	20	10
		First Day Cover	. . . .		60

153 Open Prayer Book and Text

(Des G. Lissenden. Eng P. E. Morriss. Recess)

1961 (8 Nov). *Christmas.* P 14½ × 14.

341	153	5d. brown	. . . .	10	10
		First Day Cover	. . . .		60

154 J. M. Stuart   155 Flynn's Grave and
Nursing Sister

(Des W. Jardine. Eng P. E. Morriss. Recess)

1962 (25 July). *Centenary of Stuart's Crossing of Australia from South to North.* P 14½ × 15.

342	154	5d. brown-red	. . . .	15	10
		First Day Cover	. . . .		60

(Des F. D. Manley. Photo)

1962 (5 Sept). *50th Anniv of Australian Inland Mission.* P 13½.

343	155	5d. multicoloured	. . . .	25	10
		a. Red omitted	. . . .	£350	£250
		First Day Cover	. . . .		60

The note below No. 372b also applies to No. 343a.

156 "Woman"   157 "Madonna and
Child"

(Des D. Dundas. Eng G. Lissenden. Recess)

1962 (26 Sept). *"Associated Country Women of the World" Conference, Melbourne.* P 14 × 14½.

344	156	5d. deep green	. . . .	10	10
		First Day Cover	. . . .		60

(Des and eng G. Lissenden. Recess)

1962 (17 Oct). *Christmas.* P 14½.

345	157	5d. violet	. . . .	15	10
		First Day Cover	. . . .		60

158 Perth and Kangaroo Paw   159 Arms of Perth and
(plant)   Running Track

(Des R. M. Warner (5d.), G. Hamori (2s. 3d.). Photo Harrison)

1962 (1 Nov). *Seventh British Empire and Commonwealth Games. Perth.* P 14 (5d.) or 14½ × 14 (2s. 3d.).

346	158	5d. multicoloured	. . . .	40	10
		a. Red omitted	. . . .	£375	
347	159	2s. 3d. black, red, blue and green	. . . . . .	2·50	2·50
		Set of 2	. . . .	2·75	2·50
		First Day Cover	. . . .		5·00

160 Queen Elizabeth II.   161 Queen Elizabeth II
and Duke of Edinburgh

(Des and eng after portraits by Anthony Buckley, P. E. Morriss (5d.), B. Stewart (2s. 3d.). Recess)

1963 (18 Feb). *Royal Visit.* P 14½.

348	160	5d. deep green	. . . .	35	10
349	161	2s. 3d. brown-lake	. . . .	1·90	3·00
		Set of 2	. . . .	2·25	3·00
		First Day Cover	. . . .		5·00

162 Arms of Canberra and   163 Centenary Emblem
W. B. Griffin (architect)

(Des and eng B. Stewart. Recess)

1963 (8 Mar). *50th Anniv of Canberra. P* 14½ × 14.
350	**162**	5d. deep green		15	10
		First Day Cover			50

(Des G. Hamori. Photo)

1963 (8 May). *Red Cross Centenary. P* 13½ × 13.
351	**163**	5d. red, grey-brown and blue		25	10
		First Day Cover			50

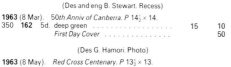

164 Blaxland, Lawson and Wentworth on Mt. York

(Des T. Alban. Eng P. E. Morriss. Recess)

1963 (28 May). *150th Anniv of First Crossing of Blue Mountains. P* 14½ × 14.
352	**164**	5d. ultramarine		15	10
		First Day Cover			50

165 "Export"   166 Queen Elizabeth II

(Des and eng B. Stewart. Recess)

1963 (28 Aug). *Export Campaign. P* 14½ × 14.
353	**165**	5d. red		10	10
		First Day Cover			50

(Des and eng P. E. Morriss from photograph by Anthony Buckley. Recess)

1963 (9 Oct)–**65**. *P* 15 × 14.
354	**166**	5d. deep green		45	10
		a. Imperf between (horiz pair) (31.7.64)		1·75	2·50
354b		5d. red (30.6.65)		40	10
		c. Coil pair (30.6.65)		14·00	18·00
		Set of 2		85	10

See notes after No. 307 re helecon ink.
The above exist in booklet panes of six stamps, with imperf outer edges, producing single stamps with one or two adjacent sides imperf.

STANLEY GIBBONS
STAMP COLLECTING SERIES

Introductory booklets on *How to Start, How to Identify Stamps* and *Collecting by Theme.* A series of well illustrated guides at a low price.
Write for details.

No. 354a comes from sheets of uncut booklet panes containing 288 stamps (16 × 18) with wide margins intersecting the sheet horizontally below each third row, alternate rows of stamps imperforate between vertically and the outer left, right and bottom margins imperforate. This means that in each sheet there are 126 pairs of stamps imperf between vertically, plus a number with wide imperforate margins attached, as shown in the illustration.

167 Tasman and *Heemskerk*   168 Dampier and *Roebuck*

169 Captain Cook   170 Flinders and *Investigator*

171 Bass and   172 Admiral King
Whaleboat   and *Mermaid*

(Des W. Jardine. Eng B. Stewart (4s., £1). E. R. M. Jones (10s.), P. E. Morriss (others), Recess)

1963–65. *No wmk (4s.) or W* **15** *(others), (sideways on* 5s., £1). *P* 14 *or* 14½ *(5s.,* £1, £2).

355	**167**	4s. ultramarine (9.10.63)	4·50	40
356	**168**	5s. red-brown (25.11.64)	6·00	60
357	**169**	7s. 6d. olive (26.8.64)	17·00	14·00
358	**170**	10s. brown-purple (26.2.64)	42·00	3·75
		a. White paper. *Deep brown-purple* (14.1.65)	55·00	6·00
359	**171**	£1 deep reddish violet (26.2.64)	48·00	12·00
		a. White paper. *Deep bluish violet* (16.11.64)	70·00	22·00
360	**172**	£2 sepia (26.8.64)	70·00	65·00
		Set of 6	£170	85·00
		Set of 4 (*Nos.* 357/60) *optd* "Specimen"	£450	

Nos. 358 and 359 were printed on a toned paper but all the other values are on white paper, the 4s. being on rather thicker paper.

173 "Peace on Earth . . ."

174 "Commonwealth Cable"

(Des R. M. Warner. Eng B. Stewart. Recess)

1963 (25 Oct). *Christmas. P* 14½.

361	**173**	5d. greenish blue	10	10
		First Day Cover		50

(Des P. E. Morriss. Photo)

1963 (3 Dec). *Opening of COMPAC (Trans-Pacific Telephone Cable). Chalky paper. P* 13½.

362	**174**	2s. 3d. red, blue, black and pale blue	3·00	3·50
		First Day Cover		5·50

175 Yellow-tailed Thornbill

176 Black-backed Magpie

177 Galah

178 Golden Whistler

179 Blue Wren

180 Scarlet Robin

181 Straw-necked Ibis

(Des Mrs. H. Temple-Watts. Photo)

1964 (11 Mar)–**65.** *Chalky paper (except No.* 367a). *P* 13½.

363	**175**	6d. brown, yellow, black and bluish green (19.8.64)	50	25
		a. Brown, yellow, black and emerald-green (12.65)	2·50	1·75
364	**176**	9d. black, grey and pale green	1·50	3·25
365	**177**	1s. 6d. pink, grey, dull purple and black . .	1·00	1·25
366	**178**	2s. yellow, black and pink (21.4.65)	2·50	50
367	**179**	2s. 5d. deep royal blue, light violet-blue, yellow-orange, grey and black	7·00	3·25
367a		2s. 5d. deep blue, light blue, orange-brown, blue-grey and black (8.65)	24·00	12·00
368	**180**	2s. 6d. black, red, grey and green (21.4.65)	3·75	2·50
		a. Red omitted (white breast)	£650	
369	**181**	3s. black, red, buff and yellow-green (21.4.65)	3·75	1·50
		Set of 8	40·00	22·00

No. 367a is from a printing on unsurfaced Wiggins Teape paper, the rest of the set being on chalk-surfaced Harrison paper. Apart from the differences in shade, the inscriptions, particularly "BLUE WREN", stand out very much more clearly on No. 367a. Although two colours are apparent in both stamps, the grey and black were printed from one plate.

See notes after No. 307 re helecon ink.

182 "Blériot" Aircraft (type flown by M. Guillaux, 1914)

Re-entry (upper plate, R. 4/4)

(Des K. McKay. Adapted and eng P. E. Morriss. Recess)

1964 (1 July). *50th Anniv of first Australian Airmail Flight. P* 14½ × 14.

370	**182**	5d. olive-green	40	10
		a. Re-entry	£100	40·00
371		2s. 3d. scarlet	2·25	2·00
		Set of 2	2·50	2·00
		First Day Cover		4·50

183 Child looking at Nativity Scene

184 "Simpson and his Donkey"

(Des P. E. Morriss and J. Mason. Photo)

1964 (21 Oct). *Christmas. Chalky paper. P* 13½.

372	**183**	5d. red, blue, buff and black	10	10
		a. Red omitted	£250	
		b. Black omitted	£250	
		First Day Cover		50

The red ink is soluble and can be removed by bleaching and it is therefore advisable to obtain a certificate from a recognised expert committee before purchasing No. 372a.

(Des C. Andrew (after statue, Shrine of Remembrance, Melbourne). Eng E. R. M. Jones. Recess)

1965 (14 Apr). *50th Anniv of Gallipoli Landing. P* 14 × 14½.

373	**184**	5d. drab	40	10
374		8d. blue	70	1·75
375		2s. 3d. reddish purple	1·25	1·75
		Set of 3	2·10	3·25
		First Day Cover		6·50

185 "Telecommunications"   186 Sir Winston Churchill

(Des J. McMahon and G. Hamori. Photo)

1965 (10 May). *I.T.U. Centenary. P* 13½.
376 185   5d. black, brown, orange-brown & bl   25   10
           a. Black (value and pylon) omitted £425
              First Day Cover   50

(Des P. E. Morriss from photo by Karsh. Photo)

1965 (24 May). *Churchill Commemoration. Chalky paper. P* 13½.
377 186   5d. black, pale grey and light blue   15   10
           a. Pale grey ("AUSTRALIA") omitted . . £350 £200
              First Day Cover   60
About half the printing was on helecon impregnated paper, differing slightly in the shade of the blue.

187 General Monash   188 Hargrave and "Seaplane" (1902)

(Des O. Foulkes and W. Walters. Photo)

1965 (23 June). *Birth Centenary of General Sir John Monash* (*engineer and soldier*). *Chalky paper. P* 13½.
378 187   5d. multicoloured   15   10
              First Day Cover   45

(Des G. Hamori. Photo)

1965 (4 Aug). *50th Death Anniv of Lawrence Hargrave* (*aviation pioneer*). *Chalky paper. P* 13½.
379 188   5d. purple-brown, blk, yell-ochre & pur . .   15   10
           a. Purple (value) omitted £140
              First Day Cover   45

189 I.C.Y. Emblem   190 "Nativity
                                Scene"

(Des H. Fallu from U.N. theme. Photo)

1965 (1 Sept). *International Co-operation Year. Chalky paper. P* 13½.
380 189   2s. 3d. emerald and light blue . . . . 1·75 2·00
              First Day Cover . . . .   3·75

(Des J. Mason. Photo)

1965 (20 Oct). *Christmas. P* 13½.
381 190   5d. multicoloured   15   10
           a. Gold omitted £250
           b. Blue omitted £225
              First Day Cover   45
No. 381a comes from the bottom row of a sheet in which the gold is completely omitted, the background appearing as black with "CHRISTMAS 1965" and "AUSTRALIA" omitted. The row above had the black missing from the lower two-fifths of the stamp.

(New Currency. 100 cents = 1 dollar)

191 Queen Elizabeth   192 Blue-faced   193 Humbug Fish
        II   Honeyeater

194 Coral Fish   195 Hermit Crab   196 Anemone Fish

197 Red-necked   198 Azure King-
    Avocet   fisher

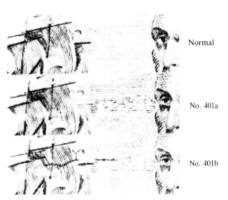

Normal

No. 401a

No. 401b

Heavy recutting between sails and eye. This is found in two variations: No. 401a Recut lines; No. 401b as before but a plate crack shown as an irregular line from sky to main sail (Lower sheet, left pane, Row 10/1).

(Des Mrs. H. Temple-Watts (6 c. T **192**, 13 c., 24 c.), Eileen Mayo (7 c. (No. **388**) to 10 c.). Recess (T **191**, 40 c. to 54 c.). Photo Chalky paper (*others*))

1966 (14 Feb)–**73**. *Decimal currency. No wmk. P* 15 × 14 (T **191**), 14 (40 c., 75 c., $1), 14½ (50 c., $2, $4) *or* 13½ (*others*).
382 191   1 c. deep red-brown   25   10
383   2 c. olive-green   90   10
384   3 c. slate-green   90   10
385   4 c. red   20   10
           a. Booklet pane. Five stamps plus one
              printed label . . . . 35·00
386 175   5 c. brown, yellow, black, & emer-grn . . .   25   10
           a. Brown (plumage) omitted £400
           b. *Brown, yellow, black & bl-grn* (1.67)   25   10

386c	191	5 c. deep blue (29.9.67)	2·50	10
		ca. Booklet pane. Five stamps plus one printed label	8·00	
		cb. Imperf in horiz strip of 3*	£550	
387	192	6 c. olive-yellow, blk, blk & pale grey	70	40
		aa. Blue (eye markings) omitted	90·00	
387a	191	6 c. orange (28.9.70)	35	10
388	193	7 c. black, grey, salmon and brown	1·50	10
388a	191	7 c. purple (1.10.71)	1·10	10
389	194	8 c. red, yell, bl-grn & blackish grn	1·50	15
390	195	9 c. brown-red, purple-brown, black and light yellow-olive	1·50	10
391	196	10 c. orange, blackish brown, pale turquoise-blue and olive-brown	1·50	10
392	197	13 c. red, black, grey & light turq-grn	3·25	25
		a. Red omitted	£325	
		b. Grey (plumage and legs) omitted . . .	£275	
393	177	15 c. rose-carmine, black, grey and light bluish green	2·50	50
		a. Rose-carmine omitted	£850	
394	178	20 c. yellow, black and pink	7·50	15
		a. Yellow (plumage) omitted	£325	
395	198	24 c. ultramarine, yellow, blk & light brn . .	90	55
396	180	25 c. black, red, grey and green	5·00	20
		a. Red omitted	£500	
397	181	30 c. black, red, buff & lt yellow-green	23·00	30
		a. Red omitted	£450	
398	167	40 c. ultramarine	12·00	10
399	168	50 c. red-brown	15·00	10
400	169	75 c. olive	1·00	1·50
401	170	$1 brown-purple (shades)	3·75	10
		a. Recut lines in sky	20·00	
		b. Recut lines and plate crack	27·00	
		c. Perf 15 × 14† (1973)	95·00	17·00
402	171	$2 deep reddish violet	10·00	30
403	172	$4 sepia	8·00	4·50
		Set of 25	90·00	8·00
		Set of 4 (Nos. 400/3) optd "Specimen"	90·00	
		Presentation Pack (Nos. 382/5, 386c, 388/91, 398/403, 405/a, 420/5) (English inscr) (7.9.70)	£400	
		Presentation Pack (Japanese inscr) .	£1100	

*This comprises two stamps imperf all round and one imperf on three sides.

†The note below No. 553 also applies to No. 401c, its exact gauge being 14·9 × 14·1. No. 401 is 14·25 × 13·95.

No. 385 is normally printed with helecon ink, the rest being on helecon paper. Early in 1967 experimental printings of No. 385 on different kinds of paper coated with helecon or Derby Luminescents phosphor were put on sale. They cannot be distinguished by the naked eye.

199　Queen Elizabeth II　　　200　"Saving Life"

1966 (14 Feb)–**67**.　Coil stamps. Photo. P 14½ × imperf.

404	199	3 c. black, light brown and green	20	40
405		4 c. black, light brown & lt vermilion	45	20
405a		5 c. black, light brown and new blue (29.9.67)	60	10
		Set of 3	1·10	60

(Des L. Mason. Photo)

1966 (6 July).　75th Anniv of Royal Life Saving Society. P 13½.

406	200	4 c. black, bright blue and blue	15	10
		First Day Cover		40

MINIMUM PRICE

The minimum price quoted is 10p which represents a handling charge rather than a basis for valuing common stamps. For further notes about prices see introductory pages.

201　"Adoration of the Shepherds"　　202 Eendracht

(Des L. Stirling, after medieval engraving. Photo)

1966 (19 Oct).　Christmas. P 13½.

407	201	4 c. black and yellow-olive	10	10
		a. Value omitted	£700	
		First Day Cover		40

No. 407a occurs as a result of a partial shift of the yellow-olive background colour in stamps of the last two vertical rows so that the value, which normally shows as white, is no longer present.

(Des F. Eidlitz. Photo)

1966 (24 Oct).　350th Anniv of Dirk Hartog's Landing in Australia. P 13½.

408	202	4 c. multicoloured	10	10
		a. Red (sphere) omitted	£800	
		First Day Cover		40

203　Open Bible　　204　Ancient Keys and Modern Lock

(Des L. Stirling. Photo)

1967 (7 Mar).　150th Anniv of British and Foreign Bible Society in Australia. P 13½.

409	203	4 c. multicoloured	10	10
		First Day Cover		40

(Des G. Andrews. Photo)

1967 (5 Apr).　150th Anniv of Australian Banking. P 13½.

410	204	4 c. black, light blue and emerald	10	10
		First Day Cover		40

205　Lions Badge and 50 Stars　　206　Y.W.C.A. Emblem

(Des M. Ripper. Photo)

1967 (7 June).　50th Anniv of Lions International. P 13½.

411	205	4 c. black, gold and blue	10	10
		First Day Cover		40

(Des H. Williamson. Photo)

1967 (21 Aug).　World Y.W.C.A. Council Meeting, Monash University, Victoria. P 13½.

412	206	4 c. dp blue, ultramarine, lt pur & lt bl	10	10
		First Day Cover		40

207 Anatomical Figures   (208)

(Des R. Ingpen. Photo)

1967 (20 Sept). *Fifth World Gynaecology and Obstetrics Congress, Sydney. P 13½.*
413   **207**   4 c. black, blue and light reddish violet ...   10   10
     First Day Cover   40

1967 (29 Sept). *No. 385 surch with T **208**.*
414   **191**   5 c. on 4 c. red   70   10
     a. Booklet pane. Five stamps plus one
       printed label ....   3·25
     No. 414 was only issued in booklets and so only occurs with one or two adjacent sides imperforate. It only exists printed with helecon ink on normal paper.

209 Christmas Bells and Gothic   210 Religious Symbols
     Arches

(Des M. Ripper (5 c.), Erica McGilchrist (25 c.). Photo)

1967. *Christmas. P 13½.*
415   **209**   5 c. multicoloured (18.10.67)   20   10
     a. Imperf three sides £800
416   **210**   25 c. multicoloured (27.11.67) ....   1·25   1·75
     Set of 2 ....   1·40   1·75
     First Day Covers (2) ....   2·50

211 Satellite in Orbit   212 World Weather Map

(Des J. Mason. Photo)

1968 (20 Mar). *World Weather Watch. P 13½.*
417   **211**   5 c. orange-brown, pl blue, bl & ochre ...   30   10
418   **212**   20 c. orange-brown, blue and black .....   1·75   3·50
     a. White (radio waves) omitted £300
     b. Orange-brown (triangle) omitted ..   £900
     Set of 2 ....   2·00   3·50
     First Day Cover ....   5·00

213 Radar Antenna

(Des R. Ingpen. Photo)

1968 (20 Mar). *World Telecommunications Intelsat II. P 13½.*
419   **213**   25 c. greenish blue, black & lt blue-green   2·75   5·00
     First Day Cover ....   6·00

214 Kangaroo Paw   215 Pink Heath   216 Tasmanian Blue
                                             Gum

217 Sturt's Desert   218 Cooktown Orchid   219 Waratah
     Pea

(Des Nell Wilson (6 c., 30 c.); R. and P. Warner (13 c., 25 c.); Dorothy Thornhill (15 c., 20 c.). Photo)

1968 (10 July)–**71.** *State Floral Emblems. Multicoloured. P 13½.*
420   **214**   6 c. Western Australia   40   35
421   **215**   13 c. Victoria   50   20
422   **216**   15 c. Tasmania ....   2·00   20
423   **217**   20 c. South Australia ....   9·00   30
424   **218**   25 c. Queensland ....   4·50   45
425   **219**   30 c. New South Wales (Type I) (*shades*) ..   1·00   10
     a. Green (leaves) omitted £350
     b. Type II (29.6.71) ....   4·50   1·50
     Set of 6 ....   16·00   1·40
     The 30 c. was reprinted in 1971 from new cylinders so that Type II shows greater areas of white in the pink tones of the petals.

220 Soil Sample Analysis

(Des R. Ingpen. Photo)

1968 (6 Aug). *International Soil Science Congress and World Medical Association Assembly. T **220** and similar horiz design. P 13 × 13½.*
426   **220**   5 c. orange-brown, stone, greenish blue & blk   10   10
     a. Nos. 426/7 se-tenant with gutter margin
       between ....   14·00   12·00
427   –   5 c. greenish blue, dull olive-yell, rose & blk   10   10
     Set of 2   20   15
     First Day Cover   70
Design:—No. 427, Rubber-gloved hands, syringe and head of Hippocrates.
     The above were printed in sheets of 100 containing a pane of 50 of each design.
     The major shades formerly listed have been deleted as there is a range of intermediate shades.

HAVE YOU READ THE NOTES AT THE BEGINNING OF THIS CATALOGUE?

These often provide answers to the enquiries we receive.

5ᶜ　AUSTRALIA

222 Athlete carrying Torch, and Sunstone Symbol

223 Sunstone Symbol and Mexican Flag

(Des H. Williamson. Photo)

1968 (2 Oct).　*Olympic Games, Mexico City. P* 13½.

428	**222**	5 c. multicoloured	20	10
429	**223**	25 c. multicoloured	35	1·50
		Set of 2	55	1·60
		First Day Cover		2·00

224 Houses and Dollar Signs

225 Church Window and View of Bethlehem

(Des Erica McGilchrist. Photo)

1968 (16 Oct).　*Building and Savings Societies Congress. P* 13½.

430	**224**	5 c. multicoloured	10	20
		First Day Cover		40

(Des G. Hamori. Photo)

1968 (23 Oct).　*Christmas. P* 13½.

431	**225**	5 c. multicoloured	10	10
		a. Green window (gold omitted)	£250	
		b. Red (inscr) omitted	£275	
		First Day Cover		40

226 Edgeworth David (geologist)

227 A. B. Paterson (poet)

228 Albert Namatjira (artist)

229 Caroline Chisholm (social worker)

(Des Note Ptg Branch (Nos. 432, 434), A. Cook (others). Recess, background litho)

1968 (6 Nov).　*Famous Australians* (1*st series*). *P* 15 × 14.

432	**226**	5 c. myrtle-green/*pale green*	75	15
		a. Booklet pane. Five stamps plus one printed label	3·75	
433	**227**	5 c. black/*pale blue*	75	15
		a. Booklet pane. Five stamps plus one printed label	3·75	

434	**228**	5 c. blackish brown/*pale buff*	75	15
		a. Booklet pane. Five stamps plus one printed label	3·75	
435	**229**	5 c. deep violet/*pale lilac*	75	15
		a. Booklet pane. Five stamps plus one printed label	3·75	
		Set of 4	2·75	55

Nos. 432/5 were only issued in booklets and only exist with one or two adjacent sides imperf.

See also Nos. 446/9, 479/82, 505/8, 537/40, 590/5, 602/7 and 637/40.

230 Macquarie Lighthouse

231 Pioneers and Modern Building, Darwin

(Des and eng Note Ptg Branch. Recess; background litho)

1968 (27 Nov).　150*th Anniv of Macquarie Lighthouse. P* 14½ × 13½.

436	**230**	5 c. black/*pale yellow*	10	15
		First Day Cover		40

Used examples are known with the pale yellow background colour omitted.

(Des Mrs. M. Lyon. Photo)

1969 (5 Feb).　*Centenary of Northern Territory Settlement. P* 13½.

437	**231**	5 c. blackish brown, yellow-olive and yellow-ochre	10	10
		First Day Cover		40

232 Melbourne Harbour

233 Concentric Circles (symbolising Management, Labour and Government)

(Des J. Mason. Photo)

1969 (26 Feb).　*Sixth Biennial Conference of International Association of Ports and Harbours. P* 13½.

438	**232**	5 c. multicoloured	15	10
		First Day Cover		40

(Des G. Hamori. Photo.)

1969 (4 June).　50*th Anniv of International Labour Organisation. P* 13½.

439	**233**	5 c. multicoloured	15	10
		a. Gold (middle circle) omitted	£350	
		First Day Cover		40

234 Sugar Cane

235 Timber

236 Wheat

237 Wool

(Des R. Ingpen. Photo)

1969 (17 Sept). *Primary Industries. P* 13½.

440	234	7 c. multicoloured	1·25	2·00
441	235	15 c. multicoloured	4·00	6·00
		a. Black ("Australia" and value) omitted	£475	
442	236	20 c. multicoloured	1·25	80
443	237	25 c. multicoloured	2·50	2·00
		Set of 4	8·00	9·75

PRESENTATION PACKS. Beginning with the following issue the Post Office released special packs containing a set of stamps with descriptive cards either in plain envelopes or protective plastic containers and these are listed.

238 "The Nativity" (stained-glass window)

239 "Tree of Life", Christ in Crib and Christmas Star (abstract)

(Des G. Hamori (5 c.), J. Coburn (25 c.). Photo)

1969 (15 Oct). *Christmas. P* 13½.

444	238	5 c. multicoloured	20	10
		a. Magenta (robe) omitted	£250	
		b. Yellow omitted	£250	
445	239	25 c. orange-red, light crimson, black and gold	1·00	2·00
		Set of 2	1·10	2·00
		Presentation Pack (10.12.69)	4·00	
		First Day Cover		3·00

240 Edmund Barton

241 Alfred Deakin

242 J. C. Watson

243 G. H. Reid

(Des from drawings by J. Santry. Recess, background litho)

1969 (22 Oct). *Famous Australians (2nd series). Prime Ministers. P* 15 × 14.

446	240	5 c. black/*pale green*	75	15
		a. Booklet pane. Five stamps plus one printed label	3·75	
447	241	5 c. black/*pale green*	75	15
		a. Booklet pane. Five stamps plus one printed label	3·75	
448	242	5 c. black/*pale green*	75	15
		a. Booklet pane. Five stamps plus one printed label	3·75	
449	243	5 c. black/*pale green*	75	15
		a. Booklet pane. Five stamps plus one printed label	3·75	
		Set of 4	2·75	55

Nos. 446/9 were only issued in booklets and only exist with one or two adjacent sides imperf.

244 Capt. Ross Smith's Vickers "Vimy", 1919

245 Lt. H. Fysh and Lt. P. McGinness 1919 survey with Ford Car

246 Capt. Wrigley and Sgt. Murphy in "BE 2E" take off to meet the Smiths

(Des E. Thake. Photo)

1969 (12 Nov). *50th Anniv of First England–Australia Flight. P* 13½.

450	244	5 c. olive-green, pale blue, black and red . .	15	10
		a. Strip of 3. Nos. 450/2	1·50	
451	245	5 c. black, red and olive-green	15	10
452	246	5 c. olive-green, black, pale blue and red . .	15	10
		Set of 3	1·50	25
		Presentation Pack (24.11.69)	2·25	
		First Day Cover		3·75

The three designs appear *se-tenant*, both horizontally and vertically, throughout the sheet.

247 Symbolic Track and Diesel Locomotive

(Des B. Sadgrove. Photo)

1970 (11 Feb). *Sydney–Perth Standard Gauge Railway Link. P* 13½.

| 453 | 247 | 5 c. multicoloured . . . . | 15 | 10 |
| | | *First Day Cover* . . . . | | 40 |

FIRST DAY COVERS. From 16 March 1970 Australia Post provided official First Day Covers for most issues. These are priced separately for Nos. 454/97. From Nos. 498/504 onwards such covers are worth the same as those produced by commercial firms.

248 Australian Pavilion, Osaka

249 "Southern Cross" and "from the Country of the South with warm feelings" (message)

(Des J. Copeland (5 c.), A. Leydin (20 c.). Photo)

1970 (16 Mar). *World Fair, Osaka. P* 13½.

454	248	5 c. multicoloured	15	10
455	249	20 c. orange-red and black	35	65
		Set of 2	50	75
		Presentation Pack (English inscr) . . .	1·75	
		(Japanese inscr) .	75·00	
		First Day Cover		1·40
		First Day Cover (official P.O. issue) . . .		80·00

251 Australian Flag

(Des P.O. Artists (5 c.), J. Mason (30 c.). Photo)

1970 (31 Mar). *Royal Visit. T* **251** *and similar horiz design. P* 13½.
456	5 c.	black and deep ochre	25	15
457	30 c.	multicoloured	75	2·00
		Set of 2	1·00	2·10
		Presentation Pack (*English inscr*)	1·75	
		(*Japanese inscr*)	38·00	
		First Day Cover		2·40
		First Day Cover (*official P.O. issue*)		60·00

Design: — 5 c. Queen Elizabeth II and Prince Philip.

252 Lucerne Plant, Bull and Sun

253 Captain Cook and H.M.S. *Endeavour*

(Des R. Ingpen. Photo)

1970 (13 Apr). *Eleventh International Grasslands Congress. P* 13½.
458	**252**	5 c. multicoloured	10	25
		First Day Cover	1·00	
		First Day Cover (*official P.O. issue*)	50·00	

(Des R. Ingpen and "Team" (T. Keneally, A. Leydin, J. R. Smith). Photo)

1970 (20 Apr). *Bicentenary of Captain Cook's Discovery of Australia's East Coast. T* **253** *and similar multicoloured designs. P* 13.
459	5 c.	Type **253**	30	10
	a.	Strip of 5. Nos. 459/63	2·50	
460	5 c.	Sextant and H.M.S. *Endeavour*	30	10
461	5 c.	Landing at Botany Bay	30	10
462	5 c.	Charting and exploring	30	10
463	5 c.	Claiming possession	30	10
464	30 c.	Captain Cook, H.M.S. *Endeavour*, sextant, aborigines and kangaroo (63 × 30 *mm*)	1·50	2·75
		Set of 6	3·25	3·00
		First Day Cover		8·00
		First Day Cover (*official P.O. issue*)		20·00
MS465	157 × 129 mm. Nos. 459/64. Imperf	13·00	15·00
		Presentation Pack (*English inscr*)	17·00	
		(*Japanese inscr*)	£225	
		First Day Cover		16·00

The 5 c. stamps were issued horizontally *se-tenant* within the sheet, to form a composite design in the order listed.

50,000 miniature sheets were made available by the Post Office to the organisers of the Australian National Philatelic Exhibition which overprinted them in the white margin at each side of the 30 c. stamp with "Souvenir Sheet AUSTRALIAN NATIONAL PHILATELIC EXHIBITION" at left and "ANPEX 1970 SYDNEY 27 APRIL—1 MAY" at right in light red-brown and they were also serially numbered. These were put on sale at the exhibition on the basis of one sheet to each visitor paying 30 c. for admission. Although still valid for pstage, since the stamps themselves had not been defaced, these sheets were not sold at post offices.

Subsequently further supplies were purchased and similarly overprinted and numbered by a private firm without the authority of the Post Office and "ANPEX 1970 SYDNEY 26 APRIL—1 MAY" at right in light red-brown This firm also had the unoverprinted sheets rouletted in colour between the stamps whilst further supplies of the normal sheets were overprinted with reproductions of old coins and others with an inscription commemorating the opening of Melbourne Airport on 1st July 1970, but all these are private productions. Further private productions have been reported.

FLUORESCENT VERY WHITE CHALKY PAPER. This paper, manufactured by Wiggins Teape Ltd at Keon Park and known as "KP5D", was first introduced for the 1971 Christmas issue, Nos. 498/504, and subsequently for other current definitives and commemoratives. They fluoresce back and front under an ultraviolet lamp and also have a strong coating of chalk on the surface. Late in 1972 this paper began to be introduced more generally and a number of stamps exist on both types of paper. The normal helecon paper does not fluoresce under the lamp but does react to the chalky test to a lesser degree. The adhesive used was gum arabic.

Stamps reprinted on the white fluorescent paper are listed in this catalogue with "Ew" prefix numbers.

Another type of paper was later introduced, designated "KP6T", similar in appearance to the "KP5D", but with blue or pink tinted PVA gum.

259 Sturt's Desert Rose

AUSTRALIA   AUSTRALIA
I.   II.

Two types of 2 c.
I. "AUSTRALIA" thin: "2c" thin; flower name lightly printed.
II. Redrawn. "AUSTRALIA" thicker; "2c" much more heavily printed; flower name thicker and bolder.

(Des Note Ptg Branch. Photo)

1970–75. *Coil Stamps. Vert designs as T* **259***. Multicoloured. P* 15 × *imperf.*
465a	2 c.	Type **259** (I) (1.10.71)	30	20
		Ew. White fluorescent paper (1972)	30	
		ab. Type II (White flugrescent paper) (1973)	30	10
466	4 c.	Type **259** (27.4.70)	70	1·25
467	5 c.	Golden Wattle (27.4.70)	20	10
		Ew. White fluorescent paper (1.10.71)	20	
468	6 c.	Type **259** (28.9.70)	1·25	1·00
	a.	Green (leaves) omitted	£200	
468b	7 c.	Sturt's Desert Pea (1.10.71)	30	20
	c.	Green (leaves) omitted	75·00	
		Ew. White fluorescent paper (1973)	30	
468d	10 c.	As 7 c. (15.1.75)	25	15
		Set of 6	2·75	2·50
		First Day Covers (4)		6·00
		First Day Covers (*official P.O. issue*) (Nos. 466/8, 468d) (3)		24·00

Nos. 465a/8d have horizontal coil perforations described after No. 191.

264 Snowy Mountains Scheme

265 Rising Flames

(Des L. Mason (7 c.), R. Ingpen (8 c., 9 c.), B. Sadgrove (10 c.). Photo)

1970 (31 Aug). *National Development* (*1st series*), *T* **264** *and similar horiz designs. Multicoloured. P* 13 × 13½.
469	7 c.	Type **264**	30	55
470	8 c.	Ord River Scheme	15	15
471	9 c.	Bauxite to aluminium	15	15
472	10 c.	Oil and Natural Gas	40	10
		Set of 4	90	85
		Presentation Pack	3·25	
		First Day Cover		1·60
		First Day Cover (*official P.O. issue*)		12·00

See also Nos. 541/4.

(Des G. Hamori. Photo)

1970 (2 Oct). *16th Commonwealth Parliamentary Association Conference, Canberra. P* 13½.
473 **265** 6 c. multicoloured 10   10
                First Day Cover   40
                First Day Cover (official P.O. issue) . . .   4·50

270 The Duigan Brothers   **271** "Theatre"
(Pioneer Aviators)

(Des A. Cook (No. 480), T. Adams (No. 482), Note Ptg Branch (others).
Recess (background litho))

1970 (16 Nov). *Famous Australians (3rd series). T* **270** *and similar vert
designs. P* 15 × 14.
479   6 c. blue . . . . 1·25   20
         a. Booklet pane. Five stamps plus one printed
            label . . . .   6·00
480   6 c. black/*flesh* . . . .   1·25   20
         a. Booklet pane. Five stamps plus one printed
            label . . . .   6·00
481   6 c. purple/*pink* . . . .   1·25   20
         a. Booklet pane. Five stamps plus one printed
            label . . . .   6·00
482   6 c. brown-lake/*pink* . . . .   1·25   20
         a. Booklet pane. Five stamps plus one printed
            label . . . .   6·00
         Set of 4 . . . .   4·50   75
         First Day Cover . . . .   1·25
         First Day Cover (official P.O. issue) . . . . . .   2·50

266 Milk Analysis and Dairy Herd

267 "The Nativity"

(Des R. Honisett. Photo)

1970 (7 Oct). *18th International Dairy Congress, Sydney. P* 13½.
474 **266** 6 c. multicoloured 10   10
                First Day Cover   40
                First Day Cover (official P.O. issue) . . .   4·75

Designs:—No. 479 Type **270**; No. 480 Lachlan Macquarie (Governor of
N.S.W.); No. 481 Adam Lindsay Gordon (poet); No. 482 E. J. Eyre
(explorer).
Nos. 479/82 were only issued in booklets and only exist with one or two
adjacent sides imperf.

(Des W. Beasley. Photo)

1970 (14 Oct). *Christmas. P* 13½.
475 **267** 6 c. multicoloured 10   10
                First Day Cover   40
                First Day Cover (official P.O. issue) . . . .   3·50

268 U.N. "Plant"   **269** Boeing "707" and Avro "504"
and Dove of Peace

(Des Monad Ltd. Photo)

1970 (19 Oct). *25th Anniv of United Nations. P* 13½.
476 **268** 6 c. multicoloured 10   10
                First Day Cover   40
                First Day Cover (official P.O. issue) . . .   2·50

Souvenir Pack 1970

1970 (19 Oct). *Containing Nos. 453, 458, 466/7 and 473/6.*
SP476a Souvenir Pack . . . . 16·00

(Des G. Hamori. Photo)

1970 (2 Nov). *50th Anniv of QANTAS Airline. T* **269** *and similar horiz
design. Multicoloured. P* 13½.
477   6 c. Type **269** 25   10
478 30 c. Avro "504" and Boeing "707" 75   1·25
         Set of 2 . . . . 1·00   1·25
         Presentation Pack . . . . 2·75
         First Day Cover . . . .   1·75
         First Day Cover (official P.O. issue) . . . . . .   2·25

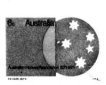

272 The Southern Cross   **273** Market "Graph"

(Des R. Beck. Photo)

1971 (21 Apr). *Centenary of Australian Natives' Association.
P* 13½.
486 **272** 6 c. black, vermilion and bright blue 10   10
                First Day Cover   40
                First Day Cover (official P.O. issue) . . .   3·50

(Des D. Annand. Photo)

1971 (6 Jan). *"Australia-Asia". T* **271** *and similar horiz designs. Multicoloured. P* 13½.
483   7 c. Type **271** 35   50
484 15 c. "Music" 60   90
485 20 c. "Sea Craft" 55   80
         Set of 3 . . . . 1·40   2·00
         Presentation Pack . . . . 4·50
         First Day Cover . . . .   2·75
         First Day Cover (official P.O. issue) . . . . . .   4·75

(Des Monad Ltd. Photo)

1971 (5 May). *Centenary of Sydney Stock Exchange. P* 13½.
487 **273** 6 c. multicoloured 10   10
                First Day Cover   40
                First Day Cover (official P.O. issue) . . .   2·50

274 Rotary Emblem   **275** "Mirage" Jets and "D.H.9a" Biplane

278 The Three Kings and the Star   **279** Andrew Fisher

(Des H. Williamson. Photo)

1971 (17 May). *50th Anniv of Rotary International in Australia. P* 13½.

488	**274**	6 c.	multicoloured	15	10
			First Day Cover		40
			First Day Cover (official P.O. issue)		2·75

(Des R. Honisett. Photo)

1971 (9 June). *50th Anniv of R.A.A.F. P* 13½.

489	**275**	6 c.	multicoloured	15	10
		a.	Black (face value and inscr) omitted	£350	
			First Day Cover		50
			First Day Cover (official P.O. issue)		2·50

276 Draught-horse, Cat and Dog   **277** Bark Painting

(Des R. Ingpen. Photo)

1971 (5 July). *Animals. T* **276** *and similar vert designs. Multicoloured. P* 13½.

490	6 c.	Type **276**	25	10
491	12 c.	Vet and lamb ("Animal Science")	45	40
492	18 c.	Red Kangaroo ("Fauna Conservation")	60	75
493	24 c.	Guide-dog ("Animals Aid to Man")	1·00	1·75
		Set of 4	2·00	2·75
		Presentation Pack	6·00	
		First Day Cover		3·25
		First Day Cover (official P.O. issue)		3·50

The 6 c. commemorated the Centenary of the Australian R.S.P.C.A., and the others were short-term definitives.

Souvenir Pack 1971

1971 (23 Aug). *Selected issues comprising Nos. 468 and 486/9.*

SP493a	Souvenir Pack	45·00

(Des J. Mason. Photo)

1971 (29 Sept). *Aboriginal Art. T* **277** *and similar multicoloured designs. P* 13½.

494	20 c.	Type **277**	20	20
	Ew.	White fluorescent paper (1973)	50	
495	25 c.	Body decoration	20	30
	a.	Black omitted*	£300	
	Ew.	White fluorescent paper (11.73)	70	
496	30 c.	Cave painting (vert)	30	20
	Ew.	White fluorescent paper (1973)	90	
497	35 c.	Grave posts (vert)	30	15
	Ew.	White fluorescent paper (late 1974)	75	
		Set of 4	90	75
		Presentation Pack	2·25	
		First Day Cover		1·40
		First Day Cover (official P.O. issue)		9·50

*The omission of the black results in the stamp being without face-value and "AUSTRALIA".

The 35 c. exists with both PVA gum and gum arabic.

(Des J. Lee. Photo)

1971 (13 Oct). *Christmas. Colours of star and colour of "AUSTRALIA" given. P* 13½.

498	**278**	7 c.	royal blue, pl mauve & pl lake-brn	1·00	15
		a.	Block of 7. Nos. 498/504	38·00	
		Ew.	White fluorescent paper	4·00	
		Ewa.	Block of 7. Nos. 498Ew/504Ew	65·00	
499		7 c.	pale mauve, pl lake-brown & white	1·00	15
		Ew.	White fluorescent paper	4·00	
500		7 c.	pale mauve, white and black	7·00	80
		Ew.	White fluorescent paper	14·00	
501		7 c.	black, green and black	1·00	15
		Ew.	White fluorescent paper	4·00	
502		7 c.	lilac, green and lilac	1·00	15
		Ew.	White fluorescent paper	4·00	
503		7 c.	black, pale lake-brown and white	1·00	15
		Ew.	White fluorescent paper	4·00	
504		7 c.	royal blue, pale mauve and green	30·00	2·25
		Ew.	White fluorescent paper	32·00	
			Set of 7	38·00	3·50
			Presentation Pack	55·00	
			First Day Cover (block of 7)		45·00

Nos. 498/504 were issued in sheets having two panes of 50 stamps. Each half pane had its stamps arranged thus:—

498	499	500	499	498
503	502	501	502	503
504	501	500	501	504
503	502	501	502	503
498	499	500	499	498

(Des J. Sandry. Recess)

1972 (8 Mar). *Famous Australians (4th series). Prime Ministers. T* **279** *and similar vert designs. P* 15×14.

505	7 c.	ultramarine (Type **279**)	60	15
	a.	Booklet pane. Five stamps plus one printed label	2·75	
506	7 c.	ultramarine. (W.M. Hughes)	60	15
	a.	Booklet pane. Five stamps plus one printed label	2·75	
507	7 c.	red (Joseph Cook)	60	15
	a.	Booklet pane. Five stamps plus one printed label	2·75	
508	7 c.	red (S. M. Bruce)	60	15
	a.	Booklet pane. Five stamps plus one printed label	2·75	
		Set of 4	2·10	55
		First Day Cover		1·25

Nos. 505/8 were issued only in booklets and exist with one or two adjacent sides imperf.

280 Cameo Brooch   **281** Fruit

(Des Mrs. V. Mason. Photo)

1972 (18 Apr). *50th Anniv of Country Women's Association. P* 13½.

509	**280**	7 c.	multicoloured	20	10
			First Day Cover		40

(Des D. Annand. Photo)

1972 (14 June). *Primary Industries. T 281 and similar horiz designs. Multicoloured. P 13½.*
510	20 c.	Type **281**	3·50	4·50
511	25 c.	Rice	3·50	5·50
512	30 c.	Fish	3·50	3·50
513	35 c.	Beef	8·00	2·00
		Set of 4	17·00	14·00
		Presentation Pack	22·00	
		First Day Cover		17·00

282 Worker in Wheelchair   **283** Telegraph Line

(Des from photographs by Barbara Ardizzone. Photo)

1972 (2 Aug). *Rehabilitation of the Disabled. T 282 and similar designs. P 13½.*
514	12 c.	yellow-brown and emerald	10	10
	Ew.	White fluorescent paper (1973)	15	
515	18 c.	sage-green and yellow-orange	40	25
516	24 c.	blue and yellow-brown	15	10
	Ew.	White fluorescent paper (1973)	25	
		Set of 3	50	40
		Presentation Pack	1·40	
		First Day Cover		90

Designs: *Horiz*—18 c. Patient and teacher. *Vert*—24 c. Boy playing with ball.

(Des J. Copeland. Photo)

1972 (22 Aug). *Centenary of Overland Telegraph Line. P 13.*
517	**283**	7 c. multicoloured	15	10
		First Day Cover		40

284 Athletics   **285** Numerals and Computer Circuit

(Des B. Sadgrove. Photo)

1972 (28 Aug). *Olympic Games, Munich. T 284 and similar vert designs. Multicoloured. P 13½.*
518	7 c.	Type **284**	25	20
519	7 c.	Rowing	25	20
520	7 c.	Swimming	25	20
521	35 c.	Equestrian	2·25	4·00
		Set of 4	2·75	4·00
		Presentation Pack	4·75	
		First Day Cover		4·75

(Des G. Andrews. Photo)

1972 (16 Oct). *Tenth International Congress of Accountants, Sydney. P 13½.*
522	**285**	7 c. multicoloured	15	10
		First Day Cover		40

286 Australian-built Harvester

(Des R. Ingpen. Photo)

1972 (15 Nov). *Pioneer Life. T 286 and similar multicoloured designs. P 13½.*
523	5 c.	Pioneer family (*vert*)	15	10
	Ew.	White fluorescent paper (1973)	30	
524	10 c.	Water-pump (*vert*)	40	10
	Ew.	White fluorescent paper (Mid 1974)	1·00	
525	15 c.	Type **286**	30	10
	a.	Black (face value and inscr) omitted	£250	
	Ew.	White fluorescent paper (1973)	50	
526	40 c.	House	30	40
	Ew.	White fluorescent paper (Mid 1974)	65	
527	50 c.	Stage-coach	80	20
	Ew.	White fluorescent paper (Mid 1974)	2·00	
528	60 c.	Morse key (*vert*)	50	75
	Ew.	White fluorescent paper (1973)	65	
529	80 c.	Gem (paddle-steamer)	60	75
	a.	Black (face-value and inscr) omitted	£375	
	Ew.	White fluorescent paper (Mid 1974)	65	
		Set of 7	2·50	2·00
		Presentation Pack	3·50	
		First Day Cover		3·00

No. 525Ew exists with either PVA gum or gum arabic.

287 Jesus with Children   **288** "Length"

(Des from drawing by Wendy Tamlyn (7 c.), L. Stirling (35 c.). Photo)

1972 (29 Nov). *Christmas. T 287 and similar vert design. Multicoloured. P 15 × 14 (7 c.) or 13½ (35 c.).*
530	7 c.	Type **287**	25	10
	a.	Brown-red ("Australia 7c") omitted	£250	
	b.	Red-brown (inscr) omitted	£250	
531	35 c.	Dove and spectrum motif	6·50	8·00
		Set of 2	6·75	8·00
		Presentation Pack	12·00	
		First Day Cover		10·00

(Des Weatherhead & Stitt Pty. Ltd. Photo)

1973 (7 Mar). *Metric Conversion. T 288 and similar multicoloured designs. P 15 × 14 (No. 535) or 14 × 15 (others).*
532	7 c.	Type **288**	40	35
533	7 c.	"Volume"	40	35
	a.	Yellow-olive omitted*	£250	
534	7 c.	"Mass"	40	35
535	7 c.	"Temperature" (*horiz*)	40	35
		Set of 4	1·40	1·25
		Presentation Pack	2·75	
		First Day Cover		1·75

*This results in the man's drink and shorts appearing white, and the colour of the stool being the same as the background.

289 Caduceus and Laurel Wreath   **290** William Wentworth (statesman and explorer)

(Des H. Williamson. Photo)

1973 (4 Apr). *25th Anniv of W.H.O. P* 15 × 14.
536   **289**   7 c. multicoloured   25   10
                    First Day Cover   40

(Des J. Santry. Recess and litho)

1973 (16 May). *Famous Australians* (5th series). *T* **290** *and similar vert designs. P* 15 × 14.
537   7 c. yellow-bistre and black   40   20
         a. Block of 4. Nos. 537/40 ....   2·50
538   7 c. lilac and black   40   20
539   7 c. yellow-bistre and black   40   20
540   7 c. lilac and black   40   20
         Set of 4 ....   2·50   70
         Presentation Pack ....   5·00
         First Day Cover ....   1·50
Designs:—No. 537, Type **290**; No. 538, Isaac Isaacs (first Australian-born Governor-General); No. 539, Mary Gilmore (writer); No. 540, Marcus Clarke (author).
Nos. 537/40 were printed in *se-tenant* blocks of four within the sheet.

291 Shipping   **292** Banded Coral Shrimp

(Des J. Copeland. Photo)

1973 (6 June). *National Development* (2nd series). *T* **291** *and similar vert designs. Multicoloured. P* 13½.
541   20 c. Type **291** ....   4·00   4·00
542   25 c. Iron ore and steel ....   4·00   4·00
543   30 c. Beef roads ....   4·75   4·50
544   35 c. Mapping ....   4·00   4·50
         Set of 4 .... 15·00   15·00
         Presentation Pack .... 19·00
         First Day Cover ....   17·00

(Des Printing Bureau artists (1 to 4 c.), J. Mason (others). Photo)

1973 (11 July)–**74**. *Marine Life and Gemstones. T* **292** *and similar multicoloured designs. P* 14 × 15 (1 to 4 c.) *or P* 15 × 14 (*others*).
545   1 c. Type **292**   10   10
         a. Black (inscr and face value) omitted .....   90·00
         b. Yellow-brown omitted £225
546   2 c. Fiddler crab   10   10
547   3 c. Coral crab   10   10
         a. Black (inscr and value) omitted £300
548   4 c. Mauve stinger   20   30
         a. Black (face value and inscr) omitted £250
549   6 c. Chrysoprase (*vert*)   20   10
550   7 c. Agate (*vert*)   20   10
         a. Black (value and "agate") omitted ......   90·00
551   8 c. Opal (*vert*)   20   10
         a. Black (face value and inscr) omitted £100
552   9 c. Rhodonite (*vert*)   25   10
552a 10 c. Star sapphire (*vert*) (16.10.74)   20   10
         ab. Black (value, inscr, etc.) omitted £100
         ac. Turquoise-blue omitted* .... 10·00
         aEd. Printed on the gummed side .... 25·00
         Set of 9 ....   1·40   70
         Presentation Pack (*Nos.* 545/52) ......   2·50
         Presentation Pack (*Nos.* 545/52a, 579)
         (1.10.75) ....   2·00
         First Day Covers (3) ....   4·00
* The turquoise-blue occurs on the gemstones, and is normally partly covered by the black.
The 1, 3, 7 and 10 c. exist with PVA gum as well as gum arabic.

293 Children at Play   **294** John Baptising Jesus

(Des G. Hamori. Photo)

1973 (5 Sept). *50th Anniv of Legacy* (*Welfare Organisation*). *P* 13½.
553   **293**   7 c. cinnamon, deep claret and emerald ..   20   10
                    First Day Cover   40

PERFORATIONS. From 1973 to 1975 two different perforating machines were used for some issues, giving gauges of 14½ × 14 or 15 × 14 (on horizontal stamps), the exact measurement being 14·4 × 14·1 or 14·9 × 14·1. The latter gauge was also used for a reprint of the $1 definitive (No. 401c).

(Des G. Hamori. Photo)

1973 (3 Oct). *Christmas. T* **294** *and similar vert design. Multicoloured. P* 14½ × 15 (7 c.) *or* 13½ (30 c.).
554   7 c. Type **294**   30   · 10
         a. Perf 14 × 15 ....   2·50   55
         aEb. Printed on the gummed side .... 55·00
555   30 c. The Good Shepherd ....   1·10   1·50
         Set of 2 ....   1·40   1·50
         Presentation Pack ....   3·00
         First Day Cover ....   2·50

295 Sydney Opera House   **296** Wireless Receiver and
                                            Speaker

(Des A. Leydin. Photo)

1973 (17 Oct). *Architecture. T* **295** *and similar designs. P* 14½ × 14 (7, 10 c.) *or* 13½ (40, 50 c.).
556   7 c. pale turquoise-blue and new blue   25   10
         a. Perf 15 × 14 ....   2·50   1·25
557   10 c. light ochre and sepia   80   70
558   40 c. black, drab and dull mauve ....   1·00   1·50
         a. Dull mauve (background) omitted £700
559   50 c. multicoloured ....   1·25   2·25
         Set of 4 ....   3·00   4·00
         Presentation Pack ....   4·00
         First Day Cover ....   4·75
Designs: *Horiz*—10 c. Buchanan's Hotel, Townsville; 40 c. Como House, Melbourne. *Vert*—50 c. St. James' Church, Sydney.

(Des E. Thake. Photo)

1973 (21 Nov). *50th Anniv of Regular Radio Broadcasting. P* 13½.
560   **296**   7 c. lt turquoise-blue, brown-red & blk ...   15   10
                    First Day Cover   40

297 Common   298 "Sergeant of Light Horse"
  Wombat   (G. Lambert)

(Des R. Bates. Photo)

1974 (13 Feb). *Animals. T* **297** *and similar vert designs. Multicoloured.*
P 14 × 15 (20, 30 *c.*) *or* 13½ (*others*).
561   20 c. Type **297**   35   10
562   25 c. Short-nosed Echidna   75   50
563   30 c. Brush-tailed Possum   40   15
        a. Carmine-red (face-value, etc) omitted £325
564   75 c. Pygmy Glider   85   75
        Set of 4 . . . .   2·10   1·25
        Presentation Pack (1.9.75) . . . .   3·00
        First Day Cover . . . .   2·25
The 20 c. exists with gum arabic as well as PVA gum.

(Des P.O. artists. Litho Asher & Co, Melbourne ($5, $10). Photo R.B.A.
(others))

1974 (24 Apr)–**79**. *Paintings. Multicoloured designs as T* **298***. P* 13½
($1, $2, $4) *or* 14½ (*others*).
565   $1 Type **298** . . . .   1·00   10
        a. Flesh omitted*
566   $2 "Red Gums of the Far North" (H. Heysen)
            (*horiz*) . . . .   1·50   25
566a $4 "Shearing the Rams" (Tom Roberts)
            (*horiz*) . . . .   3·00   2·00
        Ew. White paper (1976) . . . .   3·50
567   $5 "McMahon's Point" (Sir Arthur Streeton)
            (14.3.79) . . . .   5·50   2·00
567a $10 "Coming   South"   (Tom   Roberts)
            (19.10.77) . . . .   8·50   3·00
        ι Ew. White paper (8.80) . . . .   8·00
        Set of 5 . . . .   17·00   6·50
        Presentation Pack (*Nos.* 565/6a) (24.4.74)   20·00
        Presentation Pack (*No.* 567a) (19.10.77) . 12·00
        Presentation Pack (*No.* 567) (14.3.79) . . .   6·00
        First Day Covers (3) . . . .   28·00
  * The omission of the flesh colour results in much of the design appearing
in different shades, most notably the shirt which appears green (especially
the folds), the hillside which is green, and the man's skin which has
highlights in yellow.
  Variations of shade occur on the $1 to $4 and $10, some of them
extreme.
  The $1 and $2 exist with PVA gum as well as gum arabic.
  Printings of No. 567a during late 1987 and 1988 were on Clark or
Harrison paper. See notes below No. 1038.
  For Nos. 567/a optd "SPECIMEN" in red, see No. SP881a.

299 Supreme Court   300 Rugby Football
    Judge

(Des T. Thompson. Photo)

1974 (15 May). *150th Anniv of Australia's Third Charter of Justice.*
P 14 × 15.
568   **299** 7 c. multicoloured   20   10
        First Day Cover   40

(Des A. Leydin from drawings by D. O'Brien. Photo)

1974 (24 July). *Non-Olympic Sports. T* **300** *and similar multicoloured*
designs. P 15 × 14 (*Nos.* 569/70) *or* 14 × 15 (*others*).
569   7 c. Type **300**   50   30
570   7 c. Bowls   50   30
571   7 c. Australian football (*vert*)   50   30
572   7 c. Cricket (*vert*)   50   30
573   7 c. Golf (*vert*)   50   30
574   7 c. Surfing (*vert*)   50   30
575   7 c. Tennis (*vert*)   50   30
        Set of 7 . . . .   3·00   1·90
        Presentation Pack . . . .   4·00
        First Day Cover . . . .   2·50

301 "Transport of Mails"   302 Letter "A" and W.C.
                                       Wentworth (co-founder)

(Des J. Copeland. Photo)

1974 (9 Oct). *Centenary of Universal Postal Union. T* **301** *and similar*
vert design. Multicoloured. P 15 × 14 (7 *c.*) *or* 13½ (30 *c.*).
576   7 c. Type **301**   30   15
        a. Perf 14½ × 14   50   25
577   30 c. Three-part version of Type **301** . . . .   1·10   1·75
        Set of 2 . . . .   1·40   1·90
        Presentation Pack . . . .   1·75
        First Day Cover . . . .   2·25

(Des I. Dalton. Typo and litho)

1974 (9 Oct). *150th Anniv of First Independent Newspaper, "The*
Australian". P 14 × 15.
578   **302** 7 c. black/*light cinnamon*   30   20
        a. Perf 14 × 14½   70   35
        First Day Cover   50

=
9c
(303)   304 "The Adoration of
                          the Magi".

1974 (16 Oct). *No.* 551 *surch with T* **303***, in red.*
579   9 c. on 8 c. Opal   15   15
        First Day Cover . . . .   1·00

(Des and recess R.B.A.)

1974 (13 Nov). *Christmas. Woodcuts by Dürer. T* **304** *and similar vert*
design. P 14 × 15.
580   10 c. black/*cream*   25   10
581   35 c. black/*cream*   80   1·00
        Set of 2 . . . .   1·00   1·00
        Presentation Pack . . . .   1·75
        First Day Cover . . . .   1·75
Design:—35 c. "The Flight into Egypt".

PROCESS. All the following issues to No. 772 were printed in photogravure, *except where otherwise stated.*

305 "Pre-School Education"   **306** "Road Safety"

(Des Vivienne Binns (5 c.), Erica McGilchrist (11 c.), E. Tanner (15 c.), J. Meldrum (60 c.))

1974 (20 Nov). *Education in Australia. T 305 and similar multicoloured designs. P 13½.*

582	5 c.	Type **305**	50	40
583	11 c.	"Correspondence Schools"	50	20
584	15 c.	"Science Education"	80	40
585	60 c.	"Advanced Education" (*vert*)	1·75	2·50
		Set of 4	3·25	3·25
		Presentation Pack	3·75	
		First Day Cover		3·75

(Des G. Andrews)

1975 (29 Jan). *Environment Dangers. T 306 and similar horiz designs. Multicoloured. P 14 × 14½ (No. 586) or 14½ × 14 (others).*

586	10 c.	Type **306**	40	25
	Ea.	Printed on the gummed side	30·00	
587	10 c.	"Pollution"	40	25
	a.	Perf 15 × 14	9·00	3·00
588	10 c.	"Bush Fires"	40	25
	a.	Perf 15 × 14	1·00	75
		Set of 3	1·10	65
		First Day Cover		1·00

307 Australian Women's   **308** J. H. Scullin
Year Emblem

(Des Leonora Howlett)

1975 (12 Mar). *International Women's Year. P 14 × 15.*

589	**307**	10 c.	dp violet-blue, green & bluish vio ...	20	15
			First Day Cover		40

This stamp exists with PVA gum as well as gum arabic.

(Des B. Dunlop)

1975 (26 Mar.). *Famous Australians (6th series). Prime Ministers. T 308 and similar vert designs. Multicoloured. P 14 × 15.*

590	10 c.	Type **308**	20	25
591	10 c.	J. A. Lyons	20	25
	Ea.	Printed on the gummed side	70·00	
592	10 c.	Earle Page	20	25
593	10 c.	Arthur Fadden	20	25
594	10 c.	John Curtin	20	25
595	10 c.	J. B. Chifley	20	25
		Set of 6	1·00	1·40
		Presentation Pack	1·75	
		First Day Cover		1·50

Nos. 591/2 and 594 exist with both PVA gum and gum arabic.

THE WORLD CENTRE FOR
FINE STAMPS IS 399 STRAND

309 Atomic Absorption   **310** Logo of Australian Postal
Spectrophotometry   Commission

(Des Weatherhead & Stitt)

1975 (14 May). *Scientific Development. T 309 and similar horiz designs. Multicoloured. P 13½.*

596	11 c.	Type **309**	50	30
597	24 c.	Radio astronomy	1·25	1·75
598	33 c.	Immunology	1·50	2·00
599	48 c.	Oceanography	2·00	2·50
		Set of 4	4·75	6·00
		Presentation Pack	5·00	
		First Day Cover		6·50

(Des P. Huveneers)

1975 (1 July). *Inauguration of Australian Postal and Telecommunications Commissions. T 310 and similar horiz design. P 14½ × 14.*

600	10 c.	black, rosine and pale grey	20	10
	a.	Pair. Nos. 600/1	1·50	1·50
	b.	Perf 15 × 14	20	10
	ba.	Pair. Nos. 600b/1b	1·50	1·50
601	10 c.	black, orange-yellow and pale grey	20	10
	b.	Perf 15 × 14	20	10
		Set of 2	1·50	20
		First Day Cover		1·75

Design:—No. 601, Logo of Australian Telecommunications Commission. Nos. 600/1 were printed together, *se-tenant* in horizontal and vertical pairs throughout the sheet.

311 Edith Cowan   **312** *Helichrysum*   **313** "Tambaran"
                         thomsonii   House and Sydney
                                            Opera House

(Des D. and J. O'Brien)

1975 (6 Aug). *Famous Australians (7th series). Australian Women. T 311 and similar vert designs. Multicoloured. A. P 14 × 14½. B. P 14 × 15.*

			A		B	
602	10 c.	Type **311**	45	45	45	45
603	10 c.	Louisa Lawson	45	45	70	45
604	10 c.	Ethel Richardson	45	45	70	45
605	10 c.	Catherine Spence	45	45	55	45
606	10 c.	Constance Stone	60	45	45	45
607	10 c.	Truganini	45	45	50	45
		Set of 6	2·50	2·40	3·00	2·40
		Presentation Pack	3·25			
		First Day Cover		2·50		

No. 604 is inscribed with the *nom de plume* "Henry Handel Richardson".

(Des F. Knight)

1975 (27 Aug). *Wild Flowers. T 312 and similar multicoloured design. P 15 × 14 (18 c.) or 14 × 15 (45 c.).*

608	18 c.	Type **312**	25	10
	a.	Black omitted	25·00	
	b.	Grey (stem, etc.) omitted	20·00	
609	45 c.	*Callistemon teretifolius* (*horiz*)	50	10
	a.	Black (face value and inscr) omitted	£200	
	b.	Yellow-green (twigs) omitted		
		Set of 2	75	10
		First Day Cover		80

The 18 c. exists with both PVA gum and gum arabic.

(Des D. Annand (18 c.) or G. Hamori (25 c.))

1975 (16 Sept). *Papua New Guinea Independence. T 313 and similar horiz design. Multicoloured. P 13½.*

610	18 c.	Type **313**	30	10
611	25 c.	"Freedom" (bird in flight)	70	1·00
		Set of 2	1·00	1·10
		Presentation Pack	1·50	
		First Day Cover		1·40

314 Epiphany Scene   315 Australian Coat of Arms

I   II

Two types of No. 614:
I. Emu's legs without toes.
II. Emu showing toes. Other minor differences also occur.

(Des D. O'Brien (15 c.) or J. Milne (45 c.))

1975 (29 Oct). *Christmas. T 314 and similar horiz design. P 14 × 15 (15 c.) or 13½ (45 c.).*

612	15 c.	multicoloured	25	10
613	45 c.	reddish violet, greenish blue and silver	1·00	2·25
		Set of 2	1·25	2·25
		Presentation Pack	2·00	
		First Day Cover		3·00
Design:—45 c. "Shining Star".				

(Des J. Spatchurst)

1976 (5 Jan). *75th Anniv of Nationhood. P 15 × 14.*

614	**315**	18 c. multicoloured (I)	35	20
		a. Buff (supporters) omitted	£275	
		b. Type II	75	30
		ba. Gold (shield and star) omitted	£120	
		First Day Cover		60

316 Telephone-user, *circa* 1878   317 John Oxley

(Des R. Ingpen)

1976 (10 Mar). *Telephone Centenary. P 13½.*

615	**316**	18 c. multicoloured	20	15
		First Day Cover		50

(Des B. Dunlop)

1976 (9 June). *19th Century Explorers. T 317 and similar horiz designs. Multicoloured. P 13½.*

616	18 c.	Type **317**	35	35
617	18 c.	Hume and Hovell	35	35
618	18 c.	John Forrest	35	35
619	18 c.	Ernest Giles	35	35
620	18 c.	William Gosse	35	35
621	18 c.	Peter Warburton	35	35
		Set of 6	1·90	1·90
		Presentation Pack	2·25	
		First Day Cover		2·50

318 Measuring Stick, Graph   319 Football
and Computer Tape

(Des R. Ingpen)

1976 (15 June). *50th Anniv of Commonwealth Scientific and Industrial Research Organisation. P 15 × 14.*

622	**318**	18 c. multicoloured	20	15
		First Day Cover		50

(Des A. Leydin)

1976 (14 July). *Olympic Games. Montreal. T 319 and similar multicoloured designs. P 13½.*

623	18 c.	Type **319**	30	20
624	18 c.	Gymnastics (*vert*)	30	20
625	25 c.	Diving (*vert*)	50	50
626	40 c.	Cycling	70	70
		Set of 4	1·60	1 40
		Presentation Pack	2·00	
		First Day Cover		1·75

The 25 c. exists with gum arabic as well as PVA gum.

320 Richmond Bridge,   321 Blamire Young (designer
Tasmania   of first Australian stamp)

(Des O. Borchert)

1976 (23 Aug). *Australian Scenes. T 320 and similar designs. Multicoloured. P 14 × 15 (50 c.) or 15 × 14 (others).*

627	5 c.	Type **320**	15	10
628	25 c.	Broken Bay, N.S.W.	40	20
629	35 c.	Wittenoom Gorge, W.A.	35	20
630	50 c.	Mt. Buffalo, Victoria (*vert*)	60	30
631	70 c.	Barrier Reef	80	1·25
632	85 c.	Ayers Rock, N.T.	1·00	1·75
		Set of 6	3·00	3·50
		Presentation Pack	4·50	
		First Day Cover		4·00

(Des R. Honisett)

1976 (27 Sept). *National Stamp Week. P 13½.*

633	**321**	18 c. multicoloured	15	15
		First Day Cover		45
MS634		101 × 112 mm. No. 633 × 4	1·25	2·00
		Presentation Pack (Nos. 633/4)	1·75	
		First Day Cover		2·50

MS634 contains one stamp coloured as No. 633; the others, showing the different colour separations used in the printing, are each differently coloured.
The miniature sheet exists with "AUSTRALIAN STAMP PROMOTION COUNCIL" overprinted in red on the margin from a privately produced booklet.

322 "Virgin and Child" (detail,   323 John Gould
Simone Cantarini)

(Des C. Medlycott (15 c.), Wendy Tamlyn (45 c.))

1976 (1 Nov). *Christmas. T 322 and similar horiz design. P* 15 × 14 (15 c.) *or* 13½ (45 c.).

635	15 c. bright magenta and light azure	20	10
636	45 c. multicoloured	60	80
	Set of 2	80	80
	Presentation Pack	1·25	
	First Day Cover		1·25

Design:—45 c. Toy koala bear and decorations.

(Des B. Weatherhead)

1976 (10 Nov). *Famous Australians (8th series). T 323 and similar horiz designs. Multicoloured. P* 15 × 14.

637	18 c. Type **323**	40	35
638	18 c. Thomas Laby	40	35
	a. Red-brown ("AUSTRALIA" etc.) omitted .	£140	
639	18 c. Sir Baldwin Spencer	40	35
640	18 c. Griffith Taylor	40	35
	Set of 4	1·40	1·25
	Presentation Pack	1·75	
	First Day Cover		1·60

324 "Music"   325 Queen Elizabeth II

(Des Wendy Tamlyn)

1977 (19 Jan). *Performing Arts. T 324 and similar vert designs. Multicoloured. P* 14 × 15.

641	20 c. Type **324**	25	25
642	30 c. Drama	40	30
643	40 c. Dance	55	35
644	60 c. Opera	1·00	1·60
	Set of 4	2·00	2·25
	Presentation Pack	2·50	
	First Day Cover		2·50

(Des P.O. Artists. Litho Govt Printer, Sydney (2% of supplies) or by Norman J. Field, Melbourne)

1977 (2 Feb). *Silver Jubilee. T 325 and similar vert design. Multicoloured. P* 14 × 15.

645	18 c. Type **325**	20	10
646	45 c. The Queen and Prince Philip	50	70
	Set of 2	70	70
	Set of 2 Gutter Pairs	4·00	
	Presentation Pack	1·00	
	First Day Cover		1·10

326 Fielder and   327 Parliament House
Wicket Keeper

(Des B. Weatherhead)

1977 (9 Mar). *Australia–England Test Cricket Centenary. T 326 and similar vert designs. Multicoloured. P* 13½.

647	18 c. Type **326**	35	35
	a. Horiz strip of 5. Nos. 647/51	2·00	
648	18 c. Umpire, batsman and scoreboard	35	35
649	18 c. Fielders	35	35
650	18 c. Batsman and umpire	35	35

651	18 c. Bowler and fielder	35	35
652	45 c. Batsman awaiting delivery	75	75
	Set of 6	2·50	2·50
	Presentation Pack	3·75	
	First Day Cover		5·00

Nos. 647/51 were printed together, *se-tenant*, in horizontal strips of 5 throughout the sheet, forming a composite design.

(Des R.B.A.)

1977 (13 Apr). *50th Anniv of Opening of Parliament House, Canberra. P* 15 × 14.

653	**327**	18 c. multicoloured	15	10
		First Day Cover		40

328 Trade Unions Workers   329 Surfing Santa

(Des D. Lanyon; adapted B. Sadgrove)

1977 (9 May). *50th Anniv of Australian Council of Trade Unions. P* 13½.

654	**328**	18 c. multicoloured	15	10
		First Day Cover		40

Souvenir Pack 1977

1977 (26 Sept). *National Stamp Week. Containing Nos.* 653/4.

SP654a	Souvenir Pack	1·60

(Des R. Roberts (15 c.), J. O'Brien (45 c.))

1977 (31 Oct). *Christmas. T 329 and similar vert design. Multicoloured. P* 14 × 15 (15 c.) *or* 13½ (45 c.).

655	15 c. Type **329**	25	10
656	45 c. Madonna and Child	1·00	80
	Set of 2	1·25	80
	Presentation Pack	1·50	
	First Day Cover		1·25

330 National Flag   331 Harry Hawker and
Sopwith "Camel"

(Des Cato Hibberd Design)

1978 (26 Jan). *Australia Day. P* 13½.

657	**330**	18 c. multicoloured	20	15
		First Day Cover		50

(Litho Asher and Co, Melbourne)

1978 (19 Apr). *Early Australian Aviators. T 331 and similar horiz designs. Multicoloured. P* 15½.

658	18 c. Type **331**	35	35
	a. Imperf (horiz pair)	£200	
659	18 c. Bert Hinkler and Avro "Avian"	35	35
	a. Imperf (horiz pair)	£275	
660	18 c. Sir Charles Kingsford Smith and Southern Cross	35	35
	a. Imperf (pair)	£200	
661	18 c. Charles Ulm and *Southern Cross*	35	35
	a. Pale orange-yellow omitted		
	Set of 4	1·25	1·25
	Presentation Pack	1·75	
	First Day Cover		1·50

MS662   100 × 112 mm. Nos. 660/1 × 2. Imperf . . . .   1·50   1·75
    Presentation Pack . . . .   2·00
    First Day Cover . . . .   2·00
The design of No. 661 has the background made up of three colours,
grey, greenish yellow and pale orange-yellow. No. 661a has this last
overlay omitted, resulting from malfunction of the doctor blade—over one
vertical column.
  Forgeries of **MS662** have been reported. These can be detected,
under strong magnification, by the lack of magenta screen on the blue
panel at right and by the presence of magenta dots in the yellow
background to No. 661.

336 1928 3d. "National **337** "The Madonna and
   Stamp Exhibition"   Child" (after van Eyck)
   Commemorative

(Des Cato Hibberd Design. Litho Asher and Co, Melbourne)

1978 (25 Sept). *National Stamp Week. 50th Anniv of National Stamp
Exhibition, Melbourne. P* 15½.
694   **336**   20 c. multicoloured   25   10
    Ea. Emerald ("AUSTRALIA") printed
     double . . . .
    First Day Cover   50
MS695   78 × 113 mm. No. 694 × 4 . . . .   1·40   1·75
    Presentation Pack . . . .   1·75
    First Day Cover . . . .   2·00

Souvenir Pack 1978

1978 (25 Sept). *Containing Nos. 657, 663, 668 and 694.*
SP695a   Souvenir Pack . . . .   2·25

(Litho. Asher and Co, Melbourne)

1978 (3 Oct–1 Nov). *Christmas. Paintings. T 337 and similar vert designs.
Multicoloured. P* 14½.
696   15 c. Type **337** (1.11)   25   10
697   25 c. "The Virgin and Child" (Marmion)   35   50
698   55 c. "The Holy Family" (del Vaga) (1.11)   60   85
    Set of 3 . . . .   1·10   1·25
    Presentation Pack (1.11.78) . . . .   1·75
    First Day Covers (2) . . . .   1·75

332 Beechcraft "Baron" landing **333** Illawarra Flame Tree
   at Station Airstrip

1978 (15 May). *50th Anniv of Royal Flying Doctor Service. P* 13½.
663   **332**   18 c. multicoloured   15   15
    First Day Cover   50

(Des D. Rose)

1978 (1 June). *Trees. T 333 and similar vert designs. Multicoloured.
P* 14 × 15 (18 *c.*) *or* 13½ (*others*).
664   18 c. Type **333**   25   10
665   25 c. Ghost Gum   55   1·25
666   40 c. Grass Tree   90   1·75
667   45 c. Cootamundra Wattle   90   1·25
    Set of 4 . . . .   2·40   4·00
    Presentation Pack (19.6.78) . . . .   3·25
    First Day Cover . . . .   4·50

334 Sturt's Desert Rose **335** Hooded Plover
   and Map

(Des D. Pitt. Litho Asher and Co, Melbourne)

1978 (19 June). *Establishment of State Government for the Northern
Territory. P* 15½.
668   **334**   18 c. multicoloured   20   15
    First Day Cover   50

(Des Kay Breeden-Williams. Photo)

1978 (3 July)–**80**. *Birds* (1st series). *Multicoloured designs as T 335.
P* 15 × 14 (20 *c.* (*both*)), 14 × 15 (22 *c.*) *or* 13½ (*others*).
669   1 c. Spotted-sided Finch (17.9.79)   10   10
670   2 c. Crimson Finch (17.9.79)   10   10
671   5 c. Type **335** (17.7.78)   15   10
    a. Grey-brown (bird's back) omitted £100
672   15 c. Forest Kingfisher (*vert*) (17.9.79)   20   10
673   20 c. Australian Dabchick ("Little Grebe")   45   10
    a. Yellow (beak and eye) omitted . . . .   30·00
674   20 c. Eastern Yellow Robin (17.9.79)   20   10
675   22 c. White-tailed Kingfisher (22 × 29 *mm*)
    (31.3.80)   30   10
676   25 c. Masked Plover (17.7.78)   50   20
677   30 c. Oystercatcher (17.7.78)   65   25
678   40 c. Variegated Wren (*vert*) (17.9.79)   30   25
679   50 c. Flame Robin (*vert*) (17.9.79)   40   40
680   55 c. Comb-crested Jacana ("Lotus-bird")   85   60
    Set of 12 . . . .   3·75   2·00
    Presentation Packs (ex 22 c.) (2) . . . .   6·00
    First Day Covers (ex 22 c.) (3) . . . .   4·00
See also Nos. 734/40.

338 "Tulloch" **339** Raising the Flag, Sydney
   Cove, 26 January 1788

(Des B. Clinton)

1978 (18 Oct). *Race-horses. T 338 and similar multicoloured designs.
P* 15 × 14 (20 *c.*) *or* 13½ (*others*).
699   20 c. Type **338**   30   10
700   35 c. "Bernborough" (*vert*)   50   70
701   50 c. "Phar Lap" (*vert*)   75   1·00
702   55 c. "Peter Pan"   80   1·00
    Set of 4 . . . .   2·10   2·50
    Presentation Pack . . . .   2·75
    First Day Cover . . . .   2·75

(Des B. Clinton. Litho Asher and Co, Melbourne)

1979 (26 Jan). *Australia Day. P* 15½.
703   **339**   20 c. multicoloured   15   15
    a. Yellow omitted . . . .
    First Day Cover   50

340 P.S. *Canberra* 341 Port Campbell, Victoria

(Des O. Borchert)

1979 (14 Feb). *Ferries and Murray River Steamers. T* **340** *and similar horiz designs. Multicoloured. P* 15 × 14 (20 *c.*) *or* 13½ (*others*).

704	20 c.	Type **340**	25	10
705	35 c.	M.V. *Lady Denman*	50	75
706	50 c.	P.S. *Murray River Queen*	70	1·10
707	55 c.	H.V. *Curl Curl*	80	1·10
		Set of 4	2·00	2·75
		Presentation Pack	2·75	
		First Day Cover	3·00	

(Des M. Robinson. Litho Asher and Co, Melbourne)

1979 (9 Apr). *National Parks. T* **341** *and similar multicoloured designs. P* 15½.

708	20 c.	Type **341**	25	25
	a.	Horiz strip of 5. Nos. 708/12	1·10	
709	20 c.	Uluru, Northern Territory	25	25
710	20 c.	Royal, New South Wales	25	25
711	20 c.	Flinders Ranges, South Australia	25	25
712	20 c.	Nambung, Western Australia	25	25
713	20 c.	Girraween, Queensland (*vert*)	25	25
	a.	Horiz pair. Nos. 713/14	50	50
	ab.	Imperf (horiz pair)*	£275	
714	20 c.	Mount Field, Tasmania (*vert*)	25	25
		Set of 7	1·40	1·40
		Presentation Pack	2·00	
		First Day Cover	1·75	

Nos. 708/14 were printed together, *se-tenant;* Nos. 708/12 in horizontal strips of 5 and Nos. 713/14 in horizontal pairs, throughout separate sheets.
* The imperforate error, No. 713ab, involves the two right-hand vertical columns of the sheet only, the left-hand stamp having vertical perforations at left.

342 "Double Fairlie" Type 343 Symbolic Swan
Locomotive, Western Australia

(Des R. Honisett)

1979 (16 May). *Steam Railways. T* **342** *and similar horiz designs. Multicoloured. P* 14 × 15 (20 *c.*) *or* 13½ (*others*).

715	20 c.	Type **342**	30	10
716	35 c.	Locomotive, "Puffing Billy" Line, Victoria	55	65
717	50 c.	Locomotive, Pichi Richi Line, South Australia	80	1·00
718	55 c.	Locomotive, Zig Zag Railway, New South Wales	90	1·10
		Set of 4	2·25	2·50
		Presentation Pack	2·40	
		First Day Cover	2·75	

(Des B. Weatherhead)

1979 (6 June). *150th Anniv of Western Australia. P* 13½.

719	**343**	20 c. multicoloured	15	15
		First Day Cover		50

A regular new issue supplement to this
catalogue appears each month in

GIBBONS STAMP MONTHLY

—from your newsagent or by postal subscription
—sample copy and details on request.

344 Children playing on Slide 345 Letters and Parcels

(Des Wendy Tamlyn. Litho Asher and Co, Melbourne)

1979 (13 Aug). *International Year of the Child. P* 13½ × 13.

720	**344**	20 c. multicoloured	15	10
		First Day Cover		50

(Des A. Collins. Litho Asher and Co, Melbourne)

1979 (24 Sept–1 Nov). *Christmas. T* **345** *and similar vert designs. Multicoloured. P* 13 × 13½.

721	15 c.	Christ's Nativity (Eastern European icon) (1.11.79)	15	10
722	25 c.	Type **345**	20	40
723	55 c.	"Madonna and Child" (Buglioni) (1.11.79)	40	60
		Set of 3	65	1·00
		Presentation Pack (1.11.79)	1·40	
		First Day Covers (2)		1·75

Souvenir Pack 1979

1979 (24 Sept). *Containing Nos. 703 and 719/20.*

SP723a	Souvenir Pack	1·10

346 Fly-fishing 347 Matthew Flinders

(Des B. Clinton)

1979 (24 Oct). *Fishing. T* **346** *and similar vert designs. P* 14 × 15 (20 *c.*) *or* 13½ (*others*).

724	20 c.	multicoloured	15	10
725	35 c.	black, deep grey-blue and violet-blue	30	60
726	50 c.	multicoloured	35	80
727	55 c.	multicoloured	40	75
		Set of 4	1·10	2·00
		Presentation Pack	1·75	
		First Day Cover		2·25

Designs:—35 c. Spinning; 50 c. Deep sea game-fishing; 55 c. Surf-fishing.

(Des B. Weatherhead. Litho Asher and Co, Melbourne)

1980 (23 Jan). *Australia Day. P* 13½ × 13.

728	**347**	20 c. multicoloured	20	10
		First Day Cover		50

348 Dingo 349 Queen Elizabeth II

(Des Marg Towt. Litho Asher and Co, Melbourne)

1980 (20 Feb). *Dogs. T* **348** *and similar horiz designs. Multicoloured.*
P 13½ × 13.

729	20 c.	Type **348**	35	10
730	25 c.	Border Collie	35	35
731	35 c.	Australian Terrier	55	65
732	50 c.	Australian Cattle Dog	1·25	1·50
733	55 c.	Australian Kelpie	1·00	1·25
		Set of 5	3·25	3·50
		Presentation Pack	3·50	
		First Day Cover		3·75

(Des Kay Breeden-Williams. Litho Asher and Co, Melbourne)

1980 (31 Mar)–83. *Birds* (2nd series). *Multicoloured designs as*
T **335**. *P* 12½.

734	10 c.	Golden-shouldered Parrot (vert) (1.7.80)	30	10
	a.	Perf 14½ × 14 (5.83)	1·40	45
734b	18 c.	Spotted Catbird (vert) (17.11.80)	35	60
735	28 c.	Australian Bee Eater ("Rainbow Bird") (vert)	50	25
736	35 c.	Regent Bowerbird (vert) (1.7.80)	35	10
737	45 c.	Masked Wood Swallow (1.7.80)	40	10
	a.	Perf 14 × 14½ (5.83)	2·75	60
738	60 c.	Australian King Parrot (vert)	50	15
739	80 c.	Rainbow Pitta (1.7.80)	85	40
740	$1	Black-backed Magpie (vert) (1.7.80)	85	10
		Set of 8	3·75	1·60
		Presentation Pack (Nos. 675, 734 and 735/ 40) (1.7.80)	5·50	
		First Day Covers (3) (inc. No. 675)		5·00

Designs of Nos. 734/40 measure 22 × 29 mm (vert) or 29 × 22 mm
(horiz).

(Des B. Weatherhead. Litho Asher and Co, Melbourne)

1980 (21 Apr). *Queen Elizabeth II's Birthday. P* 13 × 13½.

741	**349**	22 c. multicoloured	20	20
		First Day Cover		50

22c **Australia**

Opening of
the High Court Building
by Her Majesty The Queen
Canberra 1980

350 "Once a jolly Swagman   **351** High Court Buildings
camp'd by a Billabong"

(Des R. Roberts. Litho Asher and Co, Melbourne)

1980 (7 May). *Folklore. Scenes and Verses from the Folksong "Waltzing*
Matilda". T **350** *and similar vert designs. Multicoloured. P* 13 × 13½.

742	22 c.	Type **350**	40	10
	a.	Horiz strip of 5. Nos. 742/6	1·75	
743	22 c.	"And he sang as he shoved that Jumbuck in his Tuckerbag"	40	10
744	22 c.	"Up rode the Squatter, mounted on his Thoroughbred"	40	10
745	22 c.	"Down came the Troopers one, two, three"	40	10
746	22 c.	"And his Ghost may be heard as you pass by that Billabong"	40	10
		Set of 5	1·75	45
		Presentation Pack	2·00	
		First Day Cover		2·00

Nos. 742/6 were printed together, *se-tenant*, in horizontal strips of 5
throughout the sheet, forming a composite design.

(Des Cato Hibberd Design. Litho Asher and Co, Melbourne)

1980 (19 May). *Opening of High Court Building, Canberra. P* 13 × 13½.

747	**351**	22 c. multicoloured	20	20
		First Day Cover		50

THE WORLD CENTRE FOR
FINE STAMPS IS 399 STRAND

352 Salvation Army   **353** Postbox, *circa* 1900

(Des J. Spatchurst. Litho Asher and Co, Melbourne)

1980 (11 Aug). *Community Welfare. T* **352** *and similar multicoloured*
designs. P 13½ × 13 *(Nos. 748, 751) or* 13 × 13½ *(others).*

748	22 c.	Type **352**	30	30
749	22 c.	St. Vincent de Paul Society (vert)	30	30
750	22 c.	Meals on Wheels (vert)	30	30
751	22 c.	"Life. Be in it"	30	30
		Set of 4	1·10	1·10
		Presentation Pack	1·40	
		First Day Cover		1·40

(Des. B. Weatherhead. Litho Asher and Co, Melbourne)

1980 (29 Sept). *National Stamp Week. T* **353** *and similar vert designs*
showing postal history, circa 1900. *Multicoloured. P* 13 × 13½.

752	22 c.	Type **353**	30	10
	a.	Horiz strip of 5. Nos. 752/6	1·40	
753	22 c.	Postman (facing left)	30	10
754	22 c.	Mail van	30	10
755	22 c.	Postman and postbox	30	10
756	22 c.	Postman (facing right)	30	10
		Set of 5	1·40	45
		Presentation Pack	1·75	
		First Day Cover		1·75
MS757	95 × 130 mm. Nos. 752, 754 and 756		1·10	1·25
	a. Error. Imperf			
		Presentation Pack	1·25	
		First Day Cover		1·50

Nos. 752/6 were printed together, *se-tenant*, in horizontal strips of 5
throughout the sheet.
Stamps from No. **MS**757 have different backgrounds to the stamps from
normal sheets.

354 "Holy Family" (painting,   **355** "Wackett", 1941
Prospero Fontana)

(Des B. Weatherhead. Litho Asher and Co, Melbourne)

1980 (1 Oct–3 Nov). *Christmas. Works of Art. T* **354** *and similar vert*
designs. Multicoloured. P 13 × 13½.

758	15 c.	"The Virgin Enthroned" (detail of painting by Justin O'Brien) (3.11)	15	10
759	28 c.	Type **354**	20	40
760	60 c.	"Madonna and Child" (sculpture by School of M. Zuern) (3.11)	45	90
		Set of 3	70	1·25
		Presentation Pack (3.11.80)	1·00	
		First Day Covers (2)		1·75

(Des O. Borchert. Litho Victorian Government Printer, Melbourne (22 c.),
Asher and Co, Melbourne (others))

1980 (19 Nov). *Aircraft. T* **355** *and similar horiz designs. Multicoloured.*
P 13½ × 14 (22 c.) *or* 13½ × 13 *(others).*

761	22 c.	Type **355**	35	10
762	40 c.	"Winjeel", 1955	50	75

763	45 c.	"Boomerang", 1944	60	85
764	60 c.	"Nomad", 1975	80	1·10
		Set of 4	2·00	2·50
		Presentation Pack	2·25	
		First Day Cover		2·75

Souvenir Pack 1980

1980 (26 Nov). *Containing Nos. 728, 741 and 747.*
SP764*a*   Souvenir Pack . . . .   1·25

356   Flag in shape of Australia   357   Caricature of
Darby Munro (jockey)

(Des B. Weatherhead. Litho Asher and Co, Melbourne)

1981 (21 Jan). *Australia Day. P* 13½ × 13.
765   **356**   22 c. multicoloured   25   20
                First Day Cover   50

(Des T. Rafty. Litho Cambec Press, Melbourne)

1981 (18 Feb). *Sports Personalities. T* **357** *and similar vert designs showing caricatures. Multicoloured. P* 14 × 13½.
766	22 c.	Type **357**	30	10
767	35 c.	Victor Trumper (cricketer)	55	65
768	55 c.	Sir Norman Brookes (tennis player)	75	85
769	60 c.	Walter Lindrum (billiards player)	80	90
		Set of 4	2·25	2·25
		Presentation Pack	2·75	
		First Day Cover		2·75

358   1931 Kingsford   359   Apex Emblem and
Smith's Flights   Map of Australia
6d. Commemorative

(Des Cato Hibberd Design. Litho Asher and Co, Melbourne)

1981 (25 Mar). *50th Anniv of Official Australia–U.K. Airmail Service. T* **358** *and similar horiz design showing* 1931 *Kingsford Smith's Flights 6d. commemorative. P* 13 × 13½ (22 c.) *or* 13½ × 13 (60 c.).
770   22 c. blackish lilac, rosine and bright blue   25   10
771   60 c. blackish lilac, rosine and ultramarine   50   90
              Set of 2   75   1·00
              Presentation Pack . . . .   1·25
              First Day Cover . . . .   1·25

(Des P. Clark)

1981 (6 Apr). *50th Anniv of Apex (young men's service club). P* 13½.
772   **359**   22 c. multicoloured   20   20
                First Day Cover   50

ASHER AND CO. From April 1981 this firm was known as Leigh-Mardon Ltd, Melbourne.

360   Queen's Personal   361   "Licence Inspected"
Standard for Australia

(Litho Leigh-Mardon Ltd, Melbourne)

1981 (21 Apr). *Queen Elizabeth II's Birthday. P* 13½ × 13.
773   **360**   22 c. multicoloured   20   20
                First Day Cover   50

(Des B. Weatherhead. Litho Leigh-Mardon Ltd, Melbourne)

1981 (20 May). *Gold Rush Era. Sketches by S. T. Gill. T* **361** *and similar vert designs. Multicoloured. P* 13 × 13½.
774	22 c.	Type **361**	20	25
775	22 c.	"Puddling"	20	25
776	22 c.	"Quality of washing stuff"	20	25
777	22 c.	"On route to deposit gold"	20	25
		Set of 4	70	90
		Presentation Pack	1·25	
		First Day Cover		1·25

362   "On the Wallaby Track"
(Fred McCubbin)

(Litho Leigh-Mardon Ltd, Melbourne)

1981 (17 June)–**84.** *T* **362** *and similar horiz design. Multicoloured. P* 15 × 14½.
778   $2   Type **362**.   1·75   30
779   $5   "A Holiday at Mentone, 1888" (Charles Con-
           der) (4.4.84) (Optd S. £2.75) . . . .   4·75   1·25
           Presentation Pack (No. 778) . . . .   1·90
           Presentation Pack (No. 779) (4.4.84) . . . . . .   5·00
           First Day Covers (2) . . . .   7·00

Printings of these stamps during 1987–89 were on Clark (both), Harrison ($2 only) or CPL (both) papers. See notes below No. 1038.
For No. 778 optd "SPECIMEN" in red, see No. SP881*a*.

363   Thylacine   363*a*   Blue Mountain
Tree Frog

363*b*   Ulysses
(butterfly)

PRINTINGS OF THE 24C. VALUE (Nos. 788/Ea). Original printings of this stamp were produced by a combination of printing processes. The centre design was first printed in photogravure by the Note Printing Branch, Reserve Bank of Australia, and then the half-printed sheets were transferred to Leigh-Marden Ltd for the inscriptions and face value to be added in lithography.

Further supplies of this value were required in late 1981, but these were printed by Leigh-Marden Ltd entirely in lithography.

The work of the two printers can be identified by the usual differences exhibited by the processes concerned; the lithography version tending to be darker in appearance with much sharper outlines.

Other specific differences are as follows:

On the *photogravure* version the front legs show a diagonal pattern of screening dots which are replaced by vertical and horizontal lines on the *litho* stamp.

The animal's eye is highlighted on the *photogravure* stamp.

The fourth and sixth bands on the animal's back are much longer on the *litho* version.

The end of the righthand twig is pointed on the *photogravure* and blunt on the *litho*.

Photogravure Centre

Lithography Centre

(Des C. McCubbin (4, 10, 20, 27 c. (No. 791), 30 c. (No. 792a), 35, 45, 60, 80 c., $1), F. Knight (5, 24, 25, 30 c. (No. 792), 50, 55 c.) or Beverley Bruen (others). Photo Note Ptg Branch, Reserve Bank of Australia and litho Leigh-Marden (early ptgs of 24 c.), litho Leigh-Mardon (3, 5, 15, 24, 25, 27 c. (both), 30 c. (both), 40, 50, 55, 65, 75, 90 c.) or Cambec Press (others))

1981 (1 July)–**84**. *Wildlife. Multicoloured designs as T 363 (5, 24, 25, 30, 50, 55 c.), T 363a (1, 3, 15, 27 (No. 70), 40, 65, 70, 75, 85, 90, 95 c.) or vert as T 363b (others). P 13½ (1, 4, 10, 20, 24, 35, 45, 60, 70, 80, 85, 95 c., $1), 14½×14 (27 c. (No. 791), 30 c. (No. 792a)) or 12½ (others).*

781	1 c. Lace Monitor (2.2.83)	10	10
782	3 c. Corroboree Frog (19.4.82)	10	10
	a. Perf 14×14½ (9.84)	40	10
783	4 c. Regent Skipper (butterfly) (*vert*) (15.6.83) . .	40	10
784	5 c. Queensland Hairy-nosed Wombat (*vert*) (15.7.81)	10	10
	a. Perf 14½×14 (3.84)	75	10
785	10 c. Cairns Birdwing (butterfly) (*vert*) (15.6.83) . .	40	10
786	15 c. Eastern Snake-necked Tortoise (16.6.82) . . .	20	25
	a. Perf 14×14½ (3.84)	50	30
787	20 c. Macleay's Swallowtail (butterfly) (*vert*) (15.6.83)	50	20
788	24 c. Type 363 (centre photo; inscr litho)	35	10
	a. Imperf (pair)	£200	
	Eb. Centre and inscr litho (12.81)	45	30
789	25 c. Common Rabbit-Bandicoot (*vert*) (15.7.81) .	35	10
	a. Perf 14½×14 (5.83)	80	25
790	27 c. Type 363a (19.4.82)	35	15
	a. Perf 14×14½ (6.82)	60	10
791	27 c. Type 363b (15.6.83)	75	15
	a. Imperf (pair)	£300	

792	30 c. Bridled Nail-tailed Wallaby (*vert*) (15.7.81)	40	15
792a	30 c. Chlorinda Hairstreak (butterfly) (*vert*) (24.10.83)	75	20
793	35 c. Blue Tiger (butterfly) (*vert*) (15.6.83) . .	60	20
794	40 c. Smooth Knob-tailed Gecko (16.6.82)	45	45
	a. Perf 14×14½ (3.84)	1·50	75
795	45 c. Big Greasy (butterfly) (*vert*) (15.6.83) . . .	60	25
796	50 c. Leadbeater's Possum (15.7.81)	50	10
	a. Perf 14×14½ (1983)	90	30
797	55 c. Stick-nest Rat (*vert*) (15.7.81)	50	20
798	60 c. Wood White (butterfly) (*vert*) (15.6.83) . .	75	25
799	65 c. Yellow-faced Whip Snake (19.4.82)	80	30
	a. Perf 14×14½ (3.84)	75	55
800	70 c. Crucifix Toad (2.2.83)	65	80
801	75 c. Eastern Water Dragon (19.4.82)	80	25
	a. Perf 14×14½ (3.84)	1·25	75
802	80 c. Amaryllis Azure (butterfly) (*vert*) (15.6.83)	1·60	90
803	85 c. Centralian Blue-tongued Lizard (2.2.83)	1·10	90
804	90 c. Freshwater Crocodile (16.6.82)	1·10	90
805	95 c. Thorny Devil (2.2.83)	1·00	90
806	$1 Sword Grass Brown (butterfly) (*vert*) (15.6.83)	1·60	20
	Set of 27	15·00	8·00
	Presentation Packs (4)	17·00	
	First Day Covers (7)	12·00	

A printing of the 1 c. in 1987 was on Harrison paper. See notes below No. 1038.

364 Prince Charles and Lady Diana Spencer 　**365** *Cortinarius cinnabarinus*

(Des B. Clinton. Litho Leigh-Mardon Ltd, Melbourne)

1981 (29 July). *Royal Wedding. P 13½ × 13.*

821	**364**	24 c. multicoloured	25	10
822		60 c. multicoloured	75	1·00
		Set of 2	1·00	1·00
		Set of 2 Gutter Pairs	6·50	
		Presentation Pack	1·25	
		First Day Cover		1·25

(Des Celia Rosser. Litho Leigh-Mardon Ltd, Melbourne)

1981 (19 Aug). *Australian Fungi. T 365 and similar vert designs. Multicoloured. P 13 × 13½.*

823	24 c. Type 365	35	10
824	35 c. Coprinus comatus	50	50
825	55 c. Armillaria luteobubalina	70	70
826	60 c. Cortinarius austro-venetus	80	80
	Set of 4	2·10	1·90
	Presentation Pack	2·40	
	First Day Cover		2·25

Australia　24c

366 Disabled People playing Basketball　**367** "Christmas Bush for His Adorning"

(Des J. Spatchurst. Litho Cambec Press, Melbourne)

1981 (16 Sept). *International Year for Disabled Persons. P 14 × 13½.*

827	**366**	24 c. multicoloured	20	20
		First Day Cover		50

(Des F. Beck. Litho Leigh-Mardon Ltd, Melbourne)

1981 (28 Sept–2 Nov). *Christmas. Scenes and Verses from Carols by W. James and J. Wheeler. T 367 and similar vert designs. Multicoloured.* P 13 × 13½.

828	18 c. Type **367** (2 Nov)	20	10
829	30 c. "The Silver Stars are in the Sky"	30	25
830	60 c. "Noeltime" (2 Nov)	50	70
	Set of 3	90	90
	Presentation Pack (2.11.81)	1·50	
	First Day Covers (2)		1·75

368 Globe depicting   369 Ocean Racing Yacht
    Australia

(Des B. Weatherhead. Litho Leigh-Mardon Ltd, Melbourne)

1981 (30 Sept). *Commonwealth Heads of Government Meeting, Melbourne.* P 13 × 13½.

831	**368**	24 c. black, pale blue and gold	20	10
832		60 c. black, pale blue and silver	50	75
		Set of 2	70	75
		Presentation Pack	1·25	
		First Day Cover		1·25

(Des R. Fletcher. Litho Leigh-Mardon Ltd, Melbourne)

1981 (14 Oct). *Yachts. T 369 and similar vert designs. Multicoloured.* P 13 × 13½.

833	24 c. Type **369**	35	10
834	35 c. "Sharpie"	50	50
835	55 c. "12 Metre"	75	85
836	60 c. "Sabot"	1·00	1·00
	Set of 4	2·40	2·25
	Presentation Pack	2·75	
	First Day Cover		2·75

Souvenir Pack 1981

1982 (20 Jan). *Containing Nos. 765, 772/3 and 827.*
SP836a Souvenir Pack . . . . 1·25

370 Aborigine, Governor Phillip   371 Humpback Whale
(founder of N.S.W., 1788)
and Post World War II Migrant

(Des B. Clinton. Litho Cambec Press, Melbourne)

1982 (20 Jan). *Australia Day. "Three Great Waves of Migration".* P 13½ × 14.

837	**370**	24 c. multicoloured	35	25
		First Day Cover		50

(Des R. and Katrina Ingpen. Litho Cambec Press, Melbourne)

1982 (17 Feb). *Whales. T 371 and similar multicoloured designs.* P 13½ × 14 (24, 60 c.) or 14 × 13½ (others).

838	24 c. Sperm Whale	40	10
839	35 c. Black Right Whale (vert)	60	60
840	55 c. Blue Whale (vert)	1·10	1·10
841	60 c. Type **371** (new blue background)	1·25	1·25
	a. Solid greenish blue background	£250	
	Set of 4	3·00	2·75
	Presentation Pack	3·50	
	First Day Cover		3·25

No. 841a comes from a small trial printing, some sheets of which were

included amongst normal stock by mistake. The correct version of the 60 c. value shows the new blue background streaked with white at top left. On No. 841a the background is in greenish blue and is without the white streaks.

Post Office Yearbook

1982 (1 Mar). *Comprises Nos. 765/78. 784, 788/9, 792, 796/7, 821/36 and Australian Antarctic Territory Nos. 38, 40, 42, 48/50 in softbound book with slip case.*
YB841a. Yearbook . . . . 50·00

372 Queen Elizabeth II   373 "Marjorie Atherton"

(Des R. Honisett. Litho Cambec Press, Melbourne)

1982 (21 Apr). *Queen Elizabeth II's Birthday.* P 14 × 13½.

842	**372**	27 c. multicoloured	30	15
		First Day Cover		50

(Des Betty Conabere. Litho Leigh-Mardon Ltd, Melbourne)

1982 (19 May). *Roses. T 373 and similar vert designs. Multicoloured.* P 13 × 13½.

843	27 c. Type **373**	40	15
844	40 c. "Imp"	55	50
845	65 c. "Minnie Watson"	95	80
846	75 c. "Satellite"	1·10	1·00
	Set of 4	2·75	2·25
	Presentation Pack	4·00	
	First Day Cover		2·75

374 Radio Announcer and   375 Forbes Post Office
1930-style Microphone

(Des Cato Hibberd Design. Litho Leigh-Mardon Ltd, Melbourne)

1982 (16 June). *50th Anniv of ABC (Australian Broadcasting Commission). T 374 and similar horiz design. Multicoloured.* P 13½ × 13.

847	27 c. Type **374**	30	40
	a. Pair. Nos. 847/8	60	80
848	27 c. ABC logo	30	40
	Set of 2	60	80
	First Day Cover		1·00

Nos. 847/8 were printed together, *se-tenant*, in horizontal and vertical pairs throughout the sheet.

(Des F. Beck. Litho Cambec Press, Melbourne)

1982 (4 Aug). *Historic Australian Post Offices. T 375 and similar multicoloured designs.* P 14 × 13½ (vert) or 13½ × 14 (horiz).

849	27 c. Type **375**	40	30
850	27 c. Flemington Post Office	40	30
851	27 c. Rockhampton Post Office	40	30
852	27 c. Kingston S.E. Post Office (horiz)	40	30
853	27 c. York Post Office (horiz)	40	30
854	27 c. Launceston Post Office	40	30
855	27 c. Old Post and Telegraph Station, Alice Springs (horiz)	40	30
	Set of 7	2·50	1·90
	Presentation Pack	2·75	
	First Day Cover		2·40

376 Early Australian   **377** Boxing
Christmas Card

(Des B. Weatherhead. Litho Leigh-Mardon Ltd, Melbourne)

1982 (15 Sept–1 Nov). *Christmas. T* **376** *and similar multicoloured designs. P* 14½.

856	21 c.	Bushman's Hotel, with Cobb's coach arriving (*horiz*) (1.11.82)	30	10
857	35 c.	Type **376**	40	50
858	75 c.	Little girl offering Christmas pudding to swagman (1.11.82)	75	1·25
		Set of 3	1·25	1·60
		Presentation Pack (1.11.82)	1·75	
		First Day Covers (2)		2·00

(Des R. Carnielye. Litho Leigh-Mardon Ltd, Melbourne)

1982 (22 Sept). *Commonwealth Games, Brisbane. T* **377** *and similar horiz designs. P* 14½.

859	27 c.	stone, lemon and bright carmine	25	20
860	27 c.	lemon, stone and emerald	25	20
861	27 c.	stone, lemon and yellow-brown	25	20
862	75 c.	multicoloured	75	90
		Set of 4	1·40	1·40
		Presentation Pack	2·10	
		First Day Cover		1·90
MS863		130 × 95 mm. Nos. 859/61. P 13½ × 13	1·10	1·25
		Presentation Pack	1·40	
		First Day Cover		1·50

Designs:—No. 859, Type **377**; No. 860, Archery; No. 861, Weightlifting; No. 862, Pole-vaulting.

378 Sydney Harbour Bridge   **379** "Yirawala" Bark
5s. Stamp of 1932   Painting

(Des Cato Hibberd Design. Litho Cambec Press, Melbourne)

1982 (27 Sept). *National Stamp Week. P* 13½ × 14.

864	**378**	27 c.	multicoloured	30	25
			First Day Cover		60

(Des Australia Post Graphic Design Section. Litho Leigh-Mardon Ltd, Melbourne)

1982 (12 Oct). *Opening of Australian National Gallery. P* 14½.

865	**379**	27 c.	multicoloured	30	25
			First Day Cover		60

380 Mimi Spirits Dancing   **381** *Eucalyptus calophylla*
"Rosea"

(Des D. Milaybuma (27 c.), L. Nabardayal (40 c.), J. Galareya (65 c.), D. Nguleingulei-Murrumurru) (75 c.). Litho Cambec Press, Melbourne)

1982 (17 Nov). *Aboriginal Culture. Music and Dance. T* **380** *and similar horiz designs depicting Aboriginal Bark Paintings of Mimi Spirits. P* 13½ × 14.

866	27 c.	multicoloured	25	10
867	40 c.	multicoloured	40	50
868	65 c.	multicoloured	70	80
869	75 c.	multicoloured	80	1·10
		Set of 4	2·00	2·25
		Presentation Pack	2·50	
		First Day Cover		2·75

(Des Elizabeth Conabere. Photo Enschedé)

1982 (17 Nov). *Booklet stamps. Eucalyptus Flowers. T* **381** *and similar horiz designs. Multicoloured. P* 12½ × 13½.

870	1 c.	Type **381**	10	15
	a.	Booklet pane. Nos. 870/1 and 874 each × 2	80	
	b.	Booklet pane. Nos. 870/1 each × 2, 872/3 and 874 × 3	2·00	
871	2 c.	*Eucalyptus casia*	10	15
872	3 c.	*Eucalyptus ficifolia*	25	40
873	10 c.	*Eucalyptus globulus*	25	40
874	27 c.	*Eucalyptus forrestiana*	30	40
		Set of 5	90	1·40
		First Day Cover		1·75

Nos. 870/4 only exist from 60 c. (pane No 870a) and $1 (pane No. 870b) stamp booklets and the stamps have one or two adjacent sides imperforate.

Souvenir Pack 1982

1982 (1 Dec). *Containing Nos. 837, 842, 847/8, 864 and 865.*

SP874a	Souvenir Pack	2·25

Post Office Yearbook

1982 (1 Dec). *Comprises Nos. 782, 786, 790, 794, 799, 801, 804, 837/74 and Australian Antarctic Territory Nos. 53/4 in hardbound book with slip case.*

YB874b	Yearbook	40·00

382 Shand Mason Steam   **383** H.M.S. *Sirius*
Fire Engine, 1891

(Des A. Puckett. Litho Cambec Press, Melbourne)

1983 (12 Jan). *Historic Fire Engines. T* **382** *and similar horiz designs. Multicoloured. P* 13½ × 14.

875	27 c.	Type **382**	30	10
876	40 c.	Hotchkiss fire engine, 1914	45	50
877	65 c.	Ahrens-Fox PS2 fire engine, 1929	80	1·00
878	75 c.	Merryweather manual fire appliance, 1851	90	1·25
		Set of 4	2·25	2·50
		Presentation Pack	2·50	
		First Day Cover		2·75

(Des J. Spatchurst. Litho Leigh-Mardon Ltd, Melbourne)

1983 (26 Jan). *Australia Day. T* **383** *and similar horiz design. Multicoloured. P* 14½.

879	27 c.	Type **383**	35	40
	a.	Pair. Nos. 879/80	70	85
	Eab.	Blue (background) and black (inscr) printed double (pair)		
880	27 c.	H.M.S. *Supply*	35	40
		Set of 2	70	80
		First Day Cover		1·25

Nos. 879/80 were printed together, *se-tenant*, in horizontal and vertical pairs throughout the sheet.

384 Stylised Kangaroo   385 Equality and Dignity
and Kiwi

(Des G. Emery. Litho Cambec Press, Melbourne)

1983 (2 Feb). *Closer Economic Relationship Agreement with New Zealand. P* 14 × 13½.
881   **384**   27 c. multicoloured   30   25
                                                 60

1983 (9 Feb). *"Ausipex 84" International Stamp Exhibition. Souvenir Pack containing Nos. 567, 567a and 778, each optd "SPECIMEN" in red. Sold at* $8.
SP881a   Souvenir Pack . . . .   9·00

(Des. G. Emery. Litho Leigh-Mardon Ltd, Melbourne)

1983 (9 Mar). *Commonwealth Day. T* **385** *and similar vert designs. Multicoloured. P* 14½.
882   27 c. Type **385**   25   25
883   27 c. Liberty and Freedom   25   25
884   27 c. Social Justice and Co-operation   25   25
885   75 c. Peace and Harmony   70   1·10
          Set of 4 . . . .   1·25   1·75
          Presentation Pack . . . .   1·60
          First Day Cover . . . .   2·00

386 R.Y. *Britannia* passing   387 "Postal and Telecom-
Sydney Opera House   munications Services"

(Des J. Richards. Litho Leigh-Mardon Ltd, Melbourne)

1983 (20 Apr). *Queen Elizabeth II's Birthday. P* 14½.
886   **386**   27 c. multicoloured   40   25
               First Day Cover   60

(Des B. Sadgrove. Litho Cambec Press, Melbourne)

1983 (18 May). *World Communications Year. P* 13½ × 14.
887   **387**   27 c. multicoloured   30   25
               First Day Cover   60

388 Badge of the Order   389 Jaycee Members and Badge
of St. John

(Des T. McCauley. Litho Cambec Press, Melbourne)

1983 (8 June). *Centenary of St. John Ambulance in Australia. P* 14 × 13½.
888   **388**   27 c. black and deep turquoise-blue   30   25
               First Day Cover   60

(Des B. Clinton. Litho Cambec Press, Melbourne)

1983 (8 June). *50th Anniv of Australian Jaycees. P* 13½ × 14.
889   **389**   27 c. multicoloured   30   25
               First Day Cover   60

Souvenir Pack 1983

1983 (8 June). *Containing Nos.* 879/81, 886/9.
SP889a   Souvenir Pack . . . .   2·40

390 "The Bloke"   391 Nativity Scene

(Des B. Clinton. Litho Leigh-Mardon Ltd, Melbourne)

1983 (3 Aug). *Folklore. "The Sentimental Bloke" (humorous poem by C. J. Dennis). T* **390** *and similar vert designs. Multicoloured. P* 14½.
890   27 c. Type **390**   40   40
      a. Horiz strip of 5. Nos. 890/4 . . . .   1·75
891   27 c. "Doreen—The Intro"   40   40
892   27 c. "The Stror 'at Coot"   40   40
893   27 c. "Hitched"   40   40
894   27 c. "The Mooch o'Life"   40   40
          Set of 5 . . . .   1·75   1·75
          Presentation Pack . . . .   2·00
          First Day Cover . . . .   2·25
Nos. 890/4 were printed together, *se-tenant*, in horizontal strips of 5 throughout the sheet.

(Des Holly Alvarez (24 c.), Deanne Head (35 c.), Justine Jacobi (85 c.). Litho Cambec Press, Melbourne)

1983 (14 Sept–2 Nov). *Christmas. Children's Paintings. T* **391** *and similar horiz designs. Multicoloured. P* 13½ × 14.
895   24 c. Type **391** (2 November)   20   10
896   35 c. Kookaburra   35   45
897   85 c. Father Christmas in sleigh over beach (2
             November)   90   1·10
          Set of 3 . . . .   1·25   1·50
          Presentation Pack (2 November) . . . .   1·90
          First Day Covers (2) . . . .   2·25

392 Sir Paul Edmund   393 Cook Family Cottage, Melbourne
de Strzelecki

(Des Dianne Quinn. Litho Leigh-Mardon Ltd, Melbourne)

1983 (26 Sept). *Explorers of Australia. T* **392** *and similar vert designs. Multicoloured. P* 14½.
898   30 c. Type **392**   35   40
899   30 c. Ludwig Leichardt   35   40
900   30 c. William John Wills and Robert O'Hara Burke   35   40
901   30 c. Alexander Forrest   35   40
          Set of 4 . . . .   1·25   1·40
          Presentation Pack . . . .   1·90
          First Day Cover . . . .   1·75

Post Office Yearbook

1983 (30 Nov). *Comprises Nos.* 781, 783, 785, 787, 791, 792a, 793, 795, 798, 800, 802/3, 805/6, 875/901 *and Australian Antarctic Territory Nos.* 55/6 *in hardbound book with slipcase.*
YB901a   Yearbook . . . .   60·00

(Des J. Quinn. Litho Cambec Press, Melbourne)

1984 (26 Jan). *Australia Day. P* 13½ × 14.

902	**393**	30 c. black and stone	30	35
		First Day Cover		80

MACHINE LABELS. From 22 February 1984 gummed labels in the above design ranging in value from 1 c. to $9.99, were available from seven automatic machines. The number at the top of the label indicates the location of the machine from which it was issued: 2000, Sydney; 2601, Canberra; 3000, Melbourne; 4000, Brisbane; 5000, Adelaide; 6000, Perth; 7000, Hobart.

These were replaced by a further series, with a background pattern of kangaroos, on 22 October 1985. This second series included 5790 (later 0800), Darwin and labels without code number.

On 25 August 1986 a further series, with a background pattern of platypuses, was issued. These exist either without code or with one of the eight numbers introduced for the earlier issues. The design was again changed on 2 September 1987 to show Echidnas to be followed by Ringtail Possums on 28 September 1988, Frill-necked Lizards on 1 September 1989 and Koalas on 3 September 1990.

394 Charles Ulm, *Faith in Australia* and Trans-Tasman Cover

(Des G. Beck and J. Quinn. Litho Cambec Press, Melbourne)

1984 (22 Feb). 50*th Anniv of First Official Airmail Flights, New Zealand–Australia and Australia–Papua New Guinea. T* **394** *and similar horiz design. Multicoloured. P* 13½.

903	45 c. Type **394**	65	90
	a. Horiz pair. Nos. 903/4	1·25	1·75
904	45 c. As Type **394** but showing flown cover to Papua New Guinea	65	90
	Set of 2	1·25	1·75
	Presentation Pack	1·40	
	First Day Cover		2·00

Nos. 903/4 were printed together, *se-tenant*, in horizontal pairs throughout the sheet.

395 Thomson "Steamer", 1898   **396** Queen Elizabeth II

(Des A. Puckett. Litho Leigh-Mardon Ltd, Melbourne)

1984 (14 Mar). *Veteran and Vintage Cars. T* **395** *and similar horiz designs. Multicoloured. P* 14½.

905	30 c. Type **395**	45	45
	a. Vert strip of 5. Nos. 905/9	2·00	
906	30 c. Tarrant, 1906	45	45
907	30 c. Gordon & Co "Australian Six", 1919	45	45
908	30 c. Summit, 1923	45	45
909	30 c. Chic, 1924	45	45
	Set of 5	2·00	2·00
	Presentation Pack	2·50	
	First Day Cover		2·50

Nos. 905/9 were printed together, *se-tenant*, in vertical strips of 5 throughout the sheet.

(Des B. Weatherhead. Litho Leigh-Mardon Ltd, Melbourne)

1984 (18 Apr). *Queen Elizabeth II's Birthday. P* 14½.

910	**396**	30 c. multicoloured	30	35
		a. Dull mauve (background) omitted . .	£325	
		First Day Cover		80

397 *Cutty Sark*   **398** Freestyle

(Des J. Earl and J. Quinn. Litho Cambec Press, Melbourne)

1984 (23 May). *Clipper Ships. T* **397** *and similar multicoloured designs. P* 14 × 13½ (30 *c.*, 85 *c.*) *or* 13½ × 14 (*others*).

911	30 c. Type **397**	40	25
912	45 c. *Orient* (*horiz*)	70	70
913	75 c. *Sobraon* (*horiz*)	1·25	1·25
914	85 c. *Thermopylae*	1·25	1·25
	Set of 4	3·25	3·00
	Presentation Pack	3·50	
	First Day Cover		3·50

(Des B. Clinton. Litho Leigh-Mardon Ltd, Melbourne)

1984 (6 June). *Skiing. T* **398** *and similar multicoloured designs. P* 14½.

915	30 c. Type **398**	40	45
916	30 c. Downhill racer	40	45
917	30 c. Slalom (*horiz*)	40	45
918	30 c. Nordic (*horiz*)	40	45
	Set of 4	1·50	1·75
	Presentation Pack	1·75	
	First Day Cover		2·00

399 Coral Hopper

(Des G. Ryan and R. Fletcher (2, 25, 30, 50, 55, 85 c.) or G. Ryan (others). Litho Leigh-Mardon Ltd, Melbourne (30, 33 c.) or Cambec Press, Melbourne (others))

1984 (18 June)–**86**. *Marine Life. T* **399** *and similar horiz designs. Multicoloured. P* 14 × 14½ (30 *c.*, 33 *c.*) *or* 13½ (*others*).

919	2 c. Type **399**	10	10
920	3 c. Jimble (11.6.86)	10	10
921	5 c. Tasselled Anglerfish (12.6.85)	10	10
922	10 c. Stonefish (11.6.86)	20	10
923	20 c. Red Handfish (12.6.85)	45	20
924	25 c. Orange-tipped Cowrie	45	15
925	30 c. Choat's Wrasse	45	15
926	33 c. Leafy Sea-dragon (20.3.85)	35	10
927	40 c. Red Velvet Fish (12.6.85)	65	40
928	45 c. Textile Cone (11.6.86)	80	25
929	50 c. Blue-lined Surgeonfish	80	35
930	55 c. Bennett's Nudibranch	80	50
	a. New blue ("BENNETTS NUDIBRANCH") omitted	†	—
931	60 c. Lionfish (11.6.86)	90	50
932	65 c. Stingaree (11.6.86)	90	55
933	70 c. Blue-ringed Octopus (11.6.86)	90	60
934	80 c. Pineapple Fish (12.6.85)	1·25	65
935	85 c. Regal Angelfish	90	50
936	90 c. Crab-eyed Goby (12.6.85)	1·00	75
937	$1 Crown of Thorns Starfish (11.6.86) (Optd S. 50p)	1·50	80
	Set of 19	11·00	6·00
	Presentation Packs (3)	13·00	
	First Day Covers (4)		13·00

No. 930a only exists used on maximum card.

During 1987 further printings on Harrison paper were made for the 2 c., 3 c., 5 c., 25 c., 50 c., 60 c., 90 c., $1 and on CPL paper for the 65 c. See notes below No. 1038.

400 Before the Event

401 Australian 1913 1d.
Kangaroo Stamp

(Des O. Schmidinger and Christine Stead. Litho Cambec Press, Melbourne)

1984 (25 July). *Olympic Games, Los Angeles.* T **400** *and similar multicoloured designs.* P 14 × 13½ *(No.* 943*) or* 13½ × 14 *(others).*

941	30 c.	Type **400**	35	35
942	30 c.	During the event	35	35
943	30 c.	After the event *(vert)*	35	35
		Set of 3	95	95
		Presentation Pack	1·40	
		First Day Cover		1·40

(Des Ken Cato Design Studio. Litho Cambec Press, Melbourne)

1984 (22 Aug–21 Sept). *"Ausipex" International Stamp Exhibition, Melbourne.* T **401** *and similar vert designs. Multicoloured.* P 14½.

944	30 c.	Type **401**	35	30
		First Day Cover		90
MS945	126 × 175 mm. 30 c. × 7, Victoria 1850 3d.			

"Half Length"; New South Wales 1850 1d. "Sydney View"; Tasmania 1853 1d.; South Australia 1855 1d.; Western Australia 1854 1d. "Black Swan"; Queensland

1860 6d.; Type **402**	3·25	4·00	
Presentation Pack (21.9.84)	3·50		
First Day Cover		4·25	

On No. **MS**945 the emblem and inscription on the sheet margin are embossed.

402 "Angel" (stained-glass window, St. Francis' Church, Melbourne)

403 "Stick Figures" (Cobar Region)

(Des Ken Cato Design Studio. Litho Cambec Press, Melbourne)

1984 (17 Sept–31 Oct). *Christmas. Stained-glass Windows.* T **402** *and similar vert designs. Multicoloured.* P 14 × 13½.

946	24 c.	"Angel and Child" (Holy Trinity Church, Sydney) (31.10.84)	40	20
947	30 c.	"Veiled Virgin and Child" (St. Mary's Catholic Church, Geelong) (31.10.84)	55	20
948	40 c.	Type **402**	70	60
949	50 c.	"Three Kings" (St. Mary's Cathedral, Sydney) (31.10.84)	90	80
950	85 c.	"Madonna and Child" (St. Batholomew's Church, Norwood) (31.10.84)	1·25	1·25
		Set of 5	3·50	2·75
		Presentation Pack (31.10.84)	4·00	
		First Day Cover (2)		4·50

(Des Elizabeth Innes. Litho Leigh-Mardon Ltd, Melbourne)

1984 (7 Nov). *Bicentenary of Australian Settlement* (1988) *(1st issue). The First Australians.* T **403** *and similar square designs showing aborigine rock paintings. Multicoloured.* P 14½.

951	30 c.	Type **403**	45	45
952	30 c.	"Bunjil" (large figure), Grampians	45	45
953	30 c.	"Quikans" (tall figures), Cape York	45	45
954	30 c.	"Wandjina Spirit and Baby Snakes" (Gibb River)	45	45
955	30 c.	"Rock Python" (Gibb River)	45	45

956	30 c.	"Silver Barramundi" (fish) (Kakadu National Park)	45	45
957	30 c.	Bicentenary emblem	45	45
958	85 c.	"Rock Possum" (Kakadu National Park)	1·10	1·25
		Set of 8	3·75	4·00
		Presentation Pack	4·00	
		First Day Cover		5·00

See also Nos. 972/6, 993/6, 1002/7, 1019/22, 1059/63, 1064/6, 1077/81, 1090/2, 1105/9, 1110, 1137/41, 1145/8 and 1149.

Bicentenary Stamp Heritage Book

1984 (7 Nov). *Comprises Nos. 951/8 in 36-page book.*
HB958*a*　Stamp Heritage Book　　　　　　　　　　7·00

404 Yellow-tufted Honeyeater

405 "Musgrave Ranges" (Sidney Nolan)

(Des G. Emery. Litho Leigh-Mardon Ltd, Melbourne)

1984 (19 Nov). *150th Anniv of Victoria.* T **404** *and similar vert design. Multicoloured.* P 14½.

959	30 c.	Type **404**	35	40
		a. Pair. Nos. 959/60	70	80
960	30 c.	Leadbeater's Possum	35	40
		Set of 2	70	80
		First Day Cover		1·00

Nos. 959/60 were issued together, *se-tenant*, in horizontal and vertical pairs throughout the sheet.

Souvenir Pack 1984

1984 (19 Nov). *Containing Nos.* 902, 910, 944 *and* 959/60.
SP960*a*　Souvenir Pack　　　　　　　　　　　　2·00

Post Office Yearbook

1984 (21 Nov). *Comprises Nos.* 779, 902/19, 924/5, 929/30, 935, 941/60 *and Australian Antarctic Territory Nos.* 61/2, 64, 68/9, 74/5 *in hardbound book with slipcase.*
YB960*b*　Yearbook　　　　　　　　　　　　　32·00

(Des Sue Titcher. Litho Leigh-Mardon Ltd, Melbourne)

1985 (25 Jan). *Australia Day. Birth Centenary of Dorothea Mackellar (author of poem "My Country"). T **405** *and similar horiz design. Multicoloured.* P 14½.

961	30 c.	Type **405**	35	45
		a. Tête-bêche (vert pair)	70	1·25
		b. Vert pair. Nos. 961/2	70	90
962	30 c.	"The Walls of China" (Russell Drysdale)	35	45
		a. Tête-bêche (vert pair)	70	1·25
		Set of 2	70	90
		First Day Cover		1·40

Nos. 961/2 were issued together, *se-tenant*, within the same sheet. In each pane of 25 No. 961 occurs in horizontal rows 1, 4, 5, 8 and 9, and No. 962 in rows 2, 3, 6, 7 and 10. Horizontal rows 3/4 and 7/8 are inverted forming *tête-bêche* pairs of the same design in addition to the vertical *se-tenant* pairs containing both designs.

STANLEY GIBBONS
STAMP COLLECTING SERIES

Introductory booklets on *How to Start, How to Identify Stamps* and *Collecting by Theme.* A series of well illustrated guides at a low price.

Write for details.

406 Young People of Different Races, and Sun

407 Royal Victorian Volunteer Artillery

(Des Derryn Vogelnest. Litho Cambec Press, Melbourne)

1985 (13 Feb). *International Youth Year. P* 14 × 13½.
963	**406**	30 c.	multicoloured	35	30
			First Day Cover		90

(Des Pam Andrews. Litho Leigh-Mardon Ltd, Melbourne)

1985 (25 Feb). *19th-Century Australian Military Uniforms. T* **407** *and similar vert designs. Multicoloured. P* 14½.
964	33 c.	Type **407**	50	50
	a.	Horiz strip of 5. Nos 964/8	2·25	
965	33 c.	Western Australian Pinjarrah Cavalry	50	50
966	33 c.	New South Wales Lancers	50	50
967	33 c.	New South Wales Contingent to the Sudan	50	50
968	33 c.	Victorian Mounted Rifles	50	50
		Set of 5	2·25	2·25
		Presentation Pack	2·50	
		First Day Cover		2·75

Nos. 964/8 were issued in horizontal strips of 5, *se-tenant*, throughout the sheet.

408 District Nurse of early 1900's

409 Sulphur-crested Cockatoos

(Des Wendy Tamlyn. Litho Leigh-Mardon Ltd, Melbourne)

1985 (13 Mar). *Centenary of District Nursing Services. P* 14½.
969	**408**	33 c.	multicoloured	40	35
			First Day Cover		1·00

(Des R. Bevers. Litho Leigh-Mardon Ltd, Melbourne)

1985 (13 Mar). *Booklet stamps. Multicoloured, background colour given. P* 14½ × *imperf.*
970	**409**	1 c.	flesh	90	1·50
		a.	Booklet pane. Nos. 970, and 971 × 3 .	2·10	
971		33 c.	pale turquoise-green	45	55
			Set of 2	1·25	2·00
			First Day Cover		2·50

Nos. 970/1 only exist from $1 stamp booklets. As stamps from these booklets have their outer edges imperforate, the end example of No. 971 is only perforated along one side.

A second printing in December 1985 produced stamps of a less glossy appearance.

ALBUM LISTS
Write for our latest lists of albums and accessories.
These will be sent free on request.

410 Abel Tasman and Journal Entry

411 Sovereign's Badge of Order of Australia

(Des G. Emery. Litho Cambec Press, Melbourne)

1985 (10 Apr). *Bicentenary of Australian Settlement* (1988) (2nd issue). *Navigators. T* **410** *and similar square designs. Multicoloured. P* 13.
972	33 c.	Type **410**	45	35
973	33 c.	Dirk Hartog's *"Eendracht"* (detail, Aert Anthonisz)	45	35
974	33 c.	"William Dampier" (detail, T. Murray)	45	35
975	90 c.	Globe and hand with extract from Dampier's journal	1·10	1·50
		Set of 4	2·25	2·25
		Presentation Pack	2·50	
		First Day Cover		2·75
MS976		150 × 115 mm. As Nos. 972/5, but with cream-coloured margins	3·00	3·00
		Presentation Pack	3·25	
		First Day Cover		3·50

(Des Elizabeth Innes. Litho Cambec Press, Melbourne)

1985 (22 Apr). *Queen Elizabeth II's Birthday. P* 14 × 13½.
977	**411**	33 c.	multicoloured	35	30
			First Day Cover		1·00

412 Tree, and Soil running through Hourglass ("Soil")

413 *Elves and Fairies* (Annie Rentoul and Ida Rentoul Outhwaite)

(Des L. Whaite and G. Jorgensen. Litho Cambec Press, Melbourne)

1985 (15 May). *Conservation. T* **412** *and similar vert designs. Multicoloured. P* 14 × 13½.
978	33 c.	Type **412**	45	20
979	50 c.	Washing on line and smog ("air")	70	85
980	80 c.	Tap and flower ("water")	1·10	1·40
981	90 c.	Chain encircling flames ("energy")	1·25	1·75
		Set of 4	3·25	3·75
		Presentation Pack	3·50	
		First Day Cover		4·00

(Des P. Leuver. Litho Leigh-Mardon Ltd, Melbourne)

1985 (17 July). *Classic Australian Children's Books. T* **413** *and similar vert designs. Multicoloured. P* 14½.
982	33 c.	Type **413**	50	50
	a.	Horiz strip of 5. Nos. 982/6	2·25	
983	33 c.	*The Magic Pudding* (Norman Lindsay)	50	50
984	33 c.	*Ginger Meggs* (James Charles Bancks)	50	50
985	33 c.	*Blinky Bill* (Dorothy Wall)	50	50
986	33 c.	*Snugglepot and Cuddlepie* (May Gibbs) . . .	50	50
		Set of 5	2·25	2·25
		Presentation Pack	2·50	
		First Day Cover		2·50

Nos. 982/6 were issued, *se-tenant*, in horizontal strips of 5 throughout the sheet.

414 Dish Aerials   **415** Angel in Sailing Ship

(Des J. Ostoja-Kotkowski. Litho Leigh-Mardon Ltd, Melbourne)

1985 (18 Sept). *Electronic Mail Service. P* 14½.
987 **414** 33 c. multicoloured   35   30
         First Day Cover   95

(Des S. Hartshorne. Litho Leigh-Mardon Ltd, Melbourne)

1985 (18 Sept–1 Nov). *Christmas. T* **415** *and similar horiz designs. Multicoloured. P* 14½.
988   27 c. Angel with holly wings (1.11)   30   15
989   33 c. Angel with bells (1.11)   35   15
990   45 c. Type **415**   50   50
991   55 c. Angel with star (1.11)   65   70
992   90 c. Angel with Christmas tree bauble (1.11) . . .   1·00   1·25
         Set of 5 . . . .   2·50   2·50
         Presentation Pack (1.11) . . . .   3·00
         First Day Covers (2) . . . .   3·75

Souvenir Pack 1985

1985 (18 Sept). *Containing Nos. 961/3, 969, 977 and 987.*
SP992*a* Souvenir Pack . . . .   2·75

416 Astrolabe (*Batavia*, 1629)   **417** Aboriginal Wandjina Spirit,
                                       Map of Australia and Egg

(Des G. Emery. Litho Cambec Press, Melbourne)

1985 (2 Oct). *Bicentenary of Australian Settlement* (1988) (*3rd issue*). *Relics from Early Shipwrecks. T* **416** *and similar square designs. Multicoloured. P* 13.
993   33 c. Type **416**   40   15
994   50 c. German beardman jug (*Vergulde Draeck*,
         1656)   70   70
995   90 c. Wooden bobbins (*Batavia*, 1629) and en-
         crusted scissors (*Zeewijk*, 1727) . . . .   1·40   1·50
996   $1 Silver and brass buckle (*Zeewijk*, 1727) . . .   1·60   1·50
         Set of 4 . . . .   3·75   3·50
         Presentation Pack . . . .   4·00
         First Day Cover . . . .   3·75

Bicentenary Stamp Heritage Book

1985 (2 Oct). *Comprises. Nos. 972/6 and 993/6 in 36-page book.*
HB996*a* Stamp Heritage Book . . . .   9·50

Post Office Yearbook

1985 (20 Nov). *Comprises Nos. 921, 923, 926/7, 934, 936, 961/96 and Australian Antarctic Territory Nos. 66, 70, 72, 76/7 in hardbound book with slipcase.*
YB996*b* Yearbook . . . .   32·00

(Des R. Meeks. Litho Leigh-Mardon Ltd, Melbourne)

1986 (24 Jan). *Australia Day. P* 14½.
997 **417** 33 c. multicoloured   40   30
         First Day Cover . . . .   1·00

418 AUSSAT Satellite,   **419** H.M.S. *Buffalo*
Moon and Earth's Surface

(Des O. Schmidinger and Christine Stead. Litho Leigh-Mardon Ltd, Melbourne)

1986 (24 Jan). *AUSSAT National Communications Satellite System. T* **418** *and similar vert design. Multicoloured. P* 14½.
998   33 c. Type **418**   50   15
999   80 c. AUSSAT satellite in orbit . . . .   1·50   1·50
         Set of 2 . . . .   2·00   1·60
         Presentation Pack . . . .   2·25
         First Day Cover . . . .   2·00

(Des I. Kidd. Litho Cambec Press, Melbourne)

1986 (12 Feb). *150th Anniv of South Australia. T* **419** *and similar horiz design. Multicoloured. P* 13½ × 14.
1000   33 c. Type **419**   60   70
         a. Pair. Nos. 1000/1 . . . .   1·10   1·40
1001   33 c. "City Sign" sculpture (Otto Hajek),
         Adelaide   60   70
         Set of 2 . . . .   1·10   1·40
         First Day Cover . . . .   1·90
Nos. 1000/1 were printed together, *se-tenant*, in horizontal and vertical pairs throughout the sheet, the background of each horizontal pair showing an extract from the colony's Letters Patent of 1836.

420 *Banksia serrata*   **421** Radio Telescope, Parkes,
                                   and Diagram of Comet's Orbit

(Des Sue Titcher. Litho Cambec Press, Melbourne)

1986 (12 Mar). *Bicentenary of Australian Settlement* (1988) (*4th issue*). *Cook's Voyage to New Holland. T* **420** *and similar horiz designs. Multicoloured. P* 13.
1002   33 c. Type **420**   60   35
1003   33 c. *Hibiscus meraukensis*   60   35
1004   50 c. *Dillenia alata*   90   80
1005   80 c. *Correa reflexa* . . . .   1·60   1·50
1006   90 c. "Joseph Banks" (botanist) (Reynolds) and
         Banks with Dr. Solander . . . .   2·00   1·75
1007   90 c. "Sydney Parkinson" (self-portrait) and
         Parkinson drawing . . . .   2·00   1·75
         Set of 6 . . . .   7·00   6·00
         Presentation Pack . . . .   7·50
         First Day Covers (2) . . . .   6·50

(Des J. Passmore. Litho Cambec Press, Melbourne)

1986 (9 Apr). *Appearance of Halley's Comet. P* 14 × 13½.
1008 **421** 33 c. multicoloured   50   35
         First Day Cover   95

THE WORLD CENTRE FOR
FINE STAMPS IS 399 STRAND

422 Queen Elizabeth II   **423** Brumbies (wild horses)

(Des Fay Plamka. Litho Leigh-Mardon Ltd, Melbourne)

1986 (21 Apr). *60th Birthday of Queen Elizabeth II. P* 14½.
1009 **422** 33 c. multicoloured 45   35
    Gutter Pair . . . . 1·00
    First Day Cover   95

(Des R. Ingpen. Litho Leigh-Mardon Ltd, Melbourne)

1986 (21 May). *Australian Horses. T* **423** *and similar horiz designs. Multicoloured. P* 14½.
1010   33 c. Type **423** 60   15
1011   80 c. Mustering . . . . 1·50 1·50
1012   90 c. Show-jumping . . . . 1·75 1·75
1013 $1 Child on pony . . . . 2·00 2·00
    Set of 4 . . . . 5·25 5·00
    Presentation Pack . . . . 5·50
    First Day Cover . . . .   5·50

424 "The Old Shearer stands"   **425** "King George III"
                                    (A. Ramsay) and Convicts

(Des R. Ingpen. Litho Leigh-Mardon Ltd, Melbourne)

1986 (21 July). *Folklore. Scenes and Verses from the Folksong "Click go the Shears". T* **424** *and similar vert designs. Multicoloured. P* 14½.
1014   33 c. Type **424** 55   55
    a. Horiz strip of 5. Nos. 1014/18 . . . . 2·50
    Eb. Black printed double (horiz strip of 5) . . . £130
1015   33 c. "The ringer looks around" 55   55
1016   33 c. "The boss of the board" 55   55
1017   33 c. "The tar-boy is there" 55   55
1018   33 c. "Shearing is all over" 55   55
    Set of 5 . . . . 2·50 2·50
    Presentation Pack . . . . 2·75
    First Day Cover . . . .   3·00
Nos. 1014/18 were printed together, *se-tenant*, in horizontal strips of 5 throughout the sheet, forming a composite design.

(Des D. Lancashire. Litho Cambec Press, Melbourne)

1986 (6 Aug). *Bicentenary of Australian Settlement* (1988) (5th Issue). *Convict Settlement in New South Wales. T* **425** *and similar horiz designs. Multicoloured. P* 13.
1019   33 c. Type **425** 70   40
1020   33 c. "Lord Sydney" (Gilbert Stuart) and con-
       victs 70   40
1021   33 c. "Captain Arthur Phillip" (F. Wheatley) and
       ship 70   40
1022 $1 "Captain John Hunter" (W. B. Bennett) and
       aborigines . . . . 2·75 2·50
    Set of 4 . . . . 4·25 3·25
    Presentation Pack . . . . 4·50
    First Day Cover . . . .   3·50

426 Red Kangaroo   **427** Royal Bluebell

(Des D. Higgins. Litho Leigh-Mardon Ltd, Melbourne)

1986 (13 Aug). *Australian Wildlife* (1st series). *T* **426** *and similar vert designs. Multicoloured. P* 14½ × 14.
1023   36 c. Type **426** 55   55
    a. Horiz strip of 5. Nos. 1023/7 . . . . 2·50
1024   36 c. Emu 55   55
1025   36 c. Koala 55   55
1026   36 c. Laughing Kookaburra 55   55
1027   36 c. Platypus 55   55
    Set of 5 . . . . 2·50 2·50
    Presentation Pack . . . . 2·75
    First Day Cover . . . .   3·00
Nos. 1023/7 were printed together, *se-tenant*, in horizontal strips of 5 throughout the sheet.
For 37 c. values see Nos. 1072/6.

(Des Betty Conabere. Litho Mercury-Walch Pty, Hobart)

1986 (25 Aug). *Booklet stamps. Alpine Wildflowers. T* **427** *and similar vert designs. Multicoloured. APWH paper. Roul.*
1028   3 c. Type **427** 20   20
    a. Booklet pane. Nos. 1028, 1029 and 1031 × 2 1·40
    b. Booklet pane. Nos. 1028, 1030 and 1031 × 2 1·50
1029   5 c. Alpine Marsh Marigold 40   50
1030   25 c. Mount Buffalo Sunray 50   60
1031   36 c. Silver Snow Daisy 50   30
    Set of 4 . . . . 1·40 1·40
    First Day Cover . . . .   1·75
Nos. 1028/31 only exist from 80 c. (pane No. 1028a) and $1 (pane No. 1028b) stamp booklets. The outer edges of the booklet panes are imperforate.
A further printing of Nos. 1028/31, reported in September 1987, was on Harrison paper. See notes below No. 1038.

Bicentenary Stamp Heritage Book

1986 (27 Aug). *Comprises Nos. 1002/7 and 1019/22 in 36-page book.*
HB1031a   Stamp Heritage Book . . . . 9·50

428 Pink Enamel Orchid   **429** *Australia II*
                               crossing Finishing Line

(Des O. Schmidinger and Christine Stead. Litho Leigh-Mardon Ltd, Melbourne)

1986 (18 Sept). *Native Australian Orchids. T* **428** *and similar vert designs. Multicoloured. P* 14½.
1032   36 c. Type **428** 70   20
1033   55 c. *Dendrobium nindii* . . . . 1·25 85
1034   90 c. Duck Orchid . . . . 1·90 1·75
1035 $1 Queen of Sheba Orchid . . . . 2·00 1·75
    Set of 4 . . . . 5·25 4·00
    Presentation Pack . . . . 5·50
    First Day Cover . . . .   4·25

(Des J. Passmore and G. Rowan. Litho Cambec Press, Melbourne)

1986 (26 Sept). *Australian Victory in America's Cup, 1983. T* **429** *and similar vert designs. Multicoloured. P* 14 × 13½.

1036	36 c. Type **429**.		65	45
1037	36 c. Boxing kangaroo flag of winning syndicate		65	45
	a. Grey (inscr and face value) omitted		£150	
1038	36 c. America's Cup trophy		65	45
	a. Grey (inscr and face value) omitted		£150	
	Set of 3		1·75	1·25
	Presentation Pack		2·00	
	First Day Cover			1·75

Attempts to imitate the missing grey errors by the use of an eraser have been reported. Such fakes invariably show damage to the paper surface and the removal of other parts of the design.

For Souvenir Postcards of this issue see after No. 1049.

CHANGES IN STAMP PAPER. Almost all issues from 1966 were printed on paper which included a phosphorescent substance, generally described as Helecon, used to activate electronic facing and sorting machinery. From 1981 an improved grade of paper, known as APWH, was introduced, produced by a mill at Ballarat. This had white gum.

During 1986 the Ballarat paper mill closed down and, after using up residual stocks of APWH paper, the two Australian security printing firms made their own alternative arrangements.

CPE Australia Ltd (formerly Cambec Press) obtained stocks of Harrison Stamp Paper from Harrison and Sons of High Wycombe.

Leigh-Mardon Ltd printings were initially on Clark Stamp Paper, also obtained from Great Britain, but after No. 1142 they also used Harrison Stamp Paper. A further phosphor paper, known as CPL, and manufactured by Coated Papers Ltd of Great Britain, was introduced from Autumn 1987 onwards.

The three papers can be identified as follows:

Harrison Stamp Paper—highly coated white paper with PVAD gum tinted in shades of blue to green. Bright white under UV light.

Clark Stamp Paper—creamy appearance with matt creamy PVA gum. Dull yellowish reaction to UV light.

CPL Paper—off-white appearance with blue tinted gum. Dull white reaction to UV light, although some printings show purple tinge.

All three papers react, to a greater or lesser extent, to the silver test for chalk-surfacing. The phosphorescent content of all the papers is said to be suitable for the Australian electronic sorting equipment.

430 Dove with Olive Branch and Sun   431 Mary and Joseph

(Des K. Cato. Litho Cambec Press, Melbourne)

1986 (22 Oct). *International Peace Year. Harrison paper. P* 14 × 13½.

1039	**430** 36 c. multicoloured	65	35
	First Day Cover		1·25

Examples with the gutter margin overprinted to commemorate the Papal visit in November 1986 were not produced by the Australian Post Office.

Souvenir Pack 1986.

1986 (22 Oct). *Containing Nos. 997, 1000/1, 1008/9, 1039 and Australian Antarctic Territory No. 78.*

SP1039a	Souvenir Pack	3·75

(Des B. Clinton. Litho Leigh-Mardon Ltd, Melbourne)

1986 (3 Nov–Dec). *Christmas. T* **431** *and similar multicoloured designs showing scenes from children's nativity play. APWH paper. P* 14½.

1040	30 c. Type **431**		40	30
	a. Perf 14 × 13½ (12.86)		30	30
1041	36 c. Three Wise Men leaving gifts		50	35
1042	60 c. Angels (horiz)		90	1·25
	Set of 3		1·60	1·75
	First Day Cover			2·25

MS1043	147 × 70 mm. 30 c. Three angels and shepherd (horiz); 30 c. Kneeling shepherds (horiz); 30 c. Mary, Joseph and three angels; 30 c. Innkeeper and two angels: 30 c. Three Wise Men (horiz)		1·90	2·25
	Presentation Pack (Nos. 1040/3)		4·00	
	First Day Cover			2·75

There were three printings of the 30 c. The first, on APWH paper, was mainly used for first day covers and presentation packs. Further supplies were then printed by Leigh-Mardon Ltd on Clark paper to be followed by a third supply, No. 1040a, printed by Cambec Press on Harrison paper with changed perforations. It is believed that this Cambec Press printing was only distributed in New South Wales, Tasmania and Victoria.

Post Office Yearbook

1986 (10 Nov). *Comprises Nos. 920, 922, 928, 931/3, 937, 997/1043 and Australian Antarctic Territory No. 78 in hardbound book with slipcase.*

YB1043a	Yearbook	38·00

432 Australian Flag on Printed Circuit Board   433 Aerial View of Yacht

(Des J. Passmore. Litho CPE Australia Ltd, Melbourne)

1987 (23 Jan). *Australia Day. T* **432** *and similar horiz design. Multi-coloured. Harrison (No. 1044) or APWH (No. 1045) paper. P* 13½ × 14.

1044	36 c. Type **432**	35	35
1045	36 c. "Australian Made" Campaign logos	35	35
	Set of 2	70	70
	First Day Cover		1·25

(Des O. Schmidinger and Christine Stead. Litho Leigh-Mardon Ltd, Melbourne)

1987 (28 Jan). *America's Cup Yachting Championship. T* **433** *and similar vert designs. Multicoloured. Clark paper. P* 14½.

1046	36 c. Type **433**	40	20
1047	55 c. Two yachts tacking	80	80
1048	90 c. Two yachts turning	1·25	1·25
1049	$1 Two yachts under full sail	1·40	1·40
	Set of 4	3·50	3·00
	Presentation Pack	3·75	
	First Day Cover		3·75
	Souvenir Postcards (Nos. 1036/8, 1046/9) (18 May)		4·50

434 Grapes and Melons   435 Livestock

(Des Susan Tilley. Litho CPE Australia Ltd, Melbourne)

1987 (11 Feb). *Australian Fruit. T* **434** *and similar vert designs. Multi-coloured. Harrison paper. P* 14 × 13½.

1050	36 c. Type **434**	40	20
1051	65 c. Tropical and sub-tropical fruits	85	85
1052	90 c. Citrus fruit, apples and pears	1·25	1·25
1053	$1 Stone and berry fruits	1·40	1·40
	Set of 4	3·50	3·25
	Presentation Pack	3·75	
	First Day Cover		4·00

(Des D. Lancashire. Litho CPE Australia Ltd, Melbourne)

1987 (10 Apr). *Agricultural Shows. T* **435** *and similar vert designs. Multicoloured. Harrison (all values) or APWH (Nos. 1055/7) paper. P* 14 × 13½.

1054	36 c. Type **435**	50	20
1055	65 c. Produce	1·00	1·00
1056	90 c. Sideshows	1·60	1·60
1057	$1 Competitions	1·75	1·75
	Set of 4	4·25	4·00
	Presentation Pack	4·50	
	First Day Cover		4·50
	Souvenir Postcards (Nos. 1050/7) (27 July)		5·50

436 Queen Elizabeth   **437** Convicts on Quay
in Australia, 1986

(Des Janet Boschen. Litho CPE Australia Ltd, Melbourne)

1987 (21 Apr). *Queen Elizabeth II's Birthday. Harrison paper. P* 13½ × 14.

1058	**436**	36 c. multicoloured	45	35
		First Day Cover		1·25

(Des Sue Passmore. Litho CPE Australia Ltd, Melbourne)

1987 (13 May). *Bicentenary of Australian Settlement* (1988) (*6th issue*). *Departure of the First Fleet. T* **437** *and similar square designs. Multicoloured. Harrison paper. P* 13.

1059	36 c. Type **437**	65	65
	a. Horiz strip of 5. Nos. 1059/63	3·00	
1060	36 c. Royal Marines officer and wife	65	65
1061	36 c. Sailors loading supplies	65	65
1062	36 c. Officers being ferried to ships	65	65
1063	36 c. Fleet in English Channel	65	65
	Set of 5	3·00	3·00
	Presentation Pack	3·25	
	First Day Cover		3·25
	Souvenir Postcards (5) (18 May)		3·25

Nos. 1059/63 were printed together, *se-tenant*, in horizontal strips of 5 throughout the sheet.
See also Nos. 1064/6, 1077/81, 1090/2 and 1105/9.

(Des Sue Passmore. Litho CPE Australia Ltd, Melbourne)

1987 (3 June). *Bicentenary of Australian Settlement* (1988) (*7th issue*). *First Fleet at Tenerife. Square designs as T* **437**. *Multicoloured. Harrison paper. P* 13.

1064	36 c. Ferrying supplies, Santa Cruz	50	50
	a. Horiz pair. Nos. 1064/5	1·00	1·00
1065	36 c. Canary Islands fishermen and departing fleet	50	50
1066	$1 Fleet arriving at Tenerife (Optd S. 50p)	1·25	1·25
	Set of 3	2·00	2·00
	Presentation Pack	2·50	
	First Day Cover		2·50
	Souvenir Postcards (3)		2·25

Nos. 1064/5 were printed together, *se-tenant*, in horizontal pairs throughout the sheet, forming a composite design.

438 "At the Station"   **439** Bionic Ear

(Des C. Lee. Litho CPE Australia Ltd, Melbourne)

1987 (24 June). *Folklore. Scenes and Verses from Poem "The Man from Snowy River". T* **438** *and similar vert designs. Multicoloured. Harrison paper. P* 14 × 13½.

1067	36 c. Type **438**	60	60
	a. Horiz strip of 5. Nos. 1067/71	2·75	
1068	36 c. "Mountain bred"	60	60
1069	36 c. "That terrible descent"	60	60
1070	36 c. "At their heels"	60	60
1071	36 c. "Brought them back"	60	60
	Set of 5	2·75	2·75
	Presentation Pack	3·00	
	First Day Cover		3·00
	Souvenir Postcards (5) (19 Aug)		3·25

Nos. 1067/71 were printed together, *se-tenant*, in horizontal strips of five throughout the sheet, forming a composite background design of mountain scenery.

(Des D. Higgins. Litho Leigh-Mardon Ltd, Melbourne)

1987 (1 July). *Australian Wildlife* (*2nd series*). *Vert designs as T* **426**. *Multicoloured. Clark paper. P* 14½ × 14.

1072	37 c. Common Brushtail Possum	35	35
	a. Horiz strip of 5. Nos. 1072/6	1·60	
1073	37 c. Sulphur-crested Cockatoo	35	35
1074	37 c. Common Wombat	35	35
1075	37 c. Crimson Rosella	35	35
1076	37 c. Echidna	35	35
	Set of 5	1·60	1·60
	Presentation Pack (6 Aug)	2·25	
	First Day Cover		2·40

Nos. 1072/6 were printed together, *se-tenant*, in horizontal strips of 5 throughout the sheet.

(Des Sue Passmore. Litho CPE Australia Ltd, Melbourne)

1987 (6 Aug). *Bicentenary of Australian Settlement* (1988) (*8th issue*). *First Fleet at Rio de Janeiro. Square designs as T* **437**. *Multicoloured. Harrison paper. P* 13.

1077	37 c. Sperm Whale and fleet	55	55
	a. Horiz strip of 5. Nos. 1077/81	2·50	
1078	37 c. Brazilian coast	55	55
1079	37 c. British officers in market	55	55
1080	37 c. Religious procession	55	55
1081	37 c. Fleet leaving Rio	55	55
	Set of 5	2·50	2·50
	Presentation Pack	2·75	
	First Day Cover		3·00
	Souvenir Postcards (5)		3·25

(Des. O. Schmidinger and Christine Stead. Litho Leigh-Mardon Ltd, Melbourne)

1987 (19 Aug). *Australian Achievements in Technology. T* **439** *and similar vert designs. Multicoloured. Clark paper. P* 14½.

1082	37 c. Type **439**	40	35
1083	53 c. Microchips	65	60
1084	63 c. Robotics	75	70
1085	68 c. Ceramics	80	75
	Set of 4	2·40	2·25
	Presentation Pack	2·75	
	First Day Cover		2·75

440 Catching Crayfish

(Des Elizabeth Honey. Litho Leigh-Mardon Ltd, Melbourne)

1987 (16 Sept). *"Aussie Kids". T* **440** *and similar horiz designs. Multicoloured. Clark paper. P* 14½.

1086	37 c. Type **440**	35	35
1087	55 c. Playing cat's cradle	65	65
1088	90 c. Young football supporters	95	95
1089	$1 Children with kangaroo (Optd S. 50p)	1·10	1·10
	Set of 4	2·75	2·75
	Presentation Pack	3·00	
	First Day Cover		3·50
	Souvenir Postcards (Nos. 1082/9) (30 Sept)		5·00

Souvenir Pack 1987.

1987 (16 Sept). *Containing Nos. 1044/5 and 1058.*

SP1089a   Souvenir Pack . . . .   1·40

(Des Sue Passmore. Litho CPE Australia Ltd, Melbourne)

1987 (13 Oct). *Bicentenary of Australian Settlement* (1988) (*9th issue*). *First Fleet at Cape of Good Hope. Square designs as T* **437**. *Multicoloured. Harrison paper. P* 13.

1090	37 c. Marine checking list of livestock	50	50
	a. Horiz pair. Nos. 1090/1	1·00	1·00
1091	37 c. Loading livestock	50	50
1092	$1 First Fleet at Cape Town (Optd S. 50p) . . .	1·25	1·25
	Set of 3	2·00	2·00
	Presentation Pack	2·25	
	First Day Cover		2·50
	Souvenir Postcards (3) (18 Nov)		2·25

Nos. 1090/1 were printed together, *se-tenant*, in horizontal and vertical pairs throughout the sheet, the former showing a composite design.

441 Detail of Spearthrower,   **442** Grandmother and
Western Australia   Granddaughters with
                         Candles

(Des J. Passmore. Litho Leigh-Mardon Ltd, Melbourne)

1987 (13 Oct). *Booklet stamps. Aboriginal Crafts. T* **441** *and similar horiz designs. Multicoloured. APWH paper. P* 15½ × *imperf.*

1093	3 c. Type **441**	15	15
	a. Booklet pane. Nos. 1093 and 1095, each × 2	1·00	
1094	15 c. Shield pattern, New South Wales	25	60
	a. Booklet pane. Nos. 1094, 1096 × 3 and 1097 × 2	2·10	
1095	37 c. Basket weave, Queensland	40	45
1096	37 c. Bowl design, Central Australia	40	45
1097	37 c. Belt pattern, Northern Territory	40	45
	Set of 5	1·40	1·90

Nos. 1093/7 only exist from 80 c. (pane No. 1093a) and $2 (pane No. 1094a) stamp booklets. The vertical edges of the booklet panes are imperforate.

(Des B. Clinton. Litho Leigh-Mardon Ltd, Melbourne (30 c.) or CPE Australia Ltd, Melbourne (37 c., 63 c.))

1987 (2 Nov). *Christmas. T* **442** *and similar multicoloured designs showing carol singing by candlelight. Clark* (30 c.) *or Harrison* (37, 63 c.) *paper. P* 14½ (30 c.) *or* 13½ × 14 (37 c., 63 c.).

1098	30 c. Type **442**	40	40
	a. Horiz strip of 5. Nos. 1098/102	1·75	
1099	30 c. Father and daughters	40	40
1100	30 c. Four children	40	40
1101	30 c. Family	40	40
1102	30 c. Six teenagers	40	40
1103	37 c. Choir (*horiz*)	45	45
1104	63 c. Father and two children (*horiz*)	75	75
	Set of 7	2·75	2·75
	Presentation Pack	3·00	
	First Day Covers (2)		3·25

Nos. 1098/1102 were printed together, *se-tenant*, in horizontal strips of five throughout the sheet.

Post Office Yearbook

1987 (2 Nov). *Comprises Nos. 1044/1104 and Australian Antarctic Territory Nos. 63, 65, 67, 71, 73 in hardbound book with slipcase.*

YB1104a   Yearbook . . . .   50·00

(Des Sue Passmore. Litho CPE Australia Ltd, Melbourne)

1988 (26 Jan). *Bicentenary of Australian Settlement* (10th issue). *Arrival of First Fleet. Square designs as T* **437**. *Multicoloured. Harrison paper. P* 13.

1105	37 c. Aborigines watching arrival of Fleet, Botany Bay	55	55
	a. Horiz strip of 5. Nos. 1105/9	2·50	

1106	37 c. Aborigine family and anchored ships	55	55
1107	37 c. Fleet arriving at Sydney Cove	55	55
1108	37 c. Ship's boat	55	55
1109	37 c. Raising the flag, Sydney Cove, 26 January 1788	55	55
	Set of 5	2·50	2·50
	Presentation Pack	2·75	
	Souvenir Pack (Nos. 1105/9, *Christmas Island Nos. 246/50, Cocos (Keeling) Islands Nos.* 175/9)	6·50	
	First Day Cover		2·75
	Souvenir Postcards (5)		3·25

Nos. 1105/9 were printed together, *se-tenant*, in horizontal strips of five throughout the sheet, forming a composite design.

Bicentenary Stamp Heritage Book

1988 (26 Jan). *Comprises Nos.* 1059/63, 1064/6, 1077/81, 1090/2 *and* 1105/9 *in 36-page book and wallet.*

HB1109a   Stamp Heritage Book . . . .   12·00

443 Koala with Stockman's Hat and   **444** "Religion" (A. Horner)
Eagle dressed as Uncle Sam

(Des R. Harvey. Litho CPE Australia Ltd, Melbourne)

1988 (26 Jan). *Bicentenary of Australian Settlement* (11th issue). *Harrison paper. P* 13.

1110	**443** 37 c. multicoloured	55	35
	Presentation Pack (*contains* 4 × *No.* 110 *and four of U.S.A. version*) . . .	2·75	
	Souvenir Book (21 June)	5·00	
	First Day Cover		75
	Souvenir Postcard		85

A stamp in a similar design was also issued by the U.S.A.

NEW PRINTINGS. From the beginning of 1990 new printings of definitive stamps were identified by small koala symbols printed on the vertical sheet margins alongside alternate rows. One koala represented the first printing after the initial issue, two koalas the second printing, and so on.

(Litho Leigh-Mardon Ltd, Melbourne (4, 5, 20, 25, 30, 37, 39, 40, 50, 53, 70, 80, 90 c., $1) or CPE Australia Ltd, Melbourne (others))

1988 (17 Feb–28 Sept). *"Living Together". T* **444** *and similar square designs showing cartoons. Multicoloured (except 30 c.) Clark* (4, 10, 20, 25, 37, 50, 53, 70, 80, 90 c., $1) *or Harrison paper* (others). *P* 14.

1111	1 c. Type **444** (16.3)	10	10
1112	2 c. "Industry" (P. Nicholson) (16.3)	10	10
1113	3 c. "Local Government" (A. Collette) (16.3) . .	10	10
1114	4 c. "Trade Unions" (Liz Honey)	10	10
1115	5 c. "Parliament" (Bronwyn Halls) (16.3)	10	10
1116	10 c. "Transport" (Meg Williams)	10	10
1117	15 c. "Sport" (G. Cook)	10	15
1118	20 c. "Commerce" (M. Atcherson)	15	20
1119	25 c. "Housing" (R. Tandberg) (black and pale rose-lilac) (16.3)	20	25
1120	30 c. "Welfare" (R. Tandberg) (black and pale rose-lilac) (16.3)	20	25
1121	37 c. "Postal Services" (P. Viska)	30	35
	a. Booklet pane. No. 1121 × 10 (4.7)	3·00	
1121b	39 c. "Tourism" (J. Spooner) (28.9)	40	35
	ba. Booklet pane. No. 1121b × 10	4·00	
1122	40 c. "Recreation" (R. Harvey) (16.3)	30	35
1123	45 c. "Health" (Jenny Coopes)	35	40
1124	50 c. "Mining" (G. Haddon)	40	45
1125	53 c. "Primary Industry" (S. Leahy)	45	50
1126	55 c. "Education" (Victoria Roberts) (16.3) . . .	60	50
1127	60 c. "Armed Forces" (B. Green) (16.3)	45	50
1128	63 c. "Police" (J. Russell) (16.3)	70	55

1129	65 c. "Telecommunications" (B. Petty) (16.3) . . .		55	60
1130	68 c. "The Media" (A. Langoulant) (16.3)		75	60
1131	70 c. "Science and Technology" (J. Hook)		80	65
1132	75 c. "Visual Arts" (G. Dazeley) (16.3)		55	60
1133	80 c. "Performing Arts" (A. Stitt)		60	65
1134	90 c. "Banking" (S. Billington)		70	75
1135	95 c. "Law" (C. Aslanis) (16.3)		70	75
1136	$1 "Rescue and Emergency" (M. Leunig) (Optd S. 50p)		85	90
	Set of 27		10·00	10·00
	Presentation Pack (16 Mar.)		14·00	
	First Day Covers (6)			15·00

Although Leigh-Mardon printed the 37 c. (Clark and later Harrison paper) and 39 c. (Clark paper) sheet stamps, together with some of the 37 c. booklet stamps (Harrison paper), booklet panes Nos. 1121a and 1121ba were produced by CPE on CPL paper. Both CPE-printed panes have the upper and lower edges imperforate so that stamps from them are imperforate at top or bottom.

Printing of the 55 c., and 75 c. and 95 c. values was switched to Leigh-Mardon Ltd during 1988. Following the purchase of CPE Australia Ltd by Leigh-Mardon Ltd in early 1989 transfers between the two plants increased so that further supplies of the 5 c., 30 c., 40 c. and $1 were produced at the Scoresby (ex-CPE) works and a printing of the 15 c. took place at the original Leigh-Mardon Moorabbin press.

Many of these new printings show changes in paper from the original stamps. Of those originally printed by Leigh-Mardon on Clark paper the 4 c., 10 c., 37 c., 50 c. (1 Koala), 70 c., 80 c., 90 c. and $1 later appeared on Harrison paper. Further printings of the 2 c., 4 c. (2 Koalas), 5 c., 10 c., 15 c. (1 Koala), 40 c., 60 c., 65 c. (2 Koalas), 75 c. (2 Koalas) and 80 c. (3 or 4 Koalas) were also made on CPL paper. For detailed descriptions of these papers see notes below No. 1038.

445 "Government House, Sydney, 1790" (George Raper)
446 Queen Elizabeth II (from photo by Tim Graham)

(Des J. Passmore. Litho CPE Australia Ltd, Melbourne)

1988 (13 Apr). *Bicentenary of Australian Settlement (12th issue). "The Early Years, 1788–1809". T 445 and similar square designs showing paintings. Multicoloured. Harrison paper. P 13.*

1137	37 c. Type 445.		45	45
	a. Horiz strip of 5. Nos. 1137/41		2·00	
1138	37 c. "Government Farm, Parramatta, 1791" ("The Port Jackson Painter")		45	45
1139	37 c. "Parramatta Road, 1796" (attr Thomas Watling)		45	45
1140	37 c. "View of Sydney Cove, c. 1800" (detail) (Edward Dayes)		45	45
1141	37 c. "Sydney Hospital, 1803", (detail) (George William Evans)		45	45
	Set of 5		2·00	2·00
	Presentation Pack		2·25	
	First Day Cover			2·50
	Souvenir Postcards (5)			3·25

Nos. 1137/41 were printed together, *se-tenant*, in horizontal strips of 5 throughout the sheet, each strip forming a composite background design from the painting, "View of Sydney from the East Side of the Cove, c. 1808" by John Eyre.

Bicentenary Stamp Heritage Book

1988 (13 Apr). *Comprises Nos. 1137/41 in 36-page book.*
HB1141a Stamp Heritage Book . . . . 7·00

(Des Sandra Baker. Litho Leigh-Mardon Ltd, Melbourne)

1988 (21 Apr). *Queen Elizabeth II's Birthday. Harrison paper. P 14½.*
1142	**446** 37 c. multicoloured		35	40
	First Day Cover			80

447 Expo '88 Logo   448 New Parliament House

(Des G. Emery. Litho CPE Australia Ltd, Melbourne)

1988 (29 Apr). *"Expo '88" World Fair, Brisbane. Harrison paper. P 13.*
1143	**447** 37 c. multicoloured		35	40
	First Day Cover			80

(Des B. Sadgrove. Litho Leigh-Mardon Ltd, Melbourne)

1988 (9 May). *Opening of New Parliament House, Canberra. Harrison paper. P 14½.*
1144	**448** 37 c. multicoloured		35	40
	First Day Cover			80
	Souvenir Postcard			1·00

449 Early Settler and Sailing Clipper   450 Kiwi and Koala at Campfire

(Des G. Emery. Litho CPE Australia Ltd, Melbourne)

1988 (21 June). *Bicentenary of Australian Settlement (13th issue). T 449 and similar square designs. Multicoloured. Harrison paper. P 13.*
1145	37 c. Type 449.		45	45
	a. Pair. Nos. 1145/6		90	90
1146	37 c. Queen Elizabeth II with British and Australian Parliament Buildings		45	45
1147	$1 W. G. Grace (cricketer) and tennis racquet		1·25	1·25
	a. Pair. Nos. 1147/8		2·50	2·50
1148	$1 Shakespeare, John Lennon (entertainer) and Sydney Opera House		1·25	1·25
	Set of 4		3·00	3·00
	Presentation Pack (Nos. 1145/8 and GB issue)		5·50	
	Souvenir Book		6·00	
	First Day Cover			3·25
	Souvenir Postcards (4)			3·25

Nos. 1145/6 and 1147/8 were printed together, *se-tenant*, in horizontal and vertical pairs throughout the sheets, each horizontal pair showing a background design of the Australian flag.

Stamps in similar designs were also issued by Great Britain.

(Des R. Harvey. Litho Leigh-Mardon Ltd, Melbourne)

1988 (21 June). *Bicentenary of Australian Settlement (14th issue). Harrison paper. P 14½.*
1149	**450** 37 c. multicoloured		45	40
	Presentation Pack (4 × No. 1149 and four of N.Z. version)		3·00	
	Souvenir Book		5·00	
	First Day Cover			80
	Souvenir Postcard			85

A stamp in a similar design was also issued by New Zealand.

THE WORLD CENTRE FOR FINE STAMPS IS 399 STRAND

451 "Bush Potato Country" (Turkey   **452** Basketball
Tolsen Tjupurrula and David
Corby Tjapaltjarri)

(Des Janet Boschen. Litho CPE Australia Ltd, Melbourne)

1988 (1 Aug). *Art of the Desert. Aboriginal Paintings from Central Australia. T* **451** *and similar square designs. Multicoloured. Harrison paper. P* 13.
1150	37 c. Type **451**	35	40
1151	55 c. "Courtship Rejected" (Limpi Puntungka Tjapangati)	55	60
1152	90 c. "Medicine Story" (artist unknown)	90	1·10
1153	$1 "Ancestor Dreaming" (Tim Leura Tjapaltjarri)	95	1·25
	Set of 4	2·50	3·00
	Presentation Pack	3·00	
	First Day Cover		3·25

(Des Sue Passmore. Litho Leigh-Mardon Ltd, Melbourne)

1988 (14 Sept). *Olympic Games, Seoul. T* **452** *and similar horiz designs. Multicoloured. Harrison paper. P* 14½.
1154	37 c. Type **452**	35	40
1155	65 c. Athlete crossing finish line	60	65
1156	$1 Gymnast with hoop	95	1·00
	Set of 3	1·75	1·90
	Presentation Pack	2·25	
	First Day Cover		2·25
	Souvenir Postcards (3)		2·40

453 Rod and Mace

(Des K. Christos. Litho Leigh-Mardon Ltd, Melbourne)
1988 (19 Sept). *34th Commonwealth Parliamentary Conference, Canberra. Harrison paper. P* 14½.
1157	**453** 37 c. multicoloured	35	40
	First Day Cover		80

454 Necklace by Peter Tully

(Des K. Christos. Litho Mercury-Walch Pty, Hobart)
1988 (28 Sept). *Booklet stamps. Australian Crafts. T* **454** *and similar horiz designs. Multicoloured. CPL paper. Roul× imperf.*
1158	2 c. Type **454**	30	35
	a. Booklet pane. Nos. 1158 and 1160×2	1·00	
1159	5 c. Vase by Colin Levy	30	35
	a. Booklet pane. Nos. 1159 and 1160×5	2·10	

1160	39 c. Teapot by Frank Bauer	40	35
	Set of 3	90	95
	First Day Cover		1·25

Nos. 1158/60 only exist from 80 c. (pane No. 1158a) and $2 (pane No. 1159a) stamp booklets. The vertical edges of the booklet panes are imperforate.

455 Pinnacles Desert   **456** "The Nativity"
(Danielle Hush)

(Des K. Christos. Litho CPE Australia Ltd, Melbourne)

1988 (17 Oct). *Panorama of Australia. T* **455** *and similar horiz designs. Multicoloured. Harrison paper. P* 13.
1161	39 c. Type **455**	40	40
1162	55 c. Flooded landscape, Arnhem Land	55	55
1163	65 c. Twelve Apostles, Victoria	65	65
1164	70 c. Mountain Ash wood	70	70
	Set of 4	2·10	2·10
	Presentation Pack	2·50	
	First Day Cover		2·40

(Des Sandra Baker. Litho CPE Australia Ltd, Melbourne (32, 39 c.) or Leigh-Mardon Ltd, Melbourne (63 c.))

1988 (31 Oct). *Christmas. T* **456** *and similar square designs. Multicoloured. Harrison paper. P* 14½ *(63 c.) or* 13 *(others).*
1165	32 c. Type **456**	30	35
1166	39 c. "Koala as Father Christmas" (Kylie Courtney)	35	40
1167	63 c. "Christmas Cockatoo" (Benjamin Stevenson)	60	65
	Set of 3	1·10	1·25
	Presentation Pack	1·60	
	First Day Cover		1·50

Souvenir Pack 1988

1988 (31 Oct). *Containing Nos.* 1121b, 1142/4 *and* 1157.
SP1167a	Souvenir Pack		2·10

Post Office Yearbook

1988 (7 Nov). *Comprises Nos.* 1105/67 *and Australian Antarctic Territory Nos.* 79/83 *in hardbound book with slipcase.*
YB1167a	Yearbook		70·00

PRINTERS. Early in 1989 Leigh-Mardon Ltd took over CPE Australia Ltd. Stamp printing continued at both the Moorabbin (original Leigh-Mardon) and Scoresby (ex-CPE) works with some stamps being printed at one and then perforated at the other. The gauges of the perforating machines used by the two plants were eventually standardised.

457 Sir Henry   **458** Bowls
Parkes

(Des R. Bevers. Litho CPE Australia Ltd, Melbourne)

1989 (25 Jan). *Australia Day. Centenary of Federation Speech by Sir Henry Parkes (N.S.W. Prime Minister). Harrison paper. P* 14×13½.
1168	**457** 39 c. multicoloured	35	40
	First Day Cover		65

(Des S. Passmore (5, 10, 20, 41, 43, 65 c., $1, $1.20), G. Cook (others). Litho Leigh-Mardon Ltd, Melbourne)

1989 (13 Feb)–**90**. *Sports.* T**458** *and similar horiz designs. Multicoloured. CPL (1 c., 39 c. (No. 1179a), 41 c. (No. 1180), 43 c., 70 c., $1.10) or Harrison paper (others). P* 13½ (5, 10, 20, 65 c., $1.20) *or* 14 × 14½ *(others).*

1169	1 c. Type **458**	10	10
	a. Perf 13½ (3.90)	10	10
1170	2 c. Tenpin-bowling	10	10
	a. Perf 13½ (9.89)	10	10
1171	3 c. Australian football	10	10
1172	5 c. Kayaking and canoeing (17.1.90)	10	10
1174	10 c. Sailboarding (17.1.90)	10	10
1176	20 c. Tennis (17.1.90)	15	20
1179	39 c. Fishing	40	40
	a. Booklet pane. No. 1179 × 10	4·00	
	b. Perf 13½ (7.89)	40	40
1180	41 c. Cycling (23.8.89)	30	35
	a. Booklet pane. No. 1180 × 10	3·00	
1181	43 c. Skateboarding (27.8.90)	35	40
	a. Booklet pane. No. 1181 × 10	3·50	
1184	55 c. Kite-flying	40	45
1187	65 c. Rock-climbing (17.1.90)	50	55
1188	70 c. Cricket	55	60
1192	$1 Fun-run (17.1.90)	75	80
1193	$1.10, Golf (Optd S. 70p)	85	90
1194	$1.20, Hang-gliding (27.8.90)	90	95
	Set of 15	4·75	5·25
	Presentation Packs (2)	5·75	
	First Day Covers (5)		7·25
	First Day Covers (*booklet panes*) (3)		11·00
	Souvenir Postcards (as Nos. 1172, 1174, 1176, 1181, 1187, 1192, 1194) (7).		6·00

The booklet panes have the upper and lower edges imperforate, so that stamps from them are imperforate at top or bottom, and have margins at both left and right.

"Koala" new printings exist for the 1 c. (No. 1169a) (1 Koala), 2 c. (No. 1170a) (2 Koalas), 41 c. (1 and 2 Koalas), 41 c. booklet pane (1, 2, 3 and 4 Koalas), 55 c. (2 Koalas), 70 c. (2 Koalas) and $1.10 (2 and 3 Koalas).

Of the stamps initially printed on CPL paper the 1 c. (No. 1169a) (1 Koala), 39 c. booklet pane (No. 1179a), 41 c. (1 Koala), 70 c. and $1.10 (3 Koalas) subsequently appeared on Harrison paper. Of those on Harrison paper there were further printings on CPL paper for the 39 c. (No. 1179b), 41 c. booklet pane (2, 3 and 4 Koalas) and $1.10 (2 and 3 Koalas).

For 41 and 43 c. stamps as Nos. 1180/1, but self-adhesive, see Nos. 1258/a.

WARNING. The coating on a batch of paper used during 1989–90 was defective so that stamps lose parts of their design if immersed in water.

459 Merino

(Des K. McEwan. Litho CPE Australia Ltd, Melbourne)

1989 (27 Feb). *Sheep in Australia.* T **459** *and similar horiz designs. Multicoloured. CPL paper. P* 13½ × 14.

1195	39 c. Type **459**	45	40
1196	39 c. Poll Dorset	45	40
1197	85 c. Polwarth	80	85
1198	$1 Corriedale (Optd S. 70p)	95	1·00
	Set of 4	2·40	2·40
	Presentation Pack	2·75	
	First Day Cover		2·75

460 Adelaide Botanic Garden

(Des J. Passmore. Eng B. Stewart. Litho Leigh-Mardon Ltd, and die-stamped Avon Graphics, both of Melbourne ($20), litho CPE Australia Ltd, Melbourne, and recess Note Ptg Branch, Reserve Bank of Australia (others))

1989 (12 Apr)–**90**. *Botanic Gardens.* T **460** *and similar horiz designs. Multicoloured. Harrison paper. P* 14.

1199	$2 Nooroo, New South Wales (13.9.89)	1·50	1·60
1200	$5 Mawarra, Victoria (13.9.89)	3·75	4·00
1201	$10 Type **460**	7·50	8·00
1201a	$20 "A View of the Artist's House and Garden in Mills Plains, Van Diemen's Land" (John Glover) (15.8.90)	15·00	16·00
	Set of 4	25·00	27·00
	Presentation Packs (2)	29·00	
	First Day Covers (4)		32·00
	Souvenir Postcard ($20)		18·00

461 "Queen Elizabeth II" (sculpture, John Dowie)

462 Arrival of Immigrant Ship, 1830's

(Des Sandra Baker. Litho Leigh-Mardon Ltd, Melbourne)

1989 (21 Apr). *Queen Elizabeth II's Birthday. Harrison paper. P* 14½.

1202	**461** 39 c. multicoloured	35	40
	First Day Cover	65	

(Des D. Lancashire. Litho Leigh-Mardon Ltd, Melbourne)

1989 (10 May). *Colonial Development* (1*st issue*). *Pastoral Era* 1810–1850. T **462** *and similar square designs. Multicoloured. Harrison paper. P* 14½.

1203	39 c. Type **462**	40	40
	a. Horiz strip of 5. Nos. 1203/7.	1·75	
1204	39 c. Pioneer cottage and wool dray	40	40
1205	39 c. Squatter's homestead	40	40
1206	39 c. Shepherd with flock (from Joseph Lycett's "Views of Australia")	40	40
1207	39 c. Explorer in desert (after watercolour by Edward Frome)	40	40
	Set of 5	1·75	1·75
	Presentation Pack	2·25	
	Souvenir Book	7·50	
	First Day Cover		2·00

Nos. 1203/7 were printed together, *se-tenant*, in horizontal strips of five throughout the sheet.

See also Nos. 1253/7 and 1262/6.

463 Gladys Moncrieff and Roy René

464 "Impression" (Tom Roberts)

(Des Sue Passmore. Litho Leigh-Mardon Ltd, Melbourne)

1989 (12 July). *Australian Stage and Screen Personalities.* T **463** *and similar vert designs. Multicoloured. CPL paper. P* 14½.

1208	39 c. Type **463**	35	40
	a. Perf 14 × 13½	3·50	3·25

1209	85 c. Charles Chauvel and Chips Rafferty	80	85
1210	$1 Nellie Stewart and J. C. Williamson	95	1·00
1211	$1.10, Lottie Lyell and Raymond Longford . . .	1·00	1·10
	Set of 4	2·75	3·00
	Set of 2 (Nos. 1210/11) optd "Specimen"	1·40	
	Presentation Pack	3·50	
	Souvenir Book	11·50	
	First Day Cover		3·25
	Souvenir Postcards		3·25

No. 1208a was from a small first printing produced at the Scoresby (ex-CPL) plant and used in presentation packs or on first day covers. The remainder were perforated at the Moorabbin works. A small part of the printing of No. 1208 was on Harrison paper.

(Des K. Christos. Litho Leigh-Mardon Ltd, Melbourne)

1989 (23 Aug). *Australian Impressionist Paintings. T 464 and similar multicoloured designs. CPL paper. P 14 × 13½ (No. 1214) or 13½ × 14 (others).*

1212	41 c. Type **464**.	40	45
1213	41 c. "Impression for Golden Summer" (Sir Arthur Streeton)	40	45
1214	41 c. "All on a Summer's Day" (Charles Conder) (vert)	40	45
1215	41 c. "Petit Déjeuner" (Frederick McCubbin) . . .	40	45
	Set of 4	1·40	1·60
	Presentation Pack	1·90	
	Souvenir Book (Nos. 567a, 778/9 and 1212/15)	19·00	
	First Day Cover		1·75
	Souvenir Postcards		3·00

465 Freeways

(Des Sally Newell and Carolyn Limonta. Litho Leigh-Mardon Ltd, Melbourne)

1989 (1 Sept). *Booklet stamps. The Urban Environment. T 465 and similar horiz designs. CPL paper. P 15½ × imperf.*

1216	41 c. black, maroon and blue-green	60	65
	a. Booklet pane. Nos. 1216 × 2, 1217 × 3 and 1218 × 2	3·75	
1217	41 c. black, maroon and magenta	60	65
1218	41 c. black, maroon and bright blue	60	65
	Set of 3	1·60	1·75
	First Day Cover		2·00

Designs:— No. 1217, City buildings, Melbourne; No. 1218, Commuter train at platform.

Nos. 1216/18 only exist from $3 stamp booklets in which the vertical edges of the pane are imperforate.

Nos. 1216/18 also exist as a 1 Koala new printing.

466 Hikers outside Youth   **467** Horse Tram, Adelaide,
Hostel   1878

(Des Priscilla Cutter. Litho Leigh-Mardon Ltd, Melbourne)

1989 (13 Sept). *50th Anniv of Australian Youth Hostels. CPL paper. P 14½.*

1219	**466** 41 c. multicoloured	45	45
	First Day Cover		65

(Des I. McKellar. Litho Leigh-Mardon Ltd, Melbourne)

1989 (11 Oct). *Historic Trams. T 467 and similar horiz designs. Multicoloured. Harrison (No. 1222a) or CPL paper. P 13½ × 14.*

1220	41 c. Type **467**	50	50
1221	41 c. Steam tram, Sydney, 1884	50	50

1222	41 c. Cable tram, Melbourne, 1886	50	50
	a. Perf 14½	70	70
	ab. Booklet pane. No. 1222a × 10	7·50	
1223	41 c. Double-deck electric tram, Hobart, 1893 . .	50	50
1224	41 c. Combination electric tram, Brisbane, 1901	50	50
	Set of 5	2·25	2·25
	Presentation Pack	2·50	
	First Day Cover		2·50

The upper and lower edges of booklet pane No. 1222ab are imperforate. It was printed and perforated at the Moorabbin plant.

"Introducing Australia" Book

1989 (18 Oct). *Comprises Nos. 1169/71, 1179/80, 1184, 1189, 1194/8 and 1203/15 in hardbound sixty page book with slipcase.*

HB1224a	"Introducing Australia" book	42·00	

468 "Annunciation"   **469** Radio Waves
(15th-century Book   and Globe
of Hours)

(Des Lynette Brown. Litho Leigh-Mardon Ltd, Melbourne)

1989 (1 Nov). *Christmas. Illuminated Manuscripts. T 468 and similar vert designs. Multicoloured. CPL paper. P 14 × 13½ (36 c.) or 14½ (others).*

1225	36 c. Type **468**	35	40
	a. Booklet pane. No. 1225 × 10	3·50	
1226	41 c. "Annunciation to the Shepherds" (Wharncliffe Book of Hours, c. 1475)	45	45
1227	80 c. "Adoration of the Magi" (15th-century Parisian Book of Hours)	95	95
	Set of 3	1·60	1·60
	Presentation Pack	1·90	
	First Day Cover		1·90

The vertical sides of booklet pane No. 1225a are imperforate.

(Des B. Sadgrove. Litho Leigh-Mardon Ltd, Melbourne)

1989 (1 Nov). *50th Anniv of Radio Australia. CPL paper. P 14 × 13½.*

1228	**469** 41 c. multicoloured	45	45
	First Day Cover		65

Souvenir Pack 1989

1989 (1 Nov). *Containing Nos. 1168, 1180, 1202, 1219 and 1228.*

SP1228a	Souvenir Pack	2·25	

Post Office Yearbook

1989 (6 Nov). *Comprises Nos. 1168/71, 1179/80, 1184, 1189, 1194/1228 and Australian Antarctic Territory Nos. 84/7 in hardbound book with slipcase.*

YB1228a	Yearbook	45·00	

470 Golden   **471** Australian
Wattle   Wildflowers

(Des Celia Rosser. Litho Leigh-Mardon Ltd, Melbourne)

1990 (17 Jan). *Australia Day. Harrison paper. P 14½.*

1229	**470** 41 c. multicoloured	45	45
	First Day Cover		65
	Souvenir Postcard		95

(Des Beverley Graham and G. Rogers. Litho Leigh-Mardon Ltd, Melbourne)

1990 (7 Feb–May).   *Greetings Stamp. CPL paper. P* 14×13½.
1230 **471** 41 c. multicoloured   45   45
     a. Booklet pane. No. 1230×10 . . . . . .   4·50
     b. Perf 14½ (May) . . . .
     ba. Booklet pane. No. 1230b×10 . . . . .
       First Day Cover   65
       Souvenir Postcard   95
The upper and lower edges of booklet panes are imperforate.
Nos. 1230b/ba were from a 1 Koala new printing produced at the Moorabbin works.

AUSTRALIA 41c
Centenary of women in medical practice. 1990

472 Dr. Constance Stone
(first Australian woman
doctor), Modern Doctor
and Nurses

473 Greater
Glider

(Des Priscilla Cutter. Litho Leigh-Mardon Ltd, Melbourne)

1990 (7 Feb).   *Centenary of Women in Medical Practice. CPL paper. P* 14½.
1231 **472** 41 c. multicoloured   45   45
       First Day Cover   65
       Souvenir Postcard   95

(Des D. Higgins. Litho Leigh-Mardon Ltd, Melbourne)

1990 (21 Feb).   *Animals of the High Country. T* **473** *and similar vert designs. Multicoloured. Harrison paper. P* 14×13½.
1232   41 c. Type **473**   55   45
1233   65 c. Tiger Cat ("Spotted-tailed Quoll")   80   75
1234   70 c. Mountain Pygmy-possum   85   80
1235   80 c. Brush-tailed Rock-wallaby   95   90
       Set of 4 . . . .   2·75   2·50
       Presentation Pack . . . .   3·00
       First Day Cover . . . .   2·75
       Souvenir Postcards (4) . . . .   4·25

474 "Stop
Smoking"

475 Soldiers from
Two World Wars

(Des A. Stitt. Litho Leigh-Mardon Ltd, Melbourne)

1990 (14 Mar).   *Community Health. T* **474** *and similar vert designs. Multicoloured. CPL paper. P* 14×13½.
1236   41 c. Type **474**   55   55
1237   41 c. "Drinking and driving don't mix"   55   55
1238   41 c. "No junk food, please"   55   55
1239   41 c. "Guess who's just had a checkup?"   55   55
       Set of 4 . . . .   2·00   2·00
       Presentation Pack . . . .   2·25
       First Day Cover . . . .   2·25
       Souvenir Postcards (4) . . . .   3·25

THE WORLD CENTRE FOR
FINE STAMPS IS 399 STRAND

(Des O. Schmidinger and Christine Stead. Litho Leigh-Mardon Ltd, Melbourne)

1990 (12 Apr).   *"The Anzac Tradition". T* **475** *and similar vert designs. Multicoloured. CPL paper. P* 14½.
1240   41 c. Type **475**   40   40
1241   41 c. Fighter pilots and munitions worker   40   40
1242   65 c. Veterans and Anzac Day parade   70   70
1243 $1 Casualty evacuation, Vietnam, and disabled
       veteran . . . .   1·00   1·10
1244 $1.10, Letters from home and returning troop-
       ships . . . .   1·10   1·25
       Set of 5 . . . .   3·25   3·50
       Presentation Pack . . . .   3·75
       Souvenir Book . . . .   17·00
       First Day Cover . . . .   3·75
       Souvenir Postcards (5) . . . .   5·25

476 Queen at Australian
Ballet Gala Performance,
London, 1988

477 New South Wales
1861 5s. Stamp

(Des Lynette Brown. Litho Leigh-Mardon Ltd, Melbourne)

1990 (19 Apr).   *Queen Elizabeth II's Birthday. CPL paper. P* 14½.
1245 **476** 41 c. multicoloured   40   40
       First Day Cover   55
       Souvenir Postcard   85

(Des J. Passmore. Litho Leigh-Mardon Ltd, Melbourne)

1990 (1 May).   *150th Anniv of the Penny Black. T* **477** *and similar horiz designs showing stamps. Multicoloured. CPL paper. P* 13½×14.
1246   41 c. Type **477**   45   55
     a. Block of 6. Nos. 1246/51 . . . .   2·40
1247   41 c. South Australia 1855 unissued 1s.   45   55
1248   41 c. Tasmania 1853 4d.   45   55
1249   41 c. Victoria 1867 5s.   45   55
1250   41 c. Queensland 1897 unissued 6d.   45   55
1251   41 c. Western Australia 1855 4d. with inverted
       frame   45   55
       Set of 6 . . . .   2·40   2·75
       Presentation Pack . . . .   2·75
       First Day Cover . . . .   2·75
       Souvenir Postcards (6) . . . .   4·75
MS1252 122×85 mm. Nos. 1246/51 . . . .   2·40   2·75
       First Day Cover . . . .   2·75
Nos. 1246/51 were printed together, *se-tenant*, throughout the sheet of 100 (two panes 5×10). The first and fifth vertical rows contained Nos. 1246 and 1249 alternately, the second and fourth rows Nos. 1247 and 1250, and the third row Nos. 1248 and 1251.
No. **MS**1252 also exists overprinted with the "Stamp World London 90" logo for sale at this International stamp exhibition.

478 Gold Miners on way to Diggings   479 Glaciology Research

(Des B. Weatherhead. Litho Leigh-Mardon Ltd, Melbourne)

1990 (16 May). *Colonial Development* (*2nd issue*). *Gold Fever.* T **478** *and similar square designs. Multicoloured. CPL paper. P* 13.

1253	41 c. Type **478**		45	45
	a. Horiz strip of 5. Nos. 1253/7	2·00		
1254	41 c. Mining camp		45	45
1255	41 c. Panning and washing for gold		45	45
1256	41 c. Gold Commissioner's tent		45	45
1257	41 c. Moving gold under escort		45	45
	Set of 5		2·00	2·00
	Presentation Pack		2·40	
	Souvenir Book		8·75	
	First Day Cover			2·40
	Souvenir Postcards (5)			4·00

Nos. 1253/7 were printed together, *se-tenant*, in horizontal strips of 5 throughout the sheet.

(Typo Pemara Labels, Victoria)

1990 (16 May–27 Aug). *As Nos.* 1180/1 *but self-adhesive. P* 11½.

1258	41 c. Cycling		30	35
1258*a*	43 c. Skateboarding (27 Aug)		35	40
	Set of 2		65	75
	First Day Covers (2)			1·00

Nos. 1258/*a* were only available in rolls of 100 from major post offices or as strips of three from philatelic counters, each stamp, with die-cut "perforations", being separate on the imperforate backing strip.

Due to the type of adhesive used examples should be retained on piece.

(Des Janet Boschen and Yu. Artsimenev. Litho Leigh-Mardon Ltd, Melbourne)

1990 (13 June). *Australian-Soviet Scientific Co-operation in Antarctica.* T **479** *and similar horiz design. Multicoloured. CPL paper. P* 14½.

1259	41 c. Type **479**		40	40
1260	$1.10, Krill (marine biology research)		1·10	1·10
	Set of 2		1·50	1·50
	Presentation Pack (*Nos. 1259/61 and Russia issue*)		4·00	
	First Day Cover			1·75
	Souvenir Postcards (2)			2·10
MS1261	85 × 65 mm. Nos. 1259/60		1·50	1·75
	Souvenir Book (*No.* **MS**1261 *and Russia miniature sheet*)		14·00	
	First Day Cover			1·90

Stamps in similar designs were also issued by Russia.

No. **MS**1261 also exists overprinted with the "New Zealand 1990" logo for sale at this international stamp exhibition in Auckland.

480 Auctioning Building Plots

(Des B. Clinton. Litho Leigh-Mardon Ltd, Melbourne)

1990 (12 July). *Colonial Development* (3rd series). *Boomtime.* T **480** *and similar square designs. Multicoloured. CPL paper. P* 13.

1262	41 c. Type **480**		35	40
	a. Horiz strip of 5. Nos. 1262/6	1·60		
1263	41 c. Colonial mansion		35	40
1264	41 c. Stock exchange		35	40
1265	41 c. Fashionable society		35	40
1266	41 c. Factories		35	40
	Set of 5		1·60	1·75
	Presentation Pack		2·10	
	Souvenir Book		8·75	
	First Day Cover			2·00
	Souvenir Postcards (5)			4·00

Nos. 1262/6 were printed together, *se-tenant*, in horizontal strips of 5 throughout the sheet.

Index to Australian Stamp Designs from 1942

The following index is intended to facilitate the identification of all Australian stamps from 1942 onwards. Portrait stamps are usually listed under surnames only, views under the name of the town or city and other issues under the main subject or a prominent word and date chosen from the inscription. Simple abbreviations have occasionally been resorted to and when the same design or subject appears on more than one stamp, only the first of each series is indicated.

STAMP BOOKLETS

PRICES given are for complete booklets. All booklets from 1953 to 1972 were stitched and stapled booklets of this period are remakes of defective stitched booklets with new covers.

Most editions exist with either printed interleaves or wax paper interleaves, the latter for use in hot areas.

Stamps from booklets Nos. B23 and B25/8 come with the watermark either upright or inverted.

1913. *Black on red cover.*
B1 2s. booklet. Twelve ½d. (No. 1) and eighteen 1d. (No. 2) in
  panes of 6 .... £600
  a. Red on pink cover £600
B2 2s. booklet. Twenty-four 1d. (No. 2) in panes of 8 .... £600

1914. *Red on pink (Nos. B3, B5) or black on green (No. B4) cover. Stapled (No. B5).*
B3 2s. booklet. Twelve ½d. (No. 29a) and eighteen 1d. (No. 30c)
  in panes of 6 .... £900
  a. Black on pink cover £900
B4 2s. booklet. Twenty-four 1d. (No. 30c) in panes of 6 ..... £600
  a. Black on red cover £600
  b. Red on green cover £600
B5 £1 booklet. Two hundred and forty 1d. (No. 30c.) in panes of
  30 .... £1500

1918. *Black on pink cover.*
B6 2s. 3d. booklet. Eighteen 1½d. (No. 58) in panes of 6 ..... £550
  a. Black on green cover £450

1919. *Black on pink (Nos. B7/8) or black on green (No. B9) cover.*
B7 2s. 3d. booklet. Eighteen 1½d. (No. 54) in panes of 6 ..... £650
  a. Black on green cover £650
B8 2s. 3d. booklet. Eighteen 1½d. (No. 59) in panes of 6 ..... £550
  a. Black on green cover £550
B9 2s. 3d. booklet. Eighteen 1½d. (No. 55) in panes of 6 ..... £600
  a. Black on blue cover £600

1920. *Black on pink cover. Stapled (No. B11).*
B10 2s. booklet. Twelve 2d. (No. 62) in panes of 6 .... £500
  a. Black on green cover £500
  b. Black on blue cover £500
B11 £1 booklet. one hundred and twenty 2d. (No. 62) in panes
  of 15 .... £1500

1922. *Black on orange cover. Stapled (Nos. B13/14).*
B12 2s. booklet. Twelve 2d. (No. 63) in panes of 6 ....
  a. Black on white cover £400
  b. Black on pink cover £400
B13 £1 booklet. Ninety 2d. (No. 63) and fifteen 4d. (No. 65) in
  panes of 15 ....
B14 £1 booklet. One hundred and twenty 2d. (No. 63) in panes
  of 15 .... £1600

1923. *Green on pale green cover. Stapled (No. B16).*
B15 2s. 3d. booklet. Eighteen 1½d. (No. 61) in panes of 6 ..... £550
  a. Black on pale green cover £550
  b. Black on pink cover £550
B16 £1 booklet. One hundred and sixty 1½d. (No. 61) in panes of
  20 .... £2000

1924. *Green on pale green cover. Stapled (No. B18).*
B17 2s. 3d. booklet. Eighteen 1½d. (No. 77) in panes of 6 ..... £250
  a. Black on pale green cover £250
B18 £1 booklet. One hundred and sixty 1½d. (No. 77) in panes of
  20 .... £950

1927. *Green on pale green cover. Stapled (No. B22).*
B19 2s. booklet. Sixteen 1½d. (No. 105) in panes of 8 .... 80·00
B20 2s. 3d. booklet. Eighteen 1½d. (No. 87) in panes of 6 ..... £300
B21 2s. 3d. booklet. Eighteen 1½d. (No. 97) in panes of 6 ..... £225
B22 £1 booklet. One hundred and sixty 1½d. (No. 97) in panes of
  20 .... £850

1928. *Green on pale green cover.*
B23 2s. 3d. booklet. Eighteen 1½d. (No. 98) in panes of 6 ..... £200

1930. *Black on blue cover inscr "Air Mail Saves Time".*
B24 3s. booklet. Twelve 3d. (No. 115) in panes of 4 plus two
  panes of air mail labels £550
  a. Cover inscr "Use the Air Mail" £600
  b. Green on pale green cover inscr "Use the Air Mail" .. £600

1930. *Green on pale green cover.*
B25 2s. booklet. Twelve 2d. (No. 99b) in panes of six £190

1931. *Green on pale green cover inscr "Use the Air Mail" on back.*
B26 2s. booklet. Twelve 2d. (No. 127) in panes of six £180
  a. Cover with parcel post rates on back £180
  b. Black on green cover inscr "Address your mail fully..."
    on front £180
  c. Black on green cover. Advertisements front and back
    for Commonwealth Savings Bank £180
  d. Black on green cover. Commonwealth Savings Bank
    advertisement on front, postage rates on back £170

1938. *Black on green cover. Stapled.*
B27 2s. booklet. Twelve 2d. (No. 184) in panes of 6 .... £150
  a. Black on buff cover £150

1942. *Black on buff cover, size 73×47½ mm. Stapled.*
B28 2s. 6d. booklet. Twelve 2½d. (No. 205) in panes of 6, upright
  within the booklet .... 60·00

1949. *Black on buff cover, size 79½×42½ mm. Stapled.*
B29 2s. 6d. booklet. Twelve 2½d. (No. 205) in panes of 6,
  sideways within the booklet .... 65·00

Type A (*Illustration reduced. Actual size 80 × 40 mm*)

1952 (June). *Vermilion and deep blue on green cover, Type A.*
B30 3s. 6d. booklet. Twelve 3½d. (No. 248) in panes of 6 .... 20·00

1953 (8 July). *Vermilion and deep blue on green cover, Type A.*
B31 3s. 6d. booklet. Twelve 3½d. (No. 263) in panes of 6 .... 9·00

1956 (24 July). *Vermilion and deep blue on green cover, Type A.*
B32 3s. 6d. booklet. Twelve 3½d. (No. 262a) in panes of 6 .... 20·00

Type B (*Illustration reduced. Actual size 80 × 40 mm*)

1957 (13 Mar). *Vermilion and deep blue on green cover, Type B. Outer edges of booklet imperf.*
B33 4s. booklet. Twelve 4d. (No. 294) in panes of 6 .... 15·00

1959 (18 Mar). *Vermilion and deep blue on green cover, Type B. Outer edges of booklet imperf.*
B34 4s. booklet. Twelve 4d. (No. 313Eb) in panes of 6 ...... 38·00

Type C (*Illustration reduced. Actual size 80 × 40 mm*)

Type D (*Illustration reduced. Actual size* 80 × 40 *mm*)

1960–62. *Outer edges of booklet imperf.*
(a) *Vermilion and deep blue on green cover, Type C*
B35 5s. booklet. Twelve 5d. (No. 314, Dies A and B) in panes of
6 (each 2 Die A, 4 Die B) (23.3.60) . . . . 17·00
(b) *Rose and emerald on green cover, Type D*
B36 5s. booklet. Same composition (7.62) . . . . 19·00
In each pane of 6 (2 × 3), the top pair is Die A, the bottom pair Die B, and
the middle pair Die B distinguishable by the first "A" in "AUSTRALIA"
which has a slight swelling on left leg and a thickened serif at bottom of
right leg.

1964 (17 June). *Rose and emerald on green cover, Type D. Outer edges
of booklet imperf.*
B37 5s. booklet. Twelve 5d. (No. 354) in panes of 6 . . . . 38·00
Stamps in No. B37 were printed in ordinary ink but have also been
reported on helecon paper and it is believed that only a few helecon
sheets were used for these booklets.

1965 (June). *Rose and emerald on green cover, Type D. Outer edges of
booklet imperf.*
B38 5s. booklet. Twelve 5d. (No. 354b) in panes of 6 . . . . 42·00
All stamps in No. B38 normally have helecon ink, but see notes *re*
helecon stamps after No. 307.

AUSTRALIAN POST OFFICE

Type E (*Illustration reduced. Actual size* 80 × 40 *mm*)

1966 (14 Feb). *Greenish blue and black on yellow-olive cover, Type E.
Outer edges of booklet imperf.*
B39 60 c. booklet. Fifteen 4 c. (No. 385) in panes of 5 with
se-tenant label . . . . 95·00
All stamps in No. B39 have helecon ink.

The booklet panes are arranged in six rows of eight, each row carrying a
different slogan on the label, as follows:
Registered Post is Safest for your Gifts
Post your Parcels–pack, wrap and tie securely
Send Money Securely by Money Order Service
Post Early–before noon and before 4 p.m.
Use Postal Orders for Small Sums of Money
9 × 4 in. and 5¾ × 3½ in. envelopes speed your mail

1967 (29 Sept). *Greenish blue and black on yellow-olive covers, as Type
E. Outer edges of booklet imperf.*
B40 50 c. booklet. (optd cover) Ten surch 5 c. (No. 414) in panes
of 5 with printed label . . . . 10·00
B41 $1 booklet. (optd cover) Twenty surch 5 c. (No. 414) in
panes of 5 with printed label . . . . 16·00
a. Cover inscription changed . . . . 15·00
Booklets B40/1a were intended as provisional issues until supplies of
the new 5 c. became available in booklet form but in the event these were
put on sale on the same date. Booklets B40/1 show covers of B39
overprinted.

B42 50 c. booklet. Ten 5 c. (No. 386c) in panes of 5 with printed
label . . . . 17·00
B43 $1 booklet. Twenty 5 c. (No. 386c) in panes of 5 with
printed label . . . . 35·00

Type F (*Illustration reduced. Actual size* 80 × 40 *mm*)

1968 (6 Nov). *Black, red, white and blue cover, Type F. Outer edges of
booklet imperf.*
B44 $1 booklet. Twenty 5 c. (five each of Nos. 432/5) in panes
of five with *se-tenant* label . . . . 18·00

Type G (*Illustration reduced. Actual size* 80 × 40 *mm*)

1969 (22 Oct). *Olive-green and black cover, as Type G. Outer edges of
booklet imperf.*
B45 $1 booklet. Twenty 5c (five each of Nos. 446/9) in panes
of five with *se-tenant* label . . . . 18·00

Type H (*Illustration reduced. Actual size* 40 × 80 *mm*)

1970 (16 Nov). *Multicoloured on white covers, as Type H. Outer edges of
booklet imperf.*
B46 60 c. booklet. Ten 6 c. (five each of Nos. 479/80) in panes
of five with *se-tenant* label . . . . 12·00
B47 60 c. booklet. Ten 6 c. (five each of Nos. 481/2) in panes
of five with *se-tenant* label . . . . 12·00
B48 $1.20, booklet. Twenty 6 c. (five each of Nos. 479/82) in
panes of five with *se-tenant* label . . . . 24·00
There are two forms of Booklet No. B48. One, with edition No. V70/3 on
the back cover, has the panes interleaved by advertisements. The other
version has no interleaves, but has postage rates on inside front cover. Both
versions come with either white or blue stitching.

1972 (8 Mar). *Covers in reddish violet (No. B49), yellowish olive (No. B50)
or blue (No. B51), with inscr in yellow-brown and black, as Type G.
Outer edges of booklet imperf.*
B49 70 c. booklet. Ten 7 c. (five each of Nos. 505/6) in panes
of five with *se-tenant* label . . . . 5·50
B50 70 c. booklet. Ten 7 c. (five each of Nos. 507/8) in panes
of five with *se-tenant* label . . . . 5·50

B51 $1.40, booklet. Twenty 7 c. (five each of Nos. 505/8) in panes of five with se-tenant label . . . .   10·00

The Australian Post Office discontinued the general use of stamp booklets in May 1973, but in April 1979 tested two stamp-vending machines in Brisbane which issued 60 c. and 80 c. folders containing three or four examples of No. 673 taken from sheet stock. These folders were withdrawn on 30 January 1981.

During 1982 experimental stamp booklet vending machines were under test at the G.P.O.'s in Melbourne and Sydney. These machines dispensed a cream card folder, without printing, containing two copies of Nos. 669/70 and 790a. The stamps, from normal sheets, were affixed to the folders by their selvedge. These 60 c. trial folders were replaced by booklets Nos. B52/3 in November 1982.

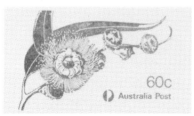

Type I (*Illustration reduced. Actual size* 80 × 45 *mm*)

1982 (17 Nov). *Eucalyptus Flowers. Covers in pale greenish yellow with olive-grey (60 c.), or rose-red ($1), as Type I. Outer edges of booklet imperf.*
B52   60 c. booklet containing No. 870a . . . .   1·00
B53 $1 booklet containing No. 870b . . . .   2·25
Nos. B52/3 were sold from vending machines.

Type J (*Illustration reduced. Actual size* 45 × 80 *mm*)

1985 (13 Mar). *Turquoise green on white cover, Type J. Outer edges of booklet imperf.*
B54 $1 booklet containing No. 970a . . . .   2·25
No. B54 was sold from vending machines.

Type K (*Illustration reduced. Actual size* 80 × 45 *mm*)

1986 (25 Aug). *Alpine Wildflowers. Apple-green (80 c.) or orange-yellow ($1) on white covers, as Type K. Outer edges of booklet panes imperf.*
B55   80 c. booklet containing No. 1028a . . . .   1·50
B56 $1 booklet containing No. 1028b . . . .   1·60
Nos. B55/6 were sold from vending machines.

Type L (*Illustration reduced. Actual size* 80 × 45 *mm*)

1987 (13 Oct). *Aboriginal Crafts. Orange-brown (80 c.) or orange-yellow ($2) on white covers, as Type L. Vertical edges of booklet panes imperf.*
B57   80 c. booklet containing No. 1093a . . . .   1·10
B58 $2 booklet containing No. 1094a . . . .   2·25
Nos. B57/8 were sold from vending machines.

Type M (*Illustration reduced. Actual size* 78 × 60 *mm*)

1988 (1 July). *Multicoloured cover, Type M.*
B59 $3.70 booklet. Ten 37 c. (No. 1121) in one pane of 10 (printed by Leigh-Mardon Ltd) . . . .   3·00
B60 $3.70 booklet containing pane No. 1121a (printed by CPE Australia Ltd, with upper and lower edges of the pane imperf and margins at left and right . . . .   3·00

1988 (28 Sept). *Multicoloured cover, as Type M, with upper and lower edges of the pane imperf and margins at left and right.*
B61 $3.90 booklet containing pane No. 1121ba . . . .   4·25

Type N (*Illustration reduced. Actual size* 80 × 45 *mm*)

1988 (28 Sept). *Australian Crafts. Orange-yellow (80 c.) or bright purple ($2) on white covers, as Type N.*
B62   80 c. booklet containing No. 1158a . . . .   1·10
B63 $2 booklet containing No. 1159a . . . .   2·25
Nos. B62/3 were sold from vending machines.

Type O (*Illustration reduced. Actual size* 77 × 50 *mm*)

1989 (13 Feb). *Multicoloured cover, Type O. Upper and lower edges of the pane imperf and margins at left and right.*
B64 $3.90 booklet containing pane No. 1179a . . . .   4·25

Type P (*Illustration reduced. Actual size* 77 × 50 *mm*)

1989 (23 Aug). *Multicoloured cover, Type P. Upper and lower edges of the pane imperf and margins at left and right.*
B65 $4.10 booklet containing pane No. 1180a . . . .   4·00

Type Q (*Illustration reduced. Actual size* 79 × 45 *mm*)

1989 (1 Sept). *Urban Environment. Black and grey-brown on white cover, Type Q. Upper and lower edges of the pane imperf and margins at left and right.*
B66 $3 booklet containing No. 1216a . . . .   4·00
No. B66 was sold from vending machines.

Type R (*Illustration reduced. Actual size* 132 × 54 *mm*)

1989 (11 Oct). *"Stampshow '89" National Stamp Exhibition, Melbourne. Multicoloured cover, Type R. Upper and lower edges of the pane imperf and margins at left and right.*
B67 $8 booklet containing pane No. 1222ab . . . .   7·50
Booklet No. B67 also contains a Melbourne Metro travel pass and entrance ticket to "Stampshow '89".

Type S (*Illustration reduced. Actual size* 94 × 52 *mm*)

1989 (1 Nov). *Christmas. Reddish brown on toned cover, Type S. Upper and lower edges of the pane imperf and margins at left and right.*
B68 $3.60 booklet containing pane No. 1225a . . . .   3·50

Type T (*Illustration reduced. Actual size* 94 × 52 *mm*)

1990 (7 Feb–May). *Greetings Stamps. Maroon and dull mauve cover, Type T. Upper and lower edges of the pane imperf and margins at left and right.*
B69 $4.10 booklet containing No. 1230a 4.50
  a. Containing pane No. 1230bc (May) . . . .
Booklet No. B69 also contains a pane of ten greetings labels.

1990 (27 Aug). *Multicoloured cover as Type P. Upper and lower edges of the pane imperf and margins at left and right.*
B70 $4.30 booklet containing pane No. 1181a . . . .   3·25

Military Post Booklets
Issued for the use of Australian Forces in Vietnam.

Type MPA (*Illustration reduced. Actual size* 110 × 54 *mm*)

1967. *Yellow-green and black on white cover, Type MPA.*
MB1   50 c. booklet. Ten 5 c. (No. 386) in one pane of 10 (30 May) . . . .   75·00
  a. Containing No. 386b (Sept) . . . .   50·00

1968 (Mar). *Yellow-green and black on white cover, Type MPA.*
MB2   50 c. booklet. Ten 5 c. (No. 386c) in one pane of 10 . . . .   60·00

POSTAGE DUE STAMPS

PRICES

Edward VII and George V issues (1902–1937)

First column = Mounted Mint
Second column = Used

POSTAGE DUE PRINTERS. Nos. D1/62 were typographed at the New South Wales Government Printing Office, Sydney.

D 1   D 2   D 3

Type D **1** adapted from plates of New South Wales Type D **1**. No letters at foot.

1902 (From July). *Chalk-surfaced paper. Wmk Type* D **2**.

(a) P 11½, 12

D 1	D **1**	½d. emerald-green	2·75	3·00
D 2		1d. emerald-green	7·50	3·50
D 3		2d. emerald-green	20·00	3·50
D 4		3d. emerald-green	35·00	16·00
D 5		4d. emerald-green	35·00	10·00
D 6		6d. emerald-green	50·00	9·00
D 7		8d. emerald-green	95·00	60·00
D 8		5s. emerald-green	£175	70·00
		Set of 8	£375	£160
		Set of 7 (Nos. D1/7) optd "Specimen" .	£200	

(b) P 11½, 12, *compound with* 11

D 9	D **1**	1d. emerald-green	55·00	15·00
D10		8d. emerald-green	50·00	14·00

(c) P 11

D12	D **1**	1d. emerald-green	£150	75·00

The ½d., 6d. and 8d. exist in dull green.
Stamps may be found showing portions of the letters "N S W" at foot.

1902–4. *Type* D **3**, *space at foot filled in, Chalk paper. Wmk Type* D **2**.

(a) P 11½, 12

D13	1d. emerald-green	45·00	25·00
D14	2d. emerald-green	45·00	20·00
D15	3d. emerald-green	60·00	20·00
D17	5d. emerald-green	27·00	9·00
D18	10d. emerald-green	50·00	12·00
D19	1s. emerald-green	50·00	9·00
D20	2s. emerald-green	85·00	16·00
D21	5s. emerald-green	£300	80·00

(b) P 11½, 12, *compound with* 11

D22	½d. emerald-green	3·25	3·00
D23	1d. emerald-green	3·75	1·25
D24	2d. emerald-green	17·00	2·50
D25	3d. emerald-green	26·00	4·00
D26	4d. emerald-green	26·00	3·50
D27	5d. emerald-green	48·00	9·50
D28	6d. emerald-green	42·00	8·50
D29	8d. emerald-green	75·00	22·00
D30	10d. emerald-green	80·00	16·00
D31	1s. emerald-green	80·00	9·50
D32	2s. emerald-green	£110	24·00
D33	5s. emerald-green	£130	17·00

(c) P 11

D34	½d. emerald-green	45·00	40·00
D35	1d. emerald-green	26·00	4·00
D36	2d. emerald-green	45·00	4·25
D37	3d. emerald-green	38·00	9·00
D38	4d. emerald-green	45·00	14·00
D39	5d. emerald-green	65·00	9·00
D40	6d. emerald-green	45·00	12·00
D41	1s. emerald-green	80·00	32·00
D42	5s. emerald-green	£225	50·00

D43	10s. emerald-green	£1400	£750
D44	20s. emerald-green	£2750	£1400
	Set of 14	£4250	£2000
	Set of 14 optd "Specimen"	£550	

Most values exist in dull green.

D **4**   D **6**

1906 (From Jan)–**08**. *Chalky paper. Wmk Type* D **4**.

(a) P 11½, 12, *compound with* 11

D45	D **3**	½d. green (1907)	5·00	3·50
D46		1d. green	7·50	2·25
D47		2d. green	16·00	3·25
D48		3d. green	£180	£100
D49		4d. green (1907)	45·00	20·00
D50		6d. green (1908)	60·00	30·00
		Set of 6	£275	£140

(b) P 11

D51	D **3**	1d. dull green	£100	30·00
D52		4d. dull green	£150	70·00
		Set of 2	£250	£100

Shades exist.

1907 (From July). *Chalky paper. W* **93** *a of Victoria. P* 11½×11.

D53	D **3**	½d. dull green	18·00	45·00
D54		1d. dull green	35·00	17·00
D55		2d. dull green	75·00	65·00
D56		4d. dull green	£140	85·00
D57		6d. dull green	£160	85·00
		Set of 5	£375	£275

1908 (Sept)–**09**. *Stroke after figure of value. Chalky paper. Wmk Type* D **4**.

(a) P 11½×11

D58	D **6**	1s. dull green (1909)	70·00	8·00
D59		5s. dull green	£200	48·00

(b) P 11

D60	D **6**	2s. dull green	£650	£650
D61		10s. dull green	£1600	£900
D62		20s. dull green	£4000	£2500
		Set of 5	£6000	£3500

Nos. D1/62 were not for use in Victoria.

D **7**

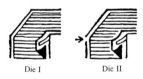

Die I   Die II

1d.

Die I   Die II
2d.

(Typo J. B. Cooke, Melbourne)

1909 (July)–**10.** Type D **7.** *Wmk Crown over A, W* **68** *of New South Wales.*

(a) *P* 12 × 12½ (*comb*) *or* 12½ (*line*)

D63	½d. rosine and yellow-green	9·00	12·00
D64	1d. rosine and yellow-green (I)	13·00	3·50
	a. Die II (7.10)	6·50	60
D65	2d. rosine and yellow-green (I)	24·00	3·50
	a. Die II (7.10)	6·50	65
D66	3d. rosine and yellow-green (1910)	18·00	8·50
D67	4d. rosine and yellow-green	18·00	4·50
D68	6d. rosine and yellow-green	25·00	6·00
D69	1s. rosine and yellow-green	30·00	4·00
D70	2s. rosine and yellow-green	70·00	16·00
D71	5s. rosine and yellow-green	75·00	20·00
D72	10s. rosine and yellow-green	£200	£130
D73	£1 rosine and yellow-green	£350	£200

(*b P* 11

D74	1d. rose and yellow-green (II)	£300	£150
D74a	2d. rose and yellow-green (II)		
D75	6d. rose and yellow-green	£1500	£650
	Set of 11	£750	£375

Only one unused example, without gum, and another pen-cancelled are known of No. D74a.
The 1d. of this printing is distinguishable from No. D78 by the colours, the green being very yellow and the rose having less of a carmine tone. The paper is thicker and slightly toned, that of No. D78 being pure white; the gum is thick and yellowish, No. D78 having thin white gum.
All later issues of the 1d. and 2d. are Die II.

(Typo J. B. Cooke and T. S. Harrison (from May 1918)

1912–23. Type D **7.** *Thin paper. White gum. W* **68** *of New South Wales.*

(a) *P* 12½.

D76	½d. scarlet and pale yellow-green (12.12)	17·00	18·00
	Wi. Wmk inverted	28·00	

(b) *P* 11

D77	½d. rosine and bright apple-green (10.14)	3·50	4·50
	a. Wmk sideways	3·25	4·50
D78	1d. rosine and bright apple-green (10.14)	2·00	55
	a. Wmk sideways	5·00	90
	Wi. Wmk inverted	16·00	

(c) *P* 14

D79	½d. rosine and bright apple-green (1914)	60·00	35·00
	a. *Carmine and apple-green* (*Harrison*) (1920) .	9·00	14·00
D80	1d. rosine and bright apple-green (10.14)	55·00	10·00
	a. *Scarlet and pale yellow-green* (1918)	16·00	3·50
	b. *Carmine and apple-green* (*Harrison*) (1919)	6·50	2·25
D81	2d. scarlet and pale yellow-green (1918)	17·00	6·00
	a. *Carmine and apple-green* (*Harrison*) (1920)	10·00	3·00
D82	3d. rosine and apple-green (5.16).	55·00	22·00
	a. Wmk sideways	£300	£275
D83b	4d. carmine and apple-green (Harrison) (1918)	55·00	35·00
	ba. *Wmk inverted*	£275	£225
	bb. *Carmine and pale yellow-green* (*Harrison*) (26.4.21)	45·00	35·00
D85	1s. scarlet and pale yellow-green (7.23)	25·00	12·00
D86	10s. scarlet and pale yellow-green (5.21)	£400	£400
D87	£1 scarlet and pale yellow-green (5.21)	£550	£500
	Set of 8	£1000	£900

Although printed by Cooke, the three higher values were not issued until some years later.

(Typo T. S. Harrison (to Feb. 1926), A. J. Mullett (to June 1927) and J. Ash (later))

1919–30. Type D **7.** *W* **6.** (a) *P* 14.

D91	½d. carmine and yellow-green (5.23)	3·75	4·50
D92	1d. carmine and yellow-green (1.3.22)	3·50	65
D93	1½d. carmine and yellow-green (3.25)	1·75	9·00
D94	2d. carmine and yellow-green (20.3.22)	3·50	1·75
D95	3d. carmine and yellow-green (12.11.19)	9·50	3·50
	Wi. Wmk inverted	45·00	

D96	4d. carmine and yellow-green (13.2.22)	30·00	10·00
D97	6d. carmine and yellow-green (13.2.22)	30·00	11·00

(b) *P* 11

D98	4d. carmine and yellow-green (9.30)	4·00	3·75
	Set of 8	75·00	40·00

All values perf 14 were printed by Harrison and all except the 4d. by Mullett and Ash. There is a wide variation of shades in this issue.

(Typo J. Ash)

1931–37. Type D **7.** *W* **15.** (a) *P* 14.

D100	1d. carmine and yellow-green (10.31)	8·50	10·00
D102	2d. carmine and yellow-green (19.10.31)	8·50	10·00

(b) *P* 11

D105	½d. carmine and yellow-green (4.34)	7·00	14·00
D106	1d. carmine and yellow-green (11.32)	4·00	60
D107	2d. carmine and yellow-green (29.9.32)	4·00	60
D108	3d. carmine and yellow-green (3.37)	70·00	60·00
D109	4d. carmine and yellow-green (26.7.34)	3·75	2·00
D110	6d. carmine and yellow-green (4.36)	£300	£225
D111	1s. carmine and yellow-green (8.34)	45·00	32·00
	Set of 7	£375	£300

<table>
<tr><td align="center">PRICES
George VI issues (1937–1952)

First column = Unmounted Mint
Second column = Mounted Mint
Third column = Used</td></tr>
</table>

D **8**    D **9**

A   B   C

The differences are found in the middle of the "D"

D    E

Type E. Larger "1" with only three background lines above; hyphen more upright.

(Frame recess. Value typo J. Ash)

1938–39. *W* **15.** *P* 14½ × 14.

D112	D **8**	½d. carmine and green (A) (1939)	2·00	1·00	2·00
D113		1d. carmine and green (A)	3·50	1·25	30
D114		2d. carmine and green (A)	4·75	2·25	1·00
D115		3d. carmine and green (B)	11·00	5·00	12·00
D116		4d. carmine and green (A)	6·00	2·75	30
D117		6d. carmine and green (A)	32·00	15·00	26·00
D118		1s. carmine and green (D)	45·00	19·00	12·00
		Set of 7	95·00	42·00	48·00

Shades exist.

1946–57. *Redrawn as Type C and E* (1*s.*). *W* **15.** *P* 14½ × 14.

D119	D **9**	½d. carmine and green (9.56)...	60	30	3·00
D120		1d. carmine and green (11.1.47)	60	30	60
D121		2d. carmine and green (9.46)...	3·25	1·10	80
D122		3d. carmine and green (25.9.46)	4·25	1·40	75
D123		4d. carmine and green (11.52) ..	4·50	1·60	1·50
D124		5d. carmine and green (12.48) ..	5·00	1·75	2·50
D125		6d. carmine and green (9.47)...	8·00	4·00	1·25

D126	D **9**	7d. carmine and green (26.8.53)	3·75	1·40	7·50
D127		8d. carmine and green (24.4.57)	10·00	5·00	22·00
D128		1s. carmine and green (9.47) . . .	13·00	6·00	1·25
		Set of 10	48·00	21·00	38·00

There are many shades in this issue.

PRICES

Elizabeth II issues (from 1953)

First column = Unmounted Mint
Second column = Used

D **10**

1953 (26 Aug)**–60.** *W* **15.** *P* 14½ × 14.

D129	D **10**	1s. carmine and yellow-green (17.2.54)	4·75	3·00
		a. *Carmine and deep green*	9·00	6·50
D130		2s. carmine and yellow-green	18·00	11·00
		a. *Carmine and deep green*	65·00	16·00
D131		5s. carmine and green	18·00	6·00
		a. *Carmine and deep green* (1960) . . .	12·00	70
		Set of 3 (*Nos.* D129/31)	35·00	18·00
		Set of 3 (*Nos.* D129a/31a)	75·00	21·00

A new die was introduced for No. D131a. This differs from the original in having a distinct gap between the two arms of the "S". On No. D131 these two features are joined.

I   II

½d. to 10d. Type I. Numeral, "D" and stop, generally unoutlined.
Type II. Clear white line separates numeral, etc. from background.

F   G

½d. Type F. Dots in figures weak or missing. Usually 6 dots in base of "2".
Type G. Dots much clearer. 7 dots in base of "2".

H   J

8d. Type H. Narrow white outlines and stop only outlined near base.
Type J. Wider outlines and stop outlined all round.

K   L

1s. Type K. "1/–" lightly outlined and only one dot in corners of oblong.
Type L. Heavier and thicker outlines and two dots in corners of oblong.

1958–60. *No wmk. P* 14½ × 14.

D132	D **9**	½d. carmine and deep green (II) (F)		
		(27.2.58)	1·00	1·75
		Ea. Type II (G) (6.59)	1·25	1·50
D133		1d. carmine and deep green (I)		
		(25.2.58)	3·00	3·25
		a. Type II (6.59)	1·00	65
D134		3d. carmine and deep green (II)		
		(25.5.60)	1·75	2·50
D135		4d. carmine and deep green (I)		
		(27.2.58)	3·75	9·00
		a. Type II (6.59)	3·00	8·50
D136		5d. carmine and deep green (I)		
		(27.2.58)	8·50	14·00
		a. Type II (6.59)	60·00	75·00
D137		6d. carmine and deep green (II)		
		(25.5.60)	2·75	2·75
D138		8d. carmine and deep green (II)		
		(H) (25.2.58)	10·00	32·00
		Ea. Type II (J) (6.59)	17·00	35·00
D139		10d. carmine and deep green (II)		
		(9.12.59)	5·50	3·25
D140	D **10**	1s. carmine and deep green (K)		
		(8.9.58)	3·00	3·50
		a. *Deep carmine & dp green* (L)		
		(6.59)	4·00	4·00
D141		2s. deep carmine and deep green		
		(8.3.60)	20·00	22·00
		Set of 10	50·00	80·00

Printings in the pence values from 1953 had the value-tablet dies re-engraved with a clear white line surrounding the numeral, "D" and stop (Type II). The first stamps to be affected were Nos. D119 and D126/7.

A second change began to occur in 1959 when the arrangement of the plates was altered from two panes each of 6 × 10 to two panes each of 5 × 12. This necessitated new plates and the opportunity was taken to recut the value as in Type II, but instead of outlining the figures on the die this was done by hand on the plate individually on each subject in a setting of 30, four identical settings being grouped together to form a plate of 120.

The alteration to Type II had already been made on the ½d. and 8d. with watermark in the 6 × 10 sheet arrangement but further changes occurred in the 5 × 12 plates giving rise to Types G and J. Type G always has 7 dots and F usually 6 although a few stamps in the sheet have 5 or 7, but in the latter case the dots at each side are extremely small. A further difference is in the shade of the centre plate which is much deeper in Type G.

In the shilling values printings from the 5 × 12 plates showed the figures heavier and sharper resulting in a deeper shade of carmine which in No. D140a coincided with the introduction of Type L.

The use of Postage Due stamps ceased on 13 January 1963.

OFFICIAL STAMPS

PRICES

First column = Mounted Mint
Second column = Used

From 1902 the departments of the Commonwealth government were issued with stamps of the various Australian States perforated "OS" to denote official use. These were replaced in 1913 by Commonwealth of Australia issues with similar perforated initials as listed below.

During the same period the administrations of the Australian States used their own stamps and those of the Commonwealth perforated with other initials for the same purpose. These States issues are outside the scope of this catalogue.

Most shades listed under the postage issues also exist perforated "OS". Only those which are worth more than the basic colour are included below.

(O 1)    (O 2) 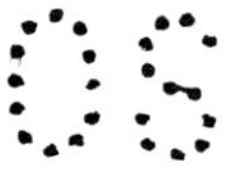   (O 3)

1913 (Jan–Apr). *Nos. 1/16 punctured as Type O **1**. W **2**. P* 12.

O1	**1**	½d. green (Die I)	6·00	3·25
		Wi. Wmk inverted	—	60·00
O2		1d. red (Die I)	8·00	1·00
		a. Wmk sideways	£200	50·00
		c. Die II	8·00	1·00
		ca. Wmk sideways	£200	50·00
		d. Die IIA	8·00	1·00
		da. Wmk sideways	£200	50·00
		Wi. Wmk inverted	25·00	2·75
O3		2d. grey (Die I)	22·00	4·50
O4		2½d. indigo (Die II)	£100	50·00
O5		3d. olive (Die I)	32·00	6·00
		d. Die II	£125	20·00
		Wi. Wmk inverted	45·00	13·00
O6		4d. orange (Die II)	45·00	18·00
		a. *Orange-yellow*	75·00	20·00
O7		5d. chestnut (Die II)	45·00	20·00
O8		6d. ultramarine (Die II)	45·00	10·00
		Wi. Wmk inverted	70·00	15·00
O9		9d. violet (Die II)	45·00	12·00
		Wi. Wmk inverted	75·00	15·00
O10		1s. emerald (Die II)	45·00	9·00
		Wi. Wmk inverted	60·00	15·00
O11		2s. brown (Die II)	£125	55·00
		a. Double print	†	—
O12		5s. grey and yellow	£250	£140
O13		10s. grey and pink	£500	£450
O14		£1 brown and blue	£1000	£800
O15		£2 black and rose	£2000	£1400
		Set of 15	£3750	£2500

1913 (June onwards). *Nos. 1/16 punctured as Type O **2**. W **2**. P* 12.

O16	**1**	½d. green (Die I)	7·00	2·25
		Wi. Wmk inverted	—	20·00
O17		1d. red (Die I)	8·00	1·25
		a. Wmk sideways	£200	35·00
		c. Die II	8·00	1·25
		ca. Wmk sideways	£200	35·00
		d. Die IIA	8·00	1·25
		da. Wmk sideways	£200	35·00
O18		2d. grey (Die I)	22·00	4·00
		Wi. Wmk inverted	24·00	6·00
O19		2½d. indigo (Die II)	60·00	38·00
O20		3d. olive (Die I)	30·00	5·00
		d. Die II	£100	22·00
		Wi. Wmk inverted	38·00	6·50
O21		4d. orange (Die II)	60·00	50·00
		a. *Orange-yellow*	£100	70·00
O22		5d. chestnut (Die II)	45·00	20·00
O23		6d. ultramarine (Die II)	40·00	10·00
		Wi. Wmk inverted	75·00	12·00
O24		9d. violet (Die II)	45·00	12·00
O25		1s. emerald (Die II)	45·00	11·00
O26		2s. brown (Die II)	£130	45·00
O27		5s. grey and yellow	£250	£100
O28		10s. grey and pink	£500	£275
O29		£1 brown and blue	£1000	£800
O30		£2 black and rose	£2000	£1400
		Set of 15	£3750	£2400

1915. *Nos. 20 and 23/7 punctured as Type O **2**. W **5**. P* 12.

O31	**1**	2d. grey (Die I)	45·00	8·50
O33		6d. ultramarine (Die II)	85·00	12·00
		b. Die IIA	£700	£110
		Wi. Wmk inverted	£130	28·00
O34		9d. violet (Die II)	£100	24·00
O35		1s. blue green (Die II)	£100	25·00
O36		2s. brown (Die II)	£350	50·00
O37		5s. grey and yellow	£350	75·00
		Wi. Wmk inverted	£375	90·00

1914–21. *Nos. 29/34 punctured as Type O **2**. W **5**. P* 14.

O38	**5a**	½d. bright green	4·00	1·75
		Wi. Wmk inverted	7·00	2·50
O39		1d. carmine-red (I)	4·50	25
		Wi. Wmk inverted	6·00	30

O40	**5a**	1d. carmine-red (II)	£250	4·00
		Wi. Wmk inverted	£325	6·00
O41		4d. orange	27·00	2·75
		a. *Yellow-orange*	27·00	5·00
		b. *Pale orange-yellow*	40·00	12·00
		c. *Lemon-yellow*	£100	20·00
		Wi. Wmk inverted	40·00	5·50
O42		5d. brown	27·00	2·00
		Wi. Wmk inverted	45·00	5·00

1915–28. *Nos. 35/45 punctured as Type O **2**. W **6**. P* 12.

O43	**1**	2d. grey (Die I)	15·00	2·00
		c. Die II	15·00	2·00
		Wi. Wmk inverted	22·00	3·75
O44		2½d. deep blue (Die II)	15·00	5·50
O45		3d. yellow-olive (Die I)	18·00	2·00
		c. Die II	50·00	15·00
		d. Die IIB	22·00	3·00
		Wi. Wmk inverted	28·00	3·50
O46		6d. ultramarine (Die II)	30·00	3·00
		a. Die IIA	£400	£100
		c. Die IIB	30·00	3·00
		Wi. Wmk inverted	45·00	5·00
O47		9d. violet (Die II)	20·00	2·75
		a. Die IIB	20·00	2·75
		Wi. Wmk inverted	—	7·00
O48		1s. blue-green (Die II)	23·00	1·75
		a. Die IIB	23·00	1·75
		Wi. Wmk inverted	—	28·00
O49		2s. brown (Die II)	90·00	9·50
		a. *Red-brown* (*aniline*)	£225	35·00
		Wi. Wmk inverted	£130	17·00
O50		5s. grey and yellow	£130	35·00
		Wi. Wmk inverted	£160	45·00
O51		10s. grey and pink	£200	60·00
		Wi. Wmk inverted	£225	70·00
O52		£1 chocolate and dull blue	£1100	£550
		ba. Wmk sideways	—	£1200
		Wi. Wmk inverted		
O53		£2 black and rose	£1800	£750
		Set of 11	£3000	£1250

1916–18. *Nos. 47/50a and 5d. as No. 34 punctured as Type O **2**. W **5**. Rough paper. P* 14.

O54	**5a**	1d. scarlet (I)	12·00	50
		Wi. Wmk inverted	16·00	75
O55		1d. deep red (I)	12·00	50
		Wi. Wmk inverted	16·00	75
O56		1d. rose-red (I)	14·00	50
		Wi. Wmk inverted	18·00	75
O57		1d. rosine (I)	55·00	4·00
O58		1d. rose-red (II)	£200	10·00
		Wi. Wmk inverted	£375	12·00
O59		1d. rosine (II)	£400	25·00
O60		5d. bright chestnut (1918)	£1100	95·00

All examples of the 5d. on this paper were perforated "OS".

1918–20. *Nos. 51 and 53/5 punctured as Type O **2**. W **6a**. P* 14.

O61	**5a**	½d. green	7·00	1·00
		Wi. Wmk inverted	12·00	2·00
O63		1d. carmine (I)	11·00	4·00
		Wi. Wmk inverted	70·00	9·50
O64		1½d. black-brown	8·00	1·00
		a. Very thin paper	12·00	4·00
		Wi. Wmk inverted	15·00	1·40
O65		1½d. red-brown	8·50	1·00
		Wi. Wmk inverted	16·00	1·90
		Set of 4	30·00	6·25

1918–23. *Nos. 56/9 and 61/6 punctured as Type O **2**. W **5**. P* 14.

O66	**5a**	½d. orange	13·00	6·00
O67		1d. violet	17·00	1·50
O68		1½d. black-brown	13·00	1·00
		Wi. Wmk inverted	18·00	1·00
O69		1½d. deep red-brown	10·00	80
		Wi. Wmk inverted	17·00	2·50
O70		1½d. green	7·00	50
O71		2d. dull orange	12·00	75
		Wi. Wmk inverted	26·00	8·50
O72		2d. bright rose-scarlet	7·50	75
		Wi. Wmk inverted	7·50	1·10
O73		4d. violet	22·00	10·00
O74		4d. ultramarine	38·00	6·50
O75		1s. 4d. pale blue	50·00	15·00
		b. *Deep turquoise*	—	£100
		Set of 10	£170	38·00

1923–24. Nos. 73/5 punctured as Type O **2**. W **6**. P 12.
O76	**1**	6d. chestnut (Die IIB)	15·00	2·00
O77		2s. maroon (Die II)	40·00	10·00
O78		£1 grey (Die IIB)	£400	£150
		Set of 3	£425	£150

1924. Nos. 76/84 punctured as Type O **2**. P 14. (a) W **5**.
O79	**5a**	1d. sage-green	4·00	40
O80		1½d. scarlet	1·00	20
		Wi. Wmk inverted	12·00	3·00
O81		2d. red-brown	20·00	5·00
		a. Bright red-brown	25·00	7·50
O82		3d. dull ultramarine	25·00	3·25
O83		4d. olive-yellow	25·00	2·50
O84		4½d. violet	30·00	5·00
		Wi. Wmk inverted	†	—

(b) W **6a**
O85	**5a**	1d. sage-green	9·00	4·50

(c) No wmk
O86	**5a**	1d. sage-green	35·00	40·00
O87		1½d. scarlet	50·00	45·00
		Set of 9	£180	95·00

1926–30. Nos. 85/104 punctured as Type O **2**. W **7**. (a) P 14.
O88	**5a**	½d. orange	65·00	50·00
O89		1d. sage-green	3·75	50
		Wi. Wmk inverted	7·50	1·00
O90		1½d. scarlet	4·75	70
		Wi. Wmk inverted	7·50	1·75
O91		1½d. golden scarlet	7·00	1·25
O92		2d. red-brown (Die I)	45·00	30·00
O93		3d. dull ultramarine	20·00	6·00
		Wi. Wmk inverted	45·00	12·00
O94		4d. yellow-olive	40·00	14·00
O95		4½d. violet	30·00	9·00
O96		1s. 4d. pale greenish blue	£120	70·00
		Set of 8	£300	£160

(b) P 13½ × 12½
O97	**5a**	½d. orange	2·25	50
O98		1d. sage-green (Die I)	2·00	35
O99		1d. sage-green (Die II)	50·00	75·00
O100		1½d. scarlet	1·75	20
O101		1½d. golden scarlet	1·75	20
O102		1½d. red-brown	3·75	1·50
O103		2d. red-brown (Die II)	9·00	4·00
O104		2d. golden scarlet (Die II)	7·00	50
O105		2d. golden scarlet (Die III)	3·75	50
		Wi. Wmk inverted	7·00	90
O106		3d. dull ultramarine (Die I)	22·00	4·00
		Wi. Wmk inverted	30·00	7·50
O107		3d. dull ultramarine (Die II)	14·00	1·25
		Wi. Wmk inverted	†	—
O108		4d. yellow-olive	17·00	3·00
O109		4½d. violet	45·00	30·00
O110		5d. orange-brown (Die II)	38·00	3·25
O111		1s. 4d. turquoise	85·00	14·00
		Set of 11	£200	50·00

1927 (9 May). Opening of Parliament House, Canberra. No. 105 punctured as Type O **3**.
O112	**8**	1½d. brownish lake	12·00	9·00

1928 (29 Oct). National Stamp Exhibition, Melbourne. No. 106 punctured as Type O **2**.
O113		3d. blue	13·00	9·00

1929–30. Nos. 107/14 punctured as Type O **2**. W **7**. P 12.
O114	**1**	6d. chestnut (Die IIB)	15·00	2·00
O115		9d. violet (Die IIB)	18·00	4·00
O116		1s. blue-green (Die IIB)	22·00	2·00
		Wi. Wmk inverted	85·00	25·00
O117		2s. maroon (Die II)	45·00	7·00
O118		5s. grey and yellow	£125	40·00
O118a		10s. grey and pink	£400	£300
O118b		£2 black and rose	£1800	£600

1929 (20 May). Air. No. 115 punctured as Type O **3**.
O119	**9**	3d. green	20·00	12·00

1929 (28 Sept). Centenary of Western Australia. No. 116 punctured as Type O **3**.
O120	**10**	1½d. dull scarlet	12·00	8·50

1930 (2 June). Centenary of Exploration of River Murray by Capt. Sturt. Nos. 117/18 punctured as Type O **2**.
O121	**11**	1½d. scarlet	6·00	4·00
O122		3d. blue	12·00	9·00
		Set of 2	18·00	13·00

(O 4)

1931 (4 May). Kingsford Smith's flights. Nos. 121/2 optd with Type O **4**.
O123	**13**	2d. rose-red	55·00	16·00
O124		3d. blue	£200	38·00

For No. 139 overprinted with Type O **4**, see No. 139a.

1932–33. Optd as Type O **4**. (a) W **7**. (i) P 13½ × 12½.
O125	**5a**	2d. golden scarlet (Die III)	6·00	70
		Wi. Wmk inverted		
O126		4d. yellow-olive	40·00	3·75

(ii) P 12
O127	**1**	6d. chestnut	80·00	65·00

(b) W **15**. (i) P 13½ × 12½
O128	**5a**	½d. orange	9·50	1·50
		a. Overprint inverted	£2000	£1100
O129		1d. green	4·00	45
O130		2d. golden scarlet (Die III)	6·00	55
		a. Overprint inverted	—	£1500
O131		3d. ultramarine (Die II) (3.33)	7·50	5·00
O132		5d. orange-brown	65·00	38·00

(ii) P 12
O133	**1**	6d. chestnut	40·00	30·00

(c) Recess. No wmk. P 11
O134	**18**	2d. scarlet	8·00	2·00
O135		3d. blue	20·00	5·50
O136	**17**	1s. green	80·00	35·00

Issue of overprinted Official stamps ceased in February 1933 and thereafter mail from the Federal administration was carried free.

BRITISH COMMONWEALTH OCCUPATION FORCE (JAPAN)

PRICES
George VI issues (1937–1952)
First column = Unmounted Mint
Second column = Mounted Mint
Third column = Used

Nos. J1/7 were used by the Australian forces occupying Japan after the Second World War. Initially their military post offices supplied unoverprinted Australian stamps, but it was decided to introduce the overprinted issue to prevent currency speculation.

The ½d., 1d. and 3d. values were first issued on 11 October 1946, and withdrawn two days later, but were re-issued together with the other values on 8 May 1947.

(1)

(2)

Wrong fount "6"
(left pane R.9/4)

Normal

Narrow "N"
(right pane R. 1/8)

1946 (11 Oct)–**48**. Stamps of Australia optd as T **1** (1d., 3d.) or T **2** (others) at British Commonwealth Command Headquarters, Kure, Japan.
J1	**27**	½d. orange (No. 179)	2·00	1·00	3·75
		a. Wrong fount "6"	25·00	10·00	32·00
		b. Narrow "N"			

J2	**46**	1d. brown-purple (No. 203)	2·00	75	1·50
		a. Error. Blue overprint	70·00	35·00	90·00
J3	**31**	3d. purple-brown (No. 187)	1·25	50	1·50
J4	**34**	6d. purple-brown (No. 189a) (8.5.47)	10·00	4·25	7·50
		a. Wrong fount "6"	70·00	30·00	85·00
		b. Stop after "JAPAN" (right pane R. 5/5)	70·00	30·00	85·00
		c. Narrow "N"			
J5	**36**	1s. grey-green (No. 191) (8.5.47). . .	10·00	4·00	8·50
		a. Wrong fount "6"	£100	42·00	£100
		b. Stop after "JAPAN" (right pane R. 5/5)	£100	42·00	£100
		c. Narrow "N"			

J6	**1**	2s. maroon (No. 212) (8.5.47).	38·00	18·00	42·00
J7	**38**	5s. claret (No. 176) (8.5.47)	£110	50·00	£130
		a. Thin rough paper (No. 176a) (1948)	£130	55·00	£150
		Set of 7	£150	70·00	£170

The following values with T **2** opt in the colours given were from proof sheets which, however, were used for postage: ½d. (red), 1d. (red or black) and 3d. (gold, red or black). (*Price from* £450 *un.*)

The use of B.C.O.F. stamps ceased on 12 February 1949.

Australian Antarctic Territory

1957 12 Pence   = 1 Shilling
      20 Shillings = 1 Australian Pound
1966 100 Cents   = 1 Australian Dollar

The area of the Antarctic situated south of 60° S. Lat. and between 160° E. long. and 45° E. with the exception of Adélie Land.

Nos. 1/7 were designed, engraved and recess-printed in Melbourne, *except where stated otherwise*. From No. 8 onwards stamps were photogravure-printed. They were also on sale and valid for use in Australia.

DATES OF ISSUE. The dates given refer to release dates in Australia. Local release dates are usually later and where known they are given in footnotes.

FIRST DAY COVER PRICES. These are for covers postmarked in the Antarctic, not those used in Australia.

1 1954 Expedition at Vestfold Hills and Map

(Des T. Lawrence; adapted by artist of the Printing Branch. Recess)

1957 (27 Mar). *P* 14½.
1   1   2s. ultramarine . . . . 1·75   60
  Issued Macquarie Island 11.12.57, Davis 6.2.58, Mawson 18.2.58, Wilkes 1.2.59.

2 Members of Shackleton Expedition at South Magnetic Pole, 1909

3 Weazel and Team

4 Dog-team and Iceberg

5 Map of Antarctica and Emperor Penguins

1959 (16 Dec). *Recess; new values surch typo (5d., 8d.). P* 14½ *(5d.),* 14½ × 14 *(8d.) or* 14 × 14½ *(others).*
2   2   5d. on 4d. black and sepia   60   15
3   3   8d. on 7d. black and indigo . . . . 4·50 2·00
4   4   1s. deep green . . . . 4·50 1·75
5   5   2s. 3d. green . . . . 10·00 4·00
            Set of 4 . . . . 18·00 7·00
  Issued Macquarie Island 26.12.59, Davis 30.1.60, Mawson 10.2.60, Wilkes 13.2.60.

6

7 Sir Douglas Mawson (Expedition leader)

1961 (5 July). *Recess. P* 14½.
6   6   5d. deep blue . . . . 1·50   15
  Issued Macquarie Island 6.12.61, Wilkes 10.1.62, Davis 20.1.62, Mawson 30.1.62.

1961 (18 Oct). *50th Anniv of* 1911–14 *Australasian Antarctic Expedition. Recess. P* 14½.
7   7   5d. myrtle-green   35   15
            First Day Cover . . . .   3·50
  Issued Macquarie Island 6.12.61, Wilkes 10.1.62, Davis 20.1.62, Mawson 30.1.62.

(New Currency. 100 cents = 1 Australian dollar)

8 Aurora and Camera Dome

9 Helicopter

10 Radio Operator

(Des J. Mason. Photo)

1966 (28 Sept)–**68.** *T* 8/10 *and similar multicoloured designs. P* 13½.
8   1 c. Type **8** (*shades*)   70   30
     Ea. Shade (1971)   80   40
9   2 c. Banding penguins (*shades*) . . . . 2·25   40
     Ea. Shade (1971) . . . . 2·50   75
10   4 c. Ship and iceberg   70   50
11   5 c. Banding Elephant-seals (25.9.68) . . . . 2·50 1·75

12	7 c.	Measuring snow strata	80	45
13	10 c.	Wind gauges	1·00	60
14	15 c.	Weather balloon	4·00	2·00
15	20 c.	Type **9**	4·25	2·25
16	25 c.	Type **10**	5·00	3·75
17	50 c.	Ice compression tests	17·00	9·00
18	$1	Parahelion ("mock sun")	42·00	15·00
		Set of 11	70·00	32·00
		Presentation Pack (English inscr) (13.7.70) .	85·00	
		Presentation Pack (Japanese inscr)	£110	

The 1 c. to 15 c. are vert as Type **8**; the 50 c. and $1 are horiz as Types **9** and **10** respectively.

Nos. 8/10 and 12/18 placed on sale locally at Macquarie Island on 11.12.66, Wilkes 9.2.67 and Mawson 16.2.67.

No. 11 issued Macquarie Island 4.12.68, Mawson 13.1.69, Wilkes/Casey 9.2.69 and Davis 20.2.69.

In No. 8*Ea* the podium is grey instead of very pale greyish blue; and on No. 9*Ea* the front penguin in the background is light blue instead of grey-blue.

11 Sastrugi (Snow Ridges)

12 Capt. Cook, Sextant and Compass

(Des J. Mason. Photo)

1971 (23 June). *Tenth Anniv of Antarctic Treaty. T* **11** *and similar horiz design.*

19	6 c.	blue and black	1·25	1·00
20	30 c.	multicoloured (Pancake ice)	6·50	6·50
		Set of 2	7·75	7·50
		Presentation Pack	9·00	
		First Day Cover		8·50

Issued Macquarie Island 23.11.71, Mawson 27.12.71, Davis 13.1.72 and Casey 17.1.72.

(Des J. Mason. Photo)

1972 (13 Sept). *Bicentenary of Cook's Circumnavigation of Antarctica. T* **12** *and similar horiz design. Multicoloured. P* 13½.

21	7 c.	Type **12**	2·00	75
22	35 c.	Chart and H.M.S. *Resolution*	8·00	6·00
		Set of 2	10·00	6·75
		Presentation Pack	12·00	
		First Day Cover		8·00

Issued Macquarie Island 19.11.72, Mawson 24.12.72, Davis 3.1.73 and Casey 22.1.73.

13 Plankton

14 Admiral Byrd (expedition leader), Aircraft and Map of South Pole

(Des G. Browning (1, 7, 9, 10, 20 c., $1), R. Honisett (others). Photo)

1973 (15 Aug). *T* **13** *and similar multicoloured designs. P* 13 × 13½ (*horiz*) *or* 13½ × 13 (*vert*).

23	1 c.	Type **13**	20	15
24	5 c.	Mawson's "Gipsy Moth", 1931	30	20
25	7 c.	Adélie Penguin	2·00	30
26	8 c.	Rymill's "Fox Moth", 1934–7	30	30
27	9 c.	Leopard Seal (*horiz*)	30	30
28	10 c.	Killer Whale (*horiz*)	5·00	1·00
	a.	Buff (oil on seals) omitted	£600	
29	20 c.	Wandering Albatross (*horiz*)	90	60
30	25 c.	Wilkins' Lockheed "Vega", 1928 (*horiz*) . . .	40	60
31	30 c.	Ellsworth's Northrop "Gamma", 1935	40	60

32	35 c.	Christensen's Avro "Avian", 1934 (*horiz*) . .	40	60
33	50 c.	Byrd's "Tri-Motor", 1929	50	60
34	$1	Sperm Whale	80	1·40
		Set of 12	10·00	6·25
		Presentation Pack	11·00	

Issued Macquarie Island 29.11.73, Mawson 30.12.73, Davis 10.1.74 and Casey 31.1.74.

(Des R. Honisett. Litho Asher and Co, Melbourne)

1979 (20 June). *50th Anniv of First Flight over South Pole. T* **14** *and similar horiz design. Multicoloured. P* 15½.

35	20 c.	Type **14**	50	40
36	55 c.	Admiral Byrd, aircraft and Antarctic terrain .	1·25	1·40
		Set of 2	1·75	1·75
		Presentation Pack	2·00	
		First Day Cover		2·00

Issued Macquarie Island 24.10.79, Davis 3.1.80, Mawson 13.1.80 and Casey 9.2.80.

15 M.V. *Thala Dan*

16 Sir Douglas Mawson in Antarctic Terrain

(Des R. Honisett. Litho Asher and Co, Melbourne)

1979 (29 Aug)–**81**. *Ships. Multicoloured designs as T* **15**. *P* 13½ × 13 (*horiz*) *or* 13 × 13½ (*vert*).

37	1 c.	S.Y. *Aurora* (*horiz*) (21.5.80)	10	10
38	2 c.	R.Y. *Penola* (9.9.81)	10	10
39	5 c.	Type **15**	15	15
40	10 c.	H.M.S. *Challenger* (*horiz*) (9.9.81)	20	10
41	15 c.	S.S. *Morning** (bow view) (*horiz*) (21.5.80)	1·40	2·25
42	15 c.	S.Y. *Nimrod* (stern view) (*horiz*) (9.9.81) . .	50	20
43	20 c.	R.R.S. *Discovery II* (*horiz*)	40	50
44	22 c.	R.Y.S. *Terra Nova* (21.5.80)	60	70
45	25 c.	S.S. *Endurance*	60	70
46	30 c.	S.S. *Fram* (*horiz*)	60	70
47	35 c.	M.S. *Nella Dan* (*horiz*) (21.5.80)	70	70
48	40 c.	M.S. *Kista Dan* (9.9.81)	70	45
49	45 c.	*L'Astrolabe* (*horiz*) (9.9.81)	70	50
50	50 c.	S.S. *Norvegia* (9.9.81)	70	55
51	55 c.	S.Y. *Discovery*	85	1·40
52	$1	H.M.S. *Resolution* (21.5.80)	1·50	2·00
		Set of 16	8·75	9·00
		Presentation Pack (5, 20, 25, 30, 55 c.) (29.8.79)	3·25	
		Presentation Pack (1, 15 (No. 41), 22, 35 c., $1) (21.5.80)	4·25	
		Presentation Pack (2, 10, 15 (No. 42), 40, 45, 50 c.) (9.9.81)	2·75	

* No. 41 is incorrectly inscribed "S.Y. *Nimrod*".

On No. 46 the S.S. *Fram* is shown flying the Icelandic ensign, instead of the Norwegian.

Nos. 37, 41, 44, 47 and 52 issued Macquarie Island 27.10.80, Casey 1.12.80, Mawson 5.12.80 and Davis 11.12.80.

Nos. 38, 40, 42 and 48/50 issued Macquarie Island 21.10.81, Mawson 25.11.81, Davis 11.1.82 and Casey 25.1.82.

Nos. 39, 43, 45/6 and 51 issued Macquarie Island 24.10.79, Davis 3.1.80, Mawson 13.1.80 and Casey 9.2.80.

(Des R. Honisett. Litho Cambec Press, Melbourne)

1982 (5 May). *Birth Centenary of Sir Douglas Mawson (Antarctic explorer). T* **16** *and similar vert design. Multicoloured. P* 14 × 13½.

53	27 c.	Type **16**	50	30
54	75 c.	Sir Douglas Mawson and map of Australian Antarctic Territory	1·50	2·00
		Set of 2	2·00	2·25
		Presentation Pack	2·25	
		First Day Cover		2·75

Issued Macquarie Island 26.10.82, Casey 16.1.83, Davis 10.2.83 and Mawson 2.3.83.

17 Light-mantled Sooty Albatross **18** Antarctic Scientist

(Des R. Honisett. Litho Leigh-Mardon Ltd, Melbourne)

1983 (6 Apr). *Regional Wildlife. T* **17** *and similar vert designs. Multicoloured. P* 14½.

55	27 c. Type **17**	70	70
	a. Horiz strip of 5. Nos. 55/9	3·25	
56	27 c. King Cormorant	70	70
57	27 c. Southern Elephant-seal	70	70
58	27 c. Royal Penguin	70	70
59	27 c. Dove Prion	70	70
	Set of 5	3·25	3·25
	Presentation Pack	3·50	
	First Day Cover		3·50

Nos. 55/9 were issued together, *se-tenant*, in horizontal strips of five, forming a composite design.
Issued Macquarie Island 21.10.83, Mawson 9.12.83, Casey 1.1.84 and Davis 2.1.84.

(Des R. Honisett. Litho Leigh-Mardon Ltd, Melbourne)

1983 (17 Sept). *12th Antarctic Treaty Consultative Meeting, Canberra. P* 14½.

60	**18** 27 c. multicoloured	60	45
	First Day Cover		1·00

Issued Macquarie Island 21.10.83, Mawson 9.12.83, Casey 1.1.84 and Davis 2.1.84.

19 Prismatic Compass and   **20** Dog Team pulling Sledge
Lloyd-Creak Dip Circle

(Des R. Fletcher. Litho Leigh-Mardon Ltd, Melbourne)

1984 (16 Jan). *75th Anniv of Magnetic Pole Expedition. T* **19** *and similar horiz design. Multicoloured. P* 14½.

61	30 c. Type **19**	75	40
62	85 c. Aneroid barometer and theodolite	1·75	1·25
	Set of 2	2·50	1·60
	Presentation Pack	2·75	
	First Day Cover		2·00

Issued Macquarie Island 23.10.84, Mawson 15.11.84, Casey 16.11.84 and Davis 1.2.85.

(Des G. Emery. Litho Leigh-Mardon Ltd (2 c., 10 c., 20 c., 36 c., 60 c.) or Cambec Press, Melbourne (others))

1984 (18 July)–**87**. *Antarctic Scenes. T* **20** *and similar multicoloured designs. P* 14½ (2 c., 10 c., 20 c., 36 c., 60 c.), 14×13½ (45 c., 90 c.) or 13½×14 (others).

63	2 c. Summer afternoon, Mawson Station (11.3.87)	10	10
64	5 c. Type **20**	10	10
65	10 c. Late summer evening, MacRobertson Land (11.3.87)	10	10
66	15 c. Prince Charles Mountains (7.8.85)	10	15
67	20 c. Summer morning, Wilkes Land (11.3.87) ...	15	20
68	25 c. Sea-ice and iceberg	20	25

69	30 c. Mount Coates	20	25
70	33 c. "Iceberg Alley", Mawson (7.8.85)	25	30
71	36 c. Early winter evening, Casey Station (11.3.87)	25	30
72	45 c. Brash ice (*vert*) (7.8.85)	35	40
73	60 c. Midwinter shadows, Casey Station (11.3.87)	45	50
74	75 c. Coastline	55	60
75	85 c. Landing strip	65	70
76	90 c. Pancake ice (*vert*) (7.8.85)	70	75
77	$1 Emperor Penguins (7.8.85) (Optd S. 50p) ...	75	80
	Set of 15	4·25	4·75
	Presentation Packs (3)	5·50	

Nos. 64, 68/9 and 74/5 issued Macquarie Island 23.10.84, Mawson 15.11.84, Casey 16.11.84 and Davis 1.2.85.

21 Prince Charles Mountains   **22** Hourglass Dolphins and
near Mawson Station   *Nella Dan*

(Des A. McGregor. Litho Cambec Press, Melbourne)

1986 (17 Sept). *25th Anniv of Antarctic Treaty. P* 14×13½.

78	**21** 36 c. multicoloured	85	35
	First Day Cover		1·00

(Des Trish Hart. Litho CPE Australia Ltd, Melbourne)

1988 (20 July). *Environment, Conservation and Technology. T* **22** *and similar square designs. Multicoloured. Harrison paper. P* 13.

79	37 c. Type **22**	55	60
	a. Horiz strip of 5. Nos. 79/83	2·50	
80	37 c. Emperor Penguins and Davis Station	55	60
81	37 c. Crabeater Seal and helicopter	55	60
82	37 c. Adelie Penguins and tracked vehicle	55	60
83	37 c. Grey-headed Albatross and photographer ..	55	60
	Set of 5	2·50	2·75
	Presentation Pack	2·75	
	First Day Cover		3·00

Nos. 79/83 were printed together, *se-tenant*, in horizontal strips of five throughout the sheet.

23 "Antarctica"

(Des Janet Boschen. Litho CPE Australia Ltd, Melbourne)

1989 (14 June). *Antarctic Landscape Paintings by Sir Sidney Nolan. T* **23** *and similar vert designs. Multicoloured. CPL paper. P* 14×13½.

84	39 c. Type **23**	50	50
85	39 c. "Iceberg Alley"	50	50
86	60 c. "Glacial Flow"	75	75
87	80 c. "Frozen Sea"	1·00	1·00
	Set of 4	2·50	2·50
	Presentation Pack	2·75	
	First Day Cover		2·75
	Souvenir Postcards		3·00

Christmas Island

1958 100 Cents = 1 Malayan Dollar
1968 100 Cents = 1 Australian Dollar

Situated in the Indian Ocean about 600 miles S. of Singapore. Formerly part of the Crown Colony of Singapore, it was transferred to Australian administration on 15 October 1958.

Stamps of the Straits Settlements and later Singapore were used on Christmas Island from 1901 until 1942 and subsequently from 1946 to 1958.

2 Map

3 Moonflower

4 Robber Crab

1 Queen Elizabeth II

5 Island Scene

6 Phosphate Train

All values. Retouch below "AUSTRALIA" resulting in thinner white frame line (Right pane, R. 4/10). (Normal illustrated at top, variety below.)

(Des G. Lissenden. Recess with name and value typo in black. Note Printing Branch, Commonwealth Bank, Melbourne)

7 Raising Phosphate

8 Flying Fish Cove

1958 (15 Oct). *No wmk. P 14½*.

1	1	2 c. yellow-orange	55	15
		Ea. Retouch	3·75	
2		4 c. brown	60	15
		Ea. Retouch	3·50	
3		5 c. deep mauve	60	15
		Ea. Retouch	3·50	
4		6 c. grey-blue	1·50	20
		Ea. Retouch	6·00	
5		8 c. black-brown	2·50	50
		Ea. Retouch	10·00	
6		10 c. violet	2·50	25
		Ea. Retouch	10·00	
7		12 c. carmine	3·00	1·25
		Ea. Retouch	12·00	
8		20 c. blue	3·00	1·50
		Ea. Retouch	12·00	
9		50 c. yellow-green	4·50	1·50
		Ea. Retouch	22·00	
10		$1 deep bluish green	5·00	1·50
		·Ea. Retouch	22·00	
		Set of 10	21·00	6·50

PRINTERS. Nos. 11/32 were printed by the Note Printing Branch. Reserve Bank of Australia, Melbourne. Nos. 33/82 were printed in photogravure by Harrison and Sons, Ltd, London.

9 Loading Cantilever

10 Christmas Island Frigate Bird

11 White-tailed Tropic Bird

(Des G. Lissenden (2, 8 c.), P. Morriss (4, 5, 10, 20 c.), B. Stewart (others) Recess)

1963 (28 Aug). *P 14½ × 14 ($1) or 14½ (others)*.

11	2	2 c. orange	40	15
12	3	4 c. red-brown	50	15
13	4	5 c. purple	50	15
14	5	6 c. indigo	40	15
15	6	8 c. black	1·60	35
16	7	10 c. violet	40	15
17	8	12 c. brown-red	40	20
18	9	20 c. blue	1·00	25
19	10	50 c. green	2·00	30
20	11	$1 yellow	4·75	60
		Set of 10	10·00	2·25

I

II

I Thick lettering

II Thinner lettering

1965. *50th Anniv of Gallipoli Landing. As T **184** of Australia, but slightly larger (22 × 34½ mm) and colour changed. Photo.*
21	10 c.	sepia, black and emerald (I) (14.4.)	30	25
	a.	Black-brown, black and light emerald (II) (24.4.)	1·50	1·25
		First Day Cover		1·25

(New Currency. 100 cents = 1 dollar (Australian))

12 Golden Striped Grouper   13 "Angel" (mosaic)

(Des G. Hamori. Photo)

1968 (6 May)–**70.** *Fishes. T **12** and similar horiz designs. Multicoloured. P 13½.*
22	1 c.	Type **12**	45	15
23	2 c.	Moorish Idol	60	20
24	3 c.	Forceps Fish	60	20
25	4 c.	Queen Triggerfish	60	20
	a.	Deep blue (face value) omitted	£475	
26	5 c.	Regal Angelfish	75	20
27	9 c.	Surgeon Fish	2·00	40
28	10 c.	Scorpion Fish	1·50	20
28a	15 c.	Saddleback Butterfly (fish) (14.12.70)	10·00	7·00
29	20 c.	Clown Butterfly (fish)	4·00	55
29a	30 c.	Ghost Pipefish (14.12.70)	10·00	7·00
30	50 c.	Blue Lined Surgeon	10·00	2·50
31	$1	Meyers Butterfly (fish)	15·00	5·00
		Set of 12	48·00	21·00

(Des G. Hamori. Photo)

1969 (10 Nov). *Christmas. P 13½.*
32	**13**	5 c. red, deep blue and gold	15	10
		First Day Cover		50

MINIMUM PRICE

The minimum price quoted is 10p which represents a handling charge rather than a basis for valuing common stamps. For further notes about prices see introductory pages.

14 "The Ansidei   15 "The Adoration of the
Madonna" (Raphael)   Shepherds" (ascr to the
School of Seville)

(Des Harrison)

1970 (26 Oct). *Christmas. Paintings. T **14** and similar vert design. Multicoloured. P 14 × 14½.*
33	3 c.	Type **14**	15	10
34	5 c.	"The Virgin and Child, St. John the Baptist and an Angel" (Morando)	15	10
		Set of 2	30	20
		First Day Cover		80

(Des Harrison)

1971 (4 Oct). *Christmas. T **15** and similar vert design. Multicoloured. W w **12**. P 14.*
35	6 c.	Type **15**	50	50
36	20 c.	"The Adoration of the Shepherds" (Reni) . .	1·00	1·00
		Set of 2	1·50	1·50
		First Day Cover		2·75

16 H.M.S. *Flying Fish*, 1887   17 Angel of Peace

(Des V. Whiteley)

1972 (7 Feb)–**73.** *Ships. Horiz designs as T **16**. Multicoloured. P 14 × 13½.*
37	1 c.	*Eagle*, 1714 (5.6.72)	20	15
38	2 c.	H.M.S. *Redpole*, 1890 (5.6.72)	25	20
39	3 c.	M.V. *Hoi Houw*, 1959 (5.6.72)	25	20
40	4 c.	*Pigot*, 1771 (6.2.73)	25	20
41	5 c.	S.S. *Valetta*, 1968 (6.2.73)	25	20
42	6 c.	Type **16**	30	25
43	7 c.	*Asia*, 1805	30	25
44	8 c.	T.S.S. *Islander*, 1929–60	35	35
45	9 c.	H.M.S. *Imperieuse**, 1888 (6.2.73)	55	40
46	10 c.	H.M.S. *Egeria*, 1887 (4.6.73)	55	40
47	20 c.	*Thomas*, 1615	85	70
48	25 c.	H.M.S. *Gordon*, 1864 (4.6.73)	1·00	75
49	30 c.	*Cygnet*, 1688 (4.6.73)	1·25	85
50	35 c.	S.S. *Triadic*, 1958 (4.6.73)	1·40	90
51	50 c.	H.M.S. *Amethyst*, 1857 (6.2.73)	2·00	1·75
52	$1	*Royal Mary*, 1643 (5.6.72)	3·00	2·25
		Set of 16	11·00	9·00
		Presentation Pack (sold at $3.75) (2.12.74) .	15·00	
		First Day Covers (4)		12·00

* The design is wrongly inscribed "H.M.S. *Imperious*".

(Des Jennifer Toombs)

1972 (2 Oct). *Christmas. T **17** and similar vert design. Multicoloured. P 14.*
53	3 c.	Type **17**	50	50
	a.	Pair. Nos. 53/4	1·00	1·00

54	3 c.	Angel of Joy	50	50
55	7 c.	Type **17**	65	65
	a.	Pair. Nos. 55/6	1·25	1·25
56	7 c.	As No. 54	65	65
		Set of 4	2·25	2·25
		First Day Cover		3·25

Nos. 53/4 and 55/6 have the two designs printed horizontally se-tenant within the sheet.

18 Virgin and Child, and Map **19** Mary and Holy Child within Christmas Star

(Des P. L. S. Cheong)

1973 (2 Oct). Christmas. P 14 × 13.

57	**18**	7 c.	multicoloured	75	35
58		25 c.	multicoloured	2·75	1·25
			Set of 2	3·50	1·60
			First Day Cover		2·75

(Des Jennifer Toombs)

1974 (2 Oct). Christmas. P 13 × 14½.

59	**19**	7 c.	mauve and grey-black	60	60
60		30 c.	light orange, bright yell & grey-blk	1·75	2·25
			Set of 2	2·25	2·75
			First Day Cover		3·75

20 "The Flight into Egypt" **21** Dove of Peace and Star of Bethlehem

(Des Jennifer Toombs)

1975 (2 Oct). Christmas. P 14 × 13.

61	**20**	10 c.	light greenish yellow, agate and gold	35	25
62		35 c.	bright rose, deep blue and gold	1·25	1·25
			Set of 2	1·60	1·50
			First Day Cover		2·25

(Des R. Bates)

1976 (2 Oct). Christmas. P 13½.

63	**21**	10 c.	cerise, lemon and bright mauve	40	40
	a.		Pair. Nos. 63/4	80	80
64	–	10 c.	cerise, lemon and bright mauve	40	40
65	**21**	35 c.	reddish violet, light greenish blue and light yellow-green	65	65
	a.		Pair. Nos. 65/6	1·25	1·25
66	–	35 c.	reddish violet, light greenish blue and light yellow-green	65	65
			Set of 4	2·00	2·00
			First Day Cover		3·50

Nos. 64 and 66 are "mirror-images" of T **21**, the two designs of each value being printed horizontally se-tenant throughout the sheet.

22 William Dampier (explorer)   **23** Australian Coat of Arms on Map of Christmas Island

(Des V. Whiteley Studio)

1977 (30 Apr)–**78**. Famous Visitors. Horiz designs as T **22** in black, vermilion and greenish yellow (45 c.) or multicoloured (others). P 14 × 13.

67	1 c.	Type **22**	10	10
68	2 c.	Capt. de Vlamingh (explorer) (22.2.78)	15	10
69	3 c.	Vice-Admiral MacLear (22.2.78)	15	10
70	4 c.	Sir John Murray (oceanographer) (22.2.78)	15	10
71	5 c.	Admiral Aldrich (31.5.78)	15	10
72	6 c.	Andrew Clunies-Ross (first settler)	15	10
73	7 c.	J. J. Lister (naturalist) (31.5.78)	20	10
74	8 c.	Admiral of the Fleet Sir William May (1.9.78)	20	15
75	9 c.	Henry Ridley (botanist)	20	15
76	10 c.	George Clunies-Ross (phosphate miner) (1.9.78)	20	15
77	20 c.	Capt. Joshua Slocum (yachtsman) (1.9.78)	40	35
78	45 c.	Charles Andrews (naturalist) (31.5.78)	85	45
79	50 c.	Richard Hanitsch (biologist) (31.5.78)	95	60
80	75 c.	Victor Purcell (scholar) (1.9.78)	85	85
81	$1	Fam Choo Beng (educator)	1·25	1·25
82	$2	Sir Harold Spencer-Jones (astronomer) (22.2.78)	2·50	2·25
		Set of 16	7·50	6·50
		Presentation Pack (sold at $6) (1.9.78)	8·00	
		First Day Covers (4)		10·00

(Des Mrs S. Muir. Litho Harrison)

1977 (2 June). Silver Jubilee. P 14½ × 13½.

83	**23**	45 c.	multicoloured	60	70
			First Day Cover		1·00

24 "A Partridge in a Pear Tree" **25** Abbott's Booby

(Des Jennifer Toombs. Litho Questa)

1977 (20 Oct)–**78**. Christmas. T **24** and similar vert designs depicting the carol "The Twelve Days of Christmas". Multicoloured. P 14.

A. No wmk. B. W w **14** (27.1.78).

			A.		B.	
84	10 c.	Type **24**	15	20	25	20
	a.	Sheetlet. Nos. 84/95	1·60	—	2·75	—
85	10 c.	"Two turtle doves"	15	20	25	20
86	10 c.	"Three French hens"	15	20	25	20
87	10 c.	"Four calling birds"	15	20	25	20
88	10 c.	"Five gold rings"	15	20	25	20
89	10 c.	"Six geese a-laying"	15	20	25	20
90	10 c.	"Seven swans a-swimming"	15	20	25	20
91	10 c.	"Eight maids a-milking"	15	20	25	20
92	10 c.	"Nine ladies dancing"	15	20	25	20
93	10 c.	"Ten lords a-leaping"	15	20	25	20
94	10 c.	"Eleven pipers piping"	15	20	25	20
95	10 c.	"Twelve drummers drumming"	15	20	25	20
		Set of 12	1·60	2·10	2·75	2·10
		First Day Cover				2·75

Nos. 84/95 were printed as a se-tenant block within a sheetlet 142 × 170 mm.

(Des Jennifer Toombs. Litho Questa)

1978 (21 Apr).   *25th Anniv of Coronation. T* **25** *and similar vert designs.*
P 15.
96	45 c.	black and bright ultramarine	60	85
	a.	Sheetlet. Nos. 96/8 × 2	3·25	
97	45 c.	multicoloured	60	85
98	45 c.	black and bright ultramarine	60	85
		Set of 3	1·60	2·25
		First Day Cover		2·40

Designs:—No. 96, White Swan of Bohun; No. 97, Queen Elizabeth II;
No. 98, Type **25.**
Nos. 96/8 were printed together in small sheets of 6, containing two *se-
tenant* strips of 3 with horizontal gutter margin between.

Souvenir Pack 1977

1978 (30 June).   *Comprises Nos. 67, 72, 75, 81, 83 and 84B/95B. Sold*
at $3.
SP98*a*   Souvenir Pack . . . .   10·00

26 "Christ Child"   **27** Chinese Children

(Des Jennifer Toombs. Litho J.W.)

1978 (2 Oct).   *Christmas. Scenes from "The Song of Christmas". T* **26**
and similar horiz designs. Multicoloured. P 14.
99	10 c.	Type **26**	15	15
	a.	Sheetlet. Nos. 99/107	1·25	
100	10 c.	"Herald Angels"	15	15
101	10 c.	"Redeemer"	15	15
102	10 c.	"Israel"	15	15
103	10 c.	"Star"	15	15
104	10 c.	"Three Wise Men"	15	15
105	10 c.	"Manger"	15	15
106	10 c.	"All He Stands For"	15	15
107	10 c.	"Shepherds Came"	15	15
		Set of 9	1·25	1·25
		First Day Cover		1·60

Nos. 99/107 were printed together, *se-tenant*, in a small sheet of 9.

Souvenir Pack 1978

1979 (31 Jan).   *Comprises Nos. 68/71, 73/4, 76/80, 82, 98a and 99/*
107. Sold at $6.75.
SP107*a*   Souvenir Pack . . . .   11·00

(Des Jennifer Toombs. Litho Questa)

1979 (20 Apr).   *International Year of the Child. T* **27** *and similar vert*
designs showing children of different races. Multicoloured, colour of
inscr given. P 14.
108	20 c.	apple-green (Type **27**)	40	40
	a.	Horiz strip of 5. Nos. 108/12	1·75	
109	20 c.	turquoise-green (Malay children)	40	40
110	20 c.	lilac (Indian children)	40	40
111	20 c.	rose (European children)	40	40
112	20 c.	orange-yellow ("Oranges and Lemons") . .	40	40
		Set of 5	1·75	1·75
		First Day Cover		2·25

Nos. 108/12 were printed together, *se-tenant*, in horizontal strips of 5
throughout the sheet, forming a composite design.

28 1958 2 c. Definitive   **29** Wise Men following Star

(Des J.W. Litho Questa)

1979 (27 Aug).   *Death Centenary of Sir Rowland Hill. T* **28** *and similar*
horiz designs showing stamps and Sir Rowland Hill. Multicoloured.
P 13½.
113	20 c.	Type **28**	25	30
	a.	Horiz strip of 5. Nos. 113/17	1·10	
114	20 c.	1963 2 c. Map definitive	25	30
115	20 c.	1965 50th anniversary of Gallipoli Landing		
		10 c. commemorative	25	30
116	20 c.	1968 4 c. Queen Triggerfish definitive	25	30
117	20 c.	1969 5 c. Christmas issue	25	30
		Set of 5	1·10	1·40
		First Day Cover		1·60

Nos. 113/17 were printed together, *se-tenant*, in horizontal strips of 5
throughout the sheet.

(Des L. Curtis. Litho Walsall)

1979 (22 Oct).   *Christmas. T* **29** *and similar horiz design. Multi-*
coloured. P 14 × 14½.
118	20 c.	Type **29**	20	25
119	55 c.	Virgin and Child	45	60
		Set of 2	65	85
		First Day Cover		1·10

30 9th Green   **31** Surveying

(Des R. Granger Barrett. Litho Format)

1980 (12 Feb).   *25th Anniv of Christmas Island Golf Club. T* **30** *and similar*
horiz design. Multicoloured. P 14½ × 14.
120	20 c.	Type **30**	50	30
121	55 c.	Clubhouse	80	65
		Set of 2	1·25	95
		First Day Cover		1·25

(Des L. Curtis. Litho Walsall)

1980 (6 May).   *Phosphate Industry* (1st issue). *T* **31** *and similar horiz*
designs. Multicoloured. P 14.
122	15 c.	Type **31**	15	15
123	22 c.	Drilling for samples	20	20
124	40 c.	Sample analysis	30	30
125	55 c.	Mine planning	40	40
		Set of 4	95	95
		First Day Cover		1·40

See also Nos. 126/9, 136/9 and 140/3.

(Des L. Curtis. Litho Walsall)

1980 (14 July).   *Phosphate Industry* (2nd issue). *Horiz designs as*
T **31.** *Multicoloured. P* 14.
126	15 c.	Jungle clearing	15	15
127	22 c.	Overburden removal	20	20
128	40 c.	Open cut mining	30	25
129	55 c.	Restoration	35	30
		Set of 4	90	80
		First Day Cover		1·25

32 Angel with Harp   **33** Skink (*Cryptoblepharus egeriae*)

(Des Jennifer Toombs. Litho Walsall)

1980 (6 Oct). *Christmas. T* **32** *and similar vert designs. Multicoloured.
P* 13½ × 13.

130	15 c.	Type **32**	15	15
	a.	Sheetlet. Nos. 130/5	1·40	
131	15 c.	Angel with wounded soldier	15	15
132	22 c.	Virgin and Child	20	20
133	22 c.	Kneeling couple	20	20
134	60 c.	Angel with harp (*different*)	45	45
135	60 c.	Angel with children	45	45
		Set of 6	1·40	1·40
		Presentation Pack	3·50	
		First Day Cover		1·90

Nos. 130/5 were printed together in small sheets of 6, containing two
se-tenant strips of 3 (Nos. 130, 132, 134 and 131, 133, 135) with horizontal
gutter margin between.

Souvenir Pack 1980

1981 (12 Jan). *Contains Nos.* 120/35. *Sold at* $5.75.

SP135*a*   Souvenir Pack ....   5·75

(Des L. Curtis. Litho Walsall)

1981 (9 Feb). *Phosphate Industry* (3rd *issue*). *Horiz designs as T* **31**.
Multicoloured. P 14.

136	22 c.	Screening and stockpiling	20	20
137	28 c.	Train loading	25	25
138	40 c.	Railing	40	40
139	60 c.	Drying	55	55
		Set of 4	1·25	1·25
		First Day Cover		1·25

(Des L. Curtis. Litho Walsall)

1981 (4 May). *Phosphate Industry* (4th *issue*). *Horiz designs as T* **31**.
Multicoloured. P 14.

140	22 c.	Crushing	25	20
141	28 c.	Conveying	35	25
142	40 c.	Bulk storage	50	40
143	60 c.	Ship loading	70	55
		Set of 4	1·60	1·25
		Presentation Pack (Nos. 122/9, 136/43)	7·00	
		(sold at $6.25)		
		First Day Cover		1·75

(Des L. Curtis. Litho Walsall)

1981 (10 Aug). *Reptiles. T* **33** *and similar horiz designs. Multicoloured.
P* 13.

144	24 c.	Type **33**	25	25
145	30 c.	Skink (*Emoia nativitata*)	30	30
146	40 c.	Gecko (*Lepidodactylus listeri*)	45	45
147	60 c.	Gecko (*Cyrtodactylus sp. nov.*)	65	65
		Set of 4	1·50	1·50
		First Day Cover		1·75

34 Scene from Carol
"Away in a Manger"

35 Eastern Reef Heron

(Des Jennifer Toombs. Litho Questa)

1981 (19 Oct). *Christmas. T* **34** *and similar horiz designs showing scenes
from carol* "Away in a Manger". *P* 14½ × 14.

148	18 c.	silver, deep blue and turquoise-blue	40	40
	a.	Sheetlet. Nos. 148/51	1·75	
149	24 c.	multicoloured	45	45
150	40 c.	multicoloured	50	50
151	60 c.	multicoloured	60	60
		Set of 4	1·75	1·75
		Presentation Pack	2·50	
		First Day Cover		2·00

Nos. 148/51 were printed together, *se-tenant*, in sheetlets of 4.

Souvenir Pack 1981

1982 (2 Feb). *Contains Nos.* 136/51. *Sold at* $6.50.

SP151*a*   Souvenir Pack ....   7·00

(Des N. Arlott. Litho Questa)

1982 (8 Mar)–**83**. *Birds. Multicoloured designs as T* **35**. *P* 14.

152	1 c.	Type **35**	15	10
153	2 c.	Common Noddy	20	10
154	3 c.	White-bellied Swiftlet (14.6.82)	20	20
155	4 c.	Christmas Island Imperial Pigeon (14.6.82)	20	20
156	5 c.	Christmas Island White Eye (21.2.83)	20	15
157	10 c.	Island Thrush (14.6.82)	20	20
158	25 c.	Red-tailed Tropic Bird	45	25
159	30 c.	Emerald Dove (21.2.83)	45	30
160	40 c.	Brown Booby (23.8.82)	60	35
161	50 c.	Red-footed Booby (23.8.82)	55	45
162	65 c.	Christmas Island Frigate Bird (23.8.82) ...	55	55
163	75 c.	White-tailed Tropic Bird (23.8.82)	65	65
164	80 c.	Australian Kestrel (*vert*) (21.2.83)	80	65
165	$1	Indonesian Hawk Owl (*vert*) (21.2.83)	1·00	90
166	$2	Australian Goshawk (*vert*) (14.6.82)	1·50	2·75
167	$4	Abbott's Booby (*vert*)	3·00	3·25
		Set of 16	9·50	10·00
		Presentation Pack (21.2.83) .... ,	11·00	
		First Day Covers (4)		15·00

36 Joseph   **37** "Mirror" Dinghy
                              and Club House

(Des Jennifer Toombs. Litho and embossed Walsall)

1982 (18 Oct). *Christmas. Origami Paper Sculptures. T* **36** *and similar
vert designs. Multicoloured. P* 14½ × 14.

168	27 c.	Type **36**	30	30
	a.	Horiz strip of 3. Nos. 168/70	1·25	
169	50 c.	Angel	45	45
170	75 c.	Mary and baby Jesus	65	65
		Set of 3	1·25	1·25
		Presentation Pack	2·00	
		First Day Cover		1·50

Nos. 168/70 were printed together, *se-tenant*, in horiz strips of 3
throughout the sheet.

Souvenir Pack 1982

1983 (7 Feb). *Contains Nos.* 152/5, 157/8, 160/3 *and* 166/70. *Sold at*
$10.90.

SP170*a*   Souvenir Pack ....   10·00

(Des L. McCombie. Litho Format)

1983 (2 May). *25th Anniv of Christmas Island Boat Club. T* **37** *and similar
multicoloured designs. P* 14 × 14½ (27, 35 c.) *or* 14½ × 14 (*others*).

171	27 c.	Type **37**	35	35
172	35 c.	Ocean-going yachts	40	40
173	50 c.	Fishing launch and cargo ship (*horiz*)	50	50
174	75 c.	Dinghy-racing and cantilever (*horiz*)	70	70
		Set of 4	1·75	1·75
		First Day Cover		2·25

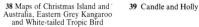

38 Maps of Christmas Island and
Australia, Eastern Grey Kangaroo
and White-tailed Tropic Bird

39 Candle and Holly

(Des A. Theobald. Litho Questa)

1983 (1 Oct). *25th Anniv of Christmas Island as an Australian Territory. T* **38** *and similar horiz designs. Multicoloured. P* 14.

175	24 c.	Type **38**	20	20
176	30 c.	Christmas Island and Australian flag	25	25
177	85 c.	Maps of Christmas Island and Australia, with Boeing "727"	70	70
		Set of 3	1·10	1·10
		First Day Cover		1·40

(Des J.W. Litho Walsall)

1983 (31 Oct). *Christmas. Candles. T* **39** *and similar vert designs. Multicoloured. P* 13.

178	24 c.	Type **39**	20	20
179	30 c.	Six gold candles	25	25
180	85 c.	Candles	70	70
		Set of 3	1·10	1·10
		Presentation Pack	1·60	
		First Day Cover		1·40

40 Feeding on Leaf   **41** *Leucocoprinus fragilissimus*

(Des L. Curtis. Litho Questa)

1984 (20 Feb). *Red Land Crab. T* **40** *and similar horiz designs showing various aspects of crab's life. Multicoloured. P* 14 × 14½.

181	30 c.	Type **40**	30	30
182	40 c.	Migration	40	40
183	55 c.	Development stages	50	50
184	85 c.	Adult female and young	70	70
		Set of 4	1·75	1·75
		First Day Cover		2·25

Souvenir Pack 1983

1984 (20 Feb). *Contains Nos.* 156, 159, 164/5 *and* 171/80. *Sold at* $7.40.

SP184*a* Souvenir Pack . . . . 9·00

(Des I. Loe. Litho Format)

1984 (30 Apr). *Fungi. T* **41** *and similar vert designs. Multicoloured. P* 14 × 14½.

185	30 c.	Type **41**	45	30
186	40 c.	*Microporus xanthopus*	55	40
187	45 c.	*Trogia anthidepas*	65	45
188	55 c.	*Haddowia longipes*	75	60
189	85 c.	*Phillipsia domingensis*	90	75
		Set of 5	3·00	2·25
		First Day Cover		2·75

42 Run-out   **43** Arrival of Father Christmas

(Des A. Theobald. Litho J.W.)

1984 (23 July). *25th Anniv of Cricket on Christmas Island. T* **42** *and similar horiz designs. Multicoloured. P* 14.

190	30 c.	Type **42**	60	35
191	40 c.	Bowled-out	70	45
192	55 c.	Batsman in action	90	65
193	85 c.	Fielder diving for catch	1·10	1·00
		Set of 4	3·00	2·25
		First Day Cover		2·75

(Des D. Slater. Litho B.D.T.)

1984 (21 Sept). *Christmas and "Auspix" International Stamp Exhibition, Melbourne. Sheet* 100 × 100 *mm containing T* **43** *and similar horiz designs. Multicoloured. P* 13½.

MS194   30 c. Type **43**; 55 c. Distribution of presents;

	85 c.	Departure of Father Christmas	2·00	2·25
		Presentation Pack	2·50	
		First Day Cover		2·50

No. **MS**194 also contains three labels horizontally *se-tenant* with the stamps and forming composite designs with them.

Souvenir Pack 1984.

1984 (1 Nov). *Contains Nos.* 181/94. *Sold at* $9.

SP194*a* Souvenir Pack . . . . 11·00

44 Robber Crab   **45** "Once in Royal David's City"

(Des L. Curtis. Litho Walsall)

1985 (30 Jan). *Crabs (1st series). T* **44** *and similar horiz designs. Multicoloured. P* 13 × 13½.

195	30 c.	Type **44**	55	40
196	40 c.	Horn-eyed Ghost Crab	65	50
197	55 c.	Purple Hermit Crab	80	65
198	85 c.	Little Nipper	1·10	1·00
		Set of 4	2·75	2·25
		First Day Cover		2·50

See also Nos. 199/202 and 203/6.

(Des L. Curtis. Litho Walsall)

1985 (29 Apr). *Crabs (2nd series). Horiz designs as T* **44**. *Multicoloured. P* 13 × 13½.

199	33 c.	Blue Crab	60	40
200	45 c.	Tawny Hermit Crab	70	50
201	60 c.	Red Nipper	85	65
202	90 c.	Smooth-handed Ghost Crab	1·25	95
		Set of 4	3·00	2·25
		First Day Cover		2·50

(Des L. Curtis. Litho Walsall)

1985 (22 July). *Crabs (3rd series). Horiz designs as T* **44**. *Multicoloured. P* 13 × 13½.

203	33 c.	Red Crab	60	55
204	45 c.	Mottled Crab	70	65
205	60 c.	Rock Hopper Crab	90	85
206	90 c.	Yellow Nipper	1·25	1·50
		Set of 4	3·00	3·25
		Presentation Pack (Nos. 195/206)	9·50	
		First Day Cover		3·50

(Des Jennifer Toombs. Litho Harrison)

1985 (28 Oct). *Christmas. Carols. T* **45** *and similar vert designs. Multicoloured. P* 14 × 14½.

207	27 c.	Type **45**	45	45
		a. Horiz strip of 5. Nos. 207/11	3·00	
208	33 c.	"While Shepherds Watched Their Flocks by Night"	55	55

209	45 c. "Away in a Manger"		65	65
210	60 c. "We Three Kings of Orient Are"		75	75
211	90 c. "Hark the Herald Angels Sing"		1·00	1·00
	Set of 5		3·00	3·00
	Presentation Pack		3·25	
	First Day Cover			3·25

Nos. 207/11 were printed together, *se-tenant* in horizontal strips of 5 throughout the sheet.

Souvenir Pack 1985

1985 (2 Dec). *Contains Nos. 195/211. Sold at $10.*
SP211*a* Souvenir Pack .... 11·00

46 Halley's Comet over   **47** Ridley's Orchid
Christmas Island

(Des L. Curtis. Litho Format)

1986 (30 Apr). *Appearance of Halley's Comet. T* **46** *and similar horiz designs. Multicoloured. P* 14.

212	33 c. Type **46**		55	55
213	45 c. Edmond Halley		70	70
214	60 c. Comet and ship loading phosphate		85	85
215	90 c. Comet over Flying Fish Cove		1·25	1·25
	Set of 4		3·00	3·00
	First Day Cover			3·25

(Des I. Loe. Litho Format)

1986 (30 June). *Native Flowers. T* **47** *and similar vert designs. Multicoloured. P* 14.

216	33 c. Type **47**		50	50
217	45 c. Hanging Flower		65	65
218	60 c. Hoya		75	75
219	90 c. Sea Hibiscus		1·10	1·10
	Set of 4		2·75	2·75
	First Day Cover			3·25

47*a* Prince Andrew and   **48** Father Christmas and
Miss Sarah Ferguson   Reindeer in Speed Boat

(Des D. Miller. Litho Walsall)

1986 (23 July). *Royal Wedding. T* **47***a and similar square design. Multicoloured. P* 14½ × 14.

220	33 c. Type **47***a*		45	35
221	90 c. Prince Andrew piloting helicopter, Digby, Canada, 1985		95	1·10
	Set of 2		1·25	1·40
	First Day Cover			1·75

(Des G. Vasarhelyi. Litho Walsall)

1986 (30 Sept). *Christmas. T* **48** *and similar horiz designs. Multicoloured. P* 13 × 13½.

222	30 c. Type **48**		40	40
223	36 c. Father Christmas and reindeer on beach		50	50
224	55 c. Father Christmas fishing		70	70
225	70 c. Playing golf		90	90
226	$1 Sleeping in hammock		1·10	1·10
	Set of 5		3·25	3·25
	Presentation Pack		3·75	
	First Day Cover			3·75

Souvenir Pack 1986

1986 (1 Dec). *Contains Nos. 212/26. Sold at $9.*
SP226*a* Souvenir Pack .... 10·00

49 H.M.S. *Flying Fish* and
Outline Map of Christmas Island

(Des L. Curtis. Litho Format)

1987 (21 Jan). *Centenary of Visits by H.M.S. "Flying Fish" and H.M.S. "Egeria". T* **49** *and similar horiz design. Multicoloured. P* 14½.

227	36 c. Type **49**		55	55
228	90 c. H.M.S. *Egeria* and outline map		1·40	1·40
	Set of 2		1·90	1·90
	First Day Cover			2·40

50 Blind Snake   **51** Children watching Father
Christmas in Sleigh

(Des G. Drummond. Litho Questa)

1987 (25 Mar)–**89**. *Wildlife. T* **50** *and similar horiz designs. Multicoloured. P* 14.

229	1 c. Type **50**		10	10
	a. Sheetlet. Nos. 229/44 (1.3.88)		12·00	
230	2 c. Blue-tailed Skink		10	10
231	3 c. Insectivorous Bat (24.6.87)		10	10
232	5 c. Green Cricket (1.3.88)		10	10
233	10 c. Christmas Island Fruit Bat (24.6.87)		10	10
234	25 c. Gecko		20	25
235	30 c. Praying Mantis (1.3.88)		30	30
236	36 c. Indonesian Hawk Owl (24.6.87)		50	50
237	40 c. Bull Mouth Helmet Shell (26.8.87)		45	45
237*a*	41 c. Nudibranch (*Phidiana* sp.) (1.9.89)		45	45
238	50 c. Textile Cone Shell (26.8.87)		45	50
239	65 c. Brittle Stars (26.8.87)		60	70
240	75 c. Royal Angelfish (26.8.87)		65	75
241	90 c. Christmas Island White (butterfly) (1.3.88)		1·00	1·00
242	$1 Mimic (butterfly) (1.3.88)		1·25	1·25
243	$2 Shrew (*Crocidura attenuata trichura*) (24.6.87)		1·75	2·00
244	$5 Green Turtle		4·50	5·00
	Set of 17		11·50	12·00
	Presentation Pack (No. 229a) (11.3.88)		15·00	
	First Day Covers (5)			17·00

No. 229*a* was originally only available from the presentation pack, but was, subsequently, sold separately by the Christmas Island Post Office. Stamps taken from it show "1988" imprint date. Examples from the ordinary sheets are without imprint date.

(Des D. Miller. Litho CPE Australia Ltd. Melbourne)

1987 (7 Oct). *Christmas. Sheet, 165 × 65 mm, containing T* **51** *and similar multicoloured designs. P* 13½.
MS245   30 c. Type **51**; 37 c. Father Christmas distributing gifts (48 × 22 mm); 90 c. Children with presents (48 × 22 mm); $1 Singing carols .... 2·50   2·75
        First Day Cover ....   3·50
The stamps within No. MS245 form a composite design of a beach scene.

Souvenir Pack 1987

1987 (25 Nov). *Contains Nos. 227/31, 233/4, 236/40 and 243/5. Sold at $14.20.*
SP245*a*   Souvenir Pack .... 15·00

(Des Sue Passmore. Litho CPE Australia Ltd, Melbourne)

1988 (26 Jan). *Bicentenary of Australian Settlement. Arrival of First Fleet. Square designs as Nos.* 1105/9 *of Australia, but each inscribed* "CHRIST-MAS ISLAND Indian Ocean" *and* "AUSTRALIA BICENTENARY".

246	37 c. Aborigines watching arrival of Fleet, Botany Bay	60	60
	a. Horiz strip of 5. Nos. 246/50	2·75	
247	37 c. Aboriginal family and anchored ships	60	60
248	37 c. Fleet arriving at Sydney Cove	60	60
249	37 c. Ship's boat	60	60
250	37 c. Raising the flag, Sydney Cove, 26 January 1788	60	60
	Set of 5	2·75	2·75
	First Day Cover		3·00

Nos. 246/50 were printed together, *se-tenant*, in horizontal strips of five throughout the sheet, forming a composite design.

52 Captain William May   53 Pony and Trap, 1910

(Des Josephine Martin. Litho Questa)

1988 (8 June). *Centenary of British Annexation. T* **52** *and similar vert designs. Multicoloured. P* 14½ × 14.

251	37 c. Type **52**	35	40
252	53 c. Annexation ceremony	50	55
253	95 c. H.M.S. *Imperieuse* firing salute	90	95
254	$1.50, Building commemorative cairn	1·40	1·50
	Set of 4	2·75	3·00
	First Day Cover		3·75

(Des L. Curtis. Litho Walsall)

1988 (24 Aug). *Centenary of Permanent Settlement. T* **53** *and similar horiz designs. Multicoloured. P* 14 × 14½.

255	37 c. Type **53**	45	40
256	55 c. Phosphate mining, 1910	60	55
257	70 c. Steam locomotive, 1914	85	70
258	$1 Arrival of first aircraft, 1957	1·25	1·00
	Set of 4	2·75	2·40
	First Day Cover		3·00

54 Beach Toys   55 Food on Table ("Good Harvesting")

(Des N. Shewring. Litho Format)

1988 (15 Nov). *Christmas. Toys and Gifts. T* **54** *and similar vert designs. Multicoloured. P* 14.

259	32 c. Type **54**	40	35
260	39 c. Flippers, snorkel and mask	50	40
261	90 c. Model soldier, doll and soft toys	1·10	90
262	$1 Models of racing car, lorry and jet aircraft . .	1·25	1·00
	Set of 4	3·00	2·40
	First Day Cover		2·75

Souvenir Pack 1988

1988 (30 Nov). *Contains Nos. 232, 235, 241/2 and 246/62. Sold at $13.*
SP262*a*   Souvenir Pack . . . . 15·00

(Des D. Miller. Litho Questa)

1989 (31 Jan). *Chinese New Year. T* **55** *and similar horiz designs. Multicoloured. P* 14 × 14½.

263	39 c. Type **55**	45	40
264	70 c. Decorations ("Prosperity")	80	70
265	90 c. Chinese girls ("Good Fortune")	1·10	90
266	$1 Lion dance ("Progress Every Year")	1·25	1·00
	Set of 4	3·25	2·75
	First Day Cover		3·25

56 Sir John Murray   57 Four Children

(Des S. Noon. Litho Walsall)

1989 (16 Mar). *75th Death Anniv of Sir John Murray* (oceanographer). *T* **56** *and similar horiz designs. Multicoloured. P* 14 × 14½.

267	39 c. Type **56**	50	50
268	80 c. Map of Christmas Island showing Murray Hill	95	95
269	$1 Oceanographic equipment	1·25	1·25
270	$1.10, H.M.S. *Challenger* (survey ship)	1·50	1·50
	Set of 4	3·75	3·75
	First Day Cover		4·25

(Des C. Burke. Litho Questa)

1989 (31 May). *Malay Hari Raya Festival. T* **57** *and similar vert designs. Multicoloured. P* 14.

271	39 c. Type **57**	50	50
272	55 c. Man playing tambourine	70	70
273	80 c. Girl in festival costume	1·00	1·00
274	$1.10, Christmas Island Mosque	1·40	1·40
	Set of 4	3·25	3·25
	First Day Cover		3·50

58 *Haperzia phlegmaria*   59 Virgin Mary and Star

(Des Kerrie Rockett. Litho Walsall)

1989 (16 Aug). *Ferns. T* **58** *and similar vert designs. Multicoloured. P* 14.

275	41 c. Type **58**	60	60
276	65 c. *Asplenium polydon*	85	85
277	80 c. Common Bracken	1·00	1·00
278	* $1.10, Birds-nest Fern	1·40	1·40
	Set of 4	3·50	3·50
	First Day Cover		4·00

(Des G. Maynard. Litho Leigh-Mardon Ltd, Melbourne)

1989 (4 Oct). *Christmas. T* **59** *and similar vert designs. Multicoloured. P* 14½.

279	36 c. Type **59**	35	40
280	41 c. Christ Child in manger	40	45

281	80 c. Shepherds and Star	75	80
282	$1.10, Three Wise Men following Star	1·00	1·10
	Set of 4	2·25	2·50
	First Day Cover		2·75

(60)   61 First
                        Sighting, 1615

1989 (18 Oct).   "Melbourne Stampshow '89". No. 237a and as No. 242, but with imprint date, optd with T **60**.

283	41 c. Nudibranch (Phidiana sp.)	40	45
284	$1 Mimic (Butterfly)	95	1·00
	Set of 2	1·40	1·50
	First Day Cover		1·75

Souvenir Pack 1989

1989 (1 Dec). Contains Nos. 237a and 263/84. Sold at $19.50.

SP284a	Souvenir Pack	19·00

(Des R. Honisett. Litho Note Ptg Branch, Reserve Bank of Australia)

1990 (31 Jan).   375th Anniv of Discovery of Christmas Island. T **61** and similar vert design. Multicoloured. P 14×15.

285	41 c. Type **61**	50	50
286	$1.10, Second sighting and naming, 1643	1·40	1·40
	Set of 2	1·90	1·90
	First Day Cover		2·25

62 Miniature Tractor pulling Phosphate   63 Male Abbott's Booby

(Des C. Lee. Litho Leigh-Mardon Ltd, Melbourne)

1990 (18 Apr–22 Aug). Christmas Island Transport. T **62** and similar multicoloured designs. P 13½ × 14 (horiz, or 14 × 13½ (vert).

287	1 c. Type **62**	10	10
288	2 c. Phosphate train (22 Aug)	10	10
289	3 c. Diesel railcar (vert)	10	10
290	5 c. Loading Road train (22 Aug)	10	10
291	10 c. Trishaw (vert)	10	10
292	15 c. Terex truck (22 Aug)	10	15
293	25 c. Articulated bus	20	25
294	30 c. Railway passenger rake (vert)	20	25
295	40 c. Passenger barge (vert)	30	35
296	50 c. Kolek (outrigger canoe)	40	45

297	65 c. Flying Doctor aircraft and ambulance (22 Aug)	50	55
298	75 c. Commercial van (22 Aug)	55	60
299	90 c. Vintage lorry (22 Aug)	70	75
300	$1 Water tanker (22 Aug)	75	80
301	$2 Traction engine (22 Aug)	1·50	1·60
302	$5 Steam locomotive and flat car	3·75	4·00
	Set of 16	8·25	9·00
	Presentation Pack	10·50	
	First Day Covers (4)		12·00

(Des N. Shewring. Litho Questa)

1990 (6 June). Abbott's Booby. T **63** and similar vert designs. Multicoloured. P 13½ × 14.

303	10 c. Type **63**	15	15
304	20 c. Juvenile male	25	25
305	29 c. Female with egg	35	35
306	41 c. Pair with chick	50	50
	Set of 4	1·10	1·10
	First Day Cover		1·50
MS307	122 × 68 mm. 41 c. Male with wings spread; 41 c. Male on branch; 41 c. Female with fledgling. P 14½	1·40	1·60
	First Day Cover		1·90

The three stamps within No. MS307 form a composite design and are without the W.W.F. logo.

Examples of No. MS307 overprinted on the selvedge with "NZ 1990 WORLD STAMP EXHIBITION AUCKLAND, NEW ZEALAND, 24 AUGUST–2 SEPTEMBER 1990" were only available from the stand at this International Philatelic Exhibition and by post from the Australian and Christmas Island Philatelic Bureaux.

64 1977 Famous Visitors 9 c. Stamp

(Des Elizabeth Innes. Litho Leigh-Mardon Ltd, Melbourne)

1990 (11 July). Centenary of Henry Ridley's Visit. T **64** and similar multicoloured design. P 15 × 14½ (41 c.) or 14½ × 15 (75 c.).

308	41 c. Type **64**	35	40
309	75 c. Ridley (botanist) in rainforest (vert)	65	70
	Set of 2	1·00	1·10
	First Day Cover		1·40

65 Corymborkus veratrifolia

(Litho Leigh-Mardon Ltd, Melbourne)

1990 (3 Oct). Christmas. Flowers. T **65** and similar horiz designs. Multicoloured. P 14½.

310	38 c. Type **65**	35	40
311	43 c. Hoya aldrichii	35	40
312	80 c. Quisqualis indica	70	75
313	$1.20, Barringtonia racemosa	1·00	1·10
	Set of 4	2·10	2·40
	First Day Cover		2·75

ALBUM LISTS

Please write for our latest lists of albums and accessories. These will be sent free on request.

Cocos (Keeling) Islands

1963   12 Pence   = 1 Shilling
        20 Shillings = 1 Australian Pound
1969   100 Cents = 1 Australian Dollar

Situated in the Indian Ocean, formerly incorporated with Singapore and transferred to Australian administration on 23 November 1955. Used Australian stamps until 1963 and again from 14 February 1966, with the introduction of decimal currency, until the appearance of the new definitives on 9 July 1969.

The stamps of the Straits Settlements were used by a postal agency operating on Cocos (Keeling) Islands from 1 April 1933 until 1 March 1937. The postal agency reopened on 2 September 1952 and used the stamps of Singapore until the islands were transferred to Australia in 1955. From 1955 until 1963 stamps of Australia were in use.

PRINTERS. All the following stamps to No. 31 were printed by the Note Printing Branch, Reserve Bank of Australia, Melbourne.

PRICES
Elizabeth II issues (from 1953)

First column = Unmounted Mint
Second column = Used

I

II

I   Thick lettering

II   Thinner lettering

1965. 50*th Anniv of Gallipoli Landing. As T* **184** *of Australia, but slightly larger* (22 × 34½ *mm) and colour changed. Photo.*

7	5d.	sepia, black and emerald (I) (14.4)	60	45
		a. Black-brown, black and light emerald (II) (24.4.)	2·00	1·25
		First Day Cover		1·60

With the introduction of decimal currency on 14 February 1966, Australian stamps were used in Cocos Islands, until the appearance of the new definitives on 9 July 1969.

1 Copra Industry

2 "Super Constellation"

3 Map of Islands

4 Palms

7 Reef Clam   **8** Great Frigate Bird

(Des L. Annois (1 c. to 6 c); P. Jones (10 c. to $1). Photo)

1969 (9 July). *Decimal Currency. T* **8** *or designs as T* **7**. *Multicoloured. P* 13½.

8	1 c.	Turban shell (*vert*)	30	20
9	2 c.	Burrowing clam (*vert*)	1·00	45
10	3 c.	Type **7**	30	15
11	4 c.	Blenny (fish)	30	15
		a. Salmon-pink omitted	£650	
12	5 c.	Coral	35	15
13	6 c.	Flying Fish	75	20
14	10 c.	Banded Rail	1·50	50
15	15 c.	Java Sparrow	1·00	20
16	20 c.	Red-tailed Tropic Bird	1·00	20
17	30 c.	Sooty Tern	1·25	25
18	50 c.	Eastern Reef Heron (*vert*)	2·00	30
19	$1	Type **8**	3·50	1·00
		Set of 12	12·00	3·25
		Presentation Pack (*English inscr*) (*plastic envelope*) (14.9.70)	15·00	
		Presentation Pack (Japanese inscr)	20·00	
		Presentation Pack (*English inscr*) (*paper envelope*) (1973)	15·00	

5 Jukong (sailboat)

6 White Tern

1963 (11 June). *Recess. P* 14½ × 14 (*5d., 2s. 3d.*) *or* 14½ (*others*).

1	**1**	3d. chocolate	1·75	1·25
2	**2**	5d. ultramarine	1·50	65
3	**3**	8d. scarlet	4·50	1·75
4	**4**	1s. green	3·00	55
5	**5**	2s. deep purple	9·00	3·00
6	**6**	2s. 3d. deep green	35·00	3·25
		Set of 6	48·00	9·50

9 *Dragon,* 1609   10 Map of Cocos (Keeling)
                                    Islands, Union Flag,
                                    Stars and Trees

(Des R. Honisett. Photo)

1976 (29 Mar).   *Ships. Multicoloured designs as T* **9**. *P* 13½.
20	1 c.	Type **9**	25	20
21	2 c.	H.M.S. *Juno,* 1857	20	20
22	5 c.	H.M.S. *Beagle,* 1836	30	20
23	10 c.	H.M.A.S. *Sydney,* 1914	35	25
24	15 c.	S.M.S. *Emden,* 1914	80	40
25	20 c.	*Ayesha,* 1907	85	50
26	25 c.	T.S.S. *Islander,* 1927	90	75
27	30 c.	M.V. *Cheshire,* 1951	1·00	75
28	35 c.	*Jukong* (sailboat)	1·00	80
29	40 c.	C.S. *Scotia,* 1900	1·00	80
30	50 c.	R.M.S. *Orontes,* 1929	1·40	90
31	$1	Royal Yacht *Gothic,* 1954	1·75	1·40
		Set of 12	8·75	6·50
		Presentation Pack	10·00	
		First Day Cover		9·00

The 2 c. to 20 c., 35 c. and 40 c. are horizontal designs.

(Des Marg Towt. Litho Asher and Co, Melbourne)

1979 (3 Sept).   *Inauguration of Independent Postal Service* (20 *c.*) *and Establishment of First Statutory Council* (50 *c.*). *T* **10** *and similar horiz design. Multicoloured. P* 15½ × 15.
32	20 c.	Type **10**	25	30
33	50 c.	Council seal and jukong (sailboat)	35	50
		Set of 2	60	80
		First Day Cover		1·00

11 Bright Yellow Long-nosed   12 "Peace on Earth"
      Butterfly Fish

(Des Marg Towt. Litho Asher and Co, Melbourne)

1979 (3 Sept)–**80**.   *Fishes. Horiz designs as T* **11**. *Multicoloured. P* 13½ × 13 (22 *c.*, 28 *c.*, 60 *c.*) *or* 15½ × 15 (*others*).
34	1 c.	Type **11**	10	25
35	2 c.	Clown Butterfly Fish (19.11.79)	20	15
36	5 c.	*Anthias sp.*	20	35
37	10 c.	Meyer's Butterfly Fish (18.2.80)	25	25
38	15 c.	Wrasse (19.11.79)	30	25
39	20 c.	Charles' Clown Fish (19.11.79)	45	30
39a	22 c.	Yellow-striped Emerald Triggerfish (1.7.80)	30	30
40	25 c.	*Cheilinus fasciatus* (18.2.80)	45	35
40a	28 c.	*Macropharyngodon meleagris* (1.7.80)	35	35
41	30 c.	*Chaetodon madagascariensis* (19.11.79)	65	45
42	35 c.	Angel Fish	45	70
43	40 c.	Hogfish (19.11.79)	70	60
44	50 c.	Wrasse (*different*) (19.11.79)	85	75
45	55 c.	*Anampses meleagrides* (18.2.80)	75	75
45a	60 c.	Grouper (1.7.80)	75	75
46	$1	Surgeon Fish	1·25	2·00
47	$2	Three-banded Butterfly Fish (18.2.80)	2·00	2·50
		Set of 17	9·00	9·50
		Presentation Pack (1.6.82)	11·00	
		First Day Covers (4)		14·00

(Des D. Pitt. Litho Asher & Co, Melbourne)

1979 (22 Oct).   *Christmas. T* **12** *and similar multicoloured design. P* 15 × 15½ (25 *c.*) *or* 15½ × 15 (55 *c.*).
48	25 c.	Type **12**	25	35
49	55 c.	"Goodwill Toward Men" (*horiz*)	40	55
		Set of 2	65	90
		First Day Cover		1·25

Souvenir Pack 1979

1980 (3 June).   *Comprises Nos. 32/3 and 48/9. Sold at* $1.80.
SP49*a*   Souvenir Pack .... 2·00

13 Star, Map of Cocos (Keeling)   14 "Administered by the
Islands and Island Landscape   British Government, 1857"

(Des P. Arnold. Litho Asher and Co, Melbourne)

1980 (22 Oct).   *Christmas. T* **13** *and similar horiz designs. Multicoloured. P* 13.
50	15 c.	Type **13**	10	10
51	28 c.	Map and Wise Men following star	15	15
52	60 c.	Map and Nativity scene	40	40
		Set of 3	60	60
		First Day Cover		95

(Des Sue Wilson. Litho Asher and Co, Melbourne)

1980 (24 Nov).   *25th Anniv of Cocos (Keeling) Islands as an Australian Territory. T* **14** *and similar horiz designs. Multicoloured. P* 13½ × 13.
53	22 c.	Type **14**	15	15
		a. Horiz strip of 5. Nos. 53/7	70	
54	22 c.	"Administered by the Government of Ceylon, 1878, 1942–6"	15	15
55	22 c.	"Administered by the Straits Settlements, 1886"	15	15
56	22 c.	"Administered by the Colony of Singapore, 1946"	15	15
57	22 c.	"Administered by the Australian Government, 1955"	15	15
		Set of 5	70	70
		Presentation Pack	1·10	
		First Day Cover		1·25

Nos. 53/7 were printed together, *se-tenant*, in horizontal strips of 5 throughout the sheet, forming a composite design.

15 *Eye of the Wind*   16 Aerial View of Animal
and Map of Cocos   Quarantine Station
(Keeling) Islands

(Des Sue Wilson. Litho Asher and Co, Melbourne)

1980 (18 Dec).   *"Operation Drake" (round the world expedition) and 400th Anniv of Sir Francis Drake's Circumnavigation of the World. T* **15** *and similar multicoloured designs. P* 13.
58	22 c.	Type **15**	20	15
59	28 c.	Map of the World showing voyage routes (*horiz*)	20	15
60	35 c.	Sir Francis Drake and *Golden Hind*	20	15
61	60 c.	Prince Charles and *Eye of the Wind*	35	30
		Set of 4	85	65
		First Day Cover		1·25

(Des Cato Hibberd Design. Litho Leigh-Mardon Ltd, Melbourne)

1981 (12 May). *Opening of Animal Quarantine Station. T* **16** *and similar horiz designs. Multicoloured. P* 13½ × 13.

62	22 c.	Type **16**	15	15
63	45 c.	Unloading livestock	30	30
64	60 c.	Livestock in pen	35	35
		Set of 3	70	70
		Presentation Pack	1·60	
		First Day Cover		1·25

17 Consolidated "Catalina" *Guba II* Flying Boat

18 Prince Charles and Lady Diana Spencer

(Des R. Honisett. Litho Leigh-Mardon Ltd, Melbourne)

1981 (23 June). *Aircraft. T* **17** *and similar horiz designs. Multicoloured. P* 13½ × 13.

65	22 c.	Type **17**	25	25
	a.	Horiz strip of 5. Nos. 65/9	1·10	
66	22 c.	Consolidated "Liberator" and Avro "Lancastrian"	25	25
67	22 c.	Douglas "DC 4 (Skymaster)" and Lockheed "Constellation"	25	25
68	22 c.	Lockheed "Electra"	25	25
69	22 c.	Boeing "727" airliners	25	25
		Set of 5	1·10	1·10
		Presentation Pack	1·60	
		First Day Cover		1·40

Nos. 65/9 were printed together, *se-tenant*, in horizontal strips of 5 throughout the sheet.

(Des B. Clinton. Litho Leigh-Mardon Ltd, Melbourne)

1981 (29 July). *Royal Wedding. P* 13½ × 13.

70	**18**	24 c. multicoloured	40	20
71		60 c. multicoloured	85	60
		Set of 2	1·25	80
		First Day Cover		1·25

19 "Angels we have heard on High"

20 *Pachyseris speciosa* and *Heliofungia actiniformis* (corals)

(Des B. Weatherhead. Litho Leigh-Mardon Ltd, Melbourne)

1981 (22 Oct). *Christmas. Scenes and Lines from Carol "Angels we have heard on High". T* **19** *and similar horiz designs. Multicoloured. P* 13½ × 13.

72	18 c.	Type **19**	10	10
73	30 c.	"Shepherds why this Jubilee?"	20	20
74	60 c.	"Come to Bethlehem and see Him"	35	35
		Set of 3	60	60
		Presentation Pack	1·10	
		First Day Cover		1·25

Souvenir Pack. "Philatelia 81", Frankfurt.

1981 (14 Nov). *Comprises Nos. 70/1.*

SP74a	Souvenir Pack	5·00	

(Des B. Weatherhead. Litho Leigh-Mardon Ltd, Melbourne)

1981 (28 Dec). *150th Anniv of Charles Darwin's Voyage. T* **20** *and similar horiz designs. Multicoloured. P* 13½ × 13.

75	24 c.	Type **20**	35	15
76	45 c.	Charles Darwin in 1853 and *Pavona cactus* (coral)	55	30
77	60 c.	H.M.S. *Beagle*, 1832, and *Lobophyllia hemprichii* (coral)	70	35
		Set of 3	1·40	70
		First Day Cover		1·25
MS78	130 × 95 mm. 24 c. Cross-section of West Island; 24 c. Cross-section of Home Island	75	85
		Presentation Pack (*Nos.* 75/8)	3·00	
		First Day Cover		1·40

21 Queen Victoria

22 Lord Baden-Powell

(Des B. Weatherhead. Litho Cambec Press, Melbourne)

1982 (31 Mar). *125th Anniv of Annexation of Cocos (Keeling) Islands to British Empire. T* **21** *and similar horiz designs. Multicoloured. P* 13½ × 14.

79	24 c.	Type **21**	20	15
80	45 c.	Union flag	35	25
81	60 c.	Capt. S. Fremantle (annexation visit, 1857) .	40	35
		Set of 3	85	65
		Presentation Pack	1·60	
		First Day Cover		1·25

(Des B. Clinton. Litho Cambec Press, Melbourne)

1982 (21 July). *75th Anniv of Boy Scout Movement. T* **22** *and similar multicoloured design. P* 13½ × 14 (27 c.) *or* 14 × 13½ (75 c.).

82	27 c.	Type **22**	30	15
83	75 c.	"75" and map of Cocos (Keeling) Islands (vert)	1·10	60
		Set of 2	1·40	75
		Presentation Pack	1·75	
		First Day Cover		1·40

23 *Precis villida*

24 "Call His Name Immanuel"

(Des B. Hargreaves. Litho Harrison)

1982 (6 Sept)–**83**. *Butterflies and Moths. T* **23** *and similar multicoloured designs. P* 14.

84	1 c.	Type **23**	25	15
85	2 c.	*Cephonodes picus* (horiz) (6.1.83)	25	15
86	5 c.	*Macroglossum corythus* (horiz)	35	15
87	10 c.	*Chasmina candida* (6.1.83)	30	15
88	20 c.	*Nagia linteola* (horiz) (6.4.83)	30	25
89	25 c.	*Eublemma rivula* (1.7.83)	30	35
90	30 c.	*Eurrhyparodes tricoloralis* (6.4.83)	35	40
91	35 c.	*Hippotion boerhaviae* (horiz)	60	50
92	40 c.	*Euploea core corinna* (6.4.83)	40	50
93	45 c.	*Psara hipponalis* (horiz) (6.4.83)	50	60
94	50 c.	*Danaus chrysippus* (horiz) (1.7.83)	55	70
95	55 c.	*Hypolimas misippus* (horiz)	60	60
96	60 c.	*Spodoptera litura* (1.7.83)	65	70
97	$1	*Achaea janata*	1·50	1·25
98	$2	*Hippotion velox* (horiz) (1.7.83)	2·00	2·25
99	$3	*Utetheisa pulchelloides* (horiz) (6.1.83) ...	2·75	2·75
		Set of 16	10·50	10·50
		Presentation Pack (21.9.83)	12·00	
		First Day Covers (4)		15·00

(Des G. Hamori. Litho Cambec Press, Melbourne)

1982 (25 Oct). *Christmas. T **24** and similar horiz designs. Multicoloured. P* 13½ × 14.

100	21 c.	Type **24**	20	20
101	35 c.	"I bring you good tidings"	35	35
102	75 c.	"Arise and flee into Egypt"	80	80
		Set of 3	1·25	1·25
		Presentation Pack	1·50	
		First Day Cover		1·50

(Des B. Clinton. Litho Cambec Press, Melbourne)

1984 (10 July). *375th Anniv of Discovery of Cocos (Keeling) Islands. T **28** and similar vert designs. Multicoloured. P* 14 × 13½.

115	30 c.	Type **28**	60	40
116	65 c.	Keeling's ship, *Hector*	1·25	90
117	95 c.	Mariner's astrolabe	1·50	1·25
118	$1.10,	Map *circa* 1666	1·60	1·50
		Set of 4	4·50	3·50
		Presentation Pack	4·75	
		First Day Cover		4·25

25 "God will look after us"   **26** Hari Raya Celebrations
(*Matt.* 1:20)

29 Malay Settlement, Home Island   **30** "Rainbow" Fish

(Des E. Roberts. Litho Cambec Press, Melbourne)

1984 (21 Sept). *"Ausipex" International Stamp Exhibition, Melbourne. T **29** and similar horiz designs. Multicoloured. P* 13½ × 14.

119	45 c.	Type **29**	65	50
120	55 c.	Airstrip, West Island	75	60
		Set of 2	1·40	1·10
		First Day Cover		1·40
MS121	130 × 95 mm. $2 Jukongs (native craft) racing		2·25	2·50
		Presentation Pack (Nos. 119/21)	4·50	
		First Day Cover		3·00

(Des R. Roberts. Litho Cambec Press, Melbourne)

1983 (25 Oct). *Christmas. Extracts from the New Testament. T **25** and similar vert designs. Multicoloured. P* 14 × 13½.

103	24 c.	Type **25**	25	30
		a. Horiz strip of 5. Nos. 103/7	1·25	
104	24 c.	"Our baby King, Jesus" (*Matthew* 2:2)	25	30
105	24 c.	"Your Saviour is born" (*Luke* 2:11)	25	30
106	24 c.	"Wise men followed the Star" (*Matthew* 2:9–10)	25	30
107	24 c.	"And worship the Lord" (*Matthew* 2:11)	25	30
		Set of 5	1·25	1·40
		Presentation Pack (31 Oct)	1·50	
		First Day Cover		1·60

Nos. 103/7 were printed together, *se-tenant*, in horizontal strips of 5 throughout the sheet.

(Des R. Roberts. Litho Cambec Press, Melbourne)

1984 (31 Oct). *Christmas. T **30** and similar horiz designs. Multicoloured. P* 13½ × 14.

122	24 c.	Type **30**	40	25
123	35 c.	"Rainbow" butterfly	70	35
124	55 c.	"Rainbow" bird	85	55
		Set of 3	1·75	1·10
		Presentation Pack	2·00	
		First Day Cover		1·60

(Des Marg Towt. Litho Cambec Press, Melbourne)

1984 (24 Jan). *Cocos-Malay Culture (1st series). Festivals. T **26** and similar vert designs. Multicoloured. P* 14 × 13½.

108	45 c.	Type **26**	45	35
109	75 c.	Melenggok dancing	65	50
110	85 c.	Cocos-Malay wedding	75	55
		Set of 3	1·75	1·25
		Presentation Pack	2·10	
		First Day Cover		2·25

See also Nos. 126/8.

31 Cocos Islanders   **32** Jukong-building

(Des B. Weatherhead. Litho Cambec Press, Melbourne)

1984 (30 Nov). *Integration of Cocos (Keeling) Islands with Australia. Sheet* 90 × 52 *mm. containing T **31** and similar horiz design. Multicoloured. P* 13½ × 14.

MS125	30 c.	Type **31**: 30 c. Australian flag on island	85	1·00
		First Day Cover		1·40

(Des Marg Towt. Litho Cambec Press, Melbourne)

1985 (30 Jan). *Cocos-Malay Culture (2nd series). Handicrafts. T **32** and similar vert designs. Multicoloured. P* 14 × 13½.

126	30 c.	Type **32**	50	25
127	45 c.	Blacksmithing	75	40
128	55 c.	Woodcarving	85	50
		Set of 3	1·90	1·10
		Presentation Pack	2·25	
		First Day Cover		1·60

27 Unpacking Barrel   **28** Captain William Keeling

(Des R. Honisett. Litho Cambec Press, Melbourne)

1984 (20 Apr). *75th Anniv of Cocos Barrel Mail. T **27** and similar horiz designs. Multicoloured. P* 13½ × 14.

111	35 c.	Type **27**	35	25
112	55 c.	Jukong awaiting mail ship	60	50
113	70 c.	P. & O. mail ship *Morea*	70	55
		Set of 3	1·50	1·10
		Presentation Pack	2·00	
		First Day Cover		1·75
MS114	125 × 95 mm. $1 Retrieving barrel		90	1·25
		First Day Cover		1·60

33 C.S. *Scotia*   34 Red-footed Booby

(Des B. Clinton. Litho Cambec Press, Melbourne)

1985 (24 Apr). *Cable-laying Ships. T* **33** *and similar horiz designs. Multicoloured. P* 13½ × 14.

129	33 c. Type **33**	60	35
130	65 c. C.S. *Anglia*	1·40	70
131	80 c. C.S. *Patrol*	1·50	90
	Set of 3	3·25	1·75
	Presentation Pack	3·75	
	First Day Cover		2·50

(Des Marg Towt. Litho Cambec Press, Melbourne)

1985 (17 July). *Birds of Cocos (Keeling) Islands. T* **34** *and similar multicoloured designs. P* 13½.

132	33 c. Type **34**	1·25	85
	a. Block of 3. Nos. 132/4	3·00	
	ab. Imperf vert (block of 3)	£500	
133	60 c. Rufous Night Heron (juvenile) (*horiz*)	1·50	1·10
134	$1 Banded Rail (*horiz*)	2·00	1·50
	Set of 3	4·25	3·00
	Presentation Pack	4·75	
	First Day Cover		3·50

Nos. 132/4 were issued together, *se-tenant*, in blocks of 3 throughout the sheet, each block forming a composite design.

35 *Trochus maculatus*

(Des G. Ray. Litho Cambec Press, Melbourne)

1985 (18 Sept)–**86**. *Shells and Molluscs. T* **35** *and similar horiz designs. Multicoloured. P* 13½ × 14.

135	1 c. Type **35**	10	10
136	2 c. *Smaragdia rangiana* (29.1.86)	10	10
137	3 c. *Chama sp.* (29.1.86)	15	15
138	4 c. *Cypraea moneta* (30.7.86)	15	15
139	5 c. *Drupa morum*	15	15
140	10 c. *Conus miles* (29.1.86)	20	20
141	15 c. *Terebra maculata* (30.4.86)	25	25
142	20 c. *Fragum fragum* (30.4.86)	30	30
143	30 c. *Turbo lajonkairii* (30.4.86)	40	40
144	33 c. *Mitra fissurata*	40	40
145	40 c. *Lambis lambis* (30.4.86)	50	50
146	50 c. *Tridacna squamosa* (30.7.86)	60	60
147	60 c. *Cypraea histrio* (30.7.86)	70	70
148	$1 *Phillidia varicosa*	1·25	1·25
149	$2 *Halgerda tessellata* (30.7.86)	2·00	2·00
150	$3 *Harminoea cymbalum* (29.1.86)	3·50	3·50
	Set of 16	9·50	9·50
	Presentation Pack (30.7.86)	12·00	
	First Day Covers (4)		14·00

36 Night Sky and Palm Trees   37 Charles Darwin, *c* 1840

(Des D. Goodwin. Litho Cambec Press, Melbourne)

1985 (30 Oct). *Christmas. Sheet* 121 × 88 *mm, containing T* **36** *and similar horiz designs. P* 13½ × 14.

MS151	27 c. × 4 multicoloured	1·75	2·00
	Presentation Pack	2·25	
	First Day Cover		2·25

The stamps within **MS**151 show a composite design of the night sky seen through a grove of palm trees. The position of the face value on the four stamps varies. Type **36** shows the top left design. The top right stamp shows the face value at bottom right, the bottom left at top left and the bottom right at top right.

(Des B. Clinton. Litho Cambec Press, Melbourne)

1986 (1 Apr). 150*th Anniv of Charles Darwin's Visit. T* **37** *and similar vert designs. Multicoloured. P* 14 × 13½.

152	33 c. Type **37**	60	40
153	60 c. Map of H.M.S. *Beagle's* route Australia to Cocos Islands	1·00	80
154	$1 H.M.S. *Beagle*	1·50	1·25
	Set of 3	2·75	2·25
	Presentation Pack	3·50	
	First Day Cover		2·75

38 Coconut Palm and Holly Sprigs   39 Jukong

(Des S. Hartshorne. Litho Cambec Press, Melbourne)

1986 (29 Oct). *Christmas. T* **38** *and similar horiz designs. Multicoloured. P* 13½ × 14.

155	30 c. Type **38**	45	30
156	90 c. Sea shell and Christmas tree bauble	1·25	1·25
157	$1 Tropical fish and bell	1·50	1·50
	Set of 3	3·00	2·75
	Presentation Pack	3·50	
	First Day Cover		3·25

(Des J. Earl. Litho Cambec Press, Melbourne)

1987 (28 Jan). *Sailing Craft. T* **39** *and similar horiz designs. Multicoloured. P* 13½ × 14.

158	36 c. Type **39**	65	65
	a. Horiz strip of 4. Nos. 158/61	2·40	
159	36 c. Ocean racing yachts	65	65
160	36 c. *Sarimanok* (replica outrigger)	65	65
161	36 c. *Ayesha* (schooner)	65	65
	Set of 4	2·40	2·40
	Presentation Pack	2·75	
	First Day Cover		2·75

Nos. 158/61 were printed together, *se-tenant*, in horizontal strips of 5 throughout the sheet, each strip forming a composite background design.

40 Beach, Direction Island   41 Radio Transmitter and
                                 Palm Trees at Sunset

(Des H. Missingham and R. Fletcher. Litho CPE Australia Ltd, Melbourne)

1987 (8 Apr).   *Cocos Islands Scenes. T **40** and similar horiz designs. Multicoloured. P 13½ × 14.*

162	70 c. Type **40**	90	75
163	90 c. Palm forest, West Island	1·25	1·00
164	$1 Golf course	1·60	1·25
	Set of 3	3·50	2·75
	Presentation Pack	4·00	
	First Day Cover		3·50

(Des R. Fletcher. Litho CPE Australia Ltd, Melbourne)

1987 (29 July).   *Communications. T **41** and similar horiz designs. Multicoloured. P 13½ × 14.*

165	70 c. Type **41**	90	90
166	75 c. Air liner at terminal	95	95
167	90 c. "Intelsat 5" satellite	1·25	1·25
168	$1 Airmail letter and globe	1·50	1·50
	Set of 4	4·25	4·25
	Presentation Pack	4·75	
	First Day Cover		4·75

42 Batik Printing   43 Hands releasing Peace Dove
                        and Map of Islands

(Des B. Clinton. Litho CPE Australia Ltd, Melbourne)

1987 (16 Sept).   *Cocos (Keeling) Islands Malay Industries. T **42** and similar horiz designs. Multicoloured. P 13½ × 14.*

169	45 c. Type **42**	65	65
170	65 c. Jukong building	85	85
171	75 c. Copra production	1·00	1·00
	Set of 3	2·25	2·25
	Presentation Pack	2·75	
	First Day Cover		2·75

(Des Marg Towt. Litho CPE Australia Ltd, Melbourne)

1987 (28 Oct).   *Christmas. T **43** and similar vert designs. Multicoloured. P 14 × 13½.*

172	30 c. Type **43**	40	30
173	90 c. Local children at Christmas party	1·25	85
174	$1 Island family and Christmas star	1·50	95
	Set of 3	2·75	1·90
	Presentation Pack	3·50	
	First Day Cover		2·75

(Des Sue Passmore. Litho CPE Australia Ltd, Melbourne)

1988 (26 Jan).   *Bicentenary of Australian Settlement. Arrival of First Fleet. Square designs as Nos. 1105/9 of Australia but each inscribed "COCOS (KEELING) ISLANDS" and "AUSTRALIA BICENTENARY".*

175	37 c. Aborigines watching arrival of Fleet, Botany Bay	60	60
	a. Horiz strip of 5. Nos. 175/9	2·75	
176	37 c. Aboriginal family and anchored ships	60	60
177	37 c. Fleet arriving at Sydney Cove	60	60
178	37 c. Ship's boat	60	60
179	37 c. Raising the flag, Sydney Cove, 26 January 1788	60	60
	Set of 5	2·75	2·75
	Presentation Pack	3·25	
	First Day Cover		3·25

Nos. 175/9 were printed together, *se-tenant,* in horizontal strips of five throughout the sheet, forming a composite design.

44 Coconut Flower   45 Copra 3d. Stamp of 1963

(Des Celia Rosser. Litho CPE Australia Ltd, Melbourne)

1988 (13 Apr).   *Life Cycle of the Coconut. T **44** and similar vert designs. Multicoloured. P 14 × 13½.*

180	37 c. Type **44**	50	40
181	65 c. Immature nuts	75	65
182	90 c. Coconut palm and mature nuts	1·10	90
183	$1 Seedlings	1·25	1·00
	Set of 4	3·25	2·75
	Presentation Pack	3·75	
	First Day Cover		3·25
MS184	102 × 91 mm. Nos. 180/3	3·25	3·50
	First Day Cover		4·00

(Des R. Fletcher. Recess and litho Note Printing Branch, Reserve Bank of Australia, Melbourne)

1988 (15 June).   *25th Anniv of First Cocos (Keeling) Islands Stamps. T **45** and similar vert designs, each showing stamp from 1963 definitive set. P 15 × 14.*

185	37 c. chocolate, black and azure	50	50
186	55 c. green, black and pale drab	70	70
187	65 c. ultramarine, black and pale grey-lilac	80	80
188	70 c. scarlet, black and bluish grey	85	85
189	90 c. deep purple, black and greenish grey	1·25	1·25
190	$1 deep green, black and light brown	1·40	1·40
	Set of 6	5·00	5·00
	Presentation Pack	6·00	
	First Day Cover		6·00

Designs:—55 c. Palms 1s.; 65 c. "Super Constellation" 5d.; 70 c. Map 8d.; 90 c. Jukong (sailboat) 2s.; $1 White Tern 2s. 3d.

46 *Pisonia grandis*   47 Beach at Sunset

(Des R. Fletcher. Litho CPE Australia Ltd, Melbourne)

1988 (29 July)**–89**.   *Flora. T **46** and similar vert designs. Multicoloured. P 14 × 13½.*

191	1 c. Type **46**	10	10
192	2 c. *Cocos nucifera* (18.1.89)	10	10
193	5 c. *Morinda citrifolia*	10	10
194	10 c. *Cordia subcordata* (18.1.89)	10	10
195	30 c. *Argusia argentea* (18.1.89)	20	25
196	37 c. *Calophyllum inophyllum*	30	35
197	40 c. *Barringtonia asiatica* (19.4.89)	30	35
198	50 c. *Caesalpinia bonduc* (19.4.89)	40	45
199	90 c. *Terminalia catappa* (19.4.89)	70	75
200	$1 *Pemphis acidula* (19.4.89)	75	80
201	$2 *Scaevola sericea* (18.1.89)	1·50	1·60
202	$3 *Hibiscus tiliaceus*	2·25	2·40
	Set of 12	6·00	6·50
	Presentation Pack (19.4.89)	7·50	
	First Day Covers (3)		9·25

(Des R. Fletcher. Litho CPE Australia Ltd, Melbourne)

1988 (30 July).   "*Sydpex '88" National Stamp Exhibition, Sydney. Sheet*
70×85 mm. Multicoloured. P 14×13½.
MS203 $3 As No. 202 . . . .   2·75   3·00
          First Day Cover . . . .   3·50

(Des T. Bland. Litho CPE Australia Ltd, Melbourne)

1988 (12 Oct).   *Christmas. P* 13½×14.
204   **47**   32 c. multicoloured   40   35
205   90 c. multicoloured . . . .   1·10   90
206          $1 multicoloured . . . .   1·25   1·00
             Set of 3 . . . .   2·50   2·00
             Presentation Pack . . . .   3·00
             First Day Cover . . . .   2·50

48 Capt. P. G. Taylor   **49** Jukong and Star

(Des B. Clinton. Litho CPE Australia Ltd, Melbourne)

1989 (19 July).   *50th Anniv of First Indian Ocean Aerial Survey. T* **48** *and*
similar vert designs. P 14×13½.
207   40 c. multicoloured   60   60
208   70 c. multicoloured   85   85
209   $1 multicoloured . . . .   1·25   1·25
210   $1.10, deep ultramarine, pale lilac and black . .   1·40   1·40
      Set of 4 . . . .   3·75   3·75
      Presentation Pack . . . .   4·00
      First Day Cover . . . .   4·00
Designs:—70 c. Consolidated Catalina "PBY2" *Guba II* and crew; $1
Guba II over Direction Island; $1.10, Unissued Australia 5s. stamp
commemorating flight.

(Des T. Bland. Litho Leigh-Mardon Ltd, Melbourne)

1989 (18 Oct).   *Christmas. P* 14×13½.
211   **49**   35 c. multicoloured   35   40
212   80 c. multicoloured   75   80
213          $1.10, multicoloured . . . .   1·00   1·10
             Set of 3 . . . .   1·90   2·10
             Presentation Pack . . . .   2·75
             First Day Cover . . . .   2·50

50 H.M.A.S. *Sydney*   **51** Xanthid Crab
        (cruiser)

(Des PCS Studios. Litho Leigh-Mardon Ltd, Melbourne)

1989 (9 Nov).   *75th Anniv of Destruction of German Cruiser* Emden. *T* **50**
and similar horiz designs. Multicoloured. P 13½×14.
214   40 c. Type **50**   55   45
      a. Horiz strip of 4, Nos. 214/17, with central
         label . . . .   3·25
215   70 c. *Emden* (German cruiser)   80   70
216   $1 *Emden's* steam launch . . . .   1·10   1·00
217   $1.10, H.M.A.S. *Sydney* and crest . . . .   1·25   1·00
      Set of 4 . . . .   3·25   3·00
      Presentation Pack . . . .   8·00
      First Day Cover . . . .   3·75
MS218   145×90 mm. Nos. 214/17 . . . .   3·50   3·50
          First Day Cover . . . .   4·00
Nos. 214/17 were printed together, *se-tenant*, in horizontal strips of
four stamps and one label throughout the sheet.

(Des Jill Ruse. Litho Leigh-Mardon Ltd, Melbourne)

1990 (31 May).   *Cocos Islands Crabs. T* **51** *and similar multicoloured*
designs. P 14½.
219   45 c. Type **51**   40   45
220   75 c. Ghost Crab   65   70
221   $1 Red-backed Mud Crab   85   90
222   $1.30, Coconut Crab (*vert*) . . . .   1·10   1·25
      Set of 4 . . . .   2·75   3·00
      Presentation Pack . . . .   3·50
      First Day Cover . . . .   3·25

52 Captain Keeling and *Hector*, 1609

(Des Elizabeth and R. Innes. Litho Note Ptg Branch, Reserve Bank of
Australia)

1990 (24 Aug).   *Navigators of the Pacific. T* **52** *and similar horiz designs.*
P 14½.
223   45 c. dull mauve   40   45
224   75 c. dull mauve and pale azure   65   70
225   $1 dull mauve and pale stone   85   90
226   $1.30, dull mauve and pale buff . . . .   1·10   1·25
      Set of 4 . . . .   2·75   3·00
      Presentation Pack . . . .   8·00
MS227   120×95 mm. As Nos. 223/6, but imperforate .   3·00   3·25
          Ea. Dull mauve printed double . . . .
Designs:—75 c. Captain Fitzroy and *Beagle*, 1836; $1 Captain Belcher
and *Samarang*, 1846; $1.30, Captain Fremantle and *Juno*, 1857.

ALBUM
LISTS

Please write for our latest lists of albums and accessories.
These will be sent free on request.

Nauru

1916 12 Pence = 1 Shilling
      20 Shillings = 1 Pound
1937 12 Pence = 1 Shilling
      20 Shillings = 1 Australian Pound
1966 100 Cents = 1 Australian Dollar

A coral island in the West Pacific, Nauru was part of the German Marshall Islands colony from 1888 until occupied by Australian forces in 1914. The island was administered as a League of Nations and United Nations Mandate from 1920 until 1968.

Stamps of Marshall Islands were used in Nauru from the opening of the German Colonial Post Office on 14 July 1908 until 8 September 1914.

Following the occupation by Australian forces the "N.W. PACIFIC ISLANDS" overprints on Australia (see Papua New Guinea) were used during the early months of 1916.

PRICES FOR STAMPS ON COVER TO 1945	
Nos. 1/12	from × 10
Nos. 13/16	from × 3
Nos. 17/25	—
Nos. 26/39	from × 6
Nos. 40/3	from × 10
Nos. 44/7	from × 15

PRICES
George V issues (1916–1935)

First column = Mounted Mint
Second column = Used

BRITISH MANDATE

NAURU **NAURU** **NAURU**
(1) (2) (3)

1916 (2 Sept)–**23**. *Stamps of Great Britain (1912–22) overprinted at Somerset House.*

(a) With T **1** (12½ mm long) at foot

1	½d. green	30	2·25
	a. "NAUP.U"	£275	
	b. Double opt, one albino	70·00	
2	1d. bright scarlet	50	2·00
	a. "NAUP.U"	£450	
2b	1d. carmine-red	10·00	
	bb. Double opt, one albino	£200	
3	1½d. red-brown (1923)	55·00	80·00
4	2d. orange (Die I)	1·75	7·00
	a. "NAUP.U"	£300	
	b. Double opt, one albino	£100	
5	2d. orange (Die II) (1923)	70·00	£100
6	2½d. blue	2·75	5·00
	a. "NAUP.U"	£375	
	b. Double opt, one albino	£200	
7	3d. bluish violet	2·00	3·50
	a. "NAUP.U"	£375	
	b. Double opt, one albino	£200	
8	4d. slate-green	2·00	7·50
	a. "NAUP.U"	£475	
	b. Double opt, one albino	£200	
9	5d. yellow-brown	2·25	8·50
	a. "NAUP.U"	£550	
	b. Double opt, one albino	£140	
10	6d. purple, **C**	3·25	10·00
	a. "NAUP.U"	£500	
	b. Double opt, one albino	£225	
11	9d. agate	7·00	18·00
	a. Double opt, one albino	£225	
12	1s. bistre-brown (Optd. £125)	7·00	18·00
	a. Double opt, one albino	£250	
	Set of 11	70·00	£130

(b) With T **2** (13½ mm long) at centre (1923)

13	½d. green	4·50	48·00
14	1d. scarlet	24·00	40·00
15	1½d. red-brown	26·00	50·00
	a. Double opt, one albino	£140	
16	2d. orange (Die II)	45·00	80·00
	Set of 4	85·00	£190

The "NAUP.U" errors occur on R. 6/2 from Control I 16 only. The ink used on this batch of overprints was shiny jet-black.

There is a constant variety consisting of short left stroke to "N" which ocurs on Nos. 1, 2, 2b, 4 (£30 each); 3 (£175); 5 (£200); 6, 7, (£38 each); 8, 9, 10 (£55 each); 11, 12 (£65 each). All unused prices.

(c) High values optd with T **3**. (i) Waterlow printing

17	5s. rose-carmine	£2750	£2250
18	10s. indigo-blue (R.) (Optd S. £1400)	£6000	£5000
	a. Double opt, one albino	£8000	£8000

(ii) De La Rue printing

19	2s. 6d. deep brown (Optd S. £300)	£500	£600
	a. Double opt, one albino	£1200	
	b. Treble opt, two albino	£1300	
20	2s. 6d. yellow-brown	65·00	90·00
21	2s. 6d. pale brown (worn plate) (Optd. S. £200)	70·00	85·00
	a. Re-entry	£1300	
22	5s. bright carmine (shades) (Optd S. £200)	£110	£150
	a. Treble opt, two albino	£550	
23	10s. pale blue (R.)	£300	£400
	a. Treble opt. (Blk. + R. + albino)		
23b	10s. deep bright blue (R.)	£600	£650
	Set of 3 (Nos. 19, 21, 22) H/S "Specimen"	£700	

(iii) Bradbury, Wilkinson printing (1919)

24	2s. 6d. chocolate-brown	75·00	£100
	a. Major re-entry		
	b. Double opt, one albino	£300	
25	2s. 6d. pale brown	60·00	85·00
	a. Double opt, one albino	£275	

AUSTRALIAN MANDATE

PRINTERS. See note at beginning of Australia.

4 *Century* (freighter)

(Des R. A. Harrison. Eng T. S. Harrison. Recess Note Printing Branch of the Treasury, Melbourne and from 1926 by the Commonwealth Bank of Australia)

1924–48. T **4**. *No wmk. P* 11.
I. Rough surfaced, greyish paper (1924–34).
II. Shiny surfaced, white paper (1937–48).

		I		II	
26	½d. chestnut	60	2·75	6·50	11·00
	a. Perf 14 (1947)		†	1·25	5·00
27	1d. green	1·50	2·75	2·50	3·00
28	1½d. scarlet	2·25	3·50	90	1·50
29	2d. orange	2·25	6·00	1·50	6·00
30	2½d. slate-blue	4·00	11·00	†	
30a	2½d. greenish blue (1934)	4·00	11·00	†	
30b	2½d. dull blue (1948)	†		1·25	3·00
	ba. Imperf between (vert pair)	†		£3750	£3750
	bb. Imperf between (horiz pair)	†		£3750	£3750
31	3d. blue	2·50	6·50	†	
31a	3d. greenish grey (1947)	†		1·50	3·50
32	4d. olive-green	3·50	8·50	3·50	5·50

		I		II	
33	5d. brown	2·50	6·00	3·25	3·75
34	6d. dull violet	3·00	11·00	3·00	3·50
35	9d. olive-brown	4·75	17·00	7·50	14·00
36	1s. brown-lake	6·00	13·00	5·00	2·75
37	2s. 6d. grey-green	25·00	35·00	24·00	27·00
38	5s. claret	48·00	70·00	35·00	48·00
39	10s. yellow	80·00	£100	80·00	80·00
	Set of 14	£180	£250		†
	Set of 15	†		£160	£180

HIS MAJESTY'S JUBILEE.

1910 - 1935

(5)   6

1935 (12 July). *Silver Jubilee.* T**4** *(shiny surfaced, white paper) optd with* T**5**.

40	1½d. scarlet	60	80
41	2d. orange	1·00	4·00
42	2½d. dull blue	1·50	1·50
43	1s. brown-lake	4·00	3·50
	Set of 4	6·50	9·00

(Recess John Ash, Melbourne)

1937 (10 May). *Coronation.* P 11.

44	**6**	1½d. scarlet	45	20	40
45		2d. orange	45	20	70
46		2½d. blue	45	20	30
47		1s. purple	60	30	70
		Set of 4	1·75	80	1·90

7 Nauruan Netting Fish   8 Anibare Bay

15 Map of Nauru

(Recess Note Printing Branch, Commonweatlh Bank, Melbourne, and from 1960 by Note Ptg Branch, Reserve Bank of Australia, Melbourne)

1954 (6 Feb)–**65**.   T**7/8**, **15** *and similar designs. Toned paper.* P 13½ × 14½ *(horiz)* or 14½ × 13½ *(vert).*

48	½d. deep violet	20	10
	a. Violet (8.5.61)	20	10
49	1d. bluish green	20	15
	a. Emerald-green (8.5.61)	20	15
	b. Deep green (1965)	35	25
50	3½d. scarlet	1·50	15
	a. Vermilion (1958)	2·25	60
51	4d. grey-blue	1·50	45
	a. Deep blue (1958)	2·50	70
52	6d. orange	70	15
53	9d. claret	50	15
54	1s. deep purple	30	15
55	2s. 6d. deep green	2·50	60
56	5s. magenta	8·00	2·00
	Set of 9	14·00	3·25

Designs: *Horiz*—3½d. Loading phosphate from cantilever; 4d. Great Frigate Bird; 6d. Nauruan canoe; 9d. Domaneab (Meeting-house); 2s. 6d. Buada lagoon. *Vert*—1s. Palm trees.

Nos. 48a, 49a/b, 50a and 51a are on white paper.

16 Micronesian Pigeon   17 Poison Nut

20 Capparis   21 White Tern

(Recess (10d., 2s. 3d.) or photo (others) Note Ptg Branch, Reserve Bank of Australia, Melbourne)

1963–65.   T**16/17**, **20/1** *and similar designs.* P 13½ × 13 (5d.), 13 × 13½ (8d.) 14 × 13½ (10d.), 15 × 14½ (1s. 3d.) or 13½ *(others).*

57	2d. black, blue, red-brown & orange-yell (3.5.65)	1·00	1·00
58	3d. multicoloured (16.4.63)	75	35
59	5d. multicoloured (22.4.63)	75	75
60	8d. black and green (1.7.63)	1·50	80
61	10d. black (16.4.64)	50	30
62	1s. 3d. blue, black and yellow-green (3.5.65) . . .	3·50	1·75
63	2s. 3d. ultramarine (16.4.64)	2·75	55
64	3s. 3d. multicoloured (3.5.65)	4·00	2·50
	Set of 8	13·00	7·00

Designs: *Vert*—5d. "Iyo" (*calophyllum*). *Horiz*—8d. Black Lizard; 2s. 3d. Coral pinnacles; 3s. 3d. Finsch's Reed Warbler.

1965 (14 Apr). *50th Anniv of Gallipoli Landing. As* T**184** *of Australia, but slightly larger* (23 × 34½ *mm). Photo.*

65	5d. sepia, black and emerald	15	10
	First Day Cover		50

STANLEY GIBBONS
STAMP COLLECTING SERIES

Introductory booklets on *How to Start, How to Identify Stamps* and *Collecting by Theme.* A series of well illustrated guides at a low price. Write for details.

(New Currency. 100 cents = $1 Australian)

24 Anibare Bay   25 "Iyo" (*calophyllum*)

(Recess (1, 2, 3, 5, 8, 19, 25 c. and $1) or photo (others))

1966 (14 Feb–25 May).   *Decimal Currency. Various stamps with values in cents and dollars as T 24/5 and some colours changed. Recess printed stamps on helecon paper.*

66	**24**	1 c. deep blue	15	10
67	**7**	2 c. brown-purple (25 May)	15	10
68	–	3 c. bluish green (as 3½d.) (25 May)	30	15
69	**25**	4 c. multicoloured	25	10
70	–	5 c. deep ultramarine (as 1s.) (25 May)	25	15
71	–	7 c. black and chestnut (as 8d.)	25	10
72	**20**	8 c. olive-green	30	10
73	–	10 c. red (as 4d.)	40	10
74	**21**	15 c. blue, black and yellow-green (25 May)	80	80
75	–	25 c. deep brown (as 2s. 3d.) (25 May)	45	40
76	**17**	30 c. multicoloured	70	30
77	–	35 c. multicoloured (as 3s. 3d.) (25 May)	1·25	35
78	**16**	50 c. multicoloured	2·50	80
79	–	$1 magenta (as 5s.)	2·00	1·00
		Set of 14	8·50	3·75

The 25 c. is as No. 63, but larger, 27½ × 24½ mm.

Nauru became an independent republic on 31 January 1968.

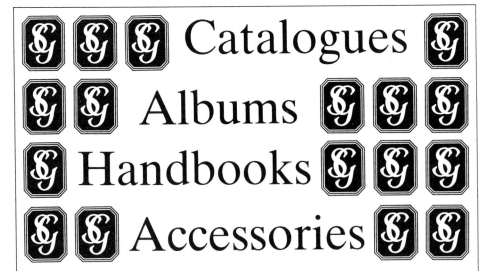

Norfolk Island

1947   12 Pence = 1 Shilling
          20 Shillings = 1 Australian Pound
1966   100 Cents = 1 Australian Dollar

A small island E. of New South Wales, administered by Australia until 1960 when a measure of local government was established.

The stamps of Tasmania were used in Norfolk Island from 1854 until 1856, such use being identified by the "72" numeral cancellation. From 1897 the stamps of New South Wales were in regular use, being replaced by issues for Australia from 1913 to 1947.

AUSTRALIAN ADMINISTRATION

PRINTERS. Nos. 1 to 42 were printed at the Note Printing Branch Reserve Bank of Australia (until 14 Jan 1960, known as the Note Printing Branch, Commonwealth Bank) by recess.

1 Ball Bay

1947 (10 June)**–59.** *Toned paper (except Nos. 6a and 12a). P 14.*

1	1	½d. orange		35	25
		a. White paper (11.56)		1·50	2·50
2		1d. bright violet		50	25
		a. White paper (11.56)		6·50	9·00
3		1½d. emerald-green		50	30
		a. White paper (11.56)		12·00	15·00
4		2d. reddish violet		55	30
		a. White paper (11.56)		£130	£120
5		2½d. scarlet		80	30
6		3d. chestnut		70	30
6a		3d. emerald-green (*white paper*) (6.7.59)		11·00	3·75
7		4d. claret		70	30
8		5½d. indigo		70	30
9		6d. purple-brown		70	30
10		9d. magenta		90	40
11		1s. grey-green		70	30
12		2s. yellow-bistre		4·00	1·00
12a		2s. deep blue (*white paper*) (6.7.59)		20·00	5·00
		Set of 14		38·00	11·50

Stamps in Type **1** perf 11 or in different colours, perf 11, are understood to have been the subject of unauthorised leakages from the Note Printing Branch and they were not issued to post offices for public use.

2 Warder's Tower   3 Airfield

4 Old Stores   5 Barracks Entrance
(Crankmill)

6 Salt House   7 Bloody Bridge

1953 (10 June). *P 14½ × 15 (vert) or 15 × 14½ (horiz).*

13	2	3½d. brown-lake		3·00	90
14	3	6½d. deep green		3·00	1·00
15	4	7½d. deep blue		4·00	3·00
16	5	8½d. chocolate		7·00	3·50
17	6	10d. reddish violet		5·00	75
18	7	5s. sepia		35·00	8·00
		Set of 6		50·00	15·00

8 Norfolk Island Seal and Pitcairners Landing

Two Types of 2s.:

Type I   Type II

Alternate stamps on each horizontal row have dot or no dot in bottom right corner.

1956 (8 June). *Centenary of Landing of Pitcairn Islanders on Norfolk Island. P 15 × 14½.*

19	8	3d. deep bluish green		1·00	30
20		2s. violet (I) (*shades*)		1·50	50
		a. Type II		1·50	50
		b. *Deep violet* (I)		2·25	1·75
		ba. Type II		2·25	1·75
		Set of 2		2·50	80
		First Day Cover			12·00

7ᵈ

NORFOLK
ISLAND

8ᵈ

(9)   (10)   (11)

1958 (1 July). *Surch with T* **9/10.**

21	**4**	7d. on 7½d. deep blue	. . . .	1·00	45
22	**5**	8d. on 8½d. chocolate	. . . .	1·00	45
		Set of 2	. . . .	2·00	90

1959 (7 Dec). *150th Anniv of Australian Post Office. No.* 331 *of Australia surch with T* **11.**

23	**143**	5d. on 4d. slate (R.)	. . . .	35	15
		First Day Cover	. . . .		2·00

12 *Hibiscus insularis*

13 *Lagunaria patersonii*

14 White Tern

15 Lantana

16 Red Hibiscus

17 Queen Elizabeth II and Cereus

18 Fringed Hibiscus

19 Solander's Petrel

20 Passion-flower

21 Rose Apple

22 Red-tailed Tropic Bird

(Design recess; centre typo (T **21**))

1960–62. *P* 14½ *or* 14½ × 14 (10s.).

24	**12**	1d. bluish green (23.5.60)	. . . .	15	10
25	**13**	2d. rose and myrtle-green (23.5.60)	. . . . .	20	10
26	**14**	3d. green (1.5.61)	. . . .	70	15
27	**15**	5d. bright purple (20.6.60)	. . . .	55	20
28	**16**	8d. red (20.6.60)	. . . .	80	50
29	**17**	9d. ultramarine (23.5.60)	. . . .	80	45
30	**6**	10d. brown and reddish violet (27.2.61)	. . .	2·50	1·25
31	**18**	1s. 1d. carmine-red (16.10.61)	. . . .	80	35
32	**19**	2s. sepia (1.5.61)	. . . .	5·50	90
33	**20**	2s. 5d. deep violet (5.2.62)	. . . .	1·00	40
34	**21**	2s. 8d. cinnamon and deep green (9.4.62)	. .	2·00	55
35	**7**	2s. sepia and deep green (27.2.61)	. . . . .	6·00	75
36	**22**	10s. emerald-green (14.8.61) (Optd S. £48)		48·00	20·00
		Set of 13	. . . .	60·00	23·00

Nos. 30 and 35 are redrawn.

The Specimen overprint on No. 36 is of similar status to those mentioned in the note at the beginning of Australia.

2/8

(23)

(24)

(25)

1960. *As Nos.* 13/15 *but colours changed, surch with T* **23/5.**

37	**2**	1s. 1d. on 3½d. deep ultramarine (26.9.60)	.	3·50	1·25
38	**3**	2s. 5d. on 6½d. bluish green (26.9.60)	. . . .	3·50	1·25
39	**4**	2s. 8d. on 7½d. sepia (29.8.60)	. . . .	7·00	2·25
		Set of 3	. . . .	12·50	4·25

26 Queen Elizabeth II and Map

27 "Tweed Trousers" (*Atypichthys latus*)

1960 (24 Oct). *Introduction of Local Government. P* 14.

40	**26**	2s. 8d. reddish purple	. . . .	14·00	6·00
		First Day Cover	. . . .		20·00

1960 (21 Nov). *Christmas. As No.* 328 *of Australia.*

41	5d. bright purple	. . . .	60	30
	First Day Cover	. . . .		2·25

1961 (20 Nov). *Christmas. As No.* 341 *of Australia.*

42	5d. slate-blue	. . . .	30	20
	First Day Cover	. . . .		1·50

PRINTERS. All the following issues to No. 233 were printed in photogravure by Harrison and Sons, Ltd, London except issues which are in the same designs as Australia, *and where otherwise stated.*

1962–63. *Fishes. Horiz designs as T* **27.** *P* 14½ × 14.

43		6d. sepia, yellow & dp bluish green (16.7.62)	.	1·00	25
44		11d. red-orange, brown and blue (25.2.63)	. . .	2·50	80
45		1s. blue, pink and yellow-olive (17.9.62)	. . . .	1·00	25
46		1s. 3d. blue, red-brown and green (15.7.63)	. .	2·50	1·00
47		1s. 6d. sepia, violet and light blue (6.5.63)	. . .	3·00	80
48		2s. 3d. dp blue, red & greenish yell (23.9.63)	. .	3·50	80
		Set of 6	. . . .	12·00	3·50

Designs:—11d. "Trumpeter"; 1s. "Po'ov"; 1s. 3d. "Dreamfish"; 1s. 6d. "Hapoéka"; 2s. 3d. "Ophie" (*carangidae*).

1962 (19 Nov). *Christmas. As Nos.* 345 *of Australia.*

49	5d. ultramarine	. . . .	30	15
	First Day Cover	. . . .		80

1963 (11 Nov). *Christmas. As No.* 361 *of Australia.*

50	5d. red	. . . .	25	15
	First Day Cover	. . . .		80

33 Overlooking Kingston

37 Norfolk Pine

1964 (24 Feb–28 Sept). *Views. Horiz designs as T* **33.** *Multicoloured. P* 14½ × 14.

51		5d. Type **33**	. . . .	50	15
52		8d. Kingston	. . . .	75	20
53		9d. The Arches (Bumboras) (11.5)	. . . .	1·75	15
54		10d. Slaughter Bay (28.9)	. . . .	3·00	25
		Set of 4	. . . .	5·50	65

(Photo Note Ptg Branch, Reserve Bank of Australia, Melbourne)

1964 (1 July). *50th Anniv of Norfolk Island as Australian Territory. P* 13½.

55	**37**	5d. black, red and orange	10	10
56		8d. black, red and grey-green	15	10
		Set of 2	25	15
		First Day Cover		60

No. 56 exists with the face value omitted due to a colour shift.

1964 (9 Nov). *Christmas. As No. 372 of Australia.*

57	5d. green, blue, buff and violet	20	10
	First Day Cover		55

1965 (14 Apr). *50th Anniv of Gallipoli Landing. As T* **184** *of Australia, but slightly larger* (22 × 34½ *mm*)*. Photo.*

58	5d. sepia, black and emerald	10	10
	First Day Cover		50

1965 (25 Oct). *Christmas. Helecon paper. As No.* 381 *of Australia.*

59	5d. multicoloured	10	10
	First Day Cover		50

(New Currency. 100 cents = $1 Australian)

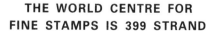

38 *Hibiscus insularis*   **39** Headstone Bridge

1966 (14 Feb). *Decimal currency. Various stamps surch in black on silver tablets, which vary slightly in size, obliterating old value as in T* **38**. *Surch typo.*

60	**38**	1 c. on 1d. bluish green (*value tablet* 4 × 5 *mm*)	20	10
		a. Value tablet larger, 5½ × 5½ mm	40	25
61	**13**	2 c. on 2d. rose and myrtle-green	20	10
62	**14**	3 c. on 3d. green	50	10
63	**15**	4 c. on 5d. bright purple	25	10
64	**16**	5 c. on 8d. red	30	10
65	**6**	10 c. on 10d. brown and reddish violet	40	15
66	**18**	15 c. on 1s. 1d. carmine-red	45	15
67	**19**	20 c. on 2s. sepia	3·50	1·50
68	**20**	25 c. on 2s. 5d. deep violet	1·25	40
69	**21**	30 c. on 2s. 8d. cinnamon and deep green . .	1·00	50
70	**7**	50 c. on 5s. sepia and deep green	4·50	75
71	**22**	$1 on 10s. emerald-green (*value tablet* 7 × 6½ *mm*)	3·50	1·75
		a. Value tablet smaller, 6½ × 4 mm	3·50	1·75
		Set of 12	14·00	5·00

1966 (27 June). *Horiz designs as T* **39**. *Multicoloured. P* 14½ × 14.

72	7 c. Type **39**	25	15
73	9 c. Cemetery Road	25	15
	Set of 2	50	30

41 St. Barnabas' Chapel   **42** St. Barnabas' Chapel
(interior)   (exterior)

1966 (23 Aug). *Centenary of Melanesian Mission. P* 14 × 14½.

74	**41**	4 c. multicoloured	10	10
75	**42**	25 c. multicoloured	15	10
		Set of 2	20	15
		First Day Cover		55

43 Star over Philip Island   **44** H.M.S. *Resolution,* 1774

(Des B.W.G. McCoy)

1966 (24 Oct). *Christmas. P* 14½.

76	**43**	4 c. multicoloured	10	10
		First Day Cover		45

(Des Harrison)

1967 (17 Apr)–**68**. *T* **44** *and similar horiz designs showing ships. Multicoloured. P* 14 × 14½.

77	1 c. Type **44**	10	10
78	2 c. *La Boussole* and *L'Astrolabe*, 1788	15	10
79	3 c. H.M.S. *Supply*, 1788	15	10
80	4 c. H.M.S. *Sirius*, 1790	15	10
81	5 c. *Norfolk* (cutter), 1798 (14.8.67)	20	10
82	7 c. H.M.S. *Mermaid* (survey cutter), 1825 (14.8.67)	20	10
83	9 c. *Lady Franklin*, 1853 (14.8.67)	20	10
84	10 c. *Morayshire*, 1856 (14.8.67)	20	20
85	15 c. *Southern Cross*, 1866 (18.3.68)	45	30
86	20 c. *Pitcairn*, 1891 (18.3.68)	60	40
87	25 c. Norfolk Island whaleboat, 1895 (18.3.68) . . .	1·00	50
88	30 c. *Iris* (cable ship), 1907 (18.6.68)	2·00	1·00
89	50 c. *Resolution*, 1926 (18.6.68)	3·00	1·75
90	$1 *Morinda*, 1931 (18.6.68).	5·50	2·50
	Set of 14	12·50	6·25
	Presentation Pack (18.6.68)	26·00	

1967 (7 June). *50th Anniv of Lions International. As No.* 411 *of Australia but colours changed.*

91	4 c. black, bluish green and olive-yellow	10	10
	First Day Cover		45

58 Prayer of John Adams and Candle

(Des B.G.W. McCoy)

1967 (16 Oct). *Christmas. P* 14.

92	**58**	5 c. black, light yellow-olive and red	10	10
		First Day Cover		40

1968 (5 Aug)–**71**. *Coil Stamps. As T* **199** *of Australia.*

93	3 c. black, light brown and vermilion	10	10
94	4 c. black, light brown and blue-green	10	10
95	5 c. black, light brown and deep violet	10	10
95a	6 c. black, lt brown & lake-brown (25.8.71)	20	25
	Set of 4	35	35

59 "Skymaster" and "Lancastrian"   **60** Bethlehem Star
Aircraft   and Flowers

(Des Harrison)

1968 (25 Sept). *21st Anniv of QANTAS Air Service, Sydney-Norfolk Island. P* 14.
96	**59**	5 c.	bluish black, carmine-red & lt blue	10	10
97		7 c.	blackish brown, carmine-red & turq	10	10
			Set of 2	15	15
			First Day Cover		40

(Des Mrs. B. L. Laing)

1968 (24 Oct). *Christmas. P* 14 × 14½.
98	**60**	5 c.	multicoloured	10	10
			First Day Cover		40

61 Captain Cook, Quadrant and Chart of Pacific Ocean

62 Van Diemen's Land, Norfolk Island and Sailing Cutter

(Des V. Whiteley from sketch by J. G. Cowan)

1969 (3 June). *Captain Cook Bicentenary (1st issue). Observation of the transit of Venus across the Sun, from Tahiti. P* 14.
99	**61**	10 c.	multicoloured	10	10
			First Day Cover		45

See also Nos. 118/19, 129, 152/5, 200/2 and 213/14.

(Des Mrs. A. Bathie and Mrs. M. J. McCoy)

1969 (29 Sept). *125th Anniv of the Annexation of Norfolk Island to Van Diemen's Land. P* 14 × 14½.
100	**62**	5 c.	multicoloured	10	10
101		30 c.	multicoloured	15	10
			Set of 2	25	15
			First Day Cover		60

63 "The Nativity" (carved mother-of-peal plaque)

64 New Zealand Grey Flyeater

(Des J. G. Cowan)

1969 (27 Oct). *Christmas. P* 14½ × 14.
102	**63**	5 c.	multicoloured	10	10
			First Day Cover		45

(Des G. Mathews)

1970–71. *Birds. T* **64** *and similar multicoloured designs. Chalk-surfaced paper. P* 14.
103	1 c.	Scarlet Robins (22.7.70)	15	10
104	2 c.	Golden Whistler (24.2.71)	25	20
105	3 c.	Type **64** (25.2.70)	25	10
106	4 c.	Long-tailed Koels (25.2.70)	25	10
107	5 c.	Red-fronted Parakeet (24.2.71)	75	45
108	7 c.	Long-tailed Triller (22.7.70)	45	10
109	9 c.	Island Thrush (25.2.70)	70	10
110	10 c.	Boobook Owl (22.7.70)	1·25	40
111	15 c.	Norfolk Island Pigeon (24.2.71)	1·50	65
112	20 c.	White-chested White Eye (16.6.71)	3·25	1·75
113	25 c.	Norfolk Island Parrots (22.7.70)	1·75	1·75
	a.	Error. Glazed, ordinary paper		
114	30 c.	Collared Grey Fantail (16.6.71)	3·00	1·75
115	45 c.	Norfolk Island Starlings (25.2.70)	3·00	80
116	50 c.	Crimson Rosella (24.2.71)	4·00	1·75
117	$1	Sacred Kingfisher (16.6.71)	8·00	6·50
		Set of 15	25·00	13·50
		Presentation Pack (11.71)	40·00	
		First Day Covers (4)		23·00

Nos. 105, 106, 109, 112, 114, 115 and 117 are horizontal, and the remainder vertical designs.

65 Capt. Cook and Map of Australia

66 First Christmas Service, 1788

(Des R. Bates)

1970 (29 Apr). *Captain Cook Bicentenary (2nd issue). Discovery of Australia's East Coast. T* **65** *and similar horiz design. Multicoloured. P* 14.
118	5 c.	Type **65**	15	10
119	10 c.	H.M.S. *Endeavour* and aborigine	20	10
		Set of 2	35	15
		First Day Cover		60

(Des R. Bates)

1970 (15 Oct). *Christmas. P* 14.
120	**66**	5 c.	multicoloured	10	10
			First Day Cover		45

67 Bishop Patteson, and Martyrdom of St. Stephen

68 Rose Window, St. Barnabas Chapel, Kingston

(Des R. Bates)

1971 (20 Sept). *Death Centenary of Bishop Patteson. T* **67** *and similar horiz designs. Multicoloured. P* 14 × 14½.
121	6 c.	Type **67**	10	10
	a.	Pair. Nos. 121/2	10	10
122	6 c.	Bible, Martyrdom of St. Stephen and knotted palm-frond	10	10
123	10 c.	Bishop Patteson and stained-glass	10	10
	a.	Pair. Nos. 123/4	20	20
124	10 c.	Cross and Bishop's Arms	10	10
		Set of 4	30	30
		First Day Cover		75

Nos. 121/2 and 123/4 were printed in *se-tenant* pairs throughout the sheet.

(Des G. Hitch. Photo Heraclio Fournier, Spain)

1971 (25 Oct). *Christmas. P* 14 × 13½.
125	**68**	6 c.	multicoloured	10	10
			First Day Cover		45

69 Map and Flag

70 "St. Mark" (stained-glass window, All Saints, Norfolk Is)

(Des G. Hitch)

1972 (7 Feb).　*25th Anniv of South Pacific Commission. P* 14 × 14½.
126　**69**　7 c. multicoloured ....　15　　10
　　　　　First Day Cover　..............　　　　　　50

(Des Mrs. M. J. McCoy)

1972 (16 Oct).　*Christmas. P* 14.
127　**70**　7 c. multicoloured ....　10　　10
　　　　　First Day Cover　.............　　　　　　50

71 Cross and Pines.
(stained-glass window,
All Saints Church)

72 H.M.S. *Resolution* in the
Antarctic

(Des Harrison)

1972 (20 Nov).　*Centenary of First Pitcairner-built Church. P* 14.
128　**71**　12 c. multicoloured ....　10　　10
　　　　a. Purple (background to dates) omitted
　　　　　First Day Cover　.............　　　　　　60

(Des G. Hitch)

1973 (17 Jan).　*Captain Cook Bicentenary (3rd issue). Crossing of the Antarctic Circle. P* 14.
129　**72**　35 c. multicoloured ....　3·00　2·00
　　　　　First Day Cover　.............　　　　　2·75

73 Child and Christmas　**74** Protestant Clergyman's
　　　　　Tree　　　　　　　　　　　Quarters

(Des B. W. McCoy (T **73**), R. Westwood (35 c.))

1973 (22 Oct).　*Christmas. T* **73** *and similar vert design. Multicoloured. P* 14.
130　　7 c. Type **73** ....　20　　10
131　　12 c. Type **73** ....　25　　10
132　　35 c. Type **73** ....　70　　80
　　　　Set of 3 ....　1·00　90
　　　　First Day Cover　.................　　　1·40

(Des G. Hitch)

1973 (19 Nov)–**75**.　*Historic Buildings. T* **74** *and similar horiz designs. Multicoloured. P* 14 × 14½.
133　　1 c. Type **74** ....　10　　10
134　　2 c. Royal Engineers' Office (1.5.74) ....　10　　10
135　　3 c. Double Quarters for Free Overseers
　　　　　(19.2.75) ....　25　　15
136　　4 c. Guard House (12.7.74) ....　20　　15
137　　5 c. Entrance to Pentagonal Gaol ....　25　　15
138　　7 c. Pentagonal Gaol (1.5.74) ....　35　　25
139　　8 c. Prisoners' Barracks (19.2.75) ....　50　　35
140　　10 c. Officers' Quarters, New Military Barracks ..　50　　35
141　　12 c. New Military Barracks (1.5.74) ......　50　　25
142　　14 c. Beach Stores (12.7.74) ....　60　　45
143　　15 c. The Magazine (19.2.75) ....　80　　50

144　　20 c. Entrance, Old Military Barracks (12.7.74) .　80　　65
145　　25 c. Old Military Barracks (19.2.75) ....　1·25　90
146　　30 c. Old Stores (Crankmill) (1.5.74) ....　1·00　60
147　　50 c. Commissariat Stores ....　1·25　1·75
148　　$1 Government House (12.7.74) ....　2·25　3·50
　　　　Set of 16 ....　9·00　9·00
　　　　First Day Covers (4) ....　　　14·00

75 Royal Couple and Map

(Des Harrison)

1974 (8 Feb).　*Royal Visit. P* 14 × 14½.
149　**75**　7 c. multicoloured ....　40　　15
150　　　25 c. multicoloured ....　1·25　75
　　　　Set of 2 ....　1·60　90
　　　　First Day Cover　..............　　　1·40

76 Chichester's *Madame Elijah*

(Des B. McCoy. Litho State Bank Note Printing Works, Helsinki)

1974 (28 Mar).　*First Aircraft Landing on Norfolk Island. P* 14.
151　**76**　14 c. multicoloured ....　1·00　　70
　　　　　First Day Cover　.............　　　1·25

77 "Captain Cook"　　　**78** Nativity Scene
(engraving　　　　　　(pearl-shell pew carving)
by J. Basire)

(Des C. I. Buffett. Litho Questa)

1974 (8 Oct).　*Captain Cook Bicentenary* (4th issue). *Discovery of Norfolk Is. T* **77** *and similar vert designs. Multicoloured. P* 14.
152　　7 c. Type **77** ....　1·25　60
153　　10 c. H.M.S. *"Resolution"* (H. Roberts) ......　2·25　1·40
154　　14 c. Norfolk Island Pine ....　2·50　1·50
155　　25 c. "Norfolk Island flax" (G. Raper) ....　3·00　2·25
　　　　Set of 4 ....　8·00　5·25
　　　　First Day Cover　.................　　　8·00

(Des G. Hitch)

1974 (18 Oct).　*Christmas. P* 14½.
156　**78**　7 c. multicoloured ....　15　　10
157　　　30 c. multicoloured ....　60　　75
　　　　Set of 2 ....　75　　85
　　　　First Day Cover　.................　　　1·25

THE WORLD CENTRE FOR
FINE STAMPS IS 399 STRAND

79 Norfolk Pine

(Manufactured by Walsall)

1974 (16 Dec).   *Centenary of Universal Postal Union. T* **79** *and similar
"island"-shaped designs. Multicoloured. Imperf (backing-paper roul
20). Self-adhesive.*
158   10 c. Type **79**   35   40
159   15 c. Offshore islands   40   45
160   35 c. Crimson Rosella and Sacred Kingfisher . . .   70   75
161   40 c. Pacific map   75   90
      Set of 4 . . . .   2·00   2·25
      First Day Cover . . . .   3·75
MS162   106 × 101 mm. Map of Norfolk Is. cut-to-shape
      with reduced-size replicas of Nos. 158/61 . . . .   18·00   23·00
      First Day Cover . . . .   30·00

80 H.M.S. *Mermaid* (survey cutter)

(Manufactured by Walsall)

1975 (18 Aug).   *150th Anniv of Second Settlement. T* **80** *and similar
"island"-shaped design. Multicoloured. Imperf (backing-paper roul 20).
Self-adhesive.*
163   10 c. Type **80**   25   20
164   35 c. Kingston, 1835 (from painting by T. Seller)   45   35
      Set of 2   70   55
      First Day Cover . . . .   1·00

81 Star on Norfolk   82 Memorial Cross
   Island Pine

(Des Harrison)

1975 (6 Oct).   *Christmas. P* 14.
165   **81**   10 c. multicoloured   15   10
166   15 c. multicoloured   20   10
167   35 c. multicoloured   30   35
         Set of 3   60   45
         First Day Cover . . . .   1·00

(Des Harrison)

1975 (24 Nov).   *Centenary of St. Barnabas Chapel. T* **82** *and similar horiz
design. Multicoloured. P* 14.
168   30 c. Type **82**   20   15
169   60 c. Laying foundation stone and Chapel in
      1975   40   40
      Set of 2   60   55
      First Day Cover . . . .   1·10

83 Launching of *Resolution*   84 Whaleship *Charles
                                     W. Morgan*

(Des Harrison)

1975 (1 Dec).   *50th Anniv of Launching of Schooner "Resolution". T* **83**
and similar horiz design. Multicoloured. P 14.
170   25 c. Type **83**   25   20
171   45 c. *Resolution* at sea   40   35
      Set of 2   65   55
      First Day Cover . . . .   1·25

(Des Harrison)

1976 (5 July).   *Bicentenary of American Revolution. T* **84** *and similar
horiz designs. Multicoloured. P* 14.
172   18 c. Type **84**   25   15
173   25 c. Thanksgiving Service   35   20
174   40 c. "Flying Fortress" over Norfolk Is   65   35
175   45 c. California Quail   75   40
      Set of 4 . . . .   1·75   1·00
      First Day Cover . . . .   1·90

85 Swallow-tailed   86 *Bassaris itea*
   Tern and Sun

(Des Harrison)

1976 (4 Oct).   *Christmas. P* 14.
176   **85**   18 c. multicoloured   25   15
177   25 c. multicoloured   40   15
178   45 c. multicoloured   85   35
         Set of 3 . . . .   1·40   60
         First Day Cover . . . .   1·25

(Des B. Hargreaves)

1976 (17 Nov)–**77**.   *Butterflies and Moths. T* **86** *and similar horiz designs.
Multicoloured. P* 14.
179   1 c. Type **86**   10   15
180   2 c. *Utetheisa pulchelloides vaga* (22.2.77) . . .   10   15
181   3 c. *Agathia asterias jowettorum* (5.7.77)   10   10
182   4 c. *Cynthia kershawi* (5.7.77)   10   15
183   5 c. *Leucania loreyimima*   15   15
184   10 c. *Hypolimnas bolina nerina*   30   15
185   14 c. *Pyrrhorachis pyrrhoyuna subscrenulata*
      (22.2.77)   30   20
186   16 c. *Austrocarea iocephala millsi*   30   20
187   17 c. *Pseudocoremia christiani* (10.5.77)   35   20
188   18 c. *Cleora idiocrossa*   35   20
189   19 c. *Simplicia caeneusalis buffetti* (10.5.77) . . .   35   20
190   20 c. *Austrocidaria ralstonae* (10.5.77)   40   20
191   30 c. *Hippotion scrofa* (22.2.77)   50   35
192   40 c. *Papilio ilioneus ilioneus* (10.5.77)   55   40
193   50 c. *Tiracola plagiata* (22.2.77)   70   50
194   $1 *Precis villida calybe* . . . .   1·00   75
195   $2 *Cepora perimale perimale* (5.7.77) . . . . . .   1·75   1·00
      Set of 17 . . . .   6·50   4·50
      Presentation Pack (31.5.78) . . . .   8·00
      First Day Covers (4) . . . .   9·50

87 Queen's View, Kingston

(Des Harrison)

1977 (10 June). *Silver Jubilee. P* 14.
196	**87**	25 c.	multicoloured	35	25
			First Day Cover		55

88 Hibiscus Flowers and Oil Lamp

89 Captain Cook (from a portrait by Nathaniel Dance)

(Des Mrs. M. J. McCoy)

1977 (4 Oct). *Christmas. P* 14 × 14½.
197	**88**	18 c.	multicoloured	15	10
198		25 c.	multicoloured	15	10
199		45 c.	multicoloured	30	35
			Set of 3	55	50
			First Day Cover		90

(Des Harrison)

1978 (18 Jan). *Captain Cook Bicentenary* (5*th issue*). *Discovery of Hawaii. T* **89** *and similar horiz designs. Multicoloured. P* 14½.
200	18 c.	Type **89**	30	20
201	25 c.	Discovery of Northern Hawaiian islands	40	30
202	80 c.	British flag against island background	90	70
		Set of 3	1·40	1·40
		First Day Cover		2·25

90 Guide Flag and Globe

(Manufactured by Walsall)

1978 (22 Feb). 50*th Anniv of Girl Guides. T* **90** *and similar "island"-shaped designs. Multicoloured. Imperf* (*backing paper roul* 20). *Self-adhesive.*
203	18 c.	Type **90**	20	15
204	25 c.	Emblem and scarf badge	35	20
		a. Horiz roul omitted (vert pair)		
205	35 c.	Emblem and Queen Elizabeth	45	25
		a. Horiz roul omitted (vert pair)		
206	45 c.	Emblem and Lady Baden-Powell	55	35
		Set of 4	1·40	85
		First Day Cover		1·60

Nos. 204a and 205a each had all horizontal roulettes omitted from the sheet of 20.

91 St. Edward's Crown

(Des Harrison)

1978 (29 June). 25*th Anniv of Coronation. T* **91** *and similar horiz design. Multicoloured. P* 14½.
207	25 c.	Type **91**	15	15
208	70 c.	Coronation regalia	40	45
		Set of 2	55	60
		First Day Cover		90

92 View of Duncombe Bay with Scout at Camp Fire

(Des S. Jensen. Manufactured by Walsall)

1978 (22 Aug). 50*th Anniv of Boy Scouts. T* **92** *and similar "island"-shaped designs. Multicoloured. Imperf* (*backing paper roul* 20). *Self-adhesive.*
209	20 c.	Type **92**	25	15
210	25 c.	View from Kingston and emblem	40	20
211	35 c.	View of Anson Bay and Link Badge	60	25
212	45 c.	Sunset scene and Lord Baden-Powell	70	35
		Set of 4	1·75	85
		First Day Cover		1·60

93 Chart showing Route of Arctic Voyage

94 Poinsettia and Bible

(Des G. Hitch)

1978 (29 Aug). *Captain Cook Bicentenary* (6*th issue*). *Northernmost Voyages. T* **93** *and similar horiz design. Multicoloured. P* 14½.
213	25 c.	Type **93**	40	30
214	90 c.	"H.M.S. *Resolution* and H.M.S. *Discovery* in Pack Ice" (painting by Webber)	1·25	80
		Set of 2	1·60	1·10
		First Day Cover		1·90

(Des Mrs. M. J. McCoy)

1978 (3 Oct). *Christmas. T* **94** *and similar vert designs. Multicoloured. P* 14½ × 14.
215	20 c.	Type **94**	15	10
216	30 c.	Native Oak and Bible	20	15
217	55 c.	Hibiscus and Bible	30	30
		Set of 3	60	50
		First Day Cover		90

95 Cook and Village of Staithes near Marton

(Des Harrison)

1978 (27 Oct). *250th Birth Anniv of Captain Cook. T* **95** *and similar horiz design. Multicoloured. P* 14½.

218	20 c.	Type **95**	35	25
219	80 c.	Cook and Whitby Harbour	1·40	1·25
		Set of 2	1·75	1·50
		First Day Cover		2·25

96 H.M.S. *Resolution*

97 Assembly Building

(Des G. Hitch)

1979 (14 Feb). *Death Bicentenary of Captain Cook. T* **96** *and similar horiz designs. Multicoloured. P* 14.

220	20 c.	Type **96**	50	30
		a. Pair. Nos. 220/1	1·00	60
221	20 c.	Cook (statue)	50	30
222	40 c.	Cook's death	70	50
		a. Pair. Nos. 222/3	1·40	1·00
223	40 c.	Cook's death (different)	70	50
		Set of 4	2·40	1·60
		First Day Cover		2·40

The 20 c. designs depict the *Resolution* and Cook's statue on a map showing the last voyage. The 40 c. designs show Cook's death from an aquatint by John Clevely.

Nos. 220/1 and 222/3 were each printed together, *se-tenant*, in horizontal pairs throughout the sheets, forming composite designs.

1979 (10 Aug). *First Norfolk Island Legislative Assembly. P* 14½ × 14.

224	**97**	$1 multicoloured	50	50
		First Day Cover		1·00

98 Tasmania 1853 1d. Stamp and Sir Rowland Hill

1979 (27 Aug). *Death Centenary of Sir Rowland Hill. T* **98** *and similar horiz designs showing stamps and Sir Rowland Hill. P* 14 × 14½.

225	20 c.	new blue and sepia	20	10
226	30 c.	brown-red and olive-grey	25	15
227	55 c.	violet and indigo	40	30
		Set of 3	75	50
		First Day Cover		1·00
MS228	142 × 91 mm. No. 227. P 14		55	65
		First Day Cover		90

Designs:—30 c. Penny Red; 55 c. 1d. "Ball Bay".

99 I.Y.C. Emblem and Map of Pacific showing Norfolk Island as Pine Tree

(Des Claire Walters. Litho Asher and Co, Melbourne)

1979 (25 Sept). *International Year of the Child. P* 15.

229	**99**	80 c. multicoloured	40	45
		First Day Cover		90

100 Emily Bay

101 Lions International Emblem

1979 (5 Nov).* *Christmas. T* **100** *and similar horiz designs showing different aspects of Emily Bay. P* 12½ × 13.

230	15 c.	multicoloured	15	15
		a. Horiz strip of 3. Nos. 230/2	40	
231	20 c.	multicoloured	15	15
232	30 c.	multicoloured	15	15
		Set of 3	40	40
		First Day Cover		80
MS233	152 × 83 mm. Nos. 230/2. P 14 × 14½		65	1·00
		First Day Cover		1·75

Nos. 230/2 were printed together, *se-tenant*, in horizontal strips of 3 throughout the sheet, forming a composite design.

* Although released by the Crown Agents in London on 2 October the stamps were not released locally until 5 November.

(Des Norfolk Island Lions Club. Litho Asher and Co, Melbourne)

1980 (25 Jan). *Lions Convention. P* 15.

234	**101**	50 c. multicoloured	35	30
		First Day Cover		75

102 Rotary International Emblem

(Des E. Lenthall. Litho Asher and Co, Melbourne)

1980 (21 Feb). *75th Anniv of Rotary International. P* 15.

235	**102**	50 c. multicoloured	35	30
		a. Black (face value and "NORFOLK ISLAND") omitted		
		First Day Cover		75

103 "D.H. 60 (Gypsy Moth)" *Mme Elijah*

(Des G. Hitch. Litho Harrison)

1980 (25 Mar)–**81.** *Aeroplanes. Horiz designs as T* **103.** *Multicoloured. P* 14½ × 14.

236	1 c.	Hawker Siddeley "H.S. 748" (3.3.81)	15	10
237	2 c.	Type **103**	15	10
238	3 c.	Curtis "P-40 Kittyhawk"	15	10
239	4 c.	Chance Vought "F4U-1 Corsair" (19.8.80)	15	10
240	5 c.	Grumman "TBF-1c Avenger" (19.8.80) ..	15	10
241	15 c.	Douglas "SBD-5 Dauntless" (19.8.80) ...	20	20
242	20 c.	Cessna "172"	25	25
243	25 c.	Lockheed "Hudson" (3.3.81)	30	30
244	30 c.	Lockheed "PV-1 Ventura" (13.1.81)	40	35
245	40 c.	Avro "York" (3.3.81)	50	45
246	50 c.	Douglas "DC-3" (13.1.81)	65	55
247	60 c.	Avro "691 Lancastrian" (13.1.81)	75	65
248	80 c.	Douglas "DC-4" (13.1.81)	95	85
249	$1	Beechcraft "Super King Air" (3.3.81) ...	1·25	90
250	$2	Fokker "F-27 Friendship" (19.8.80)	2·25	90
251	$5	Lockheed "C-130 Hercules"	5·50	2·00
		Set of 16	12·00	6·50
		First Day Covers (4)		12·00

104 Queen Elizabeth the Queen Mother

(Des K. Williams. Litho Harrison)

1980 (4 Aug). *80th Birthday of Queen Elizabeth the Queen Mother. P* 14.

252	**104**	22 c. multicoloured	30	20
253		60 c. multicoloured	65	40
		Set of 2	95	60
		First Day Cover		1·00

105 Red-tailed Tropic Birds

(Des K. Williams. Litho Harrison)

1980 (28 Oct). *Christmas. Birds. T* **105** *and similar horiz designs. Multicoloured. P* 14 × 14½.

254	15 c.	Type **105**	35	25
		a. Horiz strip of 3. Nos. 254/6	95	
255	22 c.	White Terns	35	25
256	35 c.	White-capped Noddys	35	25
257	60 c.	White Terns (*different*)	60	45
		Set of 4	1·50	1·10
		First Day Cover		1·60

Nos. 254/6 were printed together, *se-tenant*, in horizontal strips of 3 throughout the sheet.

106 *Morayshire* and View of Norfolk Island

107 Wedding Bouquet from Norfolk Island

(Des Jennifer Toombs. Litho Harrison)

1981 (5 June). *125th Anniv of Pitcairn Islanders' Migration to Norfolk Island. T* **106** *and similar horiz designs. Multicoloured. P* 14½.

258	5 c.	Type **106**	15	15
259	35 c.	Islanders arriving ashore	55	30
260	60 c.	View of new settlement	85	45
		Set of 3	1·40	80
		First Day Cover		1·40
MS261		183 × 127 mm. Nos. 258/60	1·50	1·40
		First Day Cover		2·00

(Des J.W. Litho Harrison)

1981 (22 July). *Royal Wedding. T* **107** *and similar vert designs. Multicoloured. P* 14.

262	35 c.	Type **107**	20	15
263	55 c.	Prince Charles at horse trials	35	25
264	60 c.	Prince Charles and Lady Diana Spencer ..	35	35
		Set of 3	80	65
		First Day Cover		1·40

108 Uniting Church of Australia

109 Pair of White-chested White Eyes

(Des K. Williams. Litho Harrison)

1981 (15 Sept). *Christmas. Churches. T* **108** *and similar horiz designs. Multicoloured. P* 14½ × 14.

265	18 c.	Type **108**	20	10
266	24 c.	Seventh Day Adventist Church	25	15
267	30 c.	Church of the Sacred Heart	30	20
268	$1	St. Barnabas Chapel	70	70
		Set of 4	1·25	1·00
		First Day Cover		1·75

(Des P. Slater. Litho Questa)

1981 (10 Nov). *White-chested White Eye ("Silvereye"). T* **109** *and similar horiz designs. Multicoloured. P* 14 × 14½.

269	35 c.	Type **109**	45	40
		a. Horiz strip of 5. Nos. 269/73	2·25	
270	35 c.	Bird on nest	45	40
271	35 c.	Bird with egg	45	40
272	35 c.	Parents with chicks	45	40
273	35 c.	Fledgelings	45	40
		Set of 5	2·25	2·00
		Presentation Pack	2·75	
		First Day Cover		2·25

Nos. 269/73 were printed together, *se-tenant*, in horizontal strips of 5 throughout the sheet.

110 Aerial View of Philip Island

(Des local artist. Litho Harrison)

1982 (12 Jan). *Philip and Nepean Islands. T* **110** *and similar horiz designs. Multicoloured. P* 14 × 13½.

274	24 c.	Type **110**	25	25
		a. Horiz strip of 5. Nos. 274/8	1·10	
275	24 c.	Close-up view of Philip Island landscape ..	25	25
276	24 c.	Gecko (*Phyllodactylus guentheri*), Philip Island	25	25
277	24 c.	Sooty Tern (*Sterna fuscata*), Philip Island .	25	25
278	24 c.	Philip Island Hibiscus (*Hibiscus insularis*) .	25	25
279	35 c.	Aerial view of Nepean Island	35	35
		a. Horiz strip of 5. Nos. 279/83	1·60	

280	35 c.	Close-up view of Nepean Island landscape	35	35
281	35 c.	Gecko (*Phyllodactylus guentheri*), Nepean Island	35	35
282	35 c.	Blue-faced Boobies (*Sula dactylatra*), Nepean Island	35	35
283	35 c.	*Carpobrotus glaucescens* (flower), Nepean Island	35	35
		Set of 10	2·50	2·50
		First Day Cover		3·25

The five designs of each value were printed together, *se-tenant*, in horizontal strips of 5 throughout the sheet.

111 Sperm Whale

(Des Jennifer Toombs. Litho Harrison)

1982 (23 Feb). *Whales. T 111 and similar horiz designs.* P 14½.

284	24 c.	multicoloured	45	35
285	55 c.	multicoloured	85	75
286	80 c.	black, mauve and stone	1·10	1·00
		Set of 3	2·25	1·90
		Presentation Pack	2·75	
		First Day Cover		2·25

Designs:—55 c. Black Right Whale; 80 c. Humpback Whale.

112 *Diocet*, Wrecked 20 April 1873

(Litho Harrison)

1982 (18 May–27 July). *Shipwrecks. T 112 and similar horiz designs. Multicoloured.* P 14½ × 14.

287	24 c.	H.M.S. *Sirius*, wrecked 19 March 1790 (27 July)	30	30
288	27 c.	Type **112**	30	30
289	35 c.	*Friendship*, wrecked 17 May 1835 (27 July)	40	40
290	40 c.	*Mary Hamilton*, wrecked 6 May 1873	50	50
291	55 c.	*Fairlie*, wrecked 14 February 1840 (27 July)	65	70
292	65 c.	*Warrigal*, wrecked 18 March 1918	80	85
		Set of 6	2·75	2·75
		Presentation Packs (2)	6·00	
		First Day Covers (2)		3·50

C-KURITY PAPER. The following issues up to No. 342 were all printed on this type of security paper, *unless otherwise stated.* It shows a pattern of blue fluorescent markings, resembling rosettes, on the reverse beneath the gum.

(Des A. Theobald. Litho Walsall)

1982 (7 Sept). *Christmas. 40th Anniv of first Supply-plane Landings on Norfolk Island (Christmas Day 1942). T 113 and similar horiz designs. Multicoloured.* P 14.

293	27 c.	Type **113**	30	35
294	40 c.	"Hudson" landing Christmas supplies, 1942	45	50
295	75 c.	Christmas, 1942	90	95
		Set of 3	1·50	1·60
		Presentation Pack	2·00	
		First Day Cover		1·90

(Des W. Fenton. Litho Questa)

1982 (9 Nov). *Military Uniforms. T 114 and similar vert designs. Multicoloured.* P 14½ × 14.

296	27 c.	Type **114**	30	35
297	40 c.	58th (Rutlandshire) Regiment	45	50
298	55 c.	80th (Staffordshire Volunteers) Battalion Company	65	80
299	65 c.	11th (North Devonshire) Regiment	80	1·00
		Set of 4	2·00	2·50
		Presentation Pack (14.2.83)	2·50	
		First Day Cover		2·75

115 *Panaeolus papilionaceus*

116 Beechcraft "18" Aircraft

(Des Jane Thatcher. Litho Enschedé)

1983 (29 Mar). *Fungi. T 115 and similar vert designs. Multicoloured.* P 13½ × 13.

300	27 c.	Type **115**	30	35
301	40 c.	*Coprinus domesticus*	45	50
302	55 c.	*Marasmius niveus*	65	70
303	65 c.	*Cymatoderma elegans var. lamellatum*	80	85
		Set of 4	2·00	2 25
		Presentation Pack	2·50	
		First Day Cover		2·50

(Des Walsall. Litho Format)

1983 (12 July). *Bicentenary of Manned Flight. T 116 and similar horiz designs. Multicoloured.* P 14½ × 14.

304	10 c.	Type **116**	15	15
305	27 c.	Fokker "F 28 Fellowship"	30	35
306	45 c.	French military "DC 4"	50	60
307	75 c.	Sikorsky helicopter	90	95
		Set of 4	1·60	1·90
		First Day Cover		2·25
MS308		105 × 100 mm. Nos. 304/7	1·75	2·00
		First Day Cover		2·25

113 R.N.Z.A.F. "Hudson" dropping Christmas Supplies, 1942

114 50th (Queen's Own) Regiment

117 St. Matthew

118 Cable Ship *Chantik*

(Des McCombie-Skinner Studio. Litho Format)

1983 (13 Sept). *Christmas. 150th Birth Anniv of Sir Edward Burne-Jones. T* **117** *and similar vert designs showing stained-glass windows from St. Barnabas Chapel, Norfolk Island. Multicoloured. P* 14.

309	5 c.	Type **117**	10	10
310	24 c.	St. Mark	30	30
311	30 c.	Jesus Christ	40	40
312	45 c.	St. Luke	55	55
313	85 c.	St. John	1·10	1·10
		Set of 5	2·25	2·25
		Presentation Pack	3·25	
		First Day Cover		2·50

(Des G. Drummond. Litho Format)

1983 (15 Nov). *World Communications Year. ANZCAN Cable. T* **118** *and similar horiz designs. Ordinary paper. Multicoloured. P* 14½ × 14.

314	30 c.	Type **118**	40	40
315	45 c.	*Chantik* during in-shore operations	55	55
316	75 c.	Cable ship *Mercury*	95	95
317	85 c.	Diagram of cable route	1·10	1·10
		Set of 4	2·75	2·75
		Presentation Pack	3·50	
		First Day Cover		3·00

119 Popwood   120 *Cheilodactylidae*

(Des I. Loe. Litho B.D.T.)

1984 (10 Jan–27 Mar). *Flowers. T* **119** *and similar vert designs. Multicoloured. P* 14.

318	1 c.	Type **119** (27.3)	10	15
319	2 c.	Strand Morning Glory	10	15
320	3 c.	Native Phreatia	15	15
321	4 c.	Philip Island Wisteria (27.3)	15	15
322	5 c.	Norfolk Island Palm (27.3)	15	15
323	10 c.	Evergreen	20	15
324	15 c.	Bastard Oak (27.3)	30	20
325	20 c.	Devil's Guts	35	25
326	25 c.	White Oak	40	35
327	30 c.	Ti (27.3)	55	40
328	35 c.	Philip Island Hibiscus (27.3)	55	40
329	40 c.	Native Wisteria	60	45
330	50 c.	Native Jasmine	70	50
331	$1	Norfolk Island Hibiscus (27.3)	1·10	1·00
332	$3	Native Oberonia (27.3)	3·00	2·75
333	$5	Norfolk Island Pine	4·00	4·00
		Set of 16	11·00	10·00
		Presentation Pack (27 March)	13·00	
		First Day Covers (2)		15·00

(Des Marg Towt. Litho Cambec Press, Melbourne)

1984 (17 April). *Reef Fishes. T* **120** *and similar horiz designs. Multicoloured. Ordinary paper. P* 13½ × 14.

334	30 c.	Type **120**	40	45
335	45 c.	*Pseudopeneus signatus*	60	65
336	75 c.	*Acanthuridae*	1·00	1·10
337	85 c.	*Chaeton ancinetus*	1·25	1·40
		Set of 4	2·75	3·25
		Presentation Pack	3·50	
		First Day Cover		3·50

MINIMUM PRICE

The minimum price quoted is 10p which represents a handling charge rather than a basis for valuing common stamps. For further notes about prices see introductory pages.

Norfolk Island 30c

121 Owl with Eggs   **122** 1953 7½d. and 1974 Cook Bicent
                                       10 c. Stamps

(Des P. Slater. Litho Questa)

1984 (17 July). *Boobook Owl. T* **121** *and similar vert designs. Multicoloured. P* 14.

338	30 c.	Type **121**	50	50
		a. Horiz strip of 5. Nos. 338/42	2·50	
339	30 c.	Fledgeling	50	50
340	30 c.	Young owl on stump	50	50
341	30 c.	Adult on branch	50	50
342	30 c.	Owl in flight	50	50
		Set of 5	2·50	2·50
		Presentation Pack	3·25	
		First Day Cover		3·25

Nos. 338/42 were printed together, *se-tenant*, in horizontal strips of 5 throughout the sheet.

(Des D. Miller. Litho Harrison)

1984 (18 Sept). *"Ausipex" International Stamp Exhibition, Melbourne. T* **122** *and similar horiz designs. Multicoloured. W w* **14** *(sideways). P* 14.

343	30 c.	Type **122**	30	35
344	45 c.	John Buffett commemorative postal stationery envelope	45	55
345	75 c.	Design from Presentation Pack for 1982 Military Uniforms issue	90	1·25
		Set of 3	1·50	2·00
		First Day Cover		2·50
MS346	151 × 93 mm. Nos. 343/5. P 14½		2·10	2·50
		First Day Cover		3·00

Norfolk Island 30c

5c
Norfolk Island

123 Font, Kingston   124 The Revd. Nobbs
Methodist Church   teaching Pitcairn
                             Islanders

(Des R. Murphy. Litho Questa)

1984 (9 Oct). *Christmas. Centenary of Methodist Church on Norfolk Island. T* **123** *and similar vert designs. Multicoloured. W w* **14**. *P* 14.

347	5 c.	Type **123**	10	10
348	24 c.	Church service in Old Barracks, Kingston, late 1800's	35	40
349	30 c.	The Revd. & Mrs. A. H. Phelps and sailing ship	40	45
350	45 c.	The Revd. A. H. Phelps and First Congregational Church, Chester, U.S.A.	60	65
351	85 c.	Interior of Kingston Methodist Church	1·25	1·40
		Set of 5	2·40	2·50
		First Day Cover		2·75

(Des D. Hopkins. Litho B.D.T.)

1984 (6 Nov).   *Death Centenary of the Revd. George Hunn Nobbs (leader of Pitcairn community). T **124** and similar vert designs. Multicoloured. W w **14**. P 14 × 15.*

352	30 c.	Type **124**	40	45
353	45 c.	The Revd. Nobbs with sick islander	60	65
354	75 c.	Baptising baby	1·00	1·10
355	85 c.	Presented to Queen Victoria, 1852	1·25	1·40
		Set of 4	3·00	3·25
		Presentation Pack	3·50	
		First Day Cover		3·50

125 *Fanny Fisher*

126 The Queen Mother
(from photo by Norman Parkinson)

(Des D. Hopkins. Litho Cambec Press, Melbourne)

1985 (19 Feb).   *19th-Century Whaling Ships (1st series). T **125** and similar horiz designs. Multicoloured. P 13½ × 14.*

356	5 c.	Type **125**	20	10
357	33 c.	Costa Rica Packet	55	40
358	50 c.	Splendid	80	75
359	90 c.	Onward............................	1·25	1·50
		Set of 4	2·50	2·50
		First Day Cover		3·25

See also Nos. 360/3.

(Des D. Hopkins. Litho Cambec Press, Melbourne)

1985 (30 Apr).   *19th-Century Whaling Ships (2nd series). Horiz designs as T **125**. Multicoloured. P 13½ × 14.*

360	15 c.	Waterwitch......................	40	25
361	20 c.	Canton	50	35
362	60 c.	Aladdin	1·10	85
363	80 c.	California	1·40	1·40
		Set of 4	3·00	2·50
		Presentation Pack (Nbs. 356/63)	5·75	
		First Day Cover		3·25

(Des A. Theobald ($1), C. Abbott (others). Litho Questa)

1985 (6 June).   *Life and Times of Queen Elizabeth the Queen Mother. T **126** and similar vert designs. Multicoloured. W w **16**. P 14½ × 14.*

364	5 c.	The Queen Mother (from photo by Dorothy Wilding)	10	10
365	33 c.	With Princess Anne at Trooping the Colour	35	40
366	50 c.	Type **126**	50	55
367	90 c.	With Prince Henry at his christening (from photo by Lord Snowdon)	95	1·00
		Set of 4	1·75	1·90
		First Day Cover		2·40
MS368		91 × 75 mm. $1 With Princess Anne at Ascot Races. Wmk sideways	1·10	1·25
		First Day Cover		1·50

(Des from children's paintings. Litho Cambec Press, Melbourne)

1985 (9 July).   *International Youth Year. T **127** and similar horiz design. Multicoloured. P 13½ × 14.*

369	33 c.	Type **127**	60	40
370	50 c.	"A Walk in the Country"	90	55
		Set of 2	1·50	95
		First Day Cover		1·50

(Des Flett Henderson & Arnold. Litho Cambec Press, Melbourne)

1985 (10 Sept).   *125th Anniv of Royal Norfolk Island Agricultural and Horticultural Show. T **128** and similar horiz design. Multicoloured. P 13½ × 14.*

371	80 c.	Type **128**	75	80
372	90 c.	Show exhibits	85	90
		Set of 2	1·60	1·75
		First Day Cover		2·25
MS373		132 × 85 mm. Nos. 371/2..............	1·60	2·00
		First Day Cover		2·50

129 Shepherds with Flock   **130** Long-spined Sea Urchin

(Des R. Murphy. Litho Cambec Press, Melbourne)

1985 (3 Oct).   *Christmas. T **129** and similar vert designs. Multicoloured. P 13½.*

374	27 c.	Type **129**	50	30
375	33 c.	Mary and Joseph with donkey	60	40
376	50 c.	The Three Wise Men	80	55
377	90 c.	The Nativity	1·25	90
		Set of 4	2·75	1·90
		First Day Cover		2·40

(Des L. Curtis. Litho Cambec Press, Melbourne)

1986 (14 Jan).   *Marine Life. T **130** and similar horiz designs. Multicoloured. P 13½ × 14.*

378	5 c.	Type **130**	10	10
379	33 c.	Blue Starfish	30	35
380	55 c.	Eagle Ray	50	55
381	75 c.	Moray Eel	70	75
		Set of 4	1·40	1·60
		First Day Cover		2·25
MS382		100 × 95 mm. Nos. 378/81..............	1·75	2·00
		First Day Cover		2·50

131 *Giotto* Spacecraft   **132** Isaac Robinson
(U.S. Consul 1887–1908)

127 "Swimming"   **128** Prize-winning Cow and Owner

(Des G. Revell. Litho Leigh-Mardon Ltd, Melbourne)

1986 (11 Mar). *Appearance of Halley's Comet. T* **131** *and similar vert design. Multicoloured. P* 14½ × 15.

383	$1 Type **131**	1·50	1·25
a.	Horiz pair. Nos. 383/4	3·00	2·50
384	$1 Halley's Comet	1·50	1·25
	Set of 2	3·00	2·50
	First Day Cover		3·00

Nos. 383/4 were printed together, *se-tenant*, in horizontal pairs throughout the sheet, each pair forming a composite design.

(Des G. Revell. Litho Cambec Press, Melbourne)

1986 (22 May). *"Ameripex '86" International Stamp Exhibition, Chicago. T* **132** *and similar multicoloured designs. P* 13½.

385	33 c. Type **132**	60	35
386	50 c. Ford "Model T" (first vehicle on island) (horiz)	80	50
387	80 c. Statue of Liberty	1·10	80
	Set of 3	2·25	1·50
	First Day Cover		2·25
MS388	125 × 100 mm. Nos. 385/7	2·25	2·50
	First Day Cover		3·25

No. 387 also commemorates the Centenary of the Statue of Liberty.

133 Princess Elizabeth and Dog   **134** Stylized Dove and Norfolk Island

(Des Allison Ryves. Litho Cambec Press, Melbourne)

1986 (12 June). *60th Birthday of Queen Elizabeth II. T* **133** *and similar vert designs. Multicoloured. P* 13½.

389	5 c. Type **133**	10	10
390	33 c. Queen Elizabeth II	35	35
391	80 c. Opening Norfolk Island Golf Club	85	85
392	90 c. With Duke of Edinburgh in carriage	90	90
	Set of 4	2·00	2·00
	First Day Cover		2·50

(Des Lyn Studham. Litho Cambec Press, Melbourne)

1986 (23 Sept). *Christmas. P* 13½ × 14.

393	**134** 30 c. multicoloured	25	30
394	40 c. multicoloured	35	40
395	$1 multicoloured	90	95
	Set of 3	1·40	1·50
	First Day Cover		2·00

135 British Convicts, 1787   **136** Stone Tools

(Des Josephine Martin. Litho Cambec Press, Melbourne)

1986 (14 Oct—16 Dec). *Bicentenary of Norfolk Island Settlement (1988)* (1st issue). *Governor Phillip's Commission. T* **135** *and similar vert designs. Multicoloured. P* 14 × 13½.

396	36 c. Type **135**	60	35
397	55 c. Judge passing sentence of transportation	90	55
398	90 c. Governor Phillip meeting Home Secretary (inscr "Home Society")	1·40	85

399	90 c. As No. 398, but correctly inscr "Home Secretary" (16.12)	1·40	85
400	$1 Captain Arthur Phillip	1·60	95
	Set of 5	5·50	3·25
	First Day Covers (2)		4·00

See also Nos. 401/4, 421/4, 433/5, 436/7 and 438/43.

(Des B. Clinton. Litho Cambec Press, Melbourne)

1986 (16 Dec). *Bicentenary of Norfolk Island Settlement (1988)* (2nd issue). *Pre-European Occupation. T* **136** *and similar horiz designs. Multicoloured. P* 13½.

401	36 c. Type **136**	65	35
402	36 c. Bananas and taro	65	35
403	36 c. Polynesian outrigger canoe	65	35
404	36 c. Maori chief	65	35
	Set of 4	2·40	1·25
	First Day Cover		1·75

137 Philip Island from Point Ross   **138** Male Red-fronted Parakeet

(Des C. Abbott. Litho CPE Australia Ltd, Melbourne)

1987 (17 Feb)–**88**. *Norfolk Island Scenes. T* **137** *and similar square designs. Multicoloured. P* 13½.

405	1 c. Cockpit Creek Bridge (17.5.88)	10	10
406	2 c. Cemetery Bay Beach (17.5.88)	10	10
407	3 c. Island guesthouse (17.5.88)	10	10
408	5 c. Type **137**	10	10
409	15 c. Cattle in pasture (27.7.87)	10	15
410	30 c. Rock fishing (7.4.87)	20	25
411	37 c. Old Pitcairn-style house (27.7.87)	30	35
412	40 c. Shopping centre (7.4.87)	30	35
413	50 c. Emily Bay	40	45
414	60 c. Bloody Bridge (27.7.87)	45	50
415	80 c. Pitcairner-style shop (7.4.87)	60	65
416	90 c. Government House	70	75
417	$1 Melanesian Memorial Chapel	75	80
418	$2 Convict Settlement, Kingston (7.4.87)	1·50	1·60
419	$3 Ball Bay (27.7.87)	2·25	2·40
420	$5 Northern cliffs (17.5.88)	3·75	4·00
	Set of 16	10·50	11·50
	Presentation Pack (17.5.88)	15·00	
	First Day Covers (4)		20·00
	Souvenir Postcards (set of 16)	2·25	20·00

(Des Josephine Martin. Litho CPE Australia Ltd, Melbourne)

1987 (13 May). *Bicentary of Norfolk Island Settlement (1988)* (3rd issue). *issue). The First Fleet. Vert designs as T* **135**. *Multicoloured. P* 14 × 13½.

421	5 c. Loading supplies, Deptford	15	15
422	55 c. Fleet leaving Spithead	90	75
	a. Horiz pair. Nos. 422/3	1·75	1·50
423	55 c. H.M.S. *Sirius* leaving Spithead	90	75
424	$1 Female convicts below decks	1·50	1·25
	Set of 4	3·00	2·75
	First Day Cover		3·25

Nos. 422/3 were printed together, *se-tenant*, in horizontal pairs throughout the sheet, forming a composite design.

(Des P. Slater. Litho CPE Australia Ltd, Melbourne)

1987 (16 Sept). *Red-fronted Parakeet ("Green Parrot"). T* **138** *and similar vert designs. Multicoloured. P* 14 × 13½.

425	5 c. Type **138**	25	25
	a. Horiz strip of 4. Nos. 425/8	1·60	
426	15 c. Adult with fledgeling and egg	35	35
427	36 c. Young parakeets	50	50
428	55 c. Female parakeet	70	70
	Set of 4	1·60	1·60
	First Day Cover		2·00

Nos. 425/8 were printed together, *se-tenant*, in horizontal strips of four throughout the sheet.

139 Christmas Tree and
Restored Garrison Barracks

(Des T. Bland and Alison Ryves. Litho CPE Australia Ltd, Melbourne)

1987 (13 Oct).   *Christmas. T 139 and similar horiz designs. Multicoloured.*
P 13½ × 14.

429	30 c. Type **139**	25	30
430	42 c. Children opening presents	35	40
431	58 c. Father Christmas with children	50	55
432	63 c. Children's party	55	60
	Set of 4	1·50	1·60
	First Day Cover		2·25

(Des Josephine Martin. Litho CPE Australia Ltd, Melbourne)

1987 (8 Dec).   *Bicentenary of Norfolk Island Settlement (1988) (4th issue).*
Visit of La Perouse (navigator). Vert designs as T 135. Multicoloured.
P 14 × 13½.

433	37 c. La Perouse with King Louis XVI	45	45
434	90 c. *L'Astrolabe* and *La Boussole* off Norfolk Island	1·00	1·00
435	$1 *L'Astrolabe* wrecked in Solomon Islands ..	1·25	1·25
	Set of 3	2·40	2·40
	First Day Cover		3·00

(Des Josephine Martin. Litho CPE Australia Ltd, Melbourne)

1988 (25 Jan).   *Bicentenary of Norfolk Island Settlement (5th issue).*
Arrival of First Fleet at Sydney. Vert designs as T 135. Multicoloured.
P 14 × 13½.

436	37 c. Ship's cutter approaching Port Jackson ...	50	50
437	$1 Landing at Sydney Cove	1·40	1·40
	Set of 2	1·90	1·90
	First Day Cover		2·40

(Des Josephine Martin. Litho CPE Australia Ltd, Melbourne)

1988 (4 Mar).   *Bicentenary of Norfolk Island Settlement (6th issue).*
Foundation of First Settlement. Vert designs as T 135. Multicoloured.
P 14 × 13½.

438	5 c. Lt. Philip Gidley King	10	10
439	37 c. Raising the flag. March 1788	45	45
440	55 c. King exploring	60	60
441	70 c. Landing at Sydney Bay, Norfolk Island	75	75
442	90 c. H.M.S. *Supply* (brig)	1·00	1·00
443	$1 Sydney Bay settlement, 1788	1·25	1·25
	Set of 6	3·75	3·75
	First Day Cover		4·50

140 Airliner, Container Ship
and Sydney Harbour Bridge

141 Flowers and
Decorations

(Des Janet Boschen. Litho CPE Australia Ltd, Melbourne)

1988 (30 July).   *"Sydpex '88" National Stamp Exhibition, Sydney. T 140*
and similar multicoloured designs. P 14 × 13½ (vert) or 13½ × 14 (horiz).

444	37 c. Type **140**	35	40
445	37 c. Exhibition label under magnifying glass (*horiz*)	35	40
446	37 c. Telephone and dish aerial	35	40
	Set of 3	95	1·10
	First Day Cover		1·90

MS447	118 × 84 mm. Nos. 444/6.	1·00	1·25
	First Day Cover		2·00

In No. **MS447** the horizontal design is perforated 14 at foot and 13½ on
the other three sides.

(Des Sue Pearson. Litho CPE Australia Ltd, Melbourne)

1988 (27 Sept).   *Christmas. T 141 and similar vert designs. Multicoloured.*
P 14 × 13½.

448	30 c. Type **141**	30	35
449	42 c. Flowers	40	45
450	58 c. Fishes and beach	55	60
451	63 c. Norfolk Island	60	65
	Set of 4	1·60	1·90
	First Day Cover		2·50

142 Pier Store and Boat
Shed

143 *Lamprima aenea*

(Des R. Murphy. Litho CPE Australia Ltd, Melbourne)

1988 (6 Dec).   *Restored Buildings from the Convict Era. T 142 and similar*
horiz designs. Multicoloured. P 13½ × 14.

452	39 c. Type **142**	35	40
453	55 c. Royal Engineers Building	50	55
454	90 c. Old Military Barracks	85	90
455	$1 Commissariat Store and New Military Barracks	95	1·00
	Set of 4	2·40	2·50
	First Day Cover		3·00

(Des T. Nolan. Litho CPE Australia Ltd, Melbourne)

1989 (14 Feb).   *Endemic Insects. T 143 and similar horiz designs.*
Multicoloured. P 13½ × 14.

456	39 c. Type **143**	35	40
457	55 c. *Insulascirtus nythos*	50	55
458	90 c. *Caedicia araucariae*	85	90
459	$1 *Thrincophora aridela*	95	1·00
	Set of 4	2·40	2·50
	First Day Cover		3·00

144 H.M.S. *Bounty*
off Tasmania

145 Norfolk Island
Flag

(Des C. Abbott. Litho CPE Australia Ltd, Melbourne (Nos. 460/3), B.D.T.
(No. **MS**464))

1989 (28 Apr).   *Bicentenary of the Mutiny on the Bounty. T 144 and*
similar horiz designs. Multicoloured. P 13½.

460	5 c. Type **144**	20	20
461	39 c. Mutineers and Polynesian women, Pitcairn Island	60	60
462	55 c. Lake Windermere, Cumbria (Christian's home county)	80	80
463	$1.10, "Mutineers casting Bligh adrift" (Robert Dodd)	1·60	1·60
	Set of 4	3·00	3·00
	First Day Cover		3·50
MS464	110 × 85 mm. 39 c. No. 461; 90 c. Isle of Man 1989 35p. Mutiny stamp; $1 Pitcairn Islands 1989 Settlement Bicent 90 c., P 14.	2·50	2·50
	First Day Cover		3·00

(Des R. Fletcher. Litho CPE Australia Ltd, Melbourne)

1989 (10 Aug).   *10th Anniv of Internal Self-Government. T* **145** *and similar vert designs. Multicoloured. P* 14 × 13½.
465	41 c. Type **145**		55	55
466	55 c. Old ballot box		65	65
467	$1 Norfolk Island Act, 1979		1·25	1·25
468	$1.10, Island crest		1·40	1·40
	Set of 4		3·50	3·50
	First Day Cover			4·00

146 Red Cross   **147** "Gethsemane"

(Des E. Lenthall. Litho CPE Australia Ltd, Melbourne)

1989 (25 Sept).   *75th Anniv of Red Cross on Norfolk Island. P* 13½.
469 **146**	$1 bright rose-red and ultramarine	1·25	1·25
	First Day Cover		1·60

(Des Sue Pearson. Litho CPE Australia Ltd, Melbourne)

1989 (9 Oct).   *Christmas. T* **147** *and similar horiz designs showing opening lines of hymns and local scenes. Multicoloured. P* 13½ × 14.
470	36 c. Type **147**	45	40
471	60 c. "In the Sweet Bye and Bye"	65	60
472	75 c. "Let the Lower Lights Be Burning"	85	75
473	80 c. "The Beautiful Stream"	90	80
	Set of 4	2·50	2·25
	First Day Cover		2·75

148 John Royle (first announcer)

149 H.M.S. *Bounty* on fire, Pitcairn Island, 1790

(Des Philatelic Studios. Litho Leigh-Mardon Ltd, Melbourne)

1989 (21 Nov).   *50th Anniv of Radio Australia. T* **148** *and similar vert designs each showing Kingston buildings. Multicoloured. P* 14 × 13½.
474	41 c. Type **148**	55	50
475	65 c. Radio waves linking Australia and Norfolk Island	75	70
476	$1.10, Anniversary kookaburra logo	1·25	1·10
	Set of 3	2·25	2·10
	First Day Cover		2·50

(Des G. Hitch. Litho Leigh-Mardon Ltd, Melbourne)

1990 (23 Jan).   *History of the Norfolk Islanders* (1st series). *Settlement on Pitcairn Island. T* **149** *and similar vert design. Multicoloured. P* 14½.
477	70 c. Type **149**	80	80
478	$1.10, Arms of Norfolk Island	1·25	1·25
	Set of 2	2·00	2·00
	First Day Cover		2·40

150 H.M.S. *Sirius* striking Reef

(Des Maree Edmiston. Litho Leigh-Mardon Ltd, Melbourne)

1990 (19 Mar).   *Bicentenary of Wreck of H.M.S. Sirius. T* **150** *and similar horiz designs. Multicoloured. P* 13½.
479	41 c. Type **150**	60	60
	a. Horiz pair. Nos. 479/80	1·10	1·10
480	41 c. H.M.S. *Sirius* failing to clear bay	60	60
481	65 c. Divers at work on wreck	80	80
482	$1 Recovered artifacts and chart of site	1·25	1·25
	Set of 4	2·75	2·75
	First Day Cover		3·00

Nos. 479/80 were printed together, *se-tenant*, in horizontal pairs throughout the sheet, each pair forming a composite design.

151 Unloading Lighter, Kingston

152 *Ile de Lumiere* (freighter)

(Des Philatelic Studios, Melbourne. Litho Leigh-Mardon Ltd, Melbourne)

1990 (17 July).   *Ships. T* **151** *and horiz designs as T* **152**. *P* 14 × 14½ (5, 10 *c.*) or 14½ (70 *c.*, $2).
487	**151**	5 c. purple-brown	10	10
488		10 c. ochre	10	10
492	**152**	70 c. multicoloured	55	60
497	—	$2 multicoloured	1·50	1·60
		Set of 4	2·00	2·10
		First Day Cover		2·75

Design: — $2 H.M.A.S. *Success* (supply ship).

153 Santa on House Roof

(Des G. Hitch, adapted Philatelic Studios. Litho Leigh-Mardon Ltd, Melbourne)

1990 (25 Sept).   *Christmas. T* **153** *and similar multicoloured designs. P* 14½.
499	38 c. Type **153**	35	40
500	43 c. Santa at Kingston Post Office	35	40
501	65 c. Santa over Sydney Bay, Kingston (*horiz*) . . .	55	60
502	85 c. Santa on Officers' Quarters (*horiz*)	75	80
	Set of 4	1·75	2·00
	First Day Cover		2·25

Papua New Guinea

1914 12 Pence = 1 Shilling
20 Shillings = 1 Australian Pound
1966 100 Cents = 1 Australian Dollar
1975 100 Toea = 1 Kina

NEW GUINEA

Part of the German Empire from 1888, New Guinea was occupied by Australian forces in 1914.

Stamps of Germany and later of German New Guinea were used in New Guinea from 1888 until 1914.

During the interim period between the "G.R.I." surcharges and the "N.W. PACIFIC ISLANDS" overprints, stamps of Australia perforated "OS" were utilised.

PRICES FOR STAMPS ON COVER

Nos. 1/30	from × 3
Nos. 31/2	—
Nos. 33/49	from × 3
Nos. 50/9	from × 2
Nos. 60/2	—
Nos. 63/4	from × 2
Nos. 64c/q	—
Nos. 65/81	from × 5
Nos. 83/5	—
Nos. 86/97	from × 5
No. 99	—
Nos. 100/16	from × 4
Nos. 117/18	—
Nos. 119/24	from × 4
Nos. 125/203	from × 2
Nos. 204/5	—
Nos. 206/11	from × 8
Nos. 212/25	from × 2
Nos. O1/33	from × 8

PRICES

George V issues (1914–1935)

First column = Mounted Mint
Second column = Used

AUSTRALIAN OCCUPATION

Stamps of German New Guinea surcharged

G.R.I.

2d.

(2)

G.R.I.

1s.

G.R.I.

1d.

(3)

SETTINGS. The "G.R.I." issues of New Guinea were surcharged on a small hand press which could only accommodate one horizontal row of stamps at a time. In addition to complete sheets the surcharges were also applied to multiples and individual stamps which were first lightly affixed to plain paper backing sheets. Such backing sheets could contain a mixture of denominations, some of which required further surcharges.

Specialists recognise twelve settings of the low value surcharges (1d. to 8d.):

Setting 1 (Nos. 1/4, 7/11) shows the bottom of the "R" 6 mm from the top of the "d".
Setting 2 (Nos. 16/19, 22/6) shows the bottom of the "R" 5 mm from the top of the "d".
Setting 3 was used for the Official stamps (Nos. O1/2).
Setting 4, which included the 2½d. value for the first time, and Setting 5 showed individual stamps with either 6 mm or 5 mm spacing.

These five settings were for rows of ten stamps, but the remaining seven, used on odd stamps handed in for surcharging, were applied as strips of five only. One has, so far, not been reconstructed, but of the remainder three show the 6 mm spacing, two the 5 mm and one both.

On the shilling values the surcharges were applied as horizontal rows of four and the various settings divide into two groups, one with 3½ to 4½ mm between the bottom of the "R" and the top of numeral, and the second with 5½ mm between the "R" and numeral. The first group includes the very rare initial setting on which the space is 4 to 4½ mm.

G.R.I.

2d.

"1" for "I"
(Setting 1)

G.R.I.

1d.

Short "1"
(Setting 1)

G.R.I.

1s.

Large "S"
(Setting 1)

1914 (17 Oct)–**15**. *Stamps of 1901 surch.*

(a) As T **1**. *"G.R.I." and value 6 mm apart*

1	1d. on 3 pf. brown	£200	£200
	a. "1" for "I"	£350	
	b. Short "1"	£350	
	c. "1" with straight top serif (Setting 6)	£400	
	d. "I" for "1" (Setting 12)	£450	
2	1d. on 5 pf. green	25·00	30·00
	a. "1" for "I"	£120	
	b. Short "1"	£110	
	c. "1" with straight top serif (Settings 6 and 9)	£140	
3	2d. on 10 pf. carmine	40·00	50·00
	a. "1" for "I"	£170	
4	2d. on 20 pf. ultramarine	30·00	35·00
	a. "1" for "I"	£140	
	e. Surch double, one "G.R.I." albino	£1750	
	f. Surch inverted	£2500	
5	2½d. on 10 pf. carmine (27.2.15)	60·00	£100
	a. Fraction bar omitted (Setting 9)	£1000	£1300
6	2½d. on 20 pf. ultramarine (27.2.15)	60·00	£100
7	3d. on 25 pf. black and red/*yellow*	£150	£175
	a. "1" for "I"	£325	
8	3d. on 30 pf. black and orange/*buff*	£175	£200
	a. "1" for "I"	£350	
	e. Surch double	£2500	£2500
9	4d. on 40 pf. black and carmine	£225	£250
	a. "1" for "I"	£450	
	e. Surch double	£800	£1100
	f. Surch inverted	£2500	
10	5d. on 50 pf. black and purple/*buff*	£350	£450
	a. "1" for "I"	£700	
	e. Surch double	£2500	
11	8d. on 80 pf. black and carmine/*rose*	£600	£750
	a. "1" for "I"	£1100	
	d. No stop after "d"	£1200	

(b) As T **2**. *"G.R.I." and value 3½ to 4 mm apart*

12	1s. on 1 m. carmine	£1300	£1600
	a. Large "s"	£2750	£2750
13	2s. on 2 m. blue	£1500	£1800
	a. Large "s"	£3000	£3500
	c. Error. Surch "G.R.I. 5s."	£7500	
14	3s. on 3 m. violet-black	£2750	£3250
	a. Large "s"	£4250	
	b. No stop after "I" (Setting 3)	£5000	£5000
15	5s. on 5 m. carmine and black	£4750	£5250
	a. Large "s"	£6500	
	b. No stop after "I" (Setting 3)	£6500	£8000
	c. Error. Surch "G.R.I. 1s."	£12500	

G.R.I.

3d.

Thick "3"
(Setting 2)

G.R.I.

5d.

Thin "5"
(Setting 2)

1914 (16 Dec). *Stamps of* 1901 *surch.*

(a) As T **1**. "G.R.I." *and value* 5 *mm apart*

16	1d. on 3 pf. brown	35·00	40·00
	a. "I" for "1" (Setting 11)	£100	
	b. Short "1" (Setting 2)	£150	
	c. "1" with straight top serif (Settings 2 and 6)	55·00	60·00
	e. Surch double	£250	£325
	f. Surch double, one inverted	£950	
	g. Surch inverted	£550	£850
	h. Error. Surch "G.R.I. 4d."	£3500	
17	1d. on 5 pf. green	12·00	15·00
	b. Short "1" (Setting 2)	£100	£110
	c. "1" with straight top serif (Setting 2)	27·00	35·00
	e. "d" inverted	—	£800
	f. "1d" inverted	—	£1750
	g. "G.R.I." without stops or spaces	—	£1750
	h. "G.I.R." instead of "G.R.I."	£2500	£2500
	i. Surch double	£600	
18	2d. on 10 pf. carmine	16·00	20·00
	e. No stop after "d" (Setting 2)	75·00	90·00
	f. Stop before, instead of after, "G" (Settings 4 or 5)	£2250	
	g. Surch double	£2750	£2750
	h. Surch double, one inverted	—	£1500
	i. In vert pair with No. 20	£8000	
	j. In horiz pair with No. 20	£8000	
	k. Error. Surch ".GR.I. 1d."	£2000	£2000
	l. Error. Surch "G.I.R. 3d."	£3500	
19	2d. on 20 pf. ultramarine	20·00	25·00
	e. No stop after "d" (Setting 2)	60·00	75·00
	f. No stop after "I" (Setting 11)	£350	
	g. "R" inverted (Settings 4 or 5)	—	£1750
	h. Surch double	£550	£1100
	i. Surch double, one inverted	£1100	£1200
	j. Surch inverted	£1500	£2500
	k. Albino surch (in horiz pair with normal)	£3250	
	l. In vert pair with No. 21	£4000	£5000
	m. Error. Surch "G.R.I. 1d."	£3500	£3250
20	2½d. on 10 pf. carmine (27.2.15)	£175	£225
21	2½d. on 20 pf. ultramarine (27.2.15)	£1000	£1200
22	3d. on 25 pf. black and red/*yellow*	75·00	85·00
	e. Thick "3"	£425	
	f. Surch double	£1500	£2500
	g. Surch inverted	£1500	£2500
	h. Surch omitted (in horiz pair with normal)	£4500	
	i. Error. Surch "G.R.I. 1d."	£4500	
23	3d. on 30 pf. black and orange/*buff*	70·00	80·00
	e. No stop after "d" (Setting 2)	£350	
	f. Thick "3"	£325	
	g. Surch double	£800	£1000
	h. Surch double, one inverted	£1000	£1300
	i. Surch double, both inverted	£1600	£2500
	j. Surch inverted	£1400	
	k. Albino surch	£2750	
	l. Surch omitted (in vert pair with normal)	£2500	£3250
	m. Error. Surch "G.R.I. 1d."	£2500	
24	4d. on 40 pf. black and carmine	80·00	90·00
	e. Surch double	£800	
	f. Surch double, one inverted	£1000	
	g. Surch double, both inverted	£2000	
	h. Surch inverted	£1300	
	i. Error. Surch "G.R.I. 1d."	£1500	
	j. Error. Surch "G.R.I. 3d." double	£3500	
25	5d. on 50 pf. black and purple/*buff*	£120	£130
	e. Thin "5"	£600	£1000
	f. Surch double	£800	
	g. Surch double, one inverted	£1400	
	h. Surch double, both inverted	£2250	
	i. Surch inverted	£1300	
	j. Error. Surch "G.I.R. 3d."	£4500	
26	8d. on 80 pf. black and carmine/*rose*	£400	£450
	e. Surch double	£1500	£1500
	f. Surch double, one inverted	£1500	£1500
	g. Surch triple	£1600	£1800
	h. Surch inverted	£1750	£2500
	i. Error. Surch "G.R.I. 3d."	£4500	

(b) As T **2**. "G.R.I." *and value* 5½ *mm apart*

27	1s. on 1 m. carmine	£1750	£2250
28	2s. on 2 m. blue	£1900	£2500
29	3s. on 3 m. violet-black	£3000	£3750
	a. "G.R.I." double	£8500	
30	5s. on 5 m. carmine and black	£8000	£9000

1915. *Nos.* 18 *and* 19 *further surch as in T* **3**.

31	"1" on 2d. on 10 pf.	£8000	£8000
32	"1" on 2d. on 20 pf.	£8000	£5000

OFFICIAL STAMPS

O. S.
G.R.I.
1d.

(O 3*a*)

1915 (27 Feb). *Stamps of* 1901 *surch as Type* O **3***a*. "G.R.I." *and value* 3½ *mm apart.*

O1	1 d. on 3 pf. brown	25·00	45·00
	a. "1" and "d" spaced	75·00	
	b. Surch double	£2000	
O2	1d. on 5 pf. green	75·00	£110
	a. "1" and "d" spaced	£150	

German New Guinea. Registration Labels Surcharged

4   4*a*

G.R.I.
3d.

Sans serif "G" and different "3"

1915. *Registration Labels surch* "G.R.I. 3d." *in settings of five or ten and used for postage. Each black and red on buff. Inscr* "(Deutsch Neuguinea)" *spelt in various ways as indicated.*

I. *With name of town in sans-serif letters as T* **4**

33	Rabaul "(Deutsch Neuguinea)"	£100	£120
	a. "G.R.I. 3d." double	£1000	£1100
	b. No bracket before "Deutsch"	£375	£450
	ba. No bracket and surch double	£2500	
	d. "(Deutsch-Neuguinea)"	£160	£180
	da. "G.R.I. 3d." double	£2500	£2500
	db. No stop after "I"	£550	
	dc. "G.R.I. 3d" inverted	£2000	
	dd. No bracket before "Deutsch"	£550	
	de. No bracket after "Neuguinea"	£550	
34	Deulon "(Deutsch Neuguinea)"	£4250	
35	Friedrich-Wilhelmshafen "(Deutsch Neuguinea)"	£110	£200
	a. No stop after "d"	£275	
	b. "G" omitted	£1750	
	c. Sans-serif "G"	£2500	
	d. Sans-serif "G" and different "3"	£2000	
	e. Surch inverted	—	£2250
	f. "(Deutsch-Neuguinea)"	£125	£225
	fa. No stop after "d"	£325	
36	Herbertshöhe "(Deutsch Neuguinea)"	£160	£275
	a. No stop after "d"	£375	
	b. No stop after "I"	£650	
	c. "G" omitted	£2250	
	d. Surch omitted (in horiz pair with normal)	£3250	
	e. "(Deutsch Neu-Guinea)"	£300	
37	Käwieng "(Deutsch-Neuguinea)"	£375	
	a. No bracket after "Neuguinea"	£1500	
	b. "Deutsch Neu-Guinea"	£140	£225
	ba. No stop after "d"	£325	
	bb. "G.R.I." double	£1500	
	bc. "3d." double	£1500	
	bd. "G" omitted	£3000	
38	Kieta "(Deutsch-Neuguinea)"	£300	£425
	a. No bracket before "Deutsch"	£800	£1000
	b. No stop after "d"	£650	
	c. Surch omitted (righthand stamp of horiz pair)	£2750	
	d. No stops after "R" and "I"	£900	
	e. No stop after "I"	£1500	
	f. "G" omitted	£2000	
39	Manus "(Deutsch Neuguinea)"	£170	£275
	a. "G.R.I. 3d." double	£1500	
	b. No bracket before "Deutsch"	£600	£750
40	Stephansort "(Deutsch Neu-Guinea)"	—	£1500
	a. No stop after "d"	—	£2500

II. *With name of town in letters with serifs as T* **4***a*

41	Friedrich Wilhelmshafen "(Deutsch-Neuguinea)"	£140	£225
	b. No stop after "d"	£300	£400
	c. No stop after "I"	£550	£700
	d. No bracket before "Deutsch"	£550	£700
	e. No bracket after "Neuguinea"	£550	£700
42	Käwieng "(Deutsch Neuguinea)"	£110	£190
	a. No stop after "d"	£275	
43	Manus "(Deutsch-Neuguinea)"	£1100	£1600
	a. No stop after "I"	£1900	£1900

Stamps of Marshall Islands surcharged

SETTINGS. The initial supply of Marshall Islands stamps, obtained from Nauru, was surcharged with Setting 2 (5 mm between "R" and "d") on the penny values and with the 3½ to 4 setting on the shilling stamps.

Small quantities subsequently handed in were surcharged, often on the same backing sheet as German New Guinea values, with Settings 6, 7 or 12 (all 6 mm between "R" and "d") for the penny values and with a 5½ mm setting for the shilling stamps.

1914 (16 Dec). *Stamps of* 1901 *surch.*

(*a*) *As T* **1**. "G.R.I." *and value* 5 *mm apart*

50	1d. on 3 pf. brown	35·00	40·00
	c. "1" with straight top serif (Setting 2)	80·00	90·00
	d. ".G.R.I" and "1" with straight top serif (Setting 4 or 5)	—	£2750
	e. Surch inverted	£1300	
51	1d. on 5 pf. green	40·00	45·00
	c. "1" with straight top serif (Settings 2 and 11)	90·00	
	d. "I" for "1" (Setting 11)	£325	
	e. "1" and "d" spaced	£300	
	f. Surch double	£800	£1300
	g. Surch inverted	£1000	
52	2d. on 10 pf. carmine	12·00	16·00
	e. No stop after "G" (Setting 2)	£500	
	f. Surch double	£800	£1300
	g. Surch double, one inverted	£800	£1300
	h. Surch inverted	£1200	
	i. Surch sideways	£1900	
53	2d. on 20 pf. ultramarine	13·00	18·00
	e. No stop after "d" (Setting 2)	35·00	
	g. Surch double	£700	£1300
	h. Surch double, one inverted	£1300	£1500
	i. Surch inverted	£1500	£1500
54	3d. on 25 pf. black and red/*yellow*	£250	£325
	e. No stop after "d" (Settings 2 and 11)	£500	£650
	f. Thick "3"	£650	
	g. Surch double	£1000	£1300
	h. Surch double, one inverted	£1000	
	i. Surch inverted	£1500	
55	3d. on 30 pf. black and orange/*buff*	£275	£350
	e. No stop after "d" (Setting 2)	£550	
	f. Thick "3"	£700	
	g. Surch inverted	£1300	£1500
56	4d. on 40 pf. black and carmine	80·00	£100
	e. No stop after "d" (Setting 2)	£225	£275
	f. "d" omitted (Setting 2)	—	£2000
	g. Surch double	£1200	£1300
	h. Surch triple	£2000	
	i. Surch inverted	£1300	
	j. Error. Surch "G.R.I. 1d."	£3000	
	k. Error. Surch "G.R.I. 3d."	£3000	
57	5d. on 50 pf. black and purple/*buff*	£100	£130
	e. Thin "5"	£2000	
	f. "d" omitted (Setting 2)	£600	
	g. Surch double	£1500	
	h. Surch inverted	£1800	
58	8d. on 80 pf. black and carmine/*rose*	£450	£550
	e. Surch double	£1500	
	f. Surch double, both inverted	£1700	£2000
	g. Surch triple	£2500	
	h. Surch inverted	£1400	£2000

(*b*) *As T* **2**. "G.R.I." *and value* 3½–4 *mm apart*

59	1s. on 1 m. carmine	£1400	£1700
	b. No stop after "I"	£2500	
	e. Surch double	£5500	
60	2s. on 2 m. blue	£950	£1200
	b. No stop after "I"	£2000	£2500
	e. Surch double	£5500	
	f. Surch double, one inverted	£4000	£4000
61	3s. on 3 m. violet-black	£2500	£3000
	b. No stop after "I"	£3500	
	e. Surch double	£5500	£6500
62	5s. on 5 m. carmine and black	£4750	£5500
	e. Surch double, one inverted	—	£8500

1915. *Nos.* 52 *and* 53 *further surch as in T* **3**.

63	"1" on 2d. on 10 pf. carmine	£140	£170
	a. "1" double	£5000	
	b. "1" inverted	£5000	£5000
64	"1" on 2d. on 20 pf. ultramarine	£2750	£2000
	a. On No. 53e	£4500	£2750
	b. "1" inverted	£6000	£6000

1915. *Stamps of* 1901 *surch.*

(*a*) *As T* **1**. "G.R.I." *and value* 6 *mm apart*

64c	1d. on 3 pf. brown	£425	
	cc. "1" with straight top serif (Setting 6)	—	£1100
	cd. "I" for "1" (Setting 12)	£550	
	ce. Surch inverted	£2000	
64d	1d. on 5 pf. green	£425	£700
	dc. "1" with straight top serif (Setting 6)	£550	
	dd. "I" for "1" (Setting 12)	£550	
	de. Surch inverted	£2000	
64e	2d. on 10 pf. carmine	£650	£900
64f	2d. on 20 pf. ultramarine	£550	£900
	fe. Surch inverted	£2000	
64g	2½d. on 25 pf. black and red/*yellow*	£3500	
64h	2½d. on 20 pf. ultramarine	£5000	
64i	3d. on 25 pf. black and red/*yellow*	£800	£1100
64j	3d. on 30 pf. black and orange/*buff*	£850	£1100
	je. Error. Surch "G.R.I. 1d."	£3000	
64k	4d. on 40 pf. black and carmine	£800	£1100
	ke. Surch double	£2500	
	kf. Surch inverted	£2500	
64l	5d. on 50 pf. black and purple/*buff*	£700	£1100
	le. Surch double	£2500	
64m	8d. on 80 pf. black and carmine/*rose*	£1100	£1300
	me. Surch inverted	£3000	

(*b*) *As T* **2**. "G.R.I." *and value* 5½ *mm apart*

64n	1s. on 1 m. carmine	£3250	
	na. Large "s" (Setting 5)	£4250	
64o	2s. on 2 m. blue	£2750	
	oe. Surch double, one inverted	£8500	
64p	3s. on 3 m. violet-black	£4750	
	pe. Surch inverted	£8500	
64q	5s. on 5 m. carmine and black	£7500	
	qa. Large "s" (Setting 5)	£9000	

Stamps of Australia overprinted

N. W.
**PACIFIC
ISLANDS.**

(*a*)

N. W.
**PACIFIC
ISLANDS.**

(*b*)

N. W.
**PACIFIC
ISLANDS.**

(*c*)

(**6**)

W **5** *of Australia*   *W* **2** *of Australia*

W **6** *of Australia*

1915–16. *Stamps of Australia optd in black as T* **6**(*a*), (*b*) *or* (*c*).

(i) *W* **5** *of Australia. P* 14 (4 Jan–15 March 1915)

65	5*a*	½d. green	1·00	4·25
66		½d. bright green	1·50	4·50
67		1d. pale rose (Die I) (4.1)	2·75	3·00
68		1d. dull red (Die I)	3·50	3·25
69		1d. carmine-red (Die I)	3·25	3·25
		a. Substituted cliché	—	£700
69*b*		1d. carmine-red (Die II)	£250	£200
		c. Substituted cliché	£1100	
70		4d. yellow-orange	3·25	7·50
		a. Line through "FOUR PENCE"	£400	£500
		b. Pale orange-yellow		
71		4d. chrome-yellow	£300	£325
72		5d. brown	3·00	14·00

(ii) *W* **2** *of Australia. P* 12 (4 Jan 1915–March 1916)

73	**1**	2d. grey (Die I)	14·00	24·00
74		2½d. indigo (4.1.15)	2·75	13·00
76		3d. yellow-olive (Die I)	12·00	30·00
		a. Die II	£300	£350
		ab. In pair with Die I	£500	£550
77		3d. greenish olive (Die I)	£190	£250
		a. Die II	£1300	
		ab. In pair with Die I	£2250	
78		6d. ultramarine	23·00	42·00
		a. Retouched "E"	£5000	
79		9d. violet	27·00	48·00
81		1s. green	32·00	48·00
83		5s. grey and yellow (3.16)	£750	£900
84		10s. grey and pink (12.15)	£110	£160
85		£1 brown and ultramarine (12.15)	£600	£750

(iii) *W* **5** *of Australia. P* 12 (Oct 1915–July 1916)

86	**1**	2d. grey (Die I)	5·50	11·00
87		2½d. indigo (7.16)	£9000	£8000
88		6d. ultramarine	9·00	12·00
89		9d. violet (12.15)	11·00	14·00
90		1s. emerald (12.15)	8·50	20·00
91		2s. brown (12.15)	80·00	£100
92		5s. grey and yellow (12.15)	80·00	£100

(iv) *W* **6** *of Australia. P* 12 (Dec 1915–Aug 1916)

94	**1**	2d. grey (Die I)	4·00	10·00
		a. In pair with Die IIA	£175	
96		3d. yellow-olive (Die I)	4·50	11·00
		a. Die II	75·00	90·00
		ab. In pair with Die I	£140	
97		2s. brown (8.16)	25·00	45·00
99		£1 brown and ultramarine (8.16)	£400	£500

Dates for Nos. 67 and 74 are issue dates. All other dates are those of despatch. Nos. 65/6, 68/73, 76/81 were despatched on 15 March 1915. For Die IIA of 2d. see note below Australia No. 45.

SETTINGS. Type **6** exists in three slightly different versions, illustrated above as (*a*), (*b*) and (*c*). These differ in the letters "S" of "ISLANDS" as follows:

(*a*) Both "SS" normal.
(*b*) First "S" with small head and large tail and second "S" normal.
(*c*) Both "SS" with small head and large tail.

Type **11**, which also shows the examples of "S" as the normal version, can be identified from Type **6**(*a*) by the relative position of the second and third lines of the overprint. On Type **6***a* the "P" of "PACIFIC" is exactly over the first "S" of "ISLANDS". On Type **11** the "P" appears over the space between "I" and "S".

It has been established, by the study of minor variations, that there are actually six settings of the "N.W. PACIFIC ISLANDS" overprint, including that represented by T **11**, but the following are the different arrangements of Type **6**(*a*), (*b*) and (*c*) which occur.

A. Horizontal rows 1 and 2 all Type (*a*). Row 3 all Type (*b*). Rows 4 and 5 all Type (*c*).
B. (½d. green only). As A, except that the types in the bottom row run (*c*) (*c*) (*c*) (*c*) (*b*) (*c*).
C. As A, but bottom row now shows types (*a*) (*c*) (*c*) (*c*) (*b*) (*c*).

Horizontal strips and pairs showing varieties (*a*) and (*c*) or (*b*) and (*c*) se-tenant are scarce.

The earliest printing of the 1d. and 2½d. values was made on sheets with margin attached on two sides, the later printings on sheets from which the margins had been removed. In this printing the vertical distances between the overprints are less than in later printings, so that in the lower horizontal rows of the sheet the overprint is near the top of the stamp.

The settings used on King George stamps and on the Kangaroo type are similar, but the latter stamps being smaller the overprints are closer together in the vertical rows.

PURPLE OVERPRINTS. We no longer differentiate between purple and black overprints in the above series. In our opinion the two colours are nowadays insufficiently distinct to warrant separation.

PRICES. The prices quoted for Nos. 65 to 101 apply to stamps with opts Types **6** (*a*) or **6** (*c*). Stamps with opt Type **6** (*b*) are worth a 25 per cent premium. Vertical strips of three, showing (*a*), (*b*) and (*c*), are worth from four times the prices quoted for singles as Types **6** (*a*) or **6** (*c*).

N. W.
PACIFIC
One Penny　　　　ISLANDS.
(10)　　　　　　　　　(11)

1918 (23 May). *Nos. 72 and 81 surch locally with T* **10**.

100		1d. on 5d. brown	90·00	80·00
101		1d. on 1s. green	90·00	80·00

Types **6** (*a*), (*b*), (*c*) occur on these stamps also.

1918–23. *Stamps of Australia optd with T* **11** *("P" of "PACIFIC" over space between "I" and "S" of "ISLANDS").*

(i) *T* **5***a* (*King*). *W* **5** *of Australia. P* 14

102		½d. green	50	2·75
103		1d. carmine-red (Die I)	95	1·40
		a. Substituted cliché	£800	£500
		b. Rosine. Rough paper, locally gummed (perfd "OS")	£400	£150
103*c*		1d. carmine-red (Die II)	£150	48·00
		d. Substituted cliché	£800	£500
		e. Rosine. Rough paper, locally gummed (perfd "OS")	—	£500
104		4d. yellow-orange (1919)	3·25	16·00
		a. Line through "FOUR PENCE"	£1100	£1100
105		5d. brown (1919)	£175	12·00

(ii) *T* **1** (*Kangaroo*). *W* **6** *of Australia. P* 12

106		2d. grey (Die I) (1919)	2·50	15·00
		a. Die II	9·00	30·00
107		2½d. indigo (1919)	3·00	15·00
		a. "1" of "½" omitted	£5500	£5000
108		2½d. blue (1920)	6·00	22·00
109		3d. greenish olive (Die I) (1919)	15·00	19·00
		a. Die II	38·00	55·00
		ab. In pair with Die I	£300	
		b. Light olive (Die II) (1923)	9·00	15·00
110		6d. ultramarine (1919)	4·50	14·00
111		6d. greyish ultramarine (1922)	40·00	60·00
112		9d. violet (1919)	6·50	30·00
113		1s. emerald	6·50	25·00
114		1s. pale blue-green	13·00	25·00
115		2s. brown (1919)	28·00	38·00
116		5s. grey and yellow (1919)	60·00	60·00
117		10s. grey and bright pink (1919)	£150	£200
118		£1 brown and ultramarine (1922)	£2750	

(iii) *T* **5***a*. *W* **6***a of Australia* (*Mult Crown* A). *P* 14

119		½d. green (1919)	40	3·50

Type **11** differs from Type **6**(*a*) in the position of the "P" of "PACIFIC", which is further to the left in Type **11**.

1921–22. *T* **5***a of Australia. W* **5** *of Australia. Colour changes and new value. Optd with T* **11**.

120		1d. bright violet (1922)	1·00	5·00
121		2d. orange	2·50	4·50
122		2d. scarlet (1922)	3·50	8·00
123		4d. violet (1922)	22·00	40·00
		a. "FOUR PENCE" in thinner letters	£750	
124		4d. ultramarine (1922)	10·00	38·00
		a. "FOUR PENCE" in thinner letters	£750	
		Set of 5	35·00	85·00

MANDATED TERRITORY OF NEW GUINEA

PRINTERS. See note at the beginning of Australia.

12 Native Village

(13)

(Des R. Harrison. Eng T. Harrison. Recess Note Printing Branch, Treasury, Melbourne, from 1926 Note Ptg Branch, Commonwealth Bank of Australia, Melbourne).

1925–28. *P* 11.

125	**12**	½d. orange	1·50	3·50
126		1d. green	1·50	3·50
126*a*		1½d. orange-vermilion (1926)	1·50	2·25
127		2d. claret	1·75	4·50
128		3d. blue	4·00	4·00
129		4d. olive-green	11·00	15·00
130		6d. dull yellow-brown	14·00	32·00
		a. Olive-bistre (1927)	6·00	32·00
		b. Pale yellow-bistre (1928)	4·50	32·00
131		9d. dull purple (*to* violet)	13·00	32·00
132		1s. dull blue-grey	15·00	22·00
133		2s. brown-lake	30·00	40·00
134		5s. olive-bistre	48·00	65·00
135		10s. dull rose	£110	£160
136		£1 dull olive-green	£200	£250
		Set of 13	£400	£550

1931 (8 June). *Air. Optd with T* **13**. *P* 11.

137	**12**	½d. orange	60	2·50
138		1d. green	1·25	2·50
139		1½d. orange-vermilion	1·00	4·00
140		2d. claret	1·00	7·00
141		3d. blue	1·50	8·00
142		4d. olive-green	1·25	7·50
143		6d. pale yellow-bistre	1·75	13·00
144		9d. violet	3·00	15·00
145		1s. dull blue-green	3·00	16·00
146		2s. brown-lake	7·00	25·00
147		5s. olive-bistre	20·00	48·00
148		10s. bright pink	65·00	85·00
149		£1 olive-grey	£110	£140
		Set of 13	£200	£325

14 Raggiana Bird of Paradise (Dates either side of value)   (15)

(Recess John Ash, Melbourne)

1931 (2 Aug). *Tenth Anniv of Australian Administration. T* **14** (*with dates*). *P* 11.

150	**14**	1d. green	90	40
151		1½d. vermilion	4·00	8·50
152		2d. claret	2·50	2·00
153		3d. blue	3·00	4·00
154		4d. olive-green	5·00	11·00
155		5d. deep blue-green	3·50	12·00
156		6d. bistre-brown	3·00	12·00
157		9d. violet	5·50	14·00
158		1s. pale blue-green	5·00	14·00
159		2s. brown-lake	6·50	24·00
160		5s. olive-brown	35·00	48·00
161		10s. bright pink	75·00	£120
162		£1 olive-grey	£140	£200
		Set of 13	£250	£425

1931 (2 Aug). *Air. Optd with T* **15**.

163	**14**	½d. orange	45	1·00
164		1d. green	1·00	2·25
165		1½d. vermilion	1·40	6·00
166		2d. claret	1·00	2·75
167		3d. blue	2·75	3·25
168		4d. olive-green	3·00	5·00
169		5d. deep blue-green	3·50	6·50
170		6d. bistre-brown	6·00	18·00
171		9d. violet	7·50	15·00
172		1s. pale blue-green	6·50	15·00
173		2s. dull lake	10·00	38·00
174		5s. olive-brown	30·00	55·00
175		10s. bright pink	60·00	£100
176		£1 olive-grey	£100	£170
		Set of 14	£200	£350

1932 (30 June)–**34.** *T* **14** (*redrawn without dates*). *P* 11.

177	1d. green	50	20
178	1½d. claret	60	7·00
179	2d. vermilion	55	20
179*a*	2½d. green (14.9.34)	3·50	9·00
180	3d. blue	90	80
180*a*	3½d. aniline carmine (14.9.34)	8·00	9·00
181	4d. olive-green	75	2·25
182	5d. deep blue-green	70	70
183	6d. bistre-brown	85	3·00
184	9d. violet	7·50	17·00
185	1s. blue-green	4·00	10·00
186	2s. dull lake	4·00	16·00
187	5s. olive	27·00	45·00
188	10s. pink	60·00	80·00
189	£1 olive-grey	90·00	£100
	Set of 15	£190	£250

1932 (30 June)–**34.** *Air. T* **14** (*redrawn without dates*), *optd with T* **15**. *P* 11.

190	½d. orange	40	1·50
191	1d. green	40	1·50
192	1½d. claret	55	4·50
193	2d. vermilion	60	30
193*a*	2½d. green (14.9.34)	2·75	2·25
194	3d. blue	1·10	1·60
194*a*	3½d. aniline carmine (14.9.34)	3·50	3·25
195	4d. olive-green	2·50	5·50
196	5d. deep blue-green	4·25	7·50
197	6d. bistre-brown	2·75	9·00
198	9d. violet	5·50	9·00
199	1s. pale blue-green	4·50	7·50
200	2s. dull lake	5·50	24·00
201	5s. olive-brown	30·00	45·00
202	10s. pink	65·00	70·00
203	£1 olive-grey	75·00	55·00
	Set of 16	£180	£200

Two sheets were reported of the ½d. without overprint but it is believed they were not issued (*Price* £125 *un.*).

16 Bulolo Goldfields

(Recess John Ash, Melbourne)

1935 (1 May). *Air. P* 11.

204	**16**	£2 bright violet	£225	£175
205		£5 emerald-green	£600	£500
		Set of 2	£800	£650

HIS MAJESTY'S
JUBILEE.
1910 — 1935

(17)   **18**

1935 (27 June). *Silver Jubilee. As Nos.* 177 *and* 179, *but shiny paper. Optd with T* **17**.

206	1d. green	45	35
207	2d. vermilion	55	35
	Set of 2	1·00	70

STANLEY GIBBONS
STAMP COLLECTING SERIES

Introductory booklets on *How to Start, How to Identify Stamps* and *Collecting by Theme*. A series of well illustrated guides at a low price.

Write for details.

<table>
<tr><td colspan="2">PRICES</td></tr>
</table>

PRICES

George VI issues (1937–1939)

First column = Unmounted Mint
Second column = Mounted Mint
Third column = Used

(Recess John Ash. Note Ptg Branch, Melbourne)

1937 (18 May). *Coronation. P* 11.

208	**18**	2d. scarlet	50	20	30
209		3d. blue	50	20	30
210		5d. green	50	20	35
		a. Re-entry (design completely duplicated	60·00	27·00	75·00
211		1s. purple	75	35	35
		Set of 4	2·00	85	1·10
		First Day Cover			2·50

(Recess John Ash. Note Ptg Branch, Melbourne)

1939 (1 Mar). *Air. Inscr* "AIR MAIL POSTAGE" *at foot. P* 11.

212	**16**	½d. orange	80	40	3·25
213		1d. green	1·25	50	2·00
214		1½d. claret	80	45	5·00
215		2d. vermilion	3·00	1·25	3·00
216		3d. blue	3·50	1·50	8·00
217		4d. yellow-olive	3·00	1·40	7·50
218		5d. deep-green	2·75	1·40	2·25
219		6d. bistre-brown	3·50	1·50	9·50
220		9d. violet	3·50	1·50	14·00
221		1s. pale blue-green	5·50	2·75	13·00
222		2s. dull lake	42·00	16·00	40·00
223		5s. olive-brown	80·00	38·00	85·00
224		10s. pink	£225	£110	£180
225		£1 olive-green	£120	65·00	£130
		Set of 14	£450	£225	£450

OFFICIAL STAMPS

Australian stamps perforated "O S" exist with overprint Type **11** for use in New Guinea. We do not at present list such varieties.

O S   O S

(O 1)   (O 2)

1925–31. *Optd with Type* O **1**. *P* 11.

O3	**12**	1d. green	80	4·00
O4		1½d. orange-vermilion (1931)	5·50	17·00
O5		2d. claret	1·60	3·75
O6		3d. blue	2·00	5·50
O7		4d. olive-green	3·00	8·50
O8		6d. olive-bistre	13·00	35·00
		a. Pale yellow-bistre (1931)	7·00	35·00
O9		9d. violet	3·75	35·00
O10		1s. dull blue-green	5·00	35·00
O11		2s. brown-lake	27·00	60·00
		Set of 9	50·00	£180

1931 (2 Aug). *Optd with Type* O **2**. *P* 11.

O12	**14**	1d. green	1·25	9·00
O13		1½d. vermilion	2·25	12·00
O14		2d. claret	2·75	7·00
O15		3d. blue	2·25	6·00
O16		4d. olive-green	2·25	8·50
O17		5d. deep blue-green	4·50	12·00
O18		6d. bistre-brown	7·50	17·00
O19		9d. violet	8·00	28·00
O20		1s. pale blue-green	12·00	28·00
O21		2s. brown-lake	35·00	70·00
O22		5s. olive-brown	£120	£180
		Set of 11	£180	£325

1932 (30 June)–**34**. *T* **14** (*redrawn without dates*), *optd with Type* O **2**. *P* 11.

O23		1d. green	1·50	3·50
O24		1½d. claret	2·75	12·00
O25		2d. vermilion	2·75	2·75
O26		2½d. green (14.9.34)	2·75	7·50
O27		3d. blue	4·50	11·00
O28		3½d. aniline carmine (14.9.34)	3·00	10·00
O29		4d. olive-green	4·50	13·00
O30		5d. deep blue-green	4·50	13·00
O31		6d. bistre-brown	6·00	24·00
O32		9d. violet	10·00	35·00
O33		1s. pale blue-green	15·00	28·00
O34		2s. dull lake	35·00	80·00
O35		5s. olive-brown	£120	£170
		Set of 13	£190	£375

Civil Administration in New Guinea was suspended in 1942, following the Japanese invasion. It is believed that the Japanese intended to issue various New Guinea stamps overprinted with Japanese characters and an anchor, but such issues were never made available for postal purposes.

On resumption, after the Japanese defeat in 1945, Australian stamps were used until the appearance of the issue for the combined territories of Papua & New Guinea.

PAPUA (BRITISH NEW GUINEA)

Stamps of Queensland were used in British New Guinea (Papua) from at least 1885 onwards. Post Offices were opened at Daru (1894), Kulumadau (Woodlarks) (1899), Nivani (1899), Port Moresby (1885), Samarai (1888), Sudest (1899) and Tamata (1899). Stamps were usually cancelled "N.G." (at Port Moresby from 1885) or "BNG" (without stops at Samarai or with stops at the other offices) from 1888. Queensland stamps were replaced in Papua by the issue of 1901.

PRICES FOR STAMPS ON COVER

Nos. 1/7	from × 12
No. 8	—
Nos. 9/14a	from × 15
Nos. 14c/21	from × 5
No. 22	—
Nos. 23/9a	from × 5
No. 29b	—
Nos. 30/2	from × 8
Nos. 34/8b	from × 5
No. 38c	—
Nos. 38d/71	from × 7
Nos. 72/4	—
Nos. 75/92a	from × 7
Nos. 93/8	from × 10
Nos. 99/109	from × 6
Nos. 110/11	—
Nos. 112/14	from × 6
No. 115	—
Nos. 116/28	from × 5
Nos. 130/53	from × 4
Nos. 154/7	from × 12
Nos. 158/67	from × 4
No. 168	from × 3
Nos. O1/12	from × 7

PRICES
Edward VII and George V issues 1901–1935

First column = Mounted Mint
Second column = Used

1 Lakatoi (trading canoe)
with Hanuabada Village
in Background

2 (Horizontal)

(Recess D.L.R.)

1901 (1 July)–05. *Wmk Mult Rosettes, W* **2**. *P* 14.

I. Thick paper. Wmk horizontal

1	1	½d. black and yellow-green	6·00	9·00
2		1d. black and carmine	5·00	7·00
3		2d. black and violet	7·00	7·00
4		2½d. black and ultramarine	13·00	11·00
5		4d. black and sepia	40·00	35·00
6		6d. black and myrtle-green	40·00	35·00
7		1s. black and orange	60·00	65·00
8		2s. 6d. black and brown (1905)	£600	£550

II. Thick paper. Wmk vertical

9	1	½d. black and yellow-green	3·00	3·75
10		1d. black and carmine	3·00	2·00
11		2d. black and violet	4·00	4·00
12		2½d. black and ultramarine	8·00	12·00
13		4d. black and sepia	32·00	48·00
14		6d. black and myrtle-green	48·00	70·00
14a		1s. black and orange	55·00	70·00
14b		2s. 6d. black and brown	£2000	£1600

III. Thin paper. Wmk horizontal

14c	1	½d. black and yellow-green	£140	£130
14d		2½d. black and ultramarine	£180	£150
14e		2½d. black and dull blue	£275	£200

IV. Thin paper. Wmk vertical

15	1	½d. black and yellow-green	8·00	14·00
16		1d. black and carmine		
17		2d. black and violet	42·00	16·00
18		2½d. black and ultramarine		
18a		2½d. black and dull blue		
19		4d. black and sepia	£160	
20		6d. black and myrtle-green	£475	£350
21		1s. black and orange	£450	£750
22		2s. black and brown	£550	£750
		Set of 8	£625	£625

The sheets of the ½d., 2d. and 2½d. show a variety known as "white leaves" on R. 4/5 while the 2d. and 2½d. (both R. 6/2) and the ½d. and 1s. (both R. 6/3) show what is known as the "unshaded leaves" variety.

Papua.
(3)

Papua.
(4)

1906–7. A. *Optd with T* **3** (*large opt*), at Port Moresby (8 Nov 1906).

I. Thick paper. Wmk horizontal

23	1	4d. black and sepia	£200	£200
24		6d. black and myrtle-green	32·00	35·00
25		1s. black and orange	20·00	32·00
26		2s. 6d. black and brown	£140	£150

II. Thick paper. Wmk vertical

27	1	2½d. black and ultramarine	3·75	13·00
28		4d. black and sepia	£160	£160
29		6d. black and myrtle-green	18·00	32·00
29a		1s. black and orange	£750	£650
29b		2s. 6d. black and brown	£3000	£2500

III. Thin paper. Wmk vertical

30	1	½d. black and yellow-green	4·50	5·00
31		1d. black and carmine	7·50	13·00
32		2d. black and violet	4·50	3·00
		Set of 8 (*cheapest*)	£325	£350

B. *Optd with T* **4** (*small opt*), at Brisbane (May–June 1907).

I. Thick paper. Wmk horizontal

34	1	½d. black and yellow-green	35·00	48·00
35		2½d. black and ultramarine	65·00	85·00
36		1s. black and orange	60·00	£100
37		2s. black and brown	30·00	48·00
		a. Opt reading downwards	£1900	
		c. Opt double (horiz)	—	£1800
		d. Opt triple (horiz)	—	£1500

II. Thick paper. Wmk vertical

38	1	2½d. black and ultramarine	6·00	17·00
		a. Opt double		
38b		1s. black and orange	60·00	70·00
38c		2s. 6d. black and brown	£2250	£2250

III. Thin paper. Wmk horizontal

38d	1	½d. black and yellow-green	75·00	75·00
39		2½d. black and ultramarine	18·00	40·00
		a. Opt double		
39b		2½d. black and dull blue	85·00	85·00

IV. Thin paper. Wmk vertical

40	1	½d. black and yellow-green	3·50	5·00
		a. Opt double	£1500	
41		1d. black and carmine	3·75	6·00
		a. Opt reading upwards	£750	£625
42		2d. black and violet	4·50	2·25
42a		2½d. black and ultramarine		
43		4d. black and sepia	25·00	40·00
44		6d. black and myrtle-green	21·00	35·00
		a. Opt double	£1800	£3000
45		1s. black and orange	27·00	40·00
		a. Opt double, one diagonal	—	£1800
46		2s. 6d. black and brown	35·00	48·00
		Set of 8 (*cheapest*)	£110	£150

In the overprinting of this overprint Nos. 10, 16 and 21 have the "p" of "Papua" with a defective foot or inverted "d" for "p", and in No. 17 the "pua" of "Papua" is a shade lower than the first "a".

No. 37a comes from a single sheet on which the overprints were sideways. Examples exist showing one, two or four complete or partial overprints.

PRINTERS. All the following issues were printed at Melbourne. See notes at beginning of Australia.

5 Large "PAPUA"   B   C

Three types of the 2s. 6d.:—
A. Thin top to "2" and small ball. Thin "6" and small ball. Thick uneven stroke.
B. Thin top to "2" and large, well shaped ball. Thin "6" and large ball. Very thick uneven stroke.
C. Thick top to "2" and large, badly shaped ball. Thick "6" and uneven ball. Thin even line.
Type A is not illustrated as the stamp is distinguishable by perf and watermark.
The litho stones were prepared from the engraved plates of the 1901 issue, value for value except the 2s. 6d. for which the original plate was mislaid. No. 48 containing Type A was prepared from the original ½d. plate with the value inserted on the stone and later a fresh stone was prepared from the 1d. plate and this contained Type B. Finally, the original plate of the 2s. 6d. was found and a third stone was prepared from this, and issued in 1911. These stamps show Type C.

6 Small "PAPUA"

(Litho Government Printing Office, Melbourne, from transfers from original engraved plates)

1907–10. *Wmk Crown over A, W w* **11.**

A. Large "PAPUA". *(a) Wmk upright. P* 11
47	**5**	½d. black and yellow-green (11.07)		1.00	2.75

(b) Wmk sideways. P 11
48	**5**	2s. 6d. black and chocolate (A) (12.09)		48.00	60.00
		a. "POSTAGIE" at right (R. 1/5)		£250	

B. Small "PAPUA"

I. *Wmk upright. (a) P* 11 (1907–8)
49	**6**	1d. black and rose (6.08)		4.75	2.00
50		2d. black and purple (10.08)		6.00	4.50
51		2½d. black and bright ultramarine (7.08)		12.00	20.00
		a. Black and pale ultramarine		5.00	6.50
52		4d. black and sepia (20.1.07)		4.00	6.50
53		6d. black and myrtle-green (4.08)		11.00	15.00
54		1s. black and orange (10.08)		14.00	18.00

(b) P 12½ (1907–9)
55	**6**	2d. black and purple (10.08)		10.00	6.00
56		2½d. black and bright ultramarine (7.08)		45.00	55.00
		b. Black and pale ultramarine		32.00	42.00
57		4d. black and sepia (20.1.07)		7.00	7.00
58		1s. black and orange (1.09)		45.00	65.00

II. *Wmk sideways. (a) P* 11 (1909–10)
59	**6**	½d. black and yellow-green (12.09)		2.25	2.75
		a. Black and deep green (1910)		27.00	40.00
60		1d. black and carmine (1.10)		8.00	7.00
61		2d. black and purple (1.10)		4.50	2.75
62		2½d. black and dull blue (1.10)		4.25	14.00
63		4d. black and sepia (1.10)		3.50	6.00
64		6d. black and myrtle-green (11.09)		10.00	10.00
65		1s. black and orange (3.10)		40.00	48.00

(b) P 12½ (1909–10)
66	**6**	½d. black and yellow-green (12.09)		1.40	2.00
		a. Black and deep green (1910)		27.00	35.00
67		1d. black and carmine (12.09)		5.50	6.50
68		2d. black and purple (1.10)		3.00	2.50
69		2½d. black and dull blue (1.10)		7.50	22.00
70		6d. black and myrtle-green (11.09)		£1600	£2250
71		1s. black and orange (3.10)		12.00	25.00

(c) Perf compound of 11 *and* 12½
72	**6**	½d. black and yellow-green		£1800	£1800
73		2d. black and purple		£700	

(d) Mixed perfs 11 *and* 12½
74	**6**	4d. black and sepia		£2750	

(Litho Commonwealth Stamp Printing Office, Melbourne, by J. B. Cooke, from new stones made by fresh transfers)

1910 (Sept)–**11.** *Large* "PAPUA". *W w* **11** (*upright*). *P* 12½.
75	**5**	½d. black and green (12.10)		3.50	6.00
76		1d. black and carmine		8.00	3.00
77		2d. black and dull purple (shades) (12.10)		4.00	4.00
		a. "C" for "O" in "POSTAGE" (R. 4/3)		60.00	60.00
78		2½d. black and blue-violet (10.10)		4.50	16.00
79		4d. black and sepia (10.10)		2.75	8.50
80		6d. black and myrtle-green		5.50	7.50
81		1s. black and deep orange (12.10)		5.50	15.00
82		2s. 6d. black and brown (B)		45.00	65.00
83		2s. 6d. black and brown (C) (1911)		45.00	65.00
		Set of 8		70.00	£110

A variety showing a white line or "rift" in clouds occurs on R. 5/3 in Nos. 49/74 and the "white leaves" variety mentioned below No. 22 occurs on the 2d. and 2½d. values in both issues. They are worth about four times the normal price.

ONE PENNY

8   (9)

(Typo J. B. Cooke)

1911–15. *Printed in one colour. W* **8** (*sideways*).

(a) P 12½ (1911–12)
84	**6**	½d. yellow-green		60	3.00
85		a. Green		30	1.75
85		1d. rose-pink		70	40
86		2d. bright mauve		70	75
87		2½d. bright ultramarine		4.75	8.50
		a. Dull ultramarine		5.50	8.50
88		4d. pale olive-green		2.00	10.00
89		6d. orange-brown		3.75	5.00
90		1s. yellow......................		8.50	13.00
91		2s. 6d. rose-carmine		28.00	38.00
		a. Rose-red (aniline)			
		Set of 8		45.00	70.00

No. 91a always shows the watermark Crown to right of A, *as seen from the back of the stamp.*

(b) P 14
92	**6**	1d. rose-pink (6.15).................		14.00	4.75
		a. Pale scarlet		5.00	2.00

1917. *Above issue surch with T* **9** *at Port Moresby.*
93	**6**	1d. on ½d. yellow-green		90	1.40
		a. Green		50	1.00
94		1d. on 2d. bright mauve		12.00	13.00
95		1d. on 2½d. ultramarine		1.25	3.75
96		1d. on 4d. olive-green		1.00	4.50
97		1d. on 6d. orange-brown		8.00	12.00
98		1d. on 2s. 6d. rose-carmine		1.50	8.00
		Set of 6		22.00	38.00

(Typo J. B. Cooke (1916–18), T. S. Harrison (1918–26), A. J. Mullett (No. 101a only) (1926–27), or John Ash (1927–31))

1916–31. *Printed in two colours. W* **8** (*sideways*). *P* 14.
99	**6**	½d. myrtle and apple green (Harrison and Ash)			
		(1919)		80	60
		a. Myrtle and pale olive-green (1927)		45	70
100		1d. black and carmine-red (1916)		1.40	70
		a. Grey-black and red (1918)		1.60	30
		b. Intense black and red (Harrison) (1926) ..		1.90	1.75
101		1½d. pale grey-blue (shades) and brown (1925)		80	40
		a. Cobalt and light brown (Mullett) (1927) ..		6.00	3.25
		b. Bright blue and bright brown (1929)		1.50	1.25
		c. "POSTAGE" at right (R. 1/1) (all ptgs) From		35.00	38.00
102		2d. brown-purple and brown-lake (1919)		1.25	75
		a. Deep brown-purple and lake (1931)		18.00	1.25
		b. Brown-purple and claret (1931)		2.00	75

103	6	2½d. myrtle and ultramarine (1919)	4·00	8·00
104		3d. black and bright blue-green (1916)	1·25	1·75
		a. Error. Black & dp greenish Prussian blue*	£450	£450
		b. Sepia-black and bright blue-green (Harrison)	20·00	17·00
		c. Black and blue-green (1927)	3·50	5·00
105		4d. brown and orange (1919)	2·50	4·50
		a. Light brown and orange (1927)	4·75	12·00
106		5d. bluish slate and pale brown (1931)	4·25	13·00
107		6d. dull and pale purple (1919)	2·75	7·50
		a. Dull purple and red-purple (1927)	7·50	13·00
		b. "POSTACE" at left (R. 6/2) (all ptgs) From	65·00	90·00
108		1s. sepia and olive (1919)	3·25	6·00
		a. Brown and yellow-olive (1927)	6·00	11·00
109		2s. 6d. maroon and pale pink (1919)	18·00	30·00
		a. Maroon and bright pink (shades) (1927) .	18·00	35·00
110		5s. black and deep green (1916)	40·00	45·00
111		10s. green and pale ultramarine (1925)	£140	£180
		Set of 13	£200	£250

*Beware of similar shades produced by removal of yellow pigment.

No. 104a is a colour trial, prepared by Cooke, of which, it is believed, five sheets were sold in error.

The printers of the various shades can be determined by their dates of issue. The Ash printings are on whiter paper.

For 9d. and 1s. 3d. values, see Nos. 127/8.

AIR MAIL

(10)   (11)

1929 (Oct)–**30**. *Air. Optd with T* **10** *by Govt Printer, Port Moresby.*

(a) Cooke printing. Yellowish paper

112	6	3d. black and bright blue-green	1·10	5·50
		a. Opt omitted in vert pair with normal . . .	£2250	

(b) Harrison printing. Yellowish paper

113	6	3d. sepia-black and bright blue-green	50·00	60·00

(c) Ash printing. White paper

114	6	3d. black and blue-green	80	6·00
		a. Opt omitted in horiz pair with normal . . .	£3250	
		b. Ditto, but vert pair	£2750	
		c. Opt vertical, on back	£2750	
		d. Opts tête-bêche (pair)	£1700	

1930 (15 Sept). *Air. Optd with T* **11**, *in carmine by Govt Printer, Port Moresby.* *(a) Harrison printings. Yellowish paper.*

115	6	3d. sepia-black and bright blue-green	£1100	£1800
116		6d. dull and pale purple	3·00	13·00
		a. "POSTACE" at left (R. 6/2)	65·00	£100
117		1s. sepia and olive	7·00	27·00
		a. Opt inverted	£2750	

(b) Ash printings. White paper

118	6	3d. black and blue-green	55	4·50
119		6d. dull purple and red-purple	5·50	10·00
		a. "POSTACE" at left (R. 6/2)	65·00	£100
120		1s. brown and yellow-olive	5·50	13·00
		Set of 3	10·50	25·00

5d.

TWO PENCE   FIVE PENCE
(12)   (13)

1931 (1 Jan). *Surch with T* **12** *by Govt Printer, Port Moresby.*

(a) Mullett printing

121	6	2d. on 1½d. cobalt and light brown	16·00	40·00
		a. "POSTACE" at right (R. 1/1)	£150	£250

(b) Ash printing

122	6	2d. on 1½d. bright blue and bright brown	80	2·00
		a. "POSTACE" at right (R. 1/1)	32·00	48·00

1931. *Surch as T* **13** *by Govt Printer, Port Moresby.*

(a) Cooke printing

123	6	1s. 3d. on 5s. black and deep green	4·00	9·00

(b) Harrison printing. Yellowish paper

124	6	9d. on 2s. 6d. maroon and pale pink (Dec) . . .	5·50	15·00

(c) Ash printings. White paper

125	6	5d. on 1s. brown and yellow-olive (26.7)	60	1·75
126		9d. on 2s. 6d. maroon and bright pink	5·00	8·50

(Typo J. Ash)

1932. *W* **15** *of Australia (Mult "C" of "A"). P* 11.

127	5	9d. lilac and violet	4·00	23·00
128		1s. 3d. lilac and pale greenish blue	7·00	27·00
		Set of 2 optd "Specimen"	£450	

15 Motuan Girl   18 Raggiana Bird of Paradise

20 Native Mother and Child   22 Papuan Motherhood

(Des F. E. Williams (2s., £1 and frames of other values), E. Whitehouse (2d., 4d., 6d., 1s. and 10s.); remaining centres from photos by Messrs F. E. Williams and Gibson. Recess J. Ash (all values) and W. C. G. McCracken (½d., 1d., 2d., 4d.))

1932 (14 Nov). *T* **15**, **18**, **20**, **22** *and similar designs. No wmk. P* 11.

130	½d. black and orange	35	2·25
	a. Black and buff (McCracken)	12·00	20·00
131	1d. black and green	40	25
132	1½d. black and lake	60	4·50
133	2d. red	5·50	25
134	3d. black and blue	2·00	6·50
135	4d. olive-green	3·00	8·50
136	5d. black and slate-green	2·00	4·00
137	6d. bistre-brown	4·00	7·00
138	9d. black and violet	7·00	17·00
139	1s. dull blue-green	2·50	11·00
140	1s. 3d. black and dull purple	8·50	20·00
141	2s. black and slate-green	11·00	20·00
142	2s. 6d. black and rose-mauve	24·00	38·00
143	5s. black and olive-brown	48·00	50·00
144	10s. violet	75·00	75·00
145	£1 black and olive-grey	£170	£170
	Set of 16	£325	£375

Designs: *Vert* (as *T* **15**)—1d. A Chieftain's son; 1½d. Treehouses; 3d. Papuan dandy; 5d. Masked dancer; 9d. Papuan shooting fish; 1s. 3d. Lakatoi; 2s. Papuan art; 2s. 6d. Pottery making; 5s. Native policeman; £1 Delta house. (As *T* **18**)—1s. *Dubu*—or ceremonial platform. *Horiz* (as *T* **20**)—10s. Lighting a fire.

31 Hoisting the Union Jack   32 Scene on H.M.S. *Nelson*

(Recess J. Ash)

1934 (6 Nov). *50th Anniv of Declaration of British Protectorate. P* 11.
146 **31** 1d. green . . . . 80 2·25
147 **32** 2d. scarlet . . . . 1·75 2·25
148 **31** 3d. blue . . . . 1·50 3·00
149 **32** 5d. purple . . . . 4·75 7·00
         Set of 4 . . . . 8·00 13·00

HIS MAJESTYS JUBILEE.

HIS MAJESTY'S JUBILEE.
1910   1935   **1910 — 1935**
(33)   (34)

MAJESTY'S   MAJESTY'S
Normal   "Accent" flaw
             (R. 5/4)

1935 (9 July). *Silver Jubilee. Nos* 131, 133/4 *and* 136 *optd with T* **33** *or* **34** (2*d.*).
150   1d. black and green 45 80
    a. "Accent" flaw . . . . 20·00 30·00
151   2d. scarlet 95 50
152   3d. black and blue . . . . 1·25 2·50
    a. "Accent" flaw . . . . 38·00 55·00
153   5d. black and slate-green . . . . 2·75 2·75
    a. "Accent" flaw . . . . 55·00 65·00
       Set of 4 . . . . 4·75 6·00

PRICES
George VI issues (1937–1941)
First column = Unmounted Mint
Second column = Mounted Mint
Third column = Used

---

35   36 Port Moresby

(Recess J. Ash, Note Ptg Branch, Melbourne)

1937 (14 May). *Coronation. P* 11.
154 **35** 1d. green 40 15 15
155   2d. scarlet 40 15 15
156   3d. blue 40 20 20
157   5d. purple 40 25 35
       Set of 4 . . . . 1·40 65 75
       First Day Cover . . . .   2·00

(Recess J. Ash, Note Ptg Branch, Melbourne)

1938 (6 Sept). *Air. 50th Anniv of Declaration of British Possession. P* 11.
158 **36** 2d. rose-red . . . . 2·75 1·25 2·00
159   3d. bright blue . . . . 3·00 1·25 2·00
160   5d. purple . . . . 3·50 1·50 2·75
161   8d. brown-lake . . . . 9·00 4·00 9·00
162   1s. mauve . . . . 20·00 9·00 11·00
       Set of 5 . . . . 35·00 15·00 24·00
       First Day Cover . . . .   45·00

THE WORLD CENTRE FOR
FINE STAMPS IS 399 STRAND

37 Natives poling Rafts

(Recess J. Ash, Note Ptg Branch, Melbourne)

1939 (6 Sept). *Air. P* 11.
163 **37** 2d. rose-red . . . . 3·75 1·25 2·00
164   3d. bright blue . . . . 4·50 1·60 2·25
165   5d. green . . . . 5·50 1·75 1·50
166   8d. brown-lake . . . . 6·50 2·50 2·50
167   1s. mauve . . . . 8·50 4·00 5·00

(Recess W. C. G. McCracken, Note Ptg Branch, Melbourne)

1941 (2 Jan). *Air. P* 11½.
168 **37** 1s. 6d. olive-green . . . . 38·00 19·00 30·00
       Set of 6 . . . . 60·00 27·00 35·00

OFFICIAL STAMPS

1908 (Oct). *Punctured "OS".*
O1 **1** 2s. 6d. black and brown (No. 37) . . . . — 35·00
O2   2s. 6d. black and brown (No. 38c) £1100 £1100
O3   2s. 6d. black and brown (No. 46) . . . . — £200

1909–10. *Nos. 49/71 punctured "OS". I. Wmk upright. (a) P* 11
O 4 **6** 1d. black and rose . . . . 5·00 2·00
O 5   2d. black and purple . . . . 6·50 3·25
O 6   2½d. black and bright ultramarine . . . . . . 13·00 11·00
     a. Black and pale ultramarine . . . . 5·50 4·00
O 7   4d. black and sepia . . . . 5·50 4·25
O 8   6d. black and myrtle-green . . . . 12·00 10·00
O 9   1s. black and orange . . . . 15·00 13·00
       Set of 6 . . . . 45·00 32·00

(b) P 12½
O10 **6** 2d. black and purple . . . . 8·00 4·25
O11   2½d. black and bright ultramarine . . . . . . 35·00 30·00
     b. Black and pale ultramarine . . . . 22·00 22·00
O12   4d. black and sepia . . . . 8·00 5·00
O13   1s. black and orange . . . . 48·00 38·00
       Set of 4 . . . . 75·00 65·00

II. Wmk sideways. (a) P 11
O14 **6** ½d. black and yellow-green . . . . 3·25 2·25
     a. Black and deep green . . . . 28·00 25·00
O15   1d. black and carmine . . . . 9·00 5·00
O16   2d. black and purple . . . . 5·00 2·00
O17   2½d. black and dull blue . . . . 6·50 5·00
O18   4d. black and sepia . . . . 5·50 4·00
O19   6d. black and myrtle-green . . . . 15·00 6·00
O20   1s. black and orange . . . . 45·00 28·00
       Set of 7 . . . . 80·00 48·00

(b) P 12½
O21 **6** ½d. black and yellow-green . . . . 2·00 1·50
     a. Black and deep green . . . . 28·00 24·00
O22   1d. black and carmine . . . . 6·00 4·00
O23   2d. black and purple . . . . 3·50 1·50
O24   2½d. black and dull blue . . . . 10·00 7·00
O25   6d. black and myrtle-green . . . . — £400
O26   1s. black and orange . . . . 17·00 12·00
       Set of 6 . . . . — £400

1910. *Nos. 47/8 punctured "OS".*
O27 **5** ½d. black and yellow-green (*wmk upright*) . . 2·75 3·00
O28   2s. 6d. black and chocolate (*wmk sideways*) . 85·00 75·00

1910–11. *Nos. 75/83 punctured "OS".*
O29 **5** ½d. black and green . . . . 4·50 2·00
O30   1d. black and carmine . . . . 6·50 2·00
O31   2d. black and dull purple . . . . 4·75 2·00
     a. "C" for "O" in "POSTAGE" . . . . 60·00 40·00
O32   2½d. black and blue-violet . . . . 6·50 6·00
O33   4d. black and sepia . . . . 6·50 5·00
O34   6d. black and myrtle-green . . . . 6·50 6·00
O35   1s. black and deep orange . . . . 11·00 9·00
O36   2s. 6d. black and brown (B) . . . . 48·00 35·00
O37   2s. 6d. black and brown (C) . . . . 48·00 38·00
       Set of 8 . . . . 85·00 60·00

1911–12. *Nos. 84/91 punctured "OS".*

O38	**6**	½d. yellow-green	2·25	2·00
O39		1d. rose-pink	2·25	1·00
O40		2d. bright mauve	2·25	1·00
O41		2½d. bright ultramarine	6·50	6·00
O42		4d. pale olive-green	6·50	8·00
O43		6d. orange-brown	6·50	6·00
O44		1s. yellow	11·00	10·00
O45		2s. 6d. rose-carmine	35·00	35·00
		Set of 8	65·00	65·00

1930. *Nos. 99/102a and 104c/9 punctured "OS".*

O46	**6**	½d. myrtle and apple green	1·25	1·50
O47		1d. intense black and red	1·25	1·25
O48		1½d. bright blue and bright brown	1·50	1·50
		a. "POSTAGE" at right	38·00	42·00
O49		2d. deep brown-purple and lake	1·75	1·50
O50		3d. black and blue-green	2·75	2·75
O51		4d. light brown and orange	5·00	9·00
O52		6d. dull purple and pale purple	5·00	6·50
		a. "POSTAGE" at left	75·00	85·00
O53		1s. brown and yellow-olive	7·50	11·00
O54		2s. 6d. maroon and pale pink	27·00	35·00
		Set of 9	50·00	65·00

O S

(O 1)

(Typo T. S. Harrison (1d. and 2s. 6d.) and J. Ash)

1931 (29 July)–**32**. *Optd with Type* O **1**. *W* **8** *or W* **15** *of Australia* (9d., 1s. 3d.). *P* 14 *or* 11 (9d., 1s. 3d.).

O55	**6**	½d. myrtle and apple-green	80	3·50
O56		1d. grey-black and red	4·50	8·00
		a. Intense black and red	2·50	3·25
O57		1½d. bright blue and bright brown	1·40	6·50
		a. "POSTAGE" at right	45·00	80·00
O58		2d. brown-purple and claret	2·00	7·00
O59		3d. black and blue-green	2·00	12·00
O60		4d. light brown and orange	2·00	11·00
O61		5d. bluish slate and pale brown	5·50	24·00
O62		6d. dull purple and red-purple	4·00	8·50
		a. "POSTAGE" at left	80·00	£130
O63		9d. lilac and violet (1932)	30·00	48·00
O64		1s. brown and yellow-olive	8·00	22·00
O65		1s. 3d. lilac and pale greenish blue (1932)	32·00	48·00
O66		2s. 6d. maroon and pale pink (Harrison)	32·00	60·00
		a. Maroon and bright pink (Ash)	32·00	60·00
		Set of 12	£110	£225

Civil Administration in Papua was suspended in 1942. On resumption, after the Japanese defeat in 1945, Australian stamps were used until the appearance of the issue of the combined territories of Papua & New Guinea.

PAPUA NEW GUINEA

AUSTRALIAN TRUST TERRITORY

The name of the combined territory was changed from "Papua and New Guinea" to "Papua New Guinea" at the beginning of 1972. Self-Government was attained on 1 December 1973.

SPECIMEN OVERPRINTS. These come from specimen sets in which the lower values were cancelled-to-order, but stamps above the value of 10s. were overprinted "Specimen".

> **PRICES**
> Elizabeth II issues (from 1952)
>
> First column = Unmounted Mint
> Second column = Used

1 Matschie's Tree   2 Buka Head-dresses   3 Native Youth
  Kangaroo

14 Map of Papua and New Guinea   15 Papuan shooting Fish

(Recess Note Printing Branch, Commonwealth Bank, Melbourne)

1952 (30 Oct)–**58**. *T* **1/3**, **14/15** *and similar designs. P* 14.

1	½d. emerald		30	10
2	1d. deep brown		20	10
3	2d. blue		35	10
4	2½d. orange		1·75	40
5	3d. deep green		1·25	10
6	3½d. carmine-red		60	10
6a	3½d. black (2.6.58)		9·00	4·25
7	6½d. dull purple		2·75	10
	a. Maroon (1956)		3·75	15
8	7½d. blue		10·00	4·50
9	9d. brown		6·00	60
10	1s. yellow-green		2·75	10
11	1s. 6d. deep green		12·00	80
12	2s. indigo		8·00	10
13	2s. 6d. brown-purple		7·00	40
14	10s. blue-black		60·00	11·00
15	£1 deep brown		75·00	11·00
	Set of 16		£170	30 00
	Set of 2 (Nos. 14/15) *optd "Specimen"*		£120	

Designs: *Vert* (*as T* **1**/**3**)—2½d. Greater Bird of Paradise; 3d. Native policeman; 3½d. Papuan head-dress. (*As T* **15**)—6½d. Kiriwina Chief House; 7½d. Kiriwina yam house; 1s. 6d. Rubber tapping; 2s. Sepik dancing masks. *Horiz* (*as T* **14**)—9d. Copra making; 1s. Lakatoi; 2s. 6d. Native shepherd and flock.

(16)   (17)

1957 (29 Jan). *Nos.* 4 *and* 10 *surch with T* **16** *or T* **17**.

16	4d. on 2½d. orange	20	10
17	7d. on 1s. yellow-green	15	10
	Set of 2	35	10

18 Cacao Plant   19 Klinki Plymill

28 Traffic Policeman

(Des Pamela M. Prescott, Recess Note Ptg Branch, Reserve Bank of Australia, Melbourne)

1961 (26 July)–**62**. *T* **24, 26, 28** *and similar designs. P* 14½ × 14 (1*d.*, 3*d.*, 3*s.*) *or* 14 × 14½ (*others*).
28	1d. lake		60	10
29	3d. indigo		30	10
30	1s. bronze-green		3·00	15
31	2s. maroon		45	15
32	3s. deep bluish green (5.9.62)		1·00	1·00
	Set of 5		4·75	1·25

Designs: *Vert* (*as T* **24**)—3d. Tribal Elder, Tari, Papua. (*As T* **26**)—2s. Male dancer.

20 Cattle   21 Coffee Beans

(Recess Note Ptg Branch, Commonwealth Bank, Melbourne)

1958 (2 June)–**60**. *New values. P* 14.
18	**18**	4d. vermilion	90	10
19		5d. green (10.11.60)	1·25	10
20	**19**	7d. bronze-green	9·50	10
21		8d. deep ultramarine (10.11.60)	1·50	2·00
22	**20**	1s. 7d. red-brown	30·00	20·00
23		2s. 5d. verm.lion (10.11.60)	4·00	3·25
24	**21**	5s. crimson and olive-green	8·00	1·50
		Set of 7	50·00	24·00

29 Campaign Emblem   30 Map of South Pacific

(Recess Note Ptg Branch, Reserve Bank of Australia, Melbourne)

1962 (7 Apr). *Malaria Eradication. P* 14.
33	**29**	5d. carmine-red and light blue	45	15
34		1s. red and sepia	1·00	25
35		2s. black and yellow-green	1·40	70
		Set of 3	2·50	1·00
		First Day Cover		4·50

(22)   23 Council Chamber, Port Moresby

1959 (1 Dec). *No.* 1 *surch with T* **22**.
25	**1**	5d. on ½d. emerald	20	10

(Photo Harrison)

1961 (10 Apr). *Reconstitution of Legislative Council. P* 15 × 14.
26	**23**	5d. deep green and yellow	1·50	25
27		2s. 3d. deep green and light salmon	5·50	1·50
		Set of 2	7·00	1·75
		First Day Cover		8·50

(Des Pamela M. Prescott. Recess Note Ptg Branch, Reserve Bank of Australia, Melbourne)

1962 (9 July). *Fifth South Pacific Conference, Pago Pago. P* 14½ × 14.
36	**30**	5d. scarlet and light green	70	15
37		1s. 6d. deep violet and light yellow	2·00	60
38		2s. 6d. deep green and light blue	2·00	1·00
		Set of 3	4·25	1·60
		First Day Cover		6·50

31 Throwing the Javelin   33 Runners

(Des G. Hamori. Photo Courvoisier)

1962 (24 Oct). *Seventh British Empire and Commonwealth Games, Perth. T* **31, 33** *and similar design. P* 11½.
39	5d. brown and light blue	30	10
	a. Pair. Nos. 39/40	60	50
40	5d. brown and orange	30	10
41	2s. 3d. brown and light green	1·75	75
	Set of 3	2·10	1·25
	First Day Cover		3·00

Design: (*As T* **31**)—5d. High jump.
Nos. 39/40 are arranged together *se-tenant* in sheets of 100.

24 Female, Goroka, New Guinea   26 Female Dancer

34 Raggiana
Bird of Paradise

35 Common Phalanger

36 Rabaul

37 Queen Elizabeth II

(Des S. T. Cham (10s.), A. Buckley (photo) (£1). Photo Harrison (£1), Courvoisier (others)).

1963. *P* 14½ (£1) or 11½ (*others*).
42	**34**	5d. yellow, chestnut and sepia (27 Mar)	....	1·00	10
43	**35**	6d. red, yellow-brown and grey (27 Mar)	....	80	90
44	**36**	10s. multicoloured (13 Feb)	....	14·00	7·00
45	**37**	£1 sepia, gold and blue-green (3 July)	.....	10·00	2·00
		Set of 4	....	23·00	9·00
		Set of 2 (Nos. 44/5) optd "Specimen"	..	90·00	

37a Centenary Emblem

38 Waterfront, Port Moresby

(Des. G. Hamori. Photo Note Ptg Branch, Reserve Bank of Australia, Melbourne)

1963 (1 May). *Red Cross Centenary. P* 13½ × 13.
46	**37a**	5d. red, grey-brown and bluish green	.....	60	10
		First Day Cover	....		55

(Des. J. McMahon (8d.), Pamela M. Prescott (2s. 3d.). Recess Note Ptg Branch, Reserve Bank of Australia, Melbourne)

1963 (8 May). *T* **38** *and similar horiz design. P* 14 × 13½.
47	**38**	8d. green	....	25	15
48	–	2s. 3d. ultramarine	....	25	15
		Set of 2	....	50	30

Design:—2s. 3d. Piaggio "P-166" Aircraft landing at Tapini.

PAPUA & NEW GUINEA

40 Games Emblem

41 Watam Head

(Des Pamela M. Prescott. Recess Note Ptg Branch, Reserve Bank of Australia, Melbourne)

1963 (14 Aug). *First South Pacific Games, Suva. P* 13½ × 14½.
49	**40**	5d. bistre	....	10	10
50		1s. deep green	....	20	20
		Set of 2	....	30	30
		First Day Cover	....		75

(Des Pamela M. Prescott. Photo Courvoisier)

1964 (5 Feb). *Native Artefacts. T* **41** *and similar vert designs. Multicoloured. P* 11½.
51		11d. Type **41**	....	1·00	10
52		2s. 5d. Watam Head (*different*)	....	1·00	60
53		2s. 6d. Bosmun Head	....	1·00	10
54		5s. Medina Head	....	1·25	15
		Set of 4	....	3·75	75
		First Day Cover	....		2·50

45 Casting Vote

46 "Health Centres"

(Photo Courvoisier)

1964 (4 Mar). *Common Roll Elections. P* 11½.
55	**45**	5d. brown and drab	....	10	10
56		2s. 3d. brown and pale blue	....	20	25
		Set of 2	....	25	25
		First Day Cover	....		90

(Recess Note Ptg Branch, Reserve Bank of Australia, Melbourne)

1964 (5 Aug). *Health Services. T* **46** *and similar vert designs. P* 14.
57		5d. violet	....	10	10
58		8d. bronze-green	....	10	10
59		1s. blue	....	10	10
60		1s. 2d. brown-red	....	15	30
		Set of 4	....	40	40
		First Day Cover	....		90

Designs:—8d. "School health"; 1s. "Infant, child and maternal health"; 1s. 2d. "Medical training".

50 Striped Gardener
Bowerbird

51 Emperor of Germany
Bird of Paradise

(Photo Courvoisier)

1964 (28 Oct)–**65**. *Vert designs as T* **50** (1d. to 8d.) or **51** (*others*). *Multicoloured; background colours given. P* 11½ (1d. to 8d.) or 12 × 11½ (1s. to 10s.).
61		1d. pale olive-yellow (20.1.65)	....	40	10
62		3d. light grey (20.1.65)	....	50	10
63		5d. pale red (20.1.65)	....	55	10
64		6d. pale green	....	75	10
65		8d. lilac	....	80	20
66		1s. salmon	....	90	10

67   2s. light blue (20.1.65)   85   20
68   2s. 3d. light green (20.1.65).   85   75
69   3s. pale yellow (20.1.65) . . . .   1·25   1·25
70   5s. cobalt (20.1.65) . . . .   12·00   1·75
71   10s. pale drab (Optd S. £120) . . . .   10·00   3·00
         Set of 11 . . . .   26·00   6·75
Designs:—3d. Adelbert Bowerbird; 5d. Blue Bird of Paradise; 6d. Lawes'
Parotia; 8d. Black-billed Sicklebill; 2s. Brown Sicklebill; 2s. 3d. Lesser Bird
of Paradise; 3s. Magnificent Bird of Paradise; 5s. Twelve-wired Bird of
Paradise; 10s. Magnificent Riflebird.

61 Canoe Prow

62 "Simpson and
his Donkey"

(Des Pamela M. Prescott. Photo Courvoisier)

1965 (24 Mar).   *Sepik Canoe Prows in Port Moresby Museum. T* **61** *and
similar horiz designs showing carved prows. P* 11½.
72   4d. multicoloured   40   10
73   1s. 2d. multicoloured . . . .   1·75   85
74   1s. 6d. multicoloured   50   10
75   4s. multicoloured . . . .   1·50   25
         Set of 4 . . . .   3·50   1·10
         First Day Cover . . . .   3·00

(Des C. Andrew. Photo Note Ptg Branch, Reserve Bank of Australia,
Melbourne)

1965 (14 Apr).   50*th Anniv of Gallipoli Landing. P* 14 × 14½.
76   2s. 3d. sepia, black and emerald   20   10
         First Day Cover   65

65 Urban Plan and Native House

(Des G. Hamori. Photo Courvoisier)

1965 (7 July).   *Sixth South Pacific Conference, Lae. T* **65** *and similar horiz
design. P* 11½.
77   6d. multicoloured   10   10
78   1s. multicoloured   10   10
         Set of 2   15   10
         First Day Cover   40
No. 78 is similar to T **65** but with the plan on the right and the house on
the left. Also "URBANISATION" reads downwards.

66 Mother and Child

67 Globe and U.N. Emblem

(Photo Courvoisier)

1965 (13 Oct).   20*th Anniv of U.N.O. T* **66**/**7** *and similar vert design. P* 11½.
79   6d. sepia, blue and pale turquoise-blue   10   10
80   1s. orange-brown, blue and deep reddish violet . .   10   10
81   2s. blue, blue-green and light yellow-olive   10   10
         Set of 3   15   15
         First Day Cover   60
Design:—2s. U.N. Emblem and globes.

69 Blue Emperor

71 New Guinea Birdwing

Two Types of the $1 and $2:

$1 Type I

Black line through left blue patch on wing consists of two dots only.
There are two blue lines extending from upper right edge of right wing
towards two small patches of blue.

$1 Type II

The black line through left blue patch on wing is continuous. Blue lines
at upper right edge of wing are omitted. There is an extra short faint blue
line extending from edge of lower right wing which is absent in Type I.

$2 Type I

In the lower left of the butterfly there are two short black lines from the edge to the yellow part.

In the lower part of the upper right wing there is a series of indeterminate short lines and dots.

$2 Type II

The two black lines at lower left are lacking.

There are clear fine lines of shading in place of the thicker lines.

There are numerous other minor differences between the two plates of each value and also slight variations in the shades.

(Photo Courvoisier)

1966 (14 Feb–12 Oct).   *Decimal Currency. Butterflies. Vert designs as T* **69** *(1 to 5c.), or horiz as T* **71** *(others). Multicoloured. P* 11½.

82	1 c. Type **69**	20	10
83	3 c. White-banded Map Butterfly	30	20
84	4 c. Mountain Swallowtail	35	15
85	5 c. Port Moresby Terinos	35	10
86	10 c. Type **71**	40	10
86a	12 c. Blue Crow (12.10)	2·00	2·00
87	15 c. Euchenor Butterfly	4·00	80
88	20 c. White-spotted Parthenos	2·50	25
89	25 c. Orange Jezebel	4·50	70
90	50 c. New Guinea Emperor	10·00	1·25
91	$1 Blue Spotted Leaf-wing (I)	3·50	1·25
	Ea. Type II (8.67)	4·50	2·50
92	$2 Paradise Birdwing (I)	5·50	3·00
	Ea. Type II (8.67)	8·50	7·50
	Set of 12	30·00	8·50

(Des Rev. H. A. Brown. Photo Courvoisier)

1966 (8 June).   *Folklore. Elema Art* (1st *series). T* **80** *and similar vert designs. P* 11½.

93	2 c. black and carmine	10	10
94	7 c. black, light yellow and light blue	10	10
95	30 c. black, carmine and apple-green	15	10
96	60 c. black, carmine and yellow	40	20
	Set of 4	65	35
	First Day Cover		1·40

Designs:—7 c. "Marai"; 30 c. "Meavea Kivovia"; 60 c. "Toivita Tapaivita".

See also Nos. 152/5.

(Photo Courvoisier)

1966 (31 Aug).   *South Pacific Games, Nouméa. T* **84** *and similar vert designs. Multicoloured. P* 11½.

97	5 c. Type **84**	10	10
98	10 c. Football	10	10
99	20 c. Tennis	15	10
	Set of 3	30	15
	First Day Cover		55

87 *Mucuna novoguineensis*   **91** "Fine Arts"

(Des Mrs. D. Pearce. Photo Courvoisier)

1966 (7 Dec).   *Flowers. T* **87** *and similar vert designs. Multicoloured. P* 11½.

100	5 c. Type **87**	15	10
101	10 c. *Tecomanthe dentrophila*	15	10
102	20 c. *Rhododendron macgregoriae*	25	10
103	60 c. *Rhododendron konori*	40	25
	Set of 4	85	40
	First Day Cover		1·40

(Des G. Hamori. Photo Courvoisier)

1967 (8 Feb).   *Higher Education. T* **91** *and similar horiz designs. Multicoloured. P* 12½ × 12.

104	1 c. Type **91**	10	10
105	3 c. "Surveying"	10	10
106	4 c. "Civil Engineering"	10	10
107	5 c. "Science"	10	10
108	20 c. "Law"	10	10
	Set of 5	20	20
	First Day Cover		55

80 "Molala Harai"   **84** Throwing the Discus   **96** *Sagra speciosa*   **100** Laloki River

(Des Pamela M. Prescott. Photo Courvoisier)

1967 (12 Apr). *Fauna Conservation (Beetles). T* **96** *and similar vert designs. Multicoloured. P* 11½.

109	5 c. Type **96**		15	10
110	10 c. *Eupholus schoenherri*		20	10
111	20 c. *Sphingnotus albertisi*		30	10
112	25 c. *Cyphogastra albertisi*		30	10
	Set of 4		85	25
	First Day Cover			70

(Des G. Wade. Photo Courvoisier)

1967 (28 June). *Laloki River Hydro-electric Scheme, and "New Industries". T* **100** *and similar vert designs. Multicoloured. P* 12½.

113	5 c. Type **100**		10	10
114	10 c. Pyrethrum		10	10
115	20 c. Tea Plant		10	10
116	25 c. Type **100**		10	10
	Set of 4		30	20
	First Day Cover			65

103 Air Attack at Milne Bay   107 Papuan Lory

(Des R. Hodgkinson (2 c.), F. Hodgkinson (5 c.), G. Wade (20 c., 50 c.). Photo Courvoisier)

1967 (30 Aug). *25th Anniv of the Pacific War. T* **103** *and similar multicoloured designs. P* 11½.

117	2 c. Type **103**		10	10
118	5 c. Kokoda Trail (*vert*)		10	10
119	20 c. The Coast Watchers		15	10
120	50 c. Battle of the Coral Sea		50	25
	Set of 4		60	40
	First Day Cover			1·10

(Des T. Walcot. Photo Courvoisier)

1967 (29 Nov). *Christmas. Territory Parrots. T* **107** *and similar vert designs. Multicoloured. P* 12½.

121	5 c. Type **107**		20	10
122	7 c. Pesquet's Parrot		25	15
123	20 c. Dusky Lory		60	10
124	25 c. Edward's Fig Parrot		60	10
	Set of 4		1·50	30
	First Day Cover			90

111   Chimbu Head-dresses   112

(Des P. Jones. Photo Courvoisier)

1968 (21 Feb). *"National Heritage". T* **111**/12 *and similar multicoloured designs. P* 12 × 12½ (5, 60 c.) *or* 12½ × 12 (10, 27 c.).

125	5 c. Type **111**		10	10
126	10 c. Southern Highlands Head-dress (*horiz*)		10	10
127	27 c. Western Highlands Head-dress (*horiz*)		15	10
128	60 c. Type **112**		40	20
	Set of 4		60	40
	First Day Cover			1·25

115 *Hyla thesaurensis*   119 Human Rights Emblem and Papuan Head-dress (abstract)

(Des and photo Courvoisier)

1968 (24 Apr). *Fauna Conservation (Frogs). T* **115** *and similar horiz designs. Multicoloured. P* 11½.

129	5 c. Type **115**		15	15
130	10 c. *Hyla iris*		15	10
131	15 c. *Ceratobatrachus guentheri*		15	10
132	20 c. *Nyctimystes narinosa*		20	10
	Set of 4		60	30
	First Day Cover			90

(Des G. Hamori. Litho Enschedé)

1968 (26 June). *Human Rights Year. T* **119** *and similar horiz design. Multicoloured. P* 13½ × 12½.

133	5 c. Type **119**		10	10
134	10 c. Human Rights in the World (abstract)		10	10
	Set of 2		20	15

121 Leadership (abstract)   123 Egg Cowry

(Des G. Hamori. Litho Enschedé)

1968 (26 June). *Universal Suffrage. T* **121** *and similar horiz design. Multicoloured. P* 13½ × 12½.

135	20 c. Type **121**		10	10
136	25 c. Leadership of the Community (abstract)		10	10
	Set of 2		20	15
	First Day Cover (Nos. 133/6)			80

(Des P. Jones. Photo Courvoisier)

1968–69. *Seashells. Multicoloured designs as T* **123**. *P* 12 × 12½ ($2), 12½ × 12 (1 c. *to* 20 c.) *or* 11½ (*others*).

137	1 c. Type **125** (29.1.69)		10	10
138	3 c. Laciniated Conch (30.10.68)		30	10
139	4 c. Lithograph Cone (29.1.69)		20	10
140	5 c. Marbled Cone (28.8.68)		25	10
141	7 c. Episcopal Mitre (29.1.69)		35	10
142	10 c. Red Volute (30.10.68)		45	10
143	12 c. Areola Bonnet (29.1.69)		1·50	55
144	15 c. Scorpion Conch (29.1.69)		80	25
145	20 c. Fluted Clam (28.8.68)		90	10
146	25 c. Chocolate Flamed Venus Shell (28.8.68)		90	30
147	30 c. Giant Murex (28.8.68)		1·25	35
148	40 c. Chambered Nautilus (30.10.68)		1·00	30
149	60 c. Pacific Triton (28.8.68)		1·25	20
150	$1 Emerald Snail (30.10.68)		3·00	50
151	$2 Glory of the Sea (*vert*) (2.1.69)		14·00	3·75
	Set of 15		24·00	6·00

The 1, 5, 7, 15, 40, 60 c. and $1 exist with PVA gum as well as gum arabic.

138 Tito Myth

140 Luvuapo Myth

139 Iko Myth

141 Miro Myth

(Des from native motifs by Rev. H. A. Brown. Litho Enschedé)

1969 (9 Apr). *Folklore. Elema Art (2nd series). P 12½ × 13½ × Roul 9 between se-tenant pairs.*

152	**138**	5 c. black, yellow and red	10	10
		a. Pair. Nos. 152/3	20	20
153	**139**	5 c. black, yellow and red	10	10
154	**140**	10 c. black, grey and red	15	20
		a. Pair. Nos. 154/5	30	40
155	**141**	10 c. black, grey and red	15	20
		Set of 4	50	60
		First Day Cover		1·10

Nos. 152/3 and 154/5 were issued in vertical *se-tenant* pairs, separated by a line of roulette.

142 "Fireball" Class Yacht

145 *Dendrobium ostinoglossum*

(Des J. Fallas. Recess Note Ptg Branch, Reserve Bank of Australia)

1969 (25 June). *Third South Pacific Games, Port Moresby. T* **142** *and similar designs. P 14 × 14½ (5 c.) or 14½ × 14 (others).*

156	5 c. black		10	10
157	10 c. deep bluish violet		10	10
158	20 c. myrtle-green		15	10
	Set of 3		30	20
	First Day Cover			45

Designs: *Horiz*—10 c. Swimming pool, Boroko; 20 c. Games arena, Konedobu.

(Des P. Jones. Photo Courvoisier)

1969 (27 Aug). *Flora Conservation (Orchids). T* **145** *and similar vert designs. Multicoloured. P 11½.*

159	5 c. Type **145**		25	10
160	10 c. Dendrobium lawesii		35	30
161	20 c. Dendrobium pseudofrigidum		55	45
162	30 c. Denodrobium conanthum		70	30
	Set of 4		1·75	1·00
	First Day Cover			1·50

149 Bird of Paradise

150 Native Potter

(Des G. Hamori. Photo Note Ptg Branch, Reserve Bank of Australia)

1969 (24 Sept)–**71**. *Coil stamps. P 15 × imperf.*

162a	**149**	2 c. blue, black and red (1.4.71)	10	15
163		5 c. bright green, brown and red-orange . .	10	10
		Set of 2	20	20

(Des G. Hamori. Photo Courvoisier)

1969 (24 Sept). *50th Anniv of International Labour Organization. P 11½.*

164	**150**	5 c. multicoloured	10	10
		First Day Cover		40

151 Tareko   155 Prehistoric Ambun Stone

(Des G. Hamori. Photo Courvoisier)

1969 (29 Oct). *Musical Instruments. T* **151** *and similar horiz designs. P 12½ × 12.*

165	5 c. multicoloured		10	10
166	10 c. black, olive-green and pale yellow		10	10
167	25 c. black, yellow and brown		15	10
168	30 c. multicoloured		25	10
	Set of 4		55	30
	First Day Cover			1·10

Designs:—10 c. Garamut; 25 c. Iviliko; 30 c. Kundu.

(Des R. Bates. Photo Courvoisier)

1970 (11 Feb). *"National Heritage". T* **155** *and similar horiz designs. Multicoloured. P 12½ × 12.*

169	5 c. Type **155**		15	10
170	10 c. Masawa canoe of Kula Circuit		20	15
171	25 c. Torres' Map, 1606		45	15
172	30 c. H.M.S. Basilisk (paddle-sloop), 1873		60	20
	Set of 4		1·25	50
	First Day Cover			1·50

159 King of Saxony Bird of Paradise

(Des T. Walcot. Photo Courvoisier)

1970 (13 May). *Fauna Conservation (Birds of Paradise). T* **159** *and similar vert designs. Multicoloured. P* 12 × 11½.

173	5 c. Type **159**		1·00	15
174	10 c. King Bird of Paradise		1·50	60
175	15 c. Raggiana Bird of Paradise		2·25	1·00
176	25 c. Sickle-crested Bird of Paradise		2·50	70
	Set of 4		6·50	2·25
	First Day Cover			4·25

163 McDonnell Douglas "DC-6B" and Mt Wilhelm

164 Lockheed "Electra" and Mt Yule

165 Boeing "727" and Mt Giluwe

166 Fokker "Friendship" and Manam Island

(Des D. Gentleman. Photo Harrison)

1970 (8 July). *Australian and New Guinea Air Services. T* **163/6** *and similar horiz designs. Multicoloured. P* 14½ × 14.

177	5 c. Type **163**		25	10
	a. Block of 4. Nos. 177/80		90	
178	5 c. Type **164**		25	10
179	5 c. Type **165**		25	10
180	5 c. Type **166**		25	10
181	25 c. McDonnell Douglas "DC-3" and Matupi Volcano		60	40
182	30 c. Boeing "707" and Hombrom's Bluff		70	60
	Set of 6		2·00	1·25
	First Day Cover			2·25

Nos. 177/80 were issued together, *se-tenant*, in blocks of 4 throughout the sheet.

169 N. Miklouho-Maclay (scientist) and Effigy

170 Wogeo Island Food Bowl

(Des D. Gentleman. Photo Courvoisier)

1970 (19 Aug). *42nd ANZAAS (Australian-New Zealand Association for the Advancement of Science) Congress, Port Moresby. T* **169** *and similar horiz designs. P* 11½.

183	5 c. multicoloured		10	10
184	10 c. multicoloured		15	10
185	15 c. multicoloured		50	15
186	20 c. multicoloured		50	15
	Set of 4		1·10	35
	First Day Cover			95

Designs:—10 c. B. Malinowski (anthropologist) and native hut; 15 c. T. Salvadori (ornithologist) and Dwarf Cassoway; 20 c. F. R. R. Schlechter (botanist) and flower.

(Des P. Jones. Photo Courvoisier)

1970 (28 Oct). *Native Artefacts. T* **170** *and similar multicoloured designs. P* 12½ × 12 (30 c.) or 12 × 12½ (others).

187	5 c. Type **170**		10	10
188	10 c. Lime Pot		20	10
189	15 c. Aibom Sago Storage Pot		20	10
190	30 c. Manus Island Bowl (*horiz*)		25	20
	Set of 4		70	40
	First Day Cover			1·25

171 Eastern Highlands Dwelling

172 Spotted Phalanger

(Des G. Wade. Photo Courvoisier)

1971 (27 Jan). *Native Dwellings. T* **171** *and similar vert designs showing dwellings from the places given. Multicoloured. P* 11½.

191	5 c. Type **171**		15	10
192	7 c. Milne Bay		15	15
193	10 c. Purari Delta		15	10
194	40 c. Sepik		35	50
	Set of 4		70	70
	First Day Cover			1·40

(Des R. Bates. Photo Courvoisier)

1971 (31 Mar). *Fauna Conservation. T* **172** *and similar multicoloured designs. P* 11½.

195	5 c. Type **172**		30	10
196	10 c. Long-fingered Possum		60	15
197	15 c. Feather-tailed Possum		1·25	1·00
198	25 c. Long-nosed Echidna (*horiz*)		1·75	1·00
199	30 c. Ornate Tree Kangaroo (*horiz*)		1·75	70
	Set of 5		5·00	2·50
	First Day Cover			4·25

173 "Basketball"

174 Bartering Fish for Vegetables

(Des G. Hamori. Litho D.L.R.)

1971 (9 June). *Fourth South Pacific Games, Papeete, Tahiti. T* **173** *and similar horiz designs. Multicoloured. P* 13½ × 14.

200	7 c. Type **173**		10	10
201	14 c. "Sailing"		15	20
202	21 c. "Boxing"		15	25
203	28 c. "Athletics"		15	35
	Set of 4		50	75
	First Day Cover			1·40

(Des G. Wade. Photo Courvoisier)

1971 (18 Aug). *Primary Industries. T* **174** *and similar vert designs. Multicoloured. P* 11½.

204	7 c. Type **174**		15	10
205	9 c. Man stacking yams		20	25
206	14 c. Vegetable market		30	10
207	30 c. Highlanders cultivating garden		50	50
	Set of 4		1·00	80
	First Day Cover			1·50

175 Sia Dancer   176 Papuan Flag over   179 Curtiss "Seagull MF6" Aircraft   180 New National
                      Australian Flag   and *Eureka* (schooner)   Flag

(Des Bette Hays. Photo Courvoisier)

1971 (27 Oct).   *Native Dancers. T* **175** *and similar multicoloured designs. P* 11½.
208   7 c. Type **175**   20   10
209   9 c. Urasena dancer   30   20
210   20 c. Siassi Tubuan dancers (*horiz*)   80   90
211   28 c. Sia dancers (*horiz*) . . . .   1·00   1·10
       Set of 4 . . . .   2·10   2·00
       First Day Cover . . . .   2·75

(Des R. Bates. Photo Courvoisier)

1972 (26 Jan).   *Constitutional Development. T* **176** *and similar horiz design. P* 12½ × 12.
212   **176**   7 c. multicoloured   30   10
       a. Pair. Nos. 212/13   60   90
213   –   7 c. multicoloured   30   10
       Set of 2   60   20
       First Day Cover . . . .   1·00
Design:—No. 213, Crest of Papua New Guinea and Australian coat of arms.
Nos. 212/13 were printed vertically *se-tenant* within the sheet.

177 Map of Papua New Guinea and   178 Turtle
    Flag of South Pacific Commission

(Des R. Bates. Photo Courvoisier)

1972 (26 Jan).   *25th Anniv of South Pacific Commission. T* **177** *and similar horiz design. P* 12½ × 12.
214   **177**   15 c. multicoloured   65   55
       a. Pair. Nos. 214/15 . . . .   1·25   2·00
215   –   15 c. multicoloured   65   55
       Set of 2 . . . .   1·25   1·10
       First Day Cover . . . .   2·25
Design:—No. 215, Man's face and flag of the Commission.
Nos. 214/15 were printed vertically *se-tenant* within the sheet.

(Des R. Bates. Photo Courvoisier)

1972 (17 Mar).   *Fauna Conservation (Reptiles). T* **178** *and similar horiz designs. Multicoloured. P* 11½.
216   7 c. Type **178**   40   10
217   14 c. Rainforest Dragon . . . .   1·00   1·25
218   21 c. Green Python . . . .   1·25   1·50
219   30 c. Salvador's Monitor . . . .   1·75   1·25
       Set of 4 . . . .   4·00   3·50
       First Day Cover . . . .   5·00

(Des Major L. G. Halls. Photo Courvoisier)

1972 (7 June).   *50th Anniv of Aviation. T* **179** *and similar horiz designs. Multicoloured. P* 11½.
220   7 c. Type **179**   40   10
221   14 c. De Havilland "37" and native porters . . . . .   1·00   1·25
222   20 c. Junkers "G-31" and gold dredger . . . .   1·10   1·25
223   25 c. Junkers "F-13" and mission church . . . . . .   1·10   1·25
       Set of 4 . . . .   3·25   3·50
       First Day Cover . . . .   4·50

(Des R. Bates. Photo Courvoisier)

1972 (16 Aug).   *National Day. T* **180** *and similar vert designs. Multicoloured. P* 11½.
224   7 c. Type **180**   20   10
225   10 c. Native drum   25   25
226   30 c. Blowing conch-shell   45   55
       Set of 3   80   70
       First Day Cover . . . .   1·25

181 Rev. Copland King   182 Mt Tomavatur Station

(Des G. Wade. Photo Courvoisier)

1972 (25 Oct).   *Christmas (Missionaries). T* **181** *and similar horiz designs. Multicoloured. P* 11½.
227   7 c. Type **181**   25   40
228   7 c. Rev. Dr. Flierl   25   40
229   7 c. Bishop Verjus   25   40
230   7 c. Pastor Ruatoka   25   40
       Set of 4   90   1·40
       First Day Cover . . . .   1·75

(Des R. Bates. Photo Courvoisier)

1973 (24 Jan).   *Completion of Telecommunications Project, 1968–72. T* **182** *and similar horiz designs. Multicoloured. P* 12½ (*Nos.* 231/4) *or* 11½ (*others*).
231   7 c. Type **182**   45   20
       a. Block of 4. Nos. 231/4 . . . .   1·60
232   7 c. Mt Kerigomma Station   45   20
233   7 c. Sattelburg Station   45   20
234   7 c. Wideru Station   45   20
235   9 c. Teleprinter (36 × 26 mm)   45   55
236   30 c. Network Map (36 × 26 mm) . . . .   1·25   1·50
       Set of 6 . . . .   3·00   2·50
       Presentation Pack £150
       First Day Cover . . . .   3·50
Nos. 231/4 were printed in *se-tenant* blocks of four within the sheet.

ALBUM LISTS   Please write for our latest lists of albums and accessories. These will be sent free on request.

183 Queen Carola's Parotia   184 Wood Carver

(Des W. Cooper. Photo Courvoisier)

1973 (30 Mar). *Birds of Paradise. T* **183** *and similar vert designs. Multicoloured. P* 11½.
237	7 c. Type **183**	1·25	35
238	14 c. Goldie's Bird of Paradise	2·25	1·25
239	21 c. Ribbon-tailed Bird of Paradise (18×49 mm)	2·75	2·00
240	28 c. Princess Stephanie's Bird of Paradise (18×49 mm)	3·50	2·50
	Set of 4	9·00	5·50
	Presentation Pack	75·00	
	First Day Cover		6·75

(Des R. Bates. Photo Courvoisier)

1973 (13 June)–74. *T* **184** *and similar horiz designs. Multicoloured. P* 11½.
241	1 c. Type **184**	10	10
242	3 c. Wig-makers (23.1.74)	20	10
243	5 c. Mt Bagana (22.8.73)	35	10
244	6 c. Pig Exchange (7.8.74)	50	50
245	7 c. Coastal village	20	10
246	8 c. Arawe mother (23.1.74)	35	15
247	9 c. Fire dancers	25	15
248	10 c. Tifalmin hunter (23.1.74)	45	10
249	14 c. Crocodile hunters (22.8.73)	45	30
250	15 c. Mt Elimbari	50	30
251	20 c. Canoe-racing, Manus (23.1.74)	1·00	40
252	21 c. Making sago (22.8.73)	65	45
253	25 c. Council House	70	45
254	28 c. Menyamya bowmen (22.8.73)	80	60
255	30 c. Shark-snaring (22.8.73)	1·00	75
256	40 c. Fishing canoes, Madang	1·50	80
257	60 c. Tapa cloth-making (23.1.74)	2·75	1·00
258	$1 Asaro Mudmen (23.1.74)	5·00	3·25
259	$2 Enga "Sing Sing" (7.8.74)	10·00	8·50
	Set of 19	23·00	16·00
	Presentation Packs (4)	95·00	
	First Day Covers (4)		20·00

185 Stamps of German New Guinea, 1897

(Des R. Bates. Photo (1 c.), litho and recess (6 c.) or litho (7 c.). State Printing Works, Berlin. Photo and recess D.L.R. (9 c.). Recess and typo Reserve Bank of Australia (25 and 30 c.))

1973 (24 Oct). *75th Anniv of Papua New Guinea Stamps. T* **185** *and similar horiz designs. Chalky paper* (25, 30 c.). *P* 13½ (1, 6, 7 c.), 14×13½ (9 c.) *or* 14×14½ (25, 30 c.).
260	1 c. multicoloured	15	15
261	6 c. indigo, new blue and silver	25	35
262	7 c. multicoloured	30	35
263	9 c. multicoloured	35	45
264	25 c. orange and gold	60	1·00
265	30 c. plum and silver	75	1·25
	Set of 6	2·25	3·25
	Presentation Pack	32·00	
	First Day Cover		3·75

Designs: *As T* **185**—6 c. 2 mark stamp of German New Guinea, 1900; 7 c. Surcharged registration label of New Guinea, 1914. 46×35 mm.—9 c. Papua 1s. stamp, 1901. 45×38 mm—25 c. ½d. stamp of New Guinea, 1925; 30 c. Papua 10s. stamp, 1932.

SELF-GOVERNMENT

186 Native Carved Heads   187 Queen Elizabeth II (from photograph by Karsh)

(Des G. Wade. Photo Courvoisier)

1973 (5 Dec). *Self-Government. P* 11½.
266	**186**	7 c. multicoloured	20	15
267		10 c. multicoloured	40	65
		Set of 2	60	80
		Presentation Pack	7·00	
		First Day Cover		1·25

(Des and photo Harrison)

1974 (22 Feb). *Royal Visit. P* 14×14½.
268	**187**	7 c. multicoloured	25	15
269		30 c. multicoloured	1·00	1·75
		Set of 2	1·25	1·90
		Presentation Pack	20·00	
		First Day Cover		2·40

188 Blyth's Hornbill   189 *Dendrobium bracteosum*

(Des T. Nolan. Photo Courvoisier)

1974 (12 June). *Birds' Heads. T* **188** *and similar multicoloured designs. P* 11½ (10 c.) *or* 12 (*others*).
270	7 c. Type **188**	1·50	70
271	10 c. Double-wattled Cassowary (33×49 mm)	2·75	2·75
272	30 c. New Guinea Harpy Eagle	6·00	7·50
	Set of 3	9·00	10·00
	Presentation Pack	45·00	
	First Day Cover		11·50

(Des T. Nolan. Photo Courvoisier)

1974 (20 Nov). *Flora Conservation. T* **189** *and similar vert designs. Multicoloured. P* 11½.
273	7 c. Type **189**	50	10
274	10 c. D. anosmum	1·00	50
275	20 c. D. smillieae	1·40	1·25
276	30 c. D. insigne	1·75	1·25
	Set of 4	4·25	3·25
	Presentation Pack	28·00	
	First Day Cover		3·75

190 Moto La Kaboi   191 1-toea Coin

(Des G. Wade. Photo Courvoisier)

1975 (26 Feb). *National Heritage—Canoes. T* **190** *and similar horiz designs. Multicoloured. P* 11½.

277	7 c. Type **190**	30	10
278	10 c. Tami two-master morobe	45	45
279	25 c. Aramia racing canoe	1·10	1·40
280	30 c. Buka Island canoe	1·10	1·10
	Set of 4	2·75	2·75
	Presentation Pack	17·00	
	First Day Cover		3·00

(New Currency. 100 toea = 1 kina)

(Des G. Wade. Photo Courvoisier)

1975 (21 Apr). *New Coinage. T* **191** *and similar multicoloured designs. P* 11½.

281	1 t. Type **191**	10	10
282	7 t. New 2 t. and 5 t. coins (45×26 mm)	40	10
283	10 t. New 10 t. coin	60	30
284	20 t. New 20 t. coin	1·00	80
285	1 k. New 1 k. coin (45×26 mm)	3·50	4·00
	Set of 5	5·00	4·50
	Presentation Pack	23·00	
	First Day Cover		6·50

192 *Ornithoptera alexandrae*   193 Boxing

(Des R. Bates. Photo Courvoisier)

1975 (11 June). *Fauna Conservation (Birdwing Butterflies). T* **192** *and similar vert designs. Multicoloured. P* 11½.

286	7 t. Type **192**	50	10
287	10 t. *O. victoriae regis*	80	45
288	30 t. *O. allottei*	1·75	1·50
289	40 t. *O. chimaera*	2·25	2·25
	Set of 4	4·75	3·75
	Presentation Pack	22·00	
	First Day Cover		4·25

(Des R. Bates. Photo Courvoisier)

1975 (2 Aug). *Fifth South Pacific Games, Guam. T* **193** *and similar vert designs. Multicoloured. P* 11½.

290	7 t. Type **193**	15	10
291	20 t. Running	25	30
292	25 t. Basketball	30	45
293	30 t. Swimming	35	50
	Set of 4	95	1·10
	Presentation Pack	13·00	
	First Day Cover		1·75

POSTAGE DUE STAMPS

POSTAL CHARGES

6d.

POSTAL CHARGES

IXIXIXIXIX   **3s.**

(D 1)   (D 2)

1960 (1 Mar). *Postage stamps surcharged.* (a) *No. 8 with Type D* **1**.

D1	6d. on 7½d. blue (R.)	£650	£350
	a. Surch double	£2750	£1600

(b) *Nos. 1, 4, 6a, 7/8 as Type D* **2**

D2	1d. on 6½d. maroon	14·00	5·00
D3	3d. on ½d. emerald (B.)	16·00	5·00
	a. Surch double	£450	
D4	6d. on 7½d. blue (R.)	27·00	13·00
	a. Surch double	£450	
D5	1s. 3d. on 3½d. black (O.)	24·00	13·00
D6	3s. on 2½d. orange	40·00	26·00
	Set of 6	£110	55·00

Of No. D1a, only a few copies are known from a sheet used at Goroka.

D 3

(Typo Note Ptg Branch, Reserve Bank of Australia, Melbourne)

1960 (2 June). *W* **15** *of Australia. P* 14.

D 7	D **3**	1d. orange	45	35
D 8		3d. yellow-brown	70	45
D 9		6d. blue	75	40
D10		9d. deep red	75	1·25
D11		1s. light emerald	75	50
D12		1s. 3d. violet	1·40	1·40
D13		1s. 6d. pale blue	5·50	5·00
D14		3s. yellow	6·00	1·00
		Set of 8	14·50	9·50

The use of Postal Charge stamps was discontinued on 12 February 1966, but they remained on sale at the Philatelic Bureau until 31 August 1966.

Papua New Guinea became fully independent on 16 September 1975.